CONSTELLATIONS: 1

CONSTELLATIONS: 1

AN EXQUISITE CORPSE OF DREAMS

JOSHUA D. LUNDELL

FOR: CAROL
THANKS FOR PLAYING THE
ROLE OF "THE SOUL SISTER."
I LOVE YOU ♡ ☺

[signature]

P.S.— $1000   3/16/21

Crafted with loving kindness at:

76 Divisadero St.

San Francisco, California 94117

Cover design by David Ortel

For Eleanor Faye

May your dreams be full of butterflies landing on pancakes.

"No goal is the prize.
 The practice of practice.
 A habit of habits.
 Turns ignorance, wise."

— "HERK" [1439.3 / 3932]

CONTENTS

FOREWARD

Constellation: *(noun)*
    1. An area in which a group of visible stars forms a perceived outline or pattern.
    2. A configuration of related ideas, feelings, characteristics, objects, etc.
    3. *In this work*, small clusters of dream journal entries *(and subordinated characters)*.

Exquisite Corpse: *(noun)*
    1. A surrealist technique by which a collection of words/images is collectively assembled.
    2. *In this work*, the author acts as a daily de novo contributor using a journal entry convention to frame a simple multi-year inquiry: *"What do I dream about? How much can I remember?"*

Dream: *(noun)*
    1. Images, ideas, and sensations that usually occur involuntarily in the mind during certain stages of sleep. The content and purpose of dreams are not fully understood.

* * *

This is a work of fiction. It is not based on any conscious waking-life human interactions. Space and time have been rearranged. Some imagined events have been compressed, and **all** dialogue has been recreated. Some elements may include mature, and occasionally graphic themes. While the author intends such subject matter is dealt with in a candid, compassionate and radically responsible manner, it may be troubling for some readers. Discretion is advised.
    1. Names of people familiar to the author have been changed.
    2. Public figures *(referred to as "Zeitgeist Valences")* and resemblance to persons living or dead is purely coincidental. Expressed opinions, taboos, and non-sequiturs are those of imaginal characters, not be confused with the author's. Roles, actions, and attitudes mentioned in dream narratives are entirely fictional and drawn from dream realm experiences.
    3. *"Amalgams, Hybrids, and Spirits"* appearing within the work have provided their preferred names for publication.

INTRODUCTION

Welcome to you, THE DREAMER!

I'm delighted at the fortune of meeting (*again*) for the first time. I've held it true in my heart from the start of this journey that it all could be said perfectly. Admittedly, I also must tend toward hallucination. As a helpful character will tell you: *"You're about to embark on a journey of massive self-discovery."*[0143.1 / 0334]. I'll take a cue from an influential (*and arguably troublesome*) person turned dense meme and declare, *"I'm simply going to say what needs to be said, concern free."*[0609.1 / 1539].

This work has found its way to you, its invitations are many, and it comes with a unique set of responsibilities (*and inherent risk of possible frustration*). You have the opportunity to plot your course in the manner of best fit, though a clue would be to interact with it **intuitively**. Open to any page. Flip around. Start where you are and then choose where to go next. You have the freedom to jump through this catalog at will and engage in some *"Whimsical Literary Gold Panning."*

This is not just preferred, but highly encouraged.

As THE DREAMER, you choose the path. A few options to frame your journey may be:

1. Read cover to cover (*though it may drive the analytical mind mad*).
2. Consume as much (*or as little*), as frequently (*or infrequently*) as desired.
3. Keep this bedside and read an entry (*or two*), to prime your launch into dream realm.
4. Use vignettes as prompts for your own creative expressions and remembrance.
5. Follow a constellation (*Major, Minor, 1100+ total*) ...they'll appear shortly.
6. Simply open to any page and jump to any point from there.

"All models lack correctness, though some may be useful...for a time."[0536.2 / 1319]. A simple orientation found on **page 17** will assist with grounding into the ontological oneiric frame that's presented itself for our shared purpose: **to remember what we've forgotten.**

13

The abundant content with fractional context is purposeful. Mathematically, it may be that no one will ever have the same experience as you. The group theory work hasn't been done, though I've imagined there could be more many-to-many combinations a dreamer could navigate in the pages that follow than could be read in an entire linear lifetime.

Meaning can be derived looking back at paths trodden, so journey onward. Consider each dream the dip of a thimble into an infinite river, generous with its gifts and firm in its tutelage.

Who are you, really? What have you left out? I tend to forget most of it, until gently guided back. Perhaps interacting with this work will spark an inner fire that inspires unique pursuits of things you determine to be good, true and beautiful.

Ideally more of us will stay awake! Make art! Build stuff! Serve others!

I believe: In sleep exists the potential to wake up more fully.

Though I don't know much, I trust the following are arguably certain:

1. We are in space.
2. No one knows what's going on.
3. I love you.

-THE APERTURE

⚜ MAJOR CONSTELLATIONS (22) ⚜

~Most frequently encountered reflections ~
Follow a constellation by turning to their dream of origin (#0000).

⚜ **0 - THE WEAVER** ⚜ *Encountered in 262 dreams beginning with #0010.*

⚜ **1 - THE CARPENTER** ⚜ *Encountered in 207 dreams beginning with #0012.*

⚜ **2 - THE DANCER** ⚜ *Encountered in 173 dreams beginning with #0002.*

⚜ **3 - THE CHILD** ⚜ *Encountered in 107 dreams beginning with #0102.*

⚜ **4 - THE CONNECTOR** ⚜ *Encountered in 62 dreams beginning with #0071.*

⚜ **5 - THE LAWYER** ⚜ *Encountered in 54 dreams beginning with #0080.*

⚜ **6 - THE PILOT** ⚜ *Encountered in 37 dreams beginning with #0129.*

⚜ **7 - THE WORLDBRIDGER** ⚜ *Encountered in 35 dreams beginning with #0010.*

⚜ **8 - THE ATHEIST** ⚜ *Encountered in 35 dreams beginning with #0020.*

⚜ **9 - THE FIDUCIARY** ⚜ *Encountered in 30 dreams beginning with #0007.*

⚜ **10 - THE ACTOR** ⚜ *Encountered in 29 dreams beginning with #0066.*

⚜ **11 - GRANDMA** ⚜ *Encountered in 27 dreams beginning with #0013.*

⚜ **12 - THE LITTLE PRINCE** ⚜ *Encountered in 25 dreams beginning with #0915.*

⚜ **13 - THE NURSE** ⚜ *Encountered in 24 dreams beginning with #0026.*

⚜ **14 - THE MAGICIAN** ⚜ *Encountered in 22 dreams beginning with #0472.*

⚜ **15 - THE ROMANTIC** ⚜ *Encountered in 21 dreams beginning with #0318.*

⚜ **16 - THE CONFIDANT** ⚜ *Encountered in 20 dreams beginning with #0022.*

⚜ **17 - THE LOBBYIST** ⚜ *Encountered in 18 dreams beginning with #0129.*

⚜ **18 - THE PUBLIC MEDIUM** ⚜ *Encountered in 17 dreams beginning with #0028.*

⚜ **19 - THE TRANSLATOR** ⚜ *Encountered in 17 dreams beginning with #0322.*

⚜ **20 - THE HEALER** ⚜ *Encountered in 16 dreams beginning with #0010.*

⚜ **21 - THE KIND HEART** ⚜ *Encountered in 15 dreams beginning with #0179.*

♣ MINOR CONSTELLATIONS (31) ♣
~Less frequently encountered reflections~

Reflections of Creativity & Will (8) - (♣)

THE FEELER: #0094
THE COUTURIER: #0204
THE GUITARIST: #0025
THE HILLBILLY: #0014
THE POSTMASTER: #0201
THE CATHOLIC: #0678
THE DULCE DE LECHE: #0363
THE VEGAN: #0837

Reflections of The Material World (8) - (♦)

THE JESTER: #0127
THE RAPTOR: #0176
THE NUN: #0165
THE LALA: #0561
THE VIKING ELF: #0117
THE WARD OF GAIA: #0010
THE AYURVEDIC: #0002
THE WHITE RABBIT: #0014

Reflections of Reason (7) - (♠)

THE DEVOTEE: #0384
THE PSYCHIATRIST: #0259
THE THINKER: #0056
THE PIXIE: #0115
THE KANGAROO: #0279
THE REVOLUTIONARY: #0069
THE DESIGNER: #0472

Reflections of Emotion & Love (8) - (♥)

THE ROBOT: #0176
THE ARCHITECT: #0198
GRANDPA: #0014
THE EPICUREAN: #0233
THE FARMHAND: #0201
THE FIREFIGHTER: #0668
THE RECONCILIATOR: #0317
THE NEUTRAL GUIDE: #0010

Follow a constellation by turning to their dream of origin (#0000).

ORIENTATION

As illustrated below, an ascending numerical index *(date, time, and physical location)* can assist THE DREAMER orient and navigate experiences of THE UNCONSCIOUS.

#0000 - October 4, 1582 @ 00:00 (Someplace, Somewhere)
* General commentary from THE APERTURE will be found beneath the index, if relevant *

[0000.1 / 0001] [Bracketed text indicates a dream component. Occasionally, a MAJOR or MINOR CONSTELLATION may appear, who can be followed to their next dream interaction. Encounters with ZEITGEIST VALENCES are also possible, though less frequent.
    Various ALTERNATIVES beneath each entry allow THE DREAMER to take directed *"jumps"* between dreams. Follow a concept by turning to the index number provided (#0000) *...if so desired.*]
    Note: *Characters advance prospectively. At the end of their journey, no further option is listed. Indexes provided at the back of the book help THE DREAMER locate initial character encounters.*
    [0000.2 / 0002] [*"Asterisms and Bright Stars"* appear less frequently than constellations.]

[0000.3 / 0003] [<u>"Amalgams , Hybrids, & Spirits "</u> are *(mostly)* underlined or in quotations.]

[0000.4 / 0004] [*"Dialog contributed by THE DREAMER looks like this."*
    Double hash marks indicate the end of a dream]. //

⁑

Maj. = 1- THE MAJOR CONSTELLATION(S): #2222
Min. = ♣♠♦♠ - THE MINOR CONSTELLATION(S): #3333
THE ZEITGEIST VALENCE: #4444
ALTERNATIVE: #5555
THE ASTERISM or THE BRIGHT STAR: #6666

⁑

Before every journey, it's useful for THE DREAMER to take brief pause and set an intention...

INVOCATION

I, **THE DREAMER**
of the shared dream, see and draw to me
those who will enhance our shared growth and
best support living at cause as Spirit.

Help me remember things of use for all to know.
Take me places, aligned to go.

May I be fully supported by my guides;
Angels of highest order;
to joyfully expand in knowing as the body rests.

Help me to steadfastly take my next steps,
while dreaming with trusting surrender.

Use me as a tool to do your work in a way
That serves the highest and best good of:

Everyone.
Everything.
Everywhere.
Everywhen.

I commit to end patterns of negative thinking
to fully liberate my authentic connection to true creativity.

Above all, this I shall remember:
I love you.

PART 1 - INITIATE

#0001 - #0047

"These are the days of miracle and wonder
This is the long-distance call
The way the camera follows us in slo-mo
The way we look to us all
The way we look to a distant constellation
That's dying in the corner of the sky
These are the days of miracle and wonder
And don't cry baby, don't cry."

-Paul Simon

* * *

December 20, 2017 - January 19, 2018

JOSHUA D. LUNDELL

⁂

⁂ **1.1 - THE BOOK OF SERPENS: 0001-0018** ⁂

#0001 - December 20, 2017 @ 01:30 (Montaña Larapata, Peru)

[**0001.1 / 0001**] [...Where am... hmph? ...game.show.in.an.action.movie...]

[**0001.2 / 0002**] [Elves scream, *"The head! They shot him in the fucking head! Runes! Are! Secrets!"*]

[**0001.3 / 0003**] [I'm a middle aged, culturally Jewish man, living in a fifth-floor walkup apartment in Brooklyn, New York. My wife's next to me in bed reading a magazine. She rolls it up as she turns towards me. She smacks me hard in the arm shouting, *"What the hell, Stan?"* She's my soulmate *(until that day soon, when I know she'll shoot me in the head).*]

[**0001.4 / 0004**] [THE OLD SOUL *(exuberant, wise, and conscientious)* makes a salad. She removes all the arugula after tossing it with other ingredients, except a single emerald green fern leaf that rests at the bottom of the bowl. She tilts the bowl in my direction and laughs, *"Oh well."*]

[**0001.5 / 0005**] [We're in a car. A cop car passes us on the highway.]

[**0001.6 / 0006**] [I watch a game show called, "Crook Catchers." People pursue each other on foot with handguns. I decide to participate. I leap from my chair into the TV, joining a team who first chase an unarmed man down a city street then inside a diner. My partner and I corner the unarmed man in the kitchen by a heated, greased cooktop. After a dramatic pause for a commercial break, my partner attacks "the crook." He holds the unarmed man's face to the skillet, searing the flesh from his cheek. My partner's visceral actions startle me. I leap from the game show out through the TV and back to my LA-Z-BOY. The scene feels like a gritty 1980's action film.]

[**0001.7 / 0007**] [I'm a young blonde-haired girl in Dresden, Germany. My parents were forced to breed. I'm forced to live a life of blind faith. I look up and see fire scorch the night sky as I skip and sing. The world explodes around me in flames. All goes blinding white as I watch my skin burn and bones evaporate.]

[**0001.8 / 0008**] [I compete in a home interior design challenge and lose to a gregarious and stereotypically flamboyant gay man. Though the nature of the competition feels immature, it's humorous and light hearted.] //

⁂
LA-Z-BOY: #0441
FLAMES: #0678
COPS: #0481, #0662
SALAD: #0778
THE OLD SOUL: #0937
⁂

#0002 - December 20, 2017 @ 02:45 (Montaña Larapata, Peru)

[**0002.1 / 0009**] [I'm a character in a sitcom. I make burritos and intend to share them amongst friends. *"Someone ate all of mine!"* I exclaim looking directly toward a camera. I grab my cheeks in a scripted overreaction, augmented by a pre-taped audience laugh track. The remaining burritos are full of nourishing and delicious green vegetables. *"Ugh, I have to eat*

22

this," my internal monologue huffily laments while I eat with a twinge of resentment. Simultaneously, I feel generous for letting my friends take as much as they want, without externalizing complaints.]

[0002.2 / 0010] [THE AYURVEDIC and THE DANCER take a flight to Australia. I put $40USD cash in a plastic bag and shove it in an open backpack zipper to ensure they receive payment from me as agreed. I realize I've lost my phone. I'm emotionally flat to its absence and unconcerned with its whereabouts.]

[0002.3 / 0011] [I'm shown a bushel basket of potatoes. I stare at them and hear them sing a happy song, "*We're happy! Oh, we're so happy! To Give!*" Witnessing their song is nourishing.]
//

⁎⁎
Maj. = 2- THE DANCER: #0016
Min. = ◆- THE AYURVEDIC: #0026
SONG: #0436, #0465, #0557, #0559, #0562, #0563
$: #0406, #0408, #0453, #0467, #0474, #0482, #0494, #0498, #0529, #0543
VEGETABLES: #0563
⁎⁎

#0003 - December 20, 2017 @ 04:00 (Montaña Larapata, Peru)

[0003.1 / 0012] [A whisper of a heart song emerges: "*What can I say? I was raised my father's way.*"]

[0003.2 / 0013] [Giant spinning bread logs mounted on semi-trucks pass by my driver's side car window as I cruise along a highway passage through a great green and amber splotched plain. Blue open skies expand overhead.]

[0003.3 / 0014] [THE MEDICINE WOMAN (*stoic, attentive, and deliberate*) and I plant blue corn cobs on a rocky river bed. Waters run wide and shallow. A giant Caucasian fist descends from the sky. It pounds the land causing widespread tectonic rumbles and infrequent, severe aftershocks.]

[0003.4 / 0015] ["*Cliff diving is a normal and expeditious method of parachuting all.the.way.-to.the.bottom. No fear,*" a calm deep voice whispers outward in all directions from the center of my head. I watch faceless bodies in business suits descend from a steep edge towards a sharp rocky beach below. The omniscient voice continues with a bellow, "*The descent is as basic as taking a subway or a taxi. No fear.*"]

[0003.5 / 0016] [A poem is given to me in a series of images: "*Blue Flames. Black Sky. Over My. Left Eye.*"]

[0003.6 / 0017] [I lift my hands from a bushel basket filled with singing potatoes to reveal fists full of extracted potato eyes. They rhythmically throb, pulsing like venous lungs between my hands woven through the webbing of my fingers.] //

⁎⁎
BREAD: #0014, #0057, #0216
POTATOES: #0002, #0083, #0088, #0243
BUSINESS: #0408, #0417, #0422, #0435
BEACH: #0428, #0472, #0520, #0550
THE MEDICINE WOMAN: #0046
⁎⁎

#0004 - December 20, 2017 @ 04:45 (Montaña Larapata, Peru)

[0004.1 / 0018] [THE SAMOAN (*embodied, playful, and warm*) squeals with delight at her "Step Aerobics" themed birthday party. The scene is shellacked. Shiny plants, clouds, and clothing give the space a polished live action anime quality. A doo-wop background track accompanies a swirling, outwardly panning crane shot of THE SAMOAN pedaling and waving at me in slow motion. She's mounted on a stair step machine, spinning in the opposite direction from the camera as she works her body and celebrates her wellbeing. A pica pica screen of pastel pink, blue, and white objects gives a sense of floatation, air, and effortlessness. Her circular pedestal levitates in the clouds surrounded by a cast of glittery and sparkling animated characters (*fancy piglets, miniature cacti, and tumbling stars*). I'm intrigued by the large black pig tails she wears. Each seems to be an Ensō; a single stroke from a celestial watercolor brush.]

[0004.2 / 0019] [I'm shown the onramp to a galactic launch portal. Overhead, a 4-bit banner of emerald green text reads, "**WELCOME! YOU'VE FOUND IT! THE GREEN SQUARE HOLOGRAM.**" Layers of green square outlines extend out from the epicenter in innumerable dimensions across a stark black background speckled by stars. In the midst of this fantastic distraction, I realize I'm in deep space.] //

⁂

HOLOGRAM: #0024, #0132, #0452, #0511, #0518, #0559, #0567, #0648, #0810
JAPAN: #0027, #0039, #0106, #0196, #0396, #0430, #0594, #0891
BIRTHDAY: #0607, #0637, #0647, #0679, #0712

⁂

#0005 - December 20, 2017 @ 05:00 (Montaña Larapata, Peru)

[0005.1 / 0020] [Astonished, curious, seemingly orgasmic voices chorally repeat the word "Oh! Oh! OH!" as a background of hummingbirds composed of freshly fallen leaves manifests, then rapidly decays into black nothingness].

[0005.2 / 0021] [I stand in front of a crowd to demonstrate my jumping ability. I'm in an early black and white silent motion picture. A theatre organ accompanies "Mysterioso Pizzicato" as text flashes between action sequences. I'm CHARLIE CHAPLIN, based on my style of dress, the type of shoes I wear, and the bowler hat held at chest level between my hands. I inspect my feet, placed confidently in *"ballet first position."* I press down firmly through the balls of my feet and jump repeatedly. Each bound ascends me increasingly upward, though I dare not leap higher than the 10-12-foot mark. *"If I go higher, I fear I may free myself from Earth's gravity and fly out into space!"* I exclaim while the crowd gasps as I jump to previously inconceivable heights. The mood is silly. The villain's theme is replaced by a Joplin-like ragtime piano composition as my feet flutter and heels click.]

[0005.3 / 0022] [Hundreds of years in the future, I'm encouraged by my employer to regularly bounce up to different tiers of the atmosphere from the planet's surface. On select ascents, I hover weightless in the stratosphere. Not too high. Not too low. I'm in a *"goldilocks spot"* to survey and appreciate the Earth, which dangles below me like a smooth blue and white marble.] //

CHARLIE CHAPLIN: #0587
HUMMINGBIRDS: #0481
BLACK AND WHITE: #0414, #0449, #0496, #0511, #0540, #0560, #0603, #0788, #0798
FUTURE: #0559, #0718, #0756, #0761
SPACE: #0772, #0774, #0775, #0786
✳✳

#0006 - December 20, 2017 @ 05:30 (Montaña Larapata, Peru)

[0006.1 / 0023] [A group of male newscasters engage in work conversation near a staircase. Their custom is to meet with trousers down around their ankles to disarm interpersonal conflict. *"We have nothing to hide if we're always caught with our pants down."*]

[0006.2 / 0024] [PARLIAMENT FUNKADELIC PLAYS "FLASHLIGHT" on a nearby stage in a 1970's pizzeria. *"Now I lay me down to sleep. Ooh I just can't find a beat. Ooh funk me."*
I hover above an infinitely long wooden rectangular table where a pizza cut to equal proportions has been served. Any and all are invited to take a 3" square. I eat a slice, and squint while looking down at the scrolling table that extends beyond my field of vision. As I pan back and upward, I observe a time lapse film where dozens of bodiless hands scramble in and out of frame hurriedly for their piece of the pie as the music ends in an echo.
"Everybody's got a little light...under the sun...under the sun."]

[0006.3 / 0025] [I descend the second-floor staircase of a home. At each downward step I pause to inspect small black framed, white matted photos mounted at eye level. Individual coca leaves are pressed flat under glass and immortalized, like venerated family ancestors in procession along the wall. The specific order, progression, and placement of photos weaves a robust household thesis: **"We honor those who came before."**]

[0006.4 / 0026] [The James Bond Theme plays loudly as I'm shot down a netted escape hatch. A thin white tooth floss mesh ensnares me like a Christmas tree to slow my descent. I'm a secret agent who's on assignment to venture *"all the way down."* Once at the bottom, two alle-giant black shadow beings grab me by the arms and run me crouched through a shallow underground tunnel to an idling black limousine. The rear limo door opens. The shadows pick me up and toss me into the cushioned back seat. We promptly speed away as I slide across the glossed leather seat face first into the interior of the opposite door. While I have no idea where we're going, the journey's infused with a playful sense of urgency. Seems I'm precious cargo that's been successfully retrieved. We're now on the route to a familiar home base.] //

JAMES BOND: #1123
HONOR: #0401, #0421, #0671, #0781

FLASHLIGHT: #0483
THEME: #0402, #0557, #0563, #0613
PIZZA: #0470, #0696, #0736, #0767, #0775
⁂

#0007 - December 21, 2017 @ 01:55 (Montaña Larapata, Peru)

[0007.1 / 0027] [I enter a convenience store in search of a snack. I pick up six falafels in a plastic container from a small vendor stand operated by a middle-aged White man. As I look around the convenience store it shifts into a large warehouse distribution and fulfillment hub. I complete my shopping and eat two falafels while queuing to pay. Once at the point of sale, the cashier remarks incredulously that the package of six falafels is $50 while ringing up another person's selections. I remove my falafel package from the conveyor belt and stuff it in my coat, initially intending to steal it. Before check out commences, I leave my cart in line and zip back to the cold case. I place the partially consumed package back in the chiller. I return to the checkout stand and complete my transaction. I don't pay for the falafels I consumed.]

[0007.2 / 0028] [I'm in a hotel. To allow guests to "Come Closer & Faster," the hotel provides live CCTV feeds of activity in neighboring rooms. I watch a couple have sex. I want to fuck them and discuss the prospect of inviting them over to play with my partner. He and I negotiate the four-way encounter and prepare to receive our neighbors. While preparing, the TV remains on and clicked into a livestream from another neighboring room. In this feed, I watch THE FIDUCIARY straddle across his partner THE REFLECTION with such momentum they both bounce from the bed and land on top of each other in a cummy mess on the floor. Shared laughter from my room floods across the hallway to theirs when the cleaning lady pops her head in from around her cart, offering housekeeping services. She gasps, "Ah!" at the sight of two rugged, muscular men who continue to fuck each other repeatedly. One tops, the other bottoms. They flip and repeat. Being watched turns them on.]

[0007.3 / 0029] [I'm with a group of friends. Checking our watches, we note it's 7:05pm. We're in agreement that it's time to get to "The Restaurant." We have a 7:15pm reservation for four. We speed across town in a shared car, and decide to forgo the reservation when we're still miles away and it's 7:16pm. We decide the next best option is to eat at a mall food court. *"Do you think we have time to make the event?"* remains our unanswerable telepathic discussion point.

The event is a cross-genre award show celebrating a new fusion of hip hop and country music. Tonight's zeitgeist is the popularized celebration of a recent crossover track penned by GARTH BROOKS and an as-yet-unnamed hip hop artist. It's widely assumed that this pairing and penning will give birth to "The Winner" and yield a new direction in the canon of popular music. We decide to attend, and upon arrival learn that wristbands are for purchase, $24 each. We're four white men. We're told only Black people are permitted to attend the gala. We're relegated to a "Whites Only" gathering space where we watch the opening to the show through other available sources (*big screens, wristwatches, etc.*). A transgender woman attempts to gain entry and is denied, leaving her deeply offended and vitriolic at the gate. SINBAD dons a futuristic shiny silver outfit and reports rowdily from the red carpet outside the venue.

In an effort to access the event, the four of us agree to become white gloved, tuxedo wearing servers. Once cleared through an expedited background check, we advance to collect our uniforms. I pass the falafel vendor from [0007.1 / 0027] who's changed his product offering and promotion to "5 **TENTS FOR $50!**" We pass by him quickly. I turn toward him shouting back, *"How will you make money? The margins must be menial."*]

[0007.4 / 0030] THE AFFLICTED *(pained, suffering, and late)* and I have paired up to build a small model structure. The task unfolds and completes quickly. When we step back to observe our work, we see a large multi-tier competition trophy composed of concentrically stacked squares that decrease in size as the structure rises. The piece stands roughly two meters tall. I experience it as a work of art. THE AFFLICTED relates to it with revulsion, so strongly it triggers her body into a grand mal seizure.

"THIS WILL TRAP THE DEMONS IN MY HEART!" She cries out in a stuttered sputter as her deep body catharsis amplifies. In the midst of witnessing the reaction I don't believe her. My eyes are drawn to the mid-tier of our model, which now houses a small inverted chartreuse pyramid. The pyramid glows a radioactive hue while hovering and rotating slowly in a counterclockwise direction. It doesn't appear to be impacted by gravity. I walk swiftly toward the structure and begin to kick and stomp on it, with intent to destroy it. THE AFFLICTED caterwauls, *"NO! YOU DON'T UNDERSTAND! SAVE ME! STOP!"*

Her screams gain feverish intensity as I pull my knee up and drop my foot repeatedly on what I understand was her *"demon trap."* Once shattered, dark energies flow like wispy ethereal syrup from the core of the pyramid and swarm her body. She writhes on the ground in pain. I could exorcise the demons, but instead throw a plastic bag over her head and kick her body aside. I'm instantly filled with deep feelings of self-disgust for not helping her.]

[0007.5 / 0031] [I return to my role as a tuxedo wearing awards show server. SINBAD comments between award segments from the red carpet, *"Black people award shows are more fabulous than any Sunday morning hat parades, ya know what I mean?"* He guffaws and stomps around the stage hysterically to thunderous applause from the seated crowd of tens of thousands. SINBAD is joined on the red carpet by THE ROCK. They playfully flirt and comment on each other's haute couture "Spaceship Singlets." We pass a tray of beverages to JANET JACKSON and her entourage. With the next tray I'm stunned when I hand OPRAH a glass of water and a beverage napkin.

A general undercurrent of annoyance flows from the collective towards one attendee who requested an *"obnoxious plus twelve"* for their retinue, *"and only three showed up."* The show concludes. The four of us return our uniforms and collect our stipends. We're all in agreement. *"We thoroughly enjoyed that encounter, and would definitely do it again."*] //

⁑

Maj. = 9- THE FIDUCIARY: #0021
OPRAH: #0189
JANET JACKSON: #0242
PYRAMID: #0481, #0720
THE AFFLICTED: #0064
THE REFLECTION: #0119
⁑

#0008 - December 21, 2017 @ 04:00 (Montaña Larapata, Peru)

[**0008.1 / 0032**] [I alter my agreement with gravity and test it by bounding up trees, feet first, from branch to branch.]

[**0008.2 / 0033**] [Blue sky. A field of white flowers with purple pistils emerge from a sprawling green prairie. I observe a drone cam time lapse view of a vast ocean at sunset, just prior to *"the green flash."*]

[**0008.3 / 0034**] [*"My name is "Lucas!" This is important!"* A young man with Down Syndrome declares.]

[**0008.4 / 0035**] [*"HEADLINE NEWS: AMAZON buys Whole Foods. Price of salmon drops 33%."* A ticker scrolls beneath a local news profile on the day-to-day lives of downtrodden local fisherman.]

[**0008.5 / 0036**] [*"Remember the song: 'HEYOKA HA!'"* A deep droning voice tenderly invites, in English.]//

✱✱

GRAVITY: #0428, #0544, #0575, #0788

FLOWERS: #0710, #0735

DOWN SYNDROME: #0450

TIME LAPSE: #0721

✱✱

#0009 - December 21, 2017 @ 06:55 (Montaña Larapata, Peru)

[**0009.1 / 0037**] [I look up at the elaborate facade of a luxury hotel. I've been invited to meet THE CONVERT *(composed, strong, and equanimous)* for her birthday celebration. I cross the threshold, stroll through the lobby and quickly notice the space has been fitted with cheap, garish fixtures throughout. Per invitation, I've been asked to *"bring a $20 bill with a serial number ending in '08.'"* THE CONVERT's boyfriend intends to surprise her with a marriage proposal. Once at the elevator bay, I pause and learn that to get access to a secret level of the hotel where the party will take place, attendees must allow a burlap bag to be placed over their heads. I decline. A door opens and I'm permitted to enter a hallway where dying fluorescent lights flicker intermittently overhead as though they're gasping for breath. THE CONVERT and her boyfriend have a discussion nearby that ends abruptly when she becomes notably irritated by the pulsing lights.

I exit through a different stairwell and walk up one level to an ornate ballroom. I cross a plush plum carpeted room where at its center I come upon a large chalk circle drawn on the floor. Within the chalked ensō is a heaped pile of crumpled up $20 bills, perhaps eight feet high. THE DALAI LAMA stands to the side of the ensō laughing next to a row of wooden pallets stacked waist high with cash. While wadding up bills in his hands and tossing them on the pile like used up tissues he crows with a smile, *"You have '08,' yes?"* I reply with a simple *"Yes,"* as I pull the bill from my wallet and extend my arm in his direction.

"Go ahead! We've been waiting! Ha ha!" The enlightened man giggles as he invites my contribution.

I crush the crisp bill in my hand, laughing behind closed lips as I toss it on the ever-growing pile.

"This is a game where everyone wins AND loses! Ha ha!" THE DALAI LAMA revels.

"Everyone loses, except for us your holiness. We're rich...bitch!" THE BOND TRADERS *(curt,*

28

scandalous, and entrepreneurial) say in unison with a gregarious howl. On the opposite side of the pile, they review daily orders for tranches of junk munis.

I leave the ballroom and take an elevator to a mezzanine level. As the doors part I know with fluid swiftness that I'm witness to a *"HUGE MEDIA EVENT. Like, undeniably, like...you won't believe how HUGE this event is,"* as crooned by an odd juvenile sounding *"old"* voice. I spill on to a balcony, catching a glimpse of a momentous public gathering where hundreds of thousands of beings converge for "World Communications Day." A young professionally dressed Asian woman with thick powder blue horn-rimmed glasses advances to a podium to offer opening remarks. She appears confident and practiced, steady and present, with an appropriate inner nervousness that resonates energetically deep at her core, and springs forth as youthful exuberance. Her uplifting remarks conclude with a flat transition, *"And now I present to you, the 45th President of the United States, DONALD J. TRUMP."* A staged applause track cued through a large PA system is played at high volume to wash out boos and jeers. The President's handlers know this tactic preserves his fragile ego and keeps him on message. He's a puppet. An occasional tomato is flung from the crowd at the stage.

He leans into the podium microphone and begins delivering prepared remarks. I observe from offstage, noting his bizarre overuse of the word *"compare." "COMPARE, COMPARE, COMPARE!"* is woven through his language with exhausting repetition. A gold and silver microphone appears in front of my mouth and hovers weightlessly in a white ball of light. For hours, I speak the word *"compare"* into the celestially gifted microphone in an exaggerated, mocking manner each time the President repeats the oft recited word. The President becomes increasingly flustered and frustrated by my rogue over talk. The crowd joins me in playful mockery, resulting in a further *(and swift)* decline in the President's composure. His gestures devolve into violent flails and kicks.

As an embodiment of embarrassing and immature anger, he notices me off to the side. He stops his speech and calls for another person to wrap up the address. A giant red velvet theatre curtain drops to obscure the stage. The President storms away, looking at me as I call out, *"No! Mr. President, please wait! This is a historic day to be remembered! The day the President gave his rambling, nonsensical, ridiculous 'COMPARE' speech."*

Laughter permeates the crowd from opposite the crimson curtain. The crowd responds to my derision with increasing favor. Intuitively, I begin to flow, *"Just think Mr. President, how awesome is it that every child who takes a world history class henceforth will know this was THE DAY the President gave a speech and used the word 'compare,' ...how many times, World?"* "SIX HUNDRED AND FORTY-ONE TIMES!"

The gathered crowd booms and erupts in sniggers leaving the President in a state of humiliation. He stomps offstage. *"Mr. President, I did this because I love you,"* I say stoically. Just prior to exiting the building he pauses, looks at me and sneers while mouthing the words, *"I'm going to kill you."*

I leave my body on the balcony and bilocate in spirit back to THE CONVERT's birthday party. The Asian woman from the media event attends, standing upright in an "alien box" next to other guests who follow suit. *"One body. One box."* The party concludes in an unfinished room. Carpentry tools and materials are messily strewn about. Drywall is taped and coated with rough mud. Exposed wires dangle from the ceiling where fixtures will eventually be mounted. Passed hors d'oeuvres are choked down by the many revelers. THE CONVERT eats half of a fried ravioli, places it on a cocktail napkin and reflexively vomits when she notices mealworms pouring from the pasta. *"I'm surprised you don't like it. That's our protein source now,"* I say unfazed by the movement of the live larvae on the paper.] //

⁂

DONALD TRUMP: #0088
THE DALAI LAMA: #0309
$20: #0633, #0708, #0755
THE BOND TRADERS: #0074
THE CONVERT: #0319

⁂

#0010 - December 23, 2017 @ 03:00 (Montaña Larapata, Peru)

[0010.1 / 0038] [Delight! Play! I'm a three-foot-tall plastic slide in the living room of a cozy suburban house. THE HEALER *(teacher, and friend)* and THE WARD OF GAIA *(balanced, caring, and open)* are on the opposite side of the room watching THE HARBINGER *(innocent, eager, and vulnerable)*, aged 6 months, who decides to climb up my ladder and slide down. Though he can walk, I cradle his head as he descends. His neck muscles aren't yet strong enough to hold his head up during a quick drop without risking whiplash. He squeals happily as he moves from up to down, high to low. As he rides and plays, I see the textured white ceiling above him through his eyes. At the end of a pass, he plops down forcefully at the bottom. After being momentarily stunned, he giggles and looks towards mom and dad who grin approvingly.]

[0010.2 / 0039] [I walk through a casino filled with bright pulsing lights and loud noises. Everyone is male and dressed in bespoke suiting. As I pass a bar, I'm offered multiple free cocktails, which for the time being, I politely decline. *"No alcohol tonight. Thank you,"* I say appreciatively and saunter on. THE REIKI MASTER *(clinical, distant, and willing)* spins around from a stool by a roulette table, extends his right arm out and says while pointing, *"Over there...he's by the craps table."* THE REIKI MASTER smiles as I advance on my path. When I get to my destination, a man slightly taller than me with Crayola red skin and John Wayne-like features grabs me, pulls me close and holds me tight to his torso. We soul gaze. I bask in sensations of shared gentility, benevolence, and quiet strength. I can tell by his breath pattern that he speaks with an Australian accent.]

[0010.3 / 0040] [I view a screen that has two arches of different widths extending from a common origin. They occur as abstractions of exclamation points, oriented perpendicularly, and arched like shooting stars. THE WORLDBRIDGER and THE NEUTRAL GUIDE *(consistent, flat, and available)* communicate with me in an alien telepathic language for an *"as lived, in the field"* class module. Beyond the screen, I see myself receiving the transmission while I babysit in another dimension. The language has a newness in its crispness, candor, and purity that I'm eager to engage. I'm shown that it's a transmission only accessible from *"beyond the 10th chakra."*]

[0010.4 / 0041] [I'm in a house with many children. Toys and games are strewn across the floor after a healthy day of messy play. One child resists napping and is softly reprimanded in an adjacent room. The glowing blue and green abstract representations of THE WORLD-BRIDGER and THE NEUTRAL GUIDE on my mind's screen flutter in flashes, indicating I've made appropriate *"in the field"* connections to advance to my next lesson. Glowing softly, the blue and green swaths of color flash in union. This cue points me to a small pedagogical gap to close, based on how I interpret their feedback. This download continues as THE WEAVER and I communicate telepathically in a light and collaborative manner. She and I observe a rest resistant child being scolded and go about our business of *"being the house."* We observe what's occurring, with occasional under breath bursts of lighthearted laughter when she and I begin to sort out the small mess left in the family room. Overall, we know the majority of the space is functional, well ordered, and efficient. We also know that *"to grow there always needs to be a lil' sumthin' to clean up and learn from."*]

[0010.5 / 0042] [I stand on a deck under starlight, embracing the "Red Man." I rock back and forth fully enshrouded in his brawny arms. My eyes become shrink wrapped with tears. My belly churns. My chest ripens. Butterflies flutter up and out of my throat as I surrender and share, ***"I've never had an experience where I've felt so loved."*** I bury my face in his spirituous chest. He looks down towards me with a slight smile, adoringly offering, *"I could do this for as long as you're willing."* I smile and think to myself, ***"Wow. Yes. It really can be this good."***] //

⁂

Maj. = 0- THE WEAVER: #0012, 7- THE WORLDBRIDGER: #0128, 20-THE HEALER: #0011
Min. = ◆*- THE WARD OF GAIA: #0019,* ♥*- THE NEUTRAL GUIDE: #0125*
THE HARBINGER: #0023
THE REIKI MASTER: #0153

⁂

#0011 - December 23, 2017 @ 06:00 (Montaña Larapata, Peru)

[0011.1 / 0043] [*"Ok, what's going on?"* I hear THE HEALER's *(firm, grounded, and challenging)* voice as I wake from sleeping on my left side. It's morning. We're outside. It appears I've passed out mid-interview. The feeling is calm, accepting, and patient.]

[0011.2 / 0044] [I'm on an airplane.]

[0011.3 / 0045] [The scene speeds up so much, the surrounding action slows and blurs to a tunnel of light. I get a momentary glimpse of a complex lattice of prismatic white circles. They intersect in infinite directions, planes, and dimensions. They converge and align in ways my analytical 3D mind does not comprehend, yet totally make sense to my spirit.]

[0011.4 / 0046] [I exit an aircraft and walk up the jet way behind an 11-year-old girl. She uses a walker. She has cerebral palsy. She's determined to make the journey to the terminal without help from other people. I realize I'm both the girl and her caretaker. My spirit hovers in the space between their bodies. *"Hey! You forgot this!"* a voice yells to my observing spirit. A pair of wadded up sweatpants with a solid object at the core strikes me hard in the face. The shock of pain is intense and disorienting. It hurts. My cheek could be broken. In reaction I say, ***"Thanks! You don't have to be a dick!"***] //

⁎⁎

Maj. = 20- THE HEALER: #0019
AIRPLANES: #0450, #0540, #0556
TUNNEL: #0521, #0525, #0617, #0688, #0774

⁎⁎

#0012 - December 26, 2017 @ 02:30 (Montaña Larapata, Peru)
I experience two dreams concurrently:

[0012.1 / 0047] [**PART 1 - My age is {3.22.NOW}**. I ride in the back of a classic car with leather bench seats. THE CARPENTER drives. We speed down a highway listening to rock music at high volume. Different people pop up in the passenger seat. They spin around, speak with me briefly and promptly disappear. The long chain of faces concludes when THE GREEN TARA *(relationship oriented, sensational, and snarky)* emerges, inviting the continuation of a prior conversation we had regarding *"the benefits of maintaining a regular yoga practice."* To the right of the highway, large wildfires burn intensely up to the road's shoulder. We're not concerned by the torrent of flame lapping at the car. I'm enamored with the dancing hot yellow-orange flames, and accompanying black plumes of smoke which rise up and over the freeway in a large dark scythe-like arc that mows a clear blue sky. The other side of the highway is clear, tranquil, and pastoral. *"I'm thirsty. Let's stop to get a pop,"* THE CARPENTER suggests. THE GREEN TARA agrees, *"Great timing. Pull over here. I'll take you to my favorite coffee shop."*

THE CARPENTER cuts the engine and we roll to an easy stop in front of a large nonde-script warehouse. As we enter the main door, both THE CARPENTER and THE GREEN TARA disappear. The left side of my head pulses with a dull, low-grade headache. I glance up to my left and see a morbidly obese woman whose excess skin and adipose tissues pour over the edge of a hovering mobility device that trolls inchmeal through the space. I realize she's THE WEAVER, and we're on our quarterly shopping date. The further we advance inside the building, the more attention we give to how overtly dystopian, decrepit, and unattended to the warehouse seems. It's full of junk and second-hand retail bric-a-brac. I don't want any of it. No matter, because I don't have any money. THE WEAVER wheels slowly and *(in her own unique manner)* regally up and down each aisle looking for something sexy to wear. The ware-house staff is predominantly African American women who are attentive and knowledgeable. They utilize advanced technology to help us teleport instantly between quadrants of the giant retail space. I'm annoyed by their commission driven hurriedness, but humored in some moments where they achieve telepathic coherence. The sound of their chewing gum snap-ping synchronizes, just prior to the closure of a sale.

I request a teleport to "La Cantina." I arrive in a blink to discover there are no service staff. I'm greeted by poorly stacked pallets of dusty plastic milk crates. Refrigerator cases display alluring ads for cold beverages, though the cases are unpowered and the contents are room temperature. A box full of Sprite 20 oz. bottles grabs my attention. I feel thirsty and contemplate drinking one. All the bottle caps have been twisted, rendering the soda flat. In this world, soda is illegal to sell and consume. Am I planning to steal it? I know I have no money. My intention isn't clear, and while still slightly confused I teleport back to be with THE WEAVER.

The store space, staff, and vibe are all the same, but the vast network of shelves and clothing racks are virtually empty. THE WEAVER has selected two muumuus she considers *"sexy."* They hover in front of me like two bolts of drape fabric. The associate assisting THE

32

WEAVER appears to grow impatient with her indecisive, deliberate, and contemplative process. I shoot the associate a strong, icy glare that gets her to rank and file. I feel compassion for THE WEAVER. The black and silver option she's keen on is large enough for many fat people, but I know she's simply too large to wear it. She just wants to be sexy. I disregard my thirst and let her remain in inquisitive fantasy, knowing she'll eventually feel defeated.]

[0012.2 / 0048] [PART 2 - My age is {17.NOW}. The scene is familiar, dark and palpably energized. I'm at a TOOL concert. The venue is large, easily housing more than 30,000 people. I find myself in a standard predicament: I'm a short scrappy guy. Regardless of where I stand, a very large man stands directly in front of me. No matter though, I'm going to get a spot with a great view for this performance. I recall seeing them in November 1996 at "The Garage" at Caddy's in Cincinnati, Ohio. Maybe tonight they'll revive and perform their song "Third Eye?" *"Watching them start their show with that song inspired me to join a band,"* I tell the person standing next to me. The house lights drop. The right side of my head starts to throb as the "lub dub" of a heart beat increases steadily in volume through the house speakers. The entire crowd swells with excitement.

It seems most in the audience are as delighted as I. My entire being is electrified. I make eye contact and hug other concert going strangers who instantly feel like family in our shared love for this band *(and song)*. Rumor has it, the concert will only be a performance of this single track, and then they're quitting...**forever.** I'm excited to bookend my live experiences with this song. It's a protracted affair. Each band member shows up over a 14-minute intro period. DANNY CAREY first on drums. At minute 14, JUSTIN CHANCELLOR appears, bass in hand. Minute 28, ADAM JONES plugs in his gray Les Paul guitar and strikes a chord. The crowd whips into frenzy at minute 42 when MAYNARD KEENAN steps atop a box in silhouette at the back of the stage behind a microphone stand in an elaborate indiscernible costume. I'm deeply attracted to him. He occurs as mysterious, and seems to do whatever he wants. He's incredibly generous with his voice and dismissive of fandom. As the song advances, I find myself unable to recall the lyrics. A voice within culls, *"Just scream what you know at full volume and make up the rest."* The music volume rises in a dark brooding crescendo. The collective energy amplifies to a frenetic fever pitch. We're wet with beer smelling sweat and anticipation. I look at my neighbors to each side. I'm inspired to take a leap. **"YEAH MAN! GO FOR IT!"** they yell with conciliatory smiles plastered across their faces.

In the final moments of the performance, I bound ecstatically high from the back of the venue onto the stage. I land and hear an uproar from the swooning crowd. I'm surrounded by plumes of stage smoke, laser grids and pyrotechnic cannons during the last aggressive, cacophonous bars of the song. The path to the back of the stage is abnormally deep. Realizing I'm just as likely to be tackled by a band member as a security guard, I quickly turn to observe what it's like to be under inspection by a sea of human eyes. Nervousness floods my bones. I vertically leap 30 feet and off to the right of the stage. I fear I may not have jumped high *(nor far)* enough and could very well land full force on the security fence around the stage perimeter. I pull both knees toward my chest, curling into a tight spinning ball. I hesitate for a moment, bracing for the snap and accompanying extreme pain of broken bones. I breach the barrier, graze my tailbone and take a crouched landing posture on one knee. After a one breath pause, I run with velocity towards the venue exit. I teleport instantly to the rear of the concert hall and realize the performance has concluded.

House lights gleam overhead. Thousands of delighted concert goers with giant smiles and exuding high vibes flood out the doors onto a city street.

"Did you see that leaping guy? *"Man, that guy was fucking badass!"* I overhear many overserved music fans talking about me. I've gone invisible. They'll never know I stood right beside them. To collective surprise the band comes back for an additional bow. Even more uncharacteristically, MAYNARD KEENAN takes to a mic saying,

"We thought we'd give the heartbeat of this night to that LEAPING JACKASS who seized the moment for us all."

The band presents an autographed bass drum head, with which they taunt the crowd. Together they fling it like a Frisbee to the opposite end of the venue. A rabidly joyful fan catches it. I feel happy for him. The song "Perry Mason" by OZZY OSBOURNE plays at moderate volume through house speakers. I become visible and make eye contact with a female security guard. She and I debate the rowdiest concerts we've attended. I lie when I mention two bands I've never seen live.

She says, *"No, dude...Metallica 2012 was even more...you were there, right?"*

I nod in agreement knowing I'm lying about being there too, but it feels good. I'm convinced the truth in that story doesn't matter. The shared affinity for music is where the community connection is rooted. Tonight, I'm going home satisfied with the impact I've made. It's forever changed the way the performers in this band relate to their fans.] //

⁂

Maj. = 0- THE WEAVER: #0016, 1- THE CARPENTER: #0013
OZZY OSBOURNE: #0014
TOOL: #0056
ADAM JONES: #0060
DANNY CAREY: #0060
MAYNARD KEENAN: #0060
JUSTIN CHANCELLOR: #0792
TONIGHT: #0498, #0561, #0607, #0670, #0701
THE GREEN TARA: #0302

⁂

#0013 - December 26, 2017 @ 05:55 (Montaña Larapata, Peru)

[0013.1 / 0049] [My age is {7.10.13.32}. I'm in a giant mansion, taking refuge in my tiny well-lit room. I'm at GRANDMA's house. THE OFFICIANT (*authoritative, dominating, and feminine*) sits at the foot of my bed, and with gentle reassurance insists,

"Stay here. I'll come back and read to you." THE CARPENTER enters wearing camouflage military fatigues. He places a futuristic mini-computer on my tiny desk, adjacent to my tiny twin sized bed.

"I'm sorry son. I have to go. Look after your mom and sister, ok?"

He kisses me sweetly on the forehead. I bear hug his neck blurting, **"Yes Daddy. Will do, Sir."** Tears spew from my face in an emulsion of happy, sad, afraid, and (*in some odd snot laden context*) deeply funny effluence.]

[0013.2 / 0050] [I distract myself with the new video game; a highly desired feature of the tiny computer console. I select a first-person shooter, put on a VR headset and become instantly consumed by the game's arid, post-apocalyptic industrial wasteland environment. Orange, yellow and brown hued toxic clouds swirl overhead. An acrid pall similar to that of a corpse flower burns warm and sickly vomitus in the air drawn through my nostrils. I'm an

34

outsider here. Intuition suggests imminent mortal danger, but this doesn't deter my desire to explore. Sand devils swirl up around me, making breathing more laborious. I walk down an alley lined by a dilapidated wooden fence, occasionally pock marked by rusted out 50-gallon drums decorated with colorful graffiti. I continue and pass sporadic groupings of zombies that lurch along in the same direction. None of them respond when I ask,

"*Where are we?*"

A sleek automobile pulls up slowly and silently next to me. I knock on a tinted window, which recedes and reveals a gaunt middle-aged woman in business attire. Her face is grotesquely contorted. Her eyelids are missing. She sits motionless at the wheel, which has a small holographic screen displaying an advertisement for "SUGAR." The font occurs cloud-like, happy, and full of shiny, sparkling color. No matter the tactic (*finger snaps, hand claps, and a five-finger cheek slap*), I'm unable to get her attention. She's a sugar zombie. Heavy metal accompaniment (*"Bfg Division" from the game "DOOM"*) blares at such tremendous volume it ruptures my right ear drum, rendering me mostly deaf and angry. The anger quells when I recall that I'm immersed in the virtual reality of the game and end play.]

[0013.3 / 0051] [I blink and discover myself seated at the desk in my room. The sense of hearing in my right ear is present, yet faint. I lay my head down on my pillow with the light on. Looking through the diamond shaped chef's window in my bedroom door I note GRANDMA has turned off all the other lights in her mansion. I hear screams, wailing, and sobs from other rooms in GRANDMA's house. I could go turn on lights in other rooms, but I know the house is haunted.

The prevailing on-premises rule is: "**You have to turn on your own light.**"

I don't bother helping anyone, roll over, and promptly fall asleep.] //

⁎⁎

Maj. = 1- THE CARPENTER: #0016, 11- GRANDMA: #0058
SUGAR: #0566, #0575, #0756, #0793
ZOMBIE: #0531, #0714
VIDEO GAME: #0561, #0617, #0718
SOUNDTRACK: #0448, #0529

⁎⁎

#0014 - December 27, 2017 @ 00:15 (Montaña Larapata, Peru)

[0014.1 / 0052] [I'm my current age. I attend a retreat on a mountainous Andean property. Our group's month-long collaboration has yielded a series of newly constructed treehouse meeting spaces. Each has been up fitted with a large bouncy house cushion floor. Our group has become a close-knit family. While celebrating, we know danger looms and our remaining time together on the planet is short. Our prayers have attracted assassins. THE SIRENS and THE WHITE RABBIT share a bouncy room with me. One SIREN (*diplomatic, leader, and generous of spirit*) decides to exit. Once out of sight, we know she's been murdered. Next, THE WHITE RABBIT (*adventurous, intellectual, and deeply charitable*) decides to investigate and is consequently murdered. I ask the other SIREN (*nurturing, vulnerable, and strong voiced*) what she intends to do. Without speaking, she remains seated in the center of the bouncy room floor, waiting calmly for death's arrival. As I run down to the kitchen I can feel when she leaves her body while passing THE CHEF (*meticulous, committed, and unapologetic*) who duti-

35

fully produces bread, one loaf at a time in a clay oven. THE CHEF defiantly stays where he is, even after I express fear for his life.

"I'm good," he says, attention turned to loaf upon loaf of warm nourishing bread emerging from a long conveyor belt.

Standing at the end of the conveyor belt is THE HILLBILLY *(loyal, playful, and imprecise)*. THE HILLBILLY opens a door revealing a long intricate network of pipes that pump water to a waterfall. The water pressure is low. The pipes are cracked and leak profusely, resulting in a menial low-pressure trickle. We inspect the waterfall from the other side, where we discover it empties to a firebox and pools in a basin deeply recessed within a black marble hearth. THE HILLBILLY errantly rerouted an ignited gasoline source and patched it to the water pipes.

"You idiot! This is unforgivable!" I shout with a hapless quiver.

Fearful and angry, I watch wet liquid fire erupt on to stacks of cardboard boxes full of old memories and knowledge stored in the firebox. In the midst of tragedy, we know there's a way to recover the loss.

At morning's light, I request a meeting with a small, old sinister troll who demands the utterance of a series of seven sacred words in specific memorized order. Intending to cheat, I've grabbed a book with the words inscribed from one of the salvaged fuel-soaked boxes. Light shines in through a window, illuminating dust in the air like shimmering floating glitter. From a small platform the troll chides,

"You want everything the way it was? Give me the incantation."

I look down at the book and notice the words referenced on the dog-eared fuel-soaked page are illegible. Alien characters glow and oscillate into different diffused forms on the page. The last thing I hear is a wily laugh, followed by a torrent of white light. I know I troll has killed me.]

[0014.2 / 0053] [I wake up in an office cubicle farm. Phones ring. Primped and manicured people admire a long wall of photos celebrating those who have been *"historically significant to the success of the firm."* I make small talk with a couple of employees I don't know, noticing a single small graham cracker crumb on the desk. I inspect it on the tip of my finger and realize it's a tiny cream filled cannoli. I lift my finger to my tongue and swallow the pastry without thinking as conversation continues. Some giggling ensues among my fellow workers. I'm now affiliated with a game of some sort. A slightly larger pastry appears on an adjacent table, which also I decide to eat without pause. Initially, I take no notice that every time I eat one, another slightly larger pastry appears nearby that I either compulsively eat, or feel like I must eat in order to advance through "the game."

A scenario emerges where a male co-worker can no longer eat the pastries of increasing size. The collective notices this, and all activity abruptly grinds to a halt. The man walks towards an exit door that opens to a long dock. Without hesitation he proceeds good postured and with a driving sense of purpose down the dock, off the end and into the water, drowning himself. **This is business as usual.** I continue eating pastries of increasing size, knowing compulsion will eventually lead to my demise. The current cannoli is the size of my palm. Two male co-workers and I commiserate to skirt the system. One of them is RODNEY DANGERFIELD, the other feels like the essence of GRANDPA *(stylish, captivating, suave, and manicured)* though his face is not recognizable. To avoid death by drowning, we'll screen two different films at the campus theater. RODNEY DANGERFIELD and GRANDPA are in some disagreement on the two film selections. Both are from a genre I'm not familiar with. I'm more captivated by the layout and content of a full-page advertisement we've taken out in the daily, on-demand company publication. If we can distract enough workers with the movie, they'll fail to notice the eventual stall in our pastry consumption.

The plan fails spectacularly. I drowsily rouse below deck on a boat, far out to sea. GRANDPA is nearby, but pays me no attention. RODNEY DANGERFIELD pops up from below where I stand. His arms extend up from a brightly lit room filled with abundant stock of processed snack cookies and sugary frosted cakes. RODNEY DANGERFIELD cracks jokes and makes crass comments while passing up package on package, box upon box of chocolate chip mint cookies. He believes they're an antidote for our unabashed pastry consumption. He hasn't realized that we're adrift on a vast ocean. We get lost in our quippy punch line heavy conversation. When we pause from belly laughing, we look down and realize that instead of theriac cookies, we've both scarfed super-size cannoli. RODNEY DANGERFIELD opens a hatch to the upper deck. A sheet of dark water pours in. From within the wet rush, OZZY OSBOURNE swings down to welcome us to his dark mansion while profusely cussing us out.] //

Min. = ◆- *THE WHITE RABBIT: #0026,* ♣- *THE HILLBILLY: #0026,* ♥- *GRANDPA: #0222*
OZZY OSBOURNE: #0044
PUNCH: #0461, #0545, #0558, #0683
COOKIES: #0433, #0723, #0785
THE SIREN: #0035
THE CHEF: #0035

#0015 - December 29, 2017 @ 00:01 (Montaña Larapata, Peru)

[0015.1 / 0054] [I'm on a business trip. I lodge on the cheap at THE INTERN's *(compliant, friendly, and team oriented)* home. He has a number of roommates. Though I don't recognize any, all are generally agreeable to my presence. THE INTERN departs for work, while I remain in his guest room. The walls of the room dissolve, revealing a large outdoor camping field. The soil is red and rocky like the volcanic summit of Kilimanjaro. People huddle around makeshift tables eating calorically dense, yet nutrient deficient foods supplied by government relief agencies. Interpersonal interactions occur as limbic and primal. In this reality, I remember who people are by the boots they wear, more proficiently than by face.

A blink of the eye lands me back in THE INTERN's guest room. He'll be home from work at any moment. THE INTERN walks in, but I confuse him for THE MANAGING DIRECTOR *(sharp, decisive, and grumpy)*. Photos on the wall favor THE MANAGING DIREC-TOR, yet THE INTERN walks me down his hallway taking pause to remark on various memories captured in the photos. We stop. I drop to my knees and perform oral sex on him followed by numerous other faceless men who wander in and out of scene.]

[0015.2 / 0055] [I'm on the set of a late-night talk show, which has broken from convention to broadcast live during daylight hours from the center of a heavily populated shopping mall. THE RED HOT CHILI PEPPERS are today's musical guests. They're offstage in a green room ramping each other up to perform a wild and rowdy song. They take to a series of four discrete circular stages under individual flood lights. One band member stands provocatively behind a glass wall. Another plays while screaming and leering into a brick wall. They're able to keep perfect tempo and perform masterfully. I find it odd that FLEA plays the drums. His kit is bizarrely constructed. A tiny tom sits where a normal kick drum would be. The kit looks backwards and upside down, yet the rhythms produced are solid and driving. I flirt with a shirtless, muscular and tattooed ANTHONY KEDIS by licking his leather chapped leg from below the stage. He signals he wants more interaction, so I climb onstage and give him oral sex to completion (*...and he tastes lip smacking delicious*).]

[0015.3 / 0056] [I quickly speed down a blurry highway around a series of roundabouts and public fountains. I arrive back at THE INTERN's house to discover my body still in the act of blowing him and others. The frame of the scene pulls back revealing an intricate series of large brown cement housing units, best characterized as *"dwelling sized Incan ice cube trays."* The view shifts away from the busy street.]

[0015.4 / 0057] [I masturbate. I get stuck in a sensational orgasma-loop, ejaculating a total of 14 times. I'm left wobbly kneed with sexual stupor. When centered, I'm astonished by the amount of semen I've produced.] //

✷✷

RED HOT CHILI PEPPERS: #0825
TEMPO: #0429, #0597
ORAL: #0436, #0576, #0732
MASTURBATE: #0654
BRICK WALL: #0755
TATTOOS: #0455, #0597, #0644
THE MANAGING DIRECTOR: #1131

✷✷

#0016 - December 31, 2017 @ 00:15 (Montaña Larapata, Peru)

[0016.1 / 0058] [I've signed on as a member of a new construction crew. Our shared intention is to raise a temple. Though I don't recognize most people, THE MAKER (*anxious, creative, and impatient*) is familiar and identifies himself as the lead artist. Preconstruction occurs in a forest environment. We build a simple tongue and groove facade around an abandoned woodland cabin. The wood procured for construction has a zebra striped black and white finish. It appears aged. Perhaps it's rotting, but it's sturdy enough for our purposes.]

[0016.2 / 0059] [I whisk through a movie theater arcade. Details fly by in a blur. The environment is loud with cartoon sound effects (*vibraslaps, cuicas, kazoos, whistles, and alarm bells*), giving the general impression that patrons are hyper stimulated and thoroughly enjoying themselves.]

[0016.3 / 0060] [Our family home has relocated to the Black Rock Desert in northern Nevada. We take increasing interest in what's been accomplished on a temple construction project. I've purchased four, 2-litre bottles of soda. They're in plain sight on the floor of my bedroom, but I believe them to be well hidden. I chug one quickly, neck upright and throat exposed, while walking downstairs. I pass THE DANCER in the kitchen, who sits at a card table sorting today's mail. I continue outside to inspect construction progress. I pause to draw in a few deep hot and dusty breaths. My attention turns upward to an expansive azure sky spun with white wispy threads of cirrus clouds. A new city under construction, encircles the temple. Daily status reporting for both the city and the temple state both engagements are *on track.*

I return to the house and note THE DANCER's palpable confusion by a series of payment delinquency notices for a credit card account. She's forgotten her mobile banking password and is unable to make payment. She glances up and with mild frustration mutters,

"THE CARPENTER set up that account for me. He's gotta have the password."

I shoot back with a catty remark about her lack of financial hygiene, fully intending to piss her off. When THE WEAVER mildly intervenes, I scoff with a smartass tone,

"You've never experienced me out here on MY turf." Wearing a big shit eating grin on my face, I'm not likeable nor agreeable at the moment. I continue, *"Just so you know, (and aren't surprised in the future) I can be a real jackass some of the time."*

THE WEAVER is annoyed. She's shocked and saddened by my comments. I scurry upstairs to my room and chug most of the other sodas, wondering when THE CARPENTER will get home from work. I feel cocky. I'm probably 14-16 years old based on how much I think I know *(and how little discernment I seemingly possess).*] //

⁂

Maj. = 0- THE WEAVER: #0017, 1- THE CARPENTER: #0020, 2-THE DANCER: #0024
CONSTRUCTION: #0533, #0561, #0710, #0719
THE MAKER: #0038

⁂

#0017 - December 31, 2017 @ 05:00 (Montaña Larapata, Peru)

[0017.1 / 0061] [I'm on a multi-day bus tour without a destination. I'm joined by 30-40 friends and familiar faces from different eras of my current lifetime. Numerous conversations vie for my full attention, but I keep quiet and listen to a few. At midday, the group decides to rest and stretch at a rustic bed and breakfast. A welcoming wooden sign out front draws us in. Outside, it appears quaint and cozy. Inside, the interior is vast and maze-like. An attendant grabs my vintage red Samsonite suitcases and takes them to a storage room. I'm skeptical when I'm told my bags will wind up on the correct bus for the next leg of the journey. My hunch is the staff have a habit of rummaging through and pilfering from guest luggage. I turn invisible, pass by the attendant and become a curious klepto as I wade through the room of crudely stacked bags. I see a bulge in an exterior pouch of a black roller board. I unzip it, reach in and pull out an orange vial of dank marijuana nuggets, which I open and eat.

"Damn, it's sativa," I murmur as I become catatonically stoned and increasingly anxious.

I run in a zigzag pattern out the front door, pausing behind bureaus and credenzas along the path to help ground myself.

Once outside I encounter my entire traveling posse, now dressed in Halloween costumes. Most of them wear grease paint on their faces and lurch around the autumn leaf covered lawn of the B&B. Reacting to my heightening neurosis, I further question the motives of the property managers. I become a conspiracy theorist. I scramble back indoors, running up a flight of stairs towards a gymnasium sized room where I believe I'll find my luggage. I arrive, and briefly meet a petite woman that suggests,

"Try the room furthest down on the right."

I take her cue. When I pivot to look inside, I encounter a gypsy. The furniture is dusty. The shades are drawn. A magenta scarf tossed over a nightstand lamp casts a rooty red tone on the ordinary ecru walls. Still stoned and with the gypsy present, I look through her dresser drawer. I absurdly peer down the cold air returns on the floor searching for my baggage. I'm dually motivated by desires to *"find my shit and eat more pot."* Another woman appears in the gypsy's doorway inquiring as to what I'm doing. My response is to shout myriad unkind expletives while devolving into histrionics. I know I've been cursed, perhaps forever bound to this property as I peer from the window and see the tour bus roll on without me.]

[0017.2 / 0062] [I coach the USA Women's Gymnastics team. We're at the "Co-Ed World Championships" and lined up for the opening procession. I have a red and white megaphone slung around my neck. THE WEAVER serves as assistant coach. She and I share a joint part-nership with BELA and MARTHA KARYOLI. During warm ups, I'm astonished by the skill of a male competitor who performs a new element on the parallel bars. He successfully flips forward six times, lands perfectly on his upper arms, and then swings smoothly through to his next maneuver. When completed in competition, it'll be regarded as the most challenging skill successfully executed on the world stage. The competitive field is not segmented by gender. Teams can be composed of any constellation of gender identities. There is one podium to win. My team is composed entirely of cisgender women.

Rotation one concludes and teams transition between apparatuses, accompanied by a funk track I've written *(and croon the lyrics to)* as music blares overhead. The crowd is supportive and animated. I don't know if they're responding to my singing, or the athletes. Energy in the arena is uplifting, electric and focused. I'm personal friends with the judges, which doesn't do me any favors. It creates negative scoring bias for my athletes. Their bar is higher. They'll be judged more stringently.

A male gymnast vaults and receives a '10.' One of my alternate athletes is the last to perform. In order for us to take the podium, she must also achieve a '10.' While I'm not confi-dent she can do it, I encourage her to *"go out there and do the best you can."* She tumbles effort-lessly and playfully through her routine. A slight flex in her left toe during a complex twisting element could result in a marginal deduction, and consequently a loss for the team. She steps off the floor after saluting the judges. I congratulate her with a hug. I consider the podium surrendered, then a roar emerges from the crowd. **10.0.** Music starts to play and the arena breaks out into song,

"I weave! I weave love with Yoooooooou!"
"Heyy! Heyy! Heyy! Come on, Casssayyyy!"
"Yeah, we just couldn't have picked a Claasssssic, like you!"
"Though now.... how we gonna crawwwwwl?"

The team ascends the jungle gym podium like a group of playful swinging monkeys. Once at the top we crawl prone with our butts upturned toward the crowd like a hoard of mandrills. I wear my trademark fedora. When I glance up at the roof, I see **Death** and a shadowy counterpart floating above us. I continue singing, remove my hat and forcibly offer it to **Death** by placing it on its hooded head. Tiny fear beings gnawing at the ankles of the team fall away from the podium.

The women stand confidently atop the monkey bar grid, dozens of feet up in the air. Choreographed drones hover in front of each woman and drape a gold medal around each neck. The crowd roars. Our arms extend up together. I'm amazed. Even in the midst of victory, my mind still churns with the image of what I'd seen earlier seen on the parallel bars.] //

⁂

Maj. = 0- THE WEAVER: #0020
DEATH: #0496, #0519, #0529, #0567
GYMNASTICS: #0591, #0701, #0797
GREASE PAINT: #0496
BUS: #0697, #0715, #0721, #0725

⁂

#0018 - January 1, 2018 @ 00:01 (Montaña Larapata, Peru)

[0018.1 / 0063] [I'm awash in deep resonant vibration. Kaleidoscopic fractal patterns occur sacredly and psychedelically. *"Is this a ceremonial abstraction?"* Images fade as rapidly as they rise. I lie flat like a corpse, suspended in an abyss as an out of body vibrational entity works me over like a spiritual masseur. Shamanic icaros are sung by medicine women whose vocal transmissions weave gorgeous geometric patterns across an interminable void. A tube of hexagonally milled amber is placed in my left hand. I hold it up to inspect it. Within the amber is a root that looks like a musical eighth note, suspended in time. I take a closer look. I'm not sure, but it looks like...**two fused asparagus spears?**]

[0018.2 / 0064] [I'm guided by a group of spirits to the edge of a still, vast body of water at sunset. I'm awestruck by the appearance of a giant glowing rainbow-white being. As it approaches it favors a whale shark with hundreds of giant squid tentacles extending from its gills. It glides through the water, and seamlessly emerges without a splash nor drip, soaring high to the heavens overhead. It traces a Möbius strip pattern that extends to the edge of my field of vision. The group stands to receive a blessing when the celestial shark-squid soars above us. It expels a flat crystal ribbon which descends and washes through us, tuning and purifying our spirits.] //

⁂

SUNSET: #0561, #0566, #0638, #0667
MOBIUS STRIP: #0540
MUSICAL: #0405, #0512
HEXAGONS: #0437

⁂

♣ 1.2 - THE BOOK OF OPHIUCHUS: 0019-0047 ♣

#0019 - January 1, 2018 @ 21:35 (Montaña Larapata, Peru)

[0019.1 / 0065] [I travel on a bus with a group of 10 people. THE HEALER, THE WARD OF GAIA, and THE BLUES SINGER *(soulful, pained, and estranged)* are familiar to me, while the others are not. We arrive at a hostel to rest overnight. THE HEALER and THE WARD OF GAIA take a space on a stage that has enough room for them and their newborn baby. The room is spacious and rustic, walls thickened by brown wood planks and complementary drab tones. Window screens are fashioned from mosquito nets. Others in the group set their sleeping bags side by side in a row across the length of the space. The group becomes quiet, and we fall asleep.

Everyone immediately rouses when a young man leaps up from his sleeping bag and violently strikes himself repeatedly in the face. He pulls his hair out in clumps leaving fragments of bloody scalp dripping red on the floor. The violence is unilateral and self-directed. He's not a direct physical threat to any member of the party. THE HEALER leaps down from the stage, walks towards the young man and places a hand on top of his head. After some deep breaths, the young man calms down and returns to rest in his sleeping bag.

I step out of my skin for a wider perspective. As the young man rests, THE HEALER becomes a shared entity with the disease. Space time around them distorts and flexes. I observe a cosmic vacuum flow through THE HEALER that *"sucks out old thought forms and energetic programs"* that allow the disease to latch to the body. During the process, THE WARD OF GAIA calmly waves me over to her sleeping area on the stage. She points to her left and requests, *"Can you find out what she wants?"*

I look where she points and see a gaunt, zombie looking woman crawling on her hands and knees towards the baby crib. *"54. CHUBBY. BUNNIES."* I hear her repeat scratchily under her breath through decaying vocal cords. I walk to her and offer my hand to help her stand. We share a moment face to face before I place one hand on her chest and another behind her neck. She surrenders the weight of her head to the support of my hand. As she does this, her neck lengthens until her head and face descend out of view into the bowels of a bottomless garbage can behind her. I hold her with consistent and interminable support. Her neck retracts. When our eyes meet, she appears lively and vital.

She and I connect in our own unique space-time reality. Boils and pimples rise up and flood across the surface of my skin. I experience shared pain and infernal heat with her, and allow it to flow freely through and out of the space. None of it's me. The intensity of the healing waves diminishes. Once we become neutral, I psychically disconnect from her and invite her to rest in her sleeping bag.

Rabid dogs torment and nip at the hands and arms of another young man who's walked in his sleep to the front porch of the cabin. THE HEALER and I work together to shoo the dogs and generate calm. THE HEALER is notably fatigued. He pauses to kneel while psychedelic cow eye sized boils wildly pass up and out of him like carbonation. Though tired, he's resolved and undeterred. We look right and see the baby swaddled in Shipibo weavings on the stage. He's well protected.

"They will keep him clean. They're necessary but... it's... messed up," he says.

I nod.

THE HEALER continues, *"No kids are actually trying to kill themselves. It's all interference."*

I hold silent. A sizzling sound originates from the far end of the cabin. THE BLUES SINGER stands by an oil fryer preparing yucca for breakfast. It's abundant. It looks and smells delicious. As the group sleeps, the four of us sip tea, eat our share of the yucca and wax poetic on what's next for us.

"Miracle creators need to take care of ourselves," THE HEALER plainly states. I agree.] //

⁂

Maj. = 20 - THE HEALER: #0025
Min. = ◆*- THE WARD OF GAIA: #0027*
ZOMBIE: #0714
BREAKFAST: #0482, #0556, #0633, #0640, #0716, #0728

⁂

#0020 - January 2, 2018 @ 00:45 (Montaña Larapata, Peru)

[0020.1 / 0066] [THE CARPENTER, THE WEAVER, THE ATHEIST and I sit around a card table in the kitchen making small talk. THE WEAVER poses a general question about Peru, and asks each of us to share our personal adventures. I've talked plenty. I've carried the conversation and offer *"THE ATHEIST can share just as easily as I can. He's 22 and has been there too!"*] //

⁂

Maj. = 0- THE WEAVER: #0024, 1- THE CARPENTER: #0024, 8- THE ATHEIST: #0024

⁂

#0021 - January 2, 2018 @ 02:45 (Montaña Larapata, Peru)

[0021.1 / 0067] [THE FIDUCIARY and I attend a social event at the home of a mutual friend. Our friend is male. THE FIDUCIARY has a stronger relationship with the friend than I do. I forget both the friend's name and face. We watch a large television in a dark room that has no back wall, nor roof. Abundant stars drop light on us from above. We sprawl out across a mesh of springs stretched across a steel bed frame, and find it comfortable. In other realities, the mesh grid of steel wire would stab, scratch, and pierce our backs and legs. Some guests consume craft cocktails. We've concealed our consumption of boxed theater candies as we huddle at the back of the room where a wall would ordinarily be.

We entertain ourselves by opening locker sized doors on an oversized advent calendar, extracting and quickly consuming palm sized chocolate eggs filled with peanut butter. Once we've opened all the doors, we auspiciously giggle when I bring out a five-gallon pail filled with chocolate covered nails and sharp steel bits coated in rock sugar from beneath the bed. We eat our fill, paying little attention to the fact we're not able to digest steel.]

[0021.2 / 0068] [I'm about to enter an underground sex dungeon with a group of friends. We pay our admission and descend down a narrow red lit stairwell that smells of sawdust and questionable decisions. Tonight's marquis event venerates the love and vulnerability a world-famous Russian porn star shares with his demure, quiet, lovely, and effeminately expressed male partner. In recognition of the compromises that have allowed their relationship to blossom and deepen, the demure partner has agreed to participate in one live-stream pornographic scene, on location at the club.

The partner's requests are explicit. The scene will occur: *"in a white-tiled bathroom in an*

43

undisclosed region of the club to create the illusion of privacy and intimacy." The partner is fully aware of the irony that thousands will view the scene. Our group's attention is fixed on TVs mounted over the bar where we see the performers arrive on set, one by one. The partner gives a brief wave to the camera, takes a big inhale and exhales a deep sigh. He walks towards a wall with a waist high 18-inch hole. He bends over and places his body, pelvis to crown within, leaving his legs and ass exposed. His legs spread and as the camera pans down, it shows he's placed a foot on either side of a bubble filled Jacuzzi tub.

Another young man enters, perhaps 20 years old, barely containing his excitement to be a guest star in the scene. He's a virgin. He disrobes and descends into the tub with his back toward the tile wall. He takes position directly beneath the partner's lower torso. The walls of the set aren't soundproof. Whistles and cheers from the crowd at the bar permeate the set and give rise to an anticipatory grin which peel back the upturned corners of the young bathing man's mouth. The Russian porn star steps confidently on to the set, pausing to pose towards the camera for the aroused crowd. A quick shot of the bathing boy shows a ring of black dingy soap scum occurring as a webbed halo encircling his head. The Russian porn star is large, muscular, virile, and sports a very large cock and balls. He disrobes, walks to his partner and kisses his ass while delivering a hard spank. The crowd responds with strong approval. The Russian begins penetrating his partner. The camera pans down, centering on the young virgin's face. Small droplets of blood rain down on his crown, which first pool, then streak crimson lines down his cheeks. The smile never leaves the virgin's face. He believes he's participating in something Holy and receives his sacrament.

Our attention moves off the video screen to a sexy man donning a ball cap, jock strap, athletic socks and cleats sitting on a chair atop a go-go box. He flirts with passersby. It's THE LUMBERJACK (*strong, silent, and observant*). It's been 10 years since I've seen him. He's hot. Maybe I'll tell him what I think. He's broad chested, sporting mad crazy vascularity and unmatched muscular striation. My eyes shift to his bulge. I really want to blow him. We flirt. He also flirts with THE FIDUCIARY. THE LUMBERJACK pulls his jockstrap aside, displaying an erection at my eye level. I share a glance with him and lean in to kiss it. His hand meets my forehead, and keeps my mouth from touching him.

"$50," THE LUMBERJACK says. THE FIDUCIARY backs away and appears to be momentarily revolted when I pull out a $100 bill and say, *"Fine,"* with a smile. I then spend significant time and attention inspecting, tasting, and exploring the consistency and contours of THE LUMBERJACK. Eventually I get so aroused I ejaculate in my pants without a touch to my member. THE LUMBERJACK doesn't cum.

THE FIDUCIARY taps me on the left shoulder and tells me to look up at a TV. I notice I'm on the screen, and the blowjob I gave THE LUMBERJACK has been viewed by the entire club. I'm not bothered. I stand and walk towards the bar, staffed by a butch female bartender. She laughs tongue-in-cheek while holding a device that activates different cameras strategically mounted throughout the bar.

"Hey You! You know I never signed my likeness release, right?"

I know I don't have much (*if any*) legal standing, but I make the minor threat. I gather my things and head for the parking lot, playing like I'm offended as a parody. I take a lap around the fenced lot, encountering some giggles and mild mockery from small groups of guys who sit on truck tailgates drinking beer. A couple toss empty glass bottles at me, which break at my feet. I decide to go back inside and upon entry I'm flanked by a parade of male sex workers. I can see myself between two lines in the center of a CCTV feed. I pass the club owner who talks candidly with THE LUMBERJACK. They're mid-argument, but he turns to me shouting,

"It was actually $55," handing me $45 in cash.

THE HANDYMAN (*smiley, eager, and playful*) appears like a genie to my right in a puff of smoke saying,

"If you give that to me, I'll come to your next class."

I casually pass him the cash as I'm visually taken by another guy I want to blow.] //

✢

Maj. = 9- THE FIDUCIARY: #0083

BEER: #0403, #0561, #0602, #0610, #0705, #0718

SMOKE: #0747, #0755, #0762, #0768, #0773, #0787

THE HANDYMAN: #0833

✢

#0022 - January 2, 2018 @ 05:00 (Montaña Larapata, Peru)

[0022.1 / 0069] [I observe humans being kept as house pets. An expansive, wet slate wall extends upward beyond where my eyes can see. Thick metal chains threaded through eyelets mounted to the wall just inches above the ground clasp the people's ankles. The chains are stamped with a "Gravity Enterprises" trademark. Soft gold white light illuminates the otherwise grey-blackness of the wall from the top down. Water cascades in a slight trickle to the ground where it drips and splashes at the pet-people's perpetually moistened feet. The pet-people don standard Western clothes (*gym shorts, business suits, jeans and t-shirts, etc.*). They're happy and blissfully unaware of their captivity.

I turn away from the wall and wade across a vast body of water. The depth of the water varies, but is mostly ankle deep. It's a bit perplexing. Shifts in color tones from light to dark don't correlate to the relative depth of the water. One step is shallow. The next step, I'm up to my neck as I traverse the pixelated map of turquoise and indigo. Rain falls from above and splashes up to my chin when it strikes the surface of the water. One precarious step sends me chest deep and flailing, slowing my progress towards a giant single boulder in the distance that rises over 200 feet above the waterline. With steady determination, I arrive at the boulder. When I touch it, I'm sent back to the underground sex club in dream [0021.2 / 0068].

Tonight, the club sponsors a drag revue. A drag queen rips a strand of pearls from her neck and tosses them to me at the peak of her lip-synced show tune performance. Once offstage she takes a seat next to me. We rest our heads against one another as we watch the parade of performers and appreciate their expressions of glamour.]

[0022.2 / 0070] [THE CONFIDANT and THE WRANGLER (*orderly, direct, feminine*) are drunk when I visit them one night at their future-modern urban dwelling. THE CONFIDANT just baked a yellow cake in the shape of an "ohm" in honor of his son's third birthday. I find it significant that he hasn't frosted the cake yet.]

[0022.3 / 0071] [I'm back in the chest deep water. In an instant it drains to reveal a craggy land mass composed of various grades of blue gemstones. THE SEXUAL SACRED (*flirtatious, dramatic, and opportunistic*) calls from the sex club with other friends who chime in. They're raging drunk at the drag revue. They cajole me with multiple invitations to return and

45

express how much they miss me. I stay seated on the blue rocks and watch them sparkle as the sun sets.] //

⁂

Maj. = 16- THE CONFIDANT: #0075
DRAG QUEEN: #0714, #0726
URBAN: #0473, #0566
THE SEXUAL SACRED: #0073
THE WRANGLER: #0189

⁂

#0023 - January 2, 2018 @ 20:15 (Montaña Larapata, Peru)

[0023.1 / 0072] [I'm awash in watercolor. The reality frame rate is just slow enough that I can see life advance one painted panel at a time, like a stop motion animated cartoon. Lines are blurred and diffused, giving subtle softness and union between all objects, inanimate and otherwise. It's night. The brilliant white moon radiates from above. A group has gathered on a mountain for an evening of dance and song with a shared intention to invite SAINT PETER to the party (*so long as he brings his special set of keys*). THE FLUTIST (*prayerful, musical, and curious*) leads numerous songs and offers short interludes with his instrument, calling forth muses, faeries and woodland sprites. He's designated to *"invoke the spirit."*

He verifies each person's intentions one by one, making eye contact and taking an energetic imprint of each person's soul. THE HARBINGER is a small boy, acting as THE FLUTIST's impartial third party and non-conditional validator of *"the truth."* THE FLUTIST and I connect. His pupils become dilated black saucers. He confirms my intention aligns with the group agreement. We invite a gateway in space time to open. A large steel garage door opens to reveal a cave. The night sky erupts in ribbons of bright ethereal pastel tones. THE FLUTIST's long blond hair blows back and upward when a blast of cool air roars in front of him. His eyes close and rest. His head and chin gently bob from side to side. A white globe-like bubble appears around him and expands. *"Welcome to the med-i-cine!"*

A choir of voices erupts in song. Am I at a young child's birthday party? The cacophony around me feels like Chuck E. Cheese. Animatronic puppets of various shapes and sizes pop out from behind THE FLUTIST like a massive robotic bouquet. The cave glows an alien greenish white. The group breaks into ecstatic dance. Subsequent songs and prayers match the ecstatic energy. I'm flooded with great joy and laugh until my abdomen is exhausted.] //

⁂

MOON: #0506, #0544, #0556, #0572, #0668
ALIEN: #0416, #0452, #0515, #0527
CHOIR: #0476, #0525, #0758
PASTEL: #0436, #0561
THE FLUTIST: #0039
THE HARBINGER: #0798

⁂

#0024 - January 2, 2018 @ 23:30 (Montaña Larapata, Peru)

[0024.1 / 0073] [I shop at high velocity. The environment feels like an amalgamation of

46

"far future" and "distant past." A giant labyrinth composed of dark stone the size of Manhattan is home to a large open-air market. Though "old" feeling, commercial transactions clear and settle by way of 3D holograms maintained by sentient technobots from different planets, galaxies, and dimensions. As I walk the market, I'm particularly amused by a negotiation occurring between two microscopic robots who haggle over terms of a wholesale futures contract for salt. One is displeased with how the current agreement is framed and aggressively swirls a steel arm at the other. I interject to drive up the bid and volume, then step away.

An ad for a holographic DREAM THEATER concert piques my interest. Here it's common for people to augment their 3D existence with technology that fully immerses each in their own uniquely supplemented reality. A nearby woman shops for fruit, while concurrently attending a political rally. A man wipes off a cafe table, while surrounded by a crowd at an 80's arena rock show. This is normalized life, as close to a fourth dimensional state as a human brain can navigate.

Here, people get married annually to their newest selves. I take note of the date, realizing it's THE DANCER and THE ATHEIST's wedding anniversary. They join me in the market. THE WEAVER and THE CARPENTER meet us at a busy intersection. I search for a wedding gift, while the DREAM THEATER concert I paid for starts around me. I can initially see three of the band members (JOHN MYUNG, JOHN PETRUCCI and JORDAN RUDESS). Enshrouded by a yellow gold haze, they occur as "beyond human" double exposed projections as I wander through different maker booths in the market. Music begins with a precise and thunderous symphonic flourish. The composition is complex and beautifully technical, which perfectly accompanies my shopping journey. Off to my lower right, holograms of JAMES LABRIE and MIKE MANGINI appear translucent and hover over rows of prospective gifts I contemplate purchasing for THE DANCER and THE ATHEIST. The music speeds and crescendos. I'm aware I've selected a gift, but don't know what it is. THE WEAVER and THE CARPENTER suggest we get THE DANCER and THE ATHEIST to their "spot."

We leave the market and head to a rustic woodland resort. When we arrive, signage indicates only married couples are permitted entrance. THE WEAVER and THE CARPENTER go in first. THE DANCER and THE ATHEIST follow. As I stand outside, I see the upper half of a split wooden door swing back, exposing a wood carving of the cover to the Guns 'n Roses album, "Appetite for Destruction." A vinyl banner suspended overhead reads, "WELCOME TO THE JUNGLE!" My married family members spiral up a staircase together and explore other levels of the property while I remain outside. THE WEAVER leans over a banister and calls down to me to present my wedding gift. I pull out two large pies and set one in each of my palms as an offering. It's unclear if they like or accept my gift. THE WEAVER is preoccupied with cooking something and suggests I take the pies back to the market later for a refund.]

[0024.2 / 0074] [I fly over a pristine snowcapped mountain range singing a rousing song accompanied by an orchestra. *This. Is. My. Overture!*]

[0024.3 / 0075] [I'm in a busy shopping mall looking at a wall of sweatpants, advertised as the hottest new trend. "3 TIER PENDLETON PANTS" are made of patterned panels from different dyed wool blankets. They're warm, durable and heavy. I grab a pair from a table, turning a price tag over in my hand to reveal the suggested retail price of $135.90. I put them down when a handsome and flirtatious associate named "Anthony" models a line of new "*loose knit sweaters*" that are intensely colorful and shaggy. He winks at me and invites me to join him in a changing room for a private fitting. I offer him oral sex. He promptly turns me down with a smile. I leave the changing room and see a vast collection of new shirt styles displayed on a linear series of equally sized large round wooden tables. A suggested look pairs a shaggy sweater with "3 TIER PENDLETON PANTS." After contemplating, I make a selection and walk to the sales desk. THE SURGICAL TECH (*awed, recovering, and humorous*) completes my credit transaction with a smile. I exit the store a satisfied customer.] //

⁂

Maj. = *0- THE WEAVER: #0027, 1- THE CARPENTER: #0033,*
2- THE DANCER: #0037, 8- THE ATHEIST: #0154
DREAM THEATER: #0062
JOHN MYUNG: #0971
SMILE: #0532, #0597, #0667
SHOPPING: #0522, #0678, #0728, #0769, #0773

⁂

#0025 - January 3, 2017 @ 03:50 (Montaña Larapata, Peru)

[0025.1 / 0076] [A group gathers to hear THE HEALER deliver a lecture. The venue is large, open aired and lined by striking red rock formations. It's similar to, yet distinct from Petra. The interior is a series of serpentine walkways carved into stone and gives the impression of a human scale "'M'-ant farm." THE HEALER demonstrates a technique whereby elegant tapestries can be conjured and woven, seemingly out of thin air. His sample weaving is multi-paneled, earth toned and depicts events in a scrolling timeline comparable to the Bayeux Tapestry. I find it essential to take my vitamins (*B12, C, Chlorella, and Spirulina*) as nightfall approaches.

Later, I stand with THE HEALER casually discussing the weaving process. He shares that his conjuring is an inaccurate representation, and in order to attune more clearly, we need to invite the spirit of "Ayahuasca" to guide the loom. I offer my help to him as a vine harvester. He declines because I've taken vitamins, and they'll dissuade the spirit's participation. Overlooking the red rock canyon, I'm left with THE SURGEON (*precise, caring, and open*) sharing a simple dormitory style room. THE LUCKY MAN (*bold, masculine, and nimble*) shares a quick conversation with us then departs on a journey. I believe THE SURGEON will persuade THE HEALER to let me join tonight's vine harvest. Instead, without reason he takes off his clothes, gets in bed and immediately falls asleep. I'm confused.]

[0025.2 / 0077] [I'm in a commercial garage observing a man perform maintenance on an alcohol fueled stock car. It looks like a tricked-out Chevy Camaro. Chatter in Spanish fills the space, though I hear it translated to English as it's spoken. Our team applies a modification to the vehicle to integrate learnings from recent test runs.]

[0025.3 / 0078] [I'm on a plane. I've just landed in North Korea to complete a secret mission. THE GUITARIST is my partner. I carry a bag containing a handgun, small spools of wire thread, and a variety of fuses and detonators. We disembark the plane and walk through the

48

airport terminal towards immigration and customs. The open-air terminal is grey, eerily reminiscent of Communist East Berlin, where THE GUITARIST and I have previously executed missions. Noting the metal detectors at the border, supplemented with large banners proclaiming prohibited items in black block letters I double back through a turnstile to deposit the gun, wire spools and contraband in a garbage can next to a small group of North Korean border agents who take a break.

I back away from the terminal, the parking lot and eventually the border, walking step by step in reverse until I see I've crossed the DMZ and enter South Korea. The Camaro from [0025.2 / 0077], driven by the mechanic, careens down a twisty mountain highway and stops to idle as THE GUITARIST and I jump in the back. The driver makes excited pronouncements in Spanish as he speeds down the road. I notice a small steel tube extending from the side of the car, which the three of us refer to as "the trunk." It's cloaked and carries precious cargo.

We ground ourselves, pull a 180 and drive back to North Korean customs. THE GUITARIST and I exit the car, cross an asphalt parking lot and walk towards a glowing green-white building. We're both surprised at the modernity of the facility, and our interests oddly piqued by the sleek asymmetrical haircuts donned by the female border agents. Oddly, North Koreans seem to only drive black Mercedes Benzes. THE GUITARIST and I are humored that as secret agents these minor details distract and stupefy us.] //

✲✲

Maj. = 20 - THE HEALER: #0035
Min. = ♣- THE GUITARIST: #0036
NORTH KOREA: #0700
CHEVY: #0468, #0545
THE LUCKY MAN: #0026

✲✲

#0026 - January 3, 2018 @ 05:40 (Montaña Larapata, Peru)

[0026.1 / 0079] [I attend a grand opening celebration for a yoga studio. New studio. New city. Same name. The large brick building appears to be in the transitional area of a major city. The immense space doesn't have a sign on the exterior. Passersby in cars fill the adjacent parking lot, flooding in to neighboring tenants who are all fast-food eateries (*Frisch's, Culver's, Zaxby's Chicken, etc.*). A woman drives up by me, slowing to say, *"Hey, how do you like yours? They're cheap and cost effective, right?"* I don't know what she's referring to until she points at the single green inflatable dancing "tube man" positioned outside the yoga studio doorway. A man on the upper floor of an apartment building at the far end of the parking lot shouts at us loudly, yet indecipherably. The woman in the car and I yell back, **"YEAH!"** in unison then look at each other and shrug our shoulders, not knowing what we've just affirmed.

I venture up an obstacle course slide next to the front door of the yoga studio. Camouflage netting stretched in large panels creates loose trampoline surfaces to bound upward to the entrance. There's no explicit reference to help students know this is the entry point to the studio. THE HILLBILLY is convinced the trampolines are, *"the promotional tool that will get more bodies in the door."*

THE NURSE is focused on ensuring newly installed anti-gravity stairwells have been correctly positioned and meet building code specifications. *"There should be seven steps in the front and eight in the back,"* she states. I ascend the massive structure, taking note of the hurried and haphazard construction. I consider it generally unsafe. Two single sheets of basic white printer paper have been soaked through and ruined by a water leak. One sheet of paper offers a welcome and class enrollment instructions. The other is a memorial, listing names of military veterans who have recently committed suicide. Large holes in the trampoline surfaces create imminent hazards and risk of severe injury to upward bounding patrons.

I vertically scale the exterior, and once inside the building note I'm inside a large estate home. A space within the home is designated as the yoga studio. A member reception area with a single point of sale terminal has been constructed on a small white marble countertop in a modern chef's kitchen. THE AYURVEDIC follows me in, intending to take the next scheduled class. Once she's clicked her name on the tablet computer to check in, she walks to the fridge and removes a bottle of prosecco. We sit with backs against a cupboard on a black and white art deco floor, swigging from the bottle and cracking wise. THE WHITE RABBIT enters with two attractive, fit women moments after class commences. 55 bodies are in the room. There's room for 60, so we let them pass while continuing to get lit off bubbly.

I stumble to my feet and duck around a corner, unexpectedly discovering THE NURSE and THE HILLBILLY's master suite. I pause, thinking *"What a bizarre use of such a big space."* I turn to the right and see a long corridor, at the end of which a wedding procession advances. THE LUCKY MAN (*grounded, clear, and masculine*) directs the wedding party to line up. He places a smoky dark veil over each of their faces as they pass by, which they experience as uplifting, joyous, and energizing.]

[0026.2 / 0080] [I'm on a fast-moving subterranean train. Seating is arranged perpendicular to the car similar to grandstand bleachers. The underground world zooms by at a dizzying pace, putting passengers into a slight non-ordinary state of consciousness. Someone seated in the row behind me taps me on the shoulder and with a slur asks if I'll sell him my extra ticket to Coachella. *"No. I've never been,"* I respond before dropping back under hypnosis.] //

⁎⁎

Maj. = 13- THE NURSE: #0115

Min. = ♣- *THE HILLBILLY: #0201,* ♦-*THE WHITE RABBIT: #0045,* ♦-*THE AYURVEDIC: # 0032*
TRAINS: #0466, #0689

⁎⁎

#0027 - January 4, 2018 @ 05:00 (Montaña Larapata, Peru)

[0027.1 / 0081] [I'm queued at a concession stand. I'm humored by the display and want to purchase two products. The items are regionally specific. English product names have been improperly translated from Japanese, resulting in phrases that contextually read as deeply racist and inappropriate. I want to buy them out of novelty. They're grossly absurd. One item is a small theater candy sized box. The other is a pickled vegetable, hermetically sealed in its juices. An Asian-Pacific dialect is spoken all around me, even though I communicate in English. A group of patrons gathers behind me. An Asian woman with decaying teeth makes a repeated stabbing motion with her right hand into my right lower back. The pain is acute. I react by spinning around and pushing her back at her shoulders. Though short lived, some confusion and violent energy spins up between us. When calm, we move to a cafeteria lunchroom table and sit on top. Our legs dangle back and forth at the knees in waves. The formerly abusive woman tilts her bag of "Octopus Chicharrons" towards me as a peace offering. I accept by grabbing one and chomping.]

[0027.2 / 0082] [I'm a member of a motocross stunt team with THE VICTOR (*heroic, reverent, and pained*) and MARILYN MANSON.]

[0027.3 / 0083] [I learn a technique that enables me to create beautiful jellyfish basket-like structures accentuated with strands of fairy lights. When I toss a puck sized gadget in the air then press a button on a controller held in my opposite hand, delicate web-like chandeliers open like canopies over a person in a constellation of their favorite colors. With the backdrop of a carbon black sky, I toss dozens of the pucks upward. Sparkles of light slowly cascade downward to cooing sounds of delighted customers. Contently, they meditatively walk invisible labyrinthine paths around me. Occasionally I pedal an invisible tandem bike with an invisible partner, as I deliver these special gifts. Color me a cosmic paperboy who would enjoy this job until everything in the universe fades to black.]

[0027.4 / 0084] [THE WEAVER drives a car erratically through a plat of unfinished homes. I'm in the passenger seat. It's chaotic. Large gaps in the road require tremendous speed to leap and clear. It feels like we're being pursued after committing a robbery. Maybe we've stolen the car? The homes appear to be made of simple adobe bricks. I'm not convinced, but THE WEAVER is certain she has the skills to get us to our destination.]

[0027.5 / 0085] [I watch a documentary in a theater about an English butler who becomes a world-renowned pastry chef. The film is moving and enthralling. I'm so transfixed by the narrative I fail to notice THE WARD OF GAIA seated next to me. She leans forward to ask me something. The volume of her voice is so low I can't hear her. I assume she wants me to pass the popcorn, so I do. My eyes stay pointed towards the screen.] //

✿

Maj. = 0- THE WEAVER: #0033
Min. = ◆- THE WARD OF GAIA: #0028
MARILYN MANSON: #0244
SIMPLE: #0405, #0409, #0417, #0446
THE VICTOR: #0034

✿

#0028 - January 5, 2018 @ 00:35 (Montaña Larapata, Peru)

[0028.1 / 0086] [I rapidly bilocate between two different houses in the midst of a strong overnight thunderstorm. One house is a grand manor, where I practice a sophisticated repertoire of icaros in the performance salon. I wear an interactive green camouflage mesh shirt fashioned with miniature LED panels that illuminate when I sing specific tones. Patterns skitter around the front and back like Tetris tiles. I decide to walk (*in my body*) from one house to the other. When rain touches the fragile shirt, some of the circuits short out and leave dark patches in the mesh.

The other house is a smaller thatched roof cottage. Once inside, I encounter THE PUBLIC MEDIUM, my neighbor from down the street. He contemplates ordering a car for the short drive home. We both know that few cab drivers will be out and in service during such a wild storm. I offer him a place to stay overnight, but he politely declines.

In parallel, THE VICE BROTHERS (*rough, crass, and rugged*) have taken up residence in the other, larger home and laughingly read Dr. Seuss comic books to each other. They continue reading to soften the impending blow of losing their home to flooding. THE WARD OF GAIA and THE PANDA (*gentle, analytical, and helpful*) reassure them that *"singing is the best soother."* I'm inspired to raise my voice and sing praises to the sky.] //

✿

Maj. = 18- THE PUBLIC MEDIUM: #0125
Min. = ◆- THE WARD OF GAIA: #0047
NEIGHBOR: #0417, #0580, #0607
COTTAGE: #0627, #0687
THE PANDA: #0047

✿

#0029 - January 5, 2018 @ 03:50 (Montaña Larapata, Peru)

[0029.1 / 0087] [I work in a lab, researching a new species of soap generating fungus.]

[0029.2 / 0088] [I'm out on the town for a night of partying. An African American man dressed like a suave pimp drives a pink Cadillac with gold rims, and follows me from place to place. He arrives just after me, everywhere I go. I overhear him speak, noting he's in a perpetual state of complaint. I consciously move away from him and his female companion. I go to a Lutheran church. They follow me to the basement. I attempt to ditch them by doubling back and taking an escalator to a fellowship hall. On most evenings the church transitions from a quiet contemplative daytime worship space to a raucous night club. Right now, it's late, likely past 2:00am.

I make a left turn and briskly walk down a narrow hallway, intending to exit the church. Once outside I step up to a cab. THE LITTLE BROTHER (*loving, playful, and athletic*) rolls the back window down. He's "happy drunk" and requests my help. I shred and chop boxes of lettuce and onions that block the cab door, then toss the contents in the window. I repeat this until he's up to his neck in salad inside the cab. We giggle at the absurdity. He pauses to reflect saying, *"Dude (*hiccup*), you're really...."* before he freezes. His voice trails off and his head sinks below the surface of the voluminous backseat salad. A quick turn of my head finds the pimp a few feet away accusing me of trying to steal his woman. *"Man, **you have it twisted.** I'm not hitting on her,"* I say as he lunges toward me, intending to strike my face with the handle of his cane.] //

✿

BASEMENT: #0773, #0793
CHURCH: #0542, #0758
PIMP: #0500

SALAD: #0778
THE LITTLE BROTHER: #0591

⁂

#0030 - January 5, 2018 @ 06:30 (Montaña Larapata, Peru)

[0030.1 / 0089] [It's daybreak. I play hand bells with a choir in a misty bog. THE PHYSI-CIST *(lamenting, unconfident, and cerebral)* conducts. We rehearse for tonight's ritual. When practice concludes we collectively descend slowly into the muddy water with eyes gently closed. When my eyes open, I discover myself in a lodge at a public camping area. A large man with a thick Irish accent approaches with a request to join our community. He offers and shares a special medicinal cake with the group. THE PSYCHONAUT *(non-relatable, spacey, and crazed)* requests a second portion of cake with a grin. He's scolded by the group for being greedy. I feel low grade selfishness flow from him, but nothing toxic. THE PHYSICIST enters the lodge. She thanks everyone for participating in the choir and gently reminds us, *"tonight's ceremony will be possible once we close the current funding gap of $1000."*] //

⁂

IRISH: #0603
CAKE: #0406, #0452, #0513, #0729, #0768
RITUAL: #0543, #0593, #0631
THE PSYCHONAUT: #0040
THE PHYSICIST: #0045

⁂

#0031 - January 6, 2018 @ 00:15 (Montaña Larapata, Peru)

[0031.1 / 0090] [Ants swarm my body. My arms, back, face, legs...all covered. The ants avoid my feet. A few lovingly bite my skin to trigger a mild immune response. I'm itchy and uncomfortable, then realize they're rebooting my nervous system. My nerves fire repeatedly to recalibrate, then come online with an upgraded operating system. I place my hands on my head and give myself some nourishing touch to stabilize. My colon spastically contracts causing me to repeatedly shit. Once initialized, the body powers down and goes completely offline for six hours. After this provisional rest period, the body switches on from the center line out in all directions, from point to point. The reboot is systematic and deliberate. A holographic meter suspended above my head displays the text **"Defragmentation Progress."** A completion bar inches along, filling from left to right. The scene fades to black.] //

⁂

INCHES: #0657, #0703, #0742
SHIT: #0439, #0502, #0531, #0552
NERVOUS SYSTEM: #0659, #0742

⁂

#0032 - January 6, 2018 @ 06:15 (Montaña Larapata, Peru)

[0032.1 / 0091] [The scene pivots between two different locations. The first is an outdoor promenade in mid-morning. It's lined with grand leafy trees and boasts tight concrete side-

53

walks filled with people out for a leisurely stroll. A green grassy space at the center is popu-lated with a bunch of vendor tents. The small host town looks forward to this annual fair. I'm drawn into conversation with a bald woman who staffs a tent at the far end of the park.

The other location finds me at the back of a large white stone gothic cathedral. Soft white light pours through crystal prismatic stained-glass windows. I walk towards a gift shop. A book signing is underway, and I become very interested in meeting the author for whom many have queued. I ascend a staircase and turn left, discovering a meek yet ornate room. Aside from a regal red carpet that leads to the author's table and a half dozen gold fixtures displayed on marble pedestals, it's completely empty. The author is the bald woman from the fair. A fan whispers in my ear that it's PEMA CHÖDRÖN. She's surrounded by a ringed web of soft white gold light.

I blink and discover myself standing next to her at the pop-up tent on the greenspace. I'm disoriented. We both laugh as she personalizes a book for me and gives me a red and grey yoga blanket. She also wants to sell me a "Mountain1" stainless steel water bottle. PEMA CHÖDRÖN steps away to give me space to think. I decide not to buy it because someone else's Yerba Mate residue occludes the neck of the bottle. THE AYURVEDIC appears, smiles and quietly laughs as she hands me a different unsullied bottle. PEMA CHÖDRÖN returns and autographs the new bottle, pressuring me to buy. Her smile is what closes the sale.] //

⁎⁎

Min. = ◆*- THE AYURVEDIC: #0037*
STAINED GLASS: #0459, #0535, #0748
GOTHIC CATHEDRAL: #0535

⁎⁎

#0033 - January 8, 2018 @ 04:30 (Montaña Larapata, Peru)

[0033.1 / 0092] [I've been instructed to start school over. I'm with my parents attending an elementary school open house, though the environment seems strikingly similar to the student union at Miami University in Oxford, Ohio. A campus tour spills us out on a spacious green quad lined by stately uniform red brick edifices. THE WEAVER and THE CARPENTER accompany me. They take pride in my assumed forthcoming accomplish-ments. I'm satisfied. I've achieved my desired level of realization. I consider my prior time as a student a success.

Transport around campus quickly continues. In one moment, we tour a fraternity house turned library. Next, we're courted through a recently renovated administration building. The library occurs a tad chaotic. Some drunk boys occupy one of the salons and pay little attention to the literary gems on the shelves around them. The three of us speed towards a garden where we're received by THE AUDITOR *(diplomatic, balanced, and influential).* After exchanging niceties, he directs us to follow a path, at the end of which we'll find a stone monument with our names inscribed in honoraria with others for their various and substan-tial contributions, *(but it's not clear what we've contributed).* We walk around the monument unable to find our names. A helpful ghost notes our frustration and guides us inside a build-ing, assuring us, *"Your names will eventually appear. The monument is still under construction."*

We're left at a large card catalog inside the main library and invited to sit at a nearby table. A large spool of white ticker tape spins from the card catalog and spills across the table. Even-tually the tape stops and a black triangle icon points to a section where our three names have been burned in. Magnifying glasses help us to review the microscopic font. A deeper inspec-

54

tion yields our discovery of tiny military service medals offset to the right of each printed name on the tape. The ribbons are colorful and indicate meritorious service. Each name has a different ribbon assigned.]

[0033.2 / 0093] [A futuristic shopping mall has taken inspiration from (*or has directly copied*) the layout of the Guggenheim Museum. The vertically spiraling structure is a portal one can walk, *"to experience life 50 earth years ahead of the present moment."* It evolves, instantly adapting in sleekness, form and function. *"Is it a shared reality nexus point? A pylon from which space time itself courts inspiration?"* The sky overhead holds a warm pinkish orange hue. Products sold inside the property align with a consumer's unique definition of what's currently trending in their *"N=1 experience."* Anchor clothiers, chain restaurants and tchotchke kiosks sprout up in meticulously predetermined patterns and revel in momentary newness. Products and brands mature and die in time lapse waves. I've planned for a mid-day shopping visit. I visit a convenience store in search of a snack. Inside it feels like a North African market. All products have Arabic labels. The only recognizable item is Coca Cola, but I don't buy it.

I follow signage to a food court where a vendor in the center of the space instantly appeals to me. Three teenage boys cut the line in front of me. This doesn't bother me. I'm neutral. They order a chicken dish that looks and smells delicious. I ask the woman behind the counter for a sample. I taste it. I like it. I order some. As I walk around the perimeter to a register clerk, I see my service ticket pop up on an invisible screen. Though it reads "chicken" the woman calls out, *"Sirloin!"*

She reaches beneath the counter and lifts up an entire cow's head from the lower cooler. She uses a meat cleaver to hack off a segment that includes a bovine eye and ear. A membrane in the eye snaps. It deflates like a gelatinous balloon.

"Oh, that's fine, don't worry about that," I say. I pay, accept the plate, and after a skeptical first taste decide what I've been given is delicious and an even better option than I believed the chicken would be. After eating gluttonously, I eat a micro-salad. A single sprig of parsley. It's goofily presented on a giant white paper plate. A staff member startles me with an unnecessary apology for a service delay, explaining they were *"frying sesame sugar crinkle fries."*

I didn't order any, but accept a complimentary portion.]

[0033.3 / 0094] [THE WEAVER and I are with members of the band FLEETWOOD MAC at a bizarre pop-up museum, which boasts a new Avant Garde installation that features multiple tracks from their album "Tango in the Night." As we walk through a long marble atrium, we pass a variety of small rooms with red velvet theater curtains. *"Perhaps we could be in for an old-time peep show?"* The song "Seven Wonders" plays overhead as a curtain raises to reveal a massive papier mâché head of BENJAMIN FRANKLIN. It dances slowly from stage edge to stage edge, while its giant lower jaw raises and lowers in time with the lyrics as though it's lip synching. As other cartoon puppets surround BENJAMIN FRANKLIN, the scene has a similar feel to an animated sequence in an episode of Monty Python's Flying Circus. Other curtains rise and fall revealing blank, projection-less silver screens. The song "Everywhere" plays overhead as we exit down a long sloping switchback ramp. THE WEAVER and I agree, we enjoyed what we saw though it was bizarre and we didn't really get it.

"You should see the original video for that song. They were on a LOT of drugs."

I intend for the comment to be funny, but it embarrasses the band members who overhear. They turn back toward the museum and walk away from us. I wasn't aware they were listening.] //

✷✷

Maj. = 0- THE WEAVER: #0036, 1- THE CARPENTER: #0051
MUSEUM: #0746
UNIVERSITY: #0461, #0468, #0483, #0747
LIBRARY: #0406, #0484, #0538, #0554
FOOD COURT: #0726

✷✷

#0034 - January 9, 2018 @ 01:55 (Montaña Larapata, Peru)

[0034.1 / 0095] [I'm on a flight. The interior of the plane is irrationally large. Stone lined retaining walls sporting flat grassy tops give it the look of an Incan agricultural plot. Airplane seats are anchored directly in the center of each grassy flat. The cabin is sparsely populated. I recognize most passengers from a retreat I recently attended. It's decided we'll play a game while in flight. Together, we release our seat belts and begin bouncing freely around the cabin and off the walls. A studio audience watches from the periphery and cajoles us to compete. We're guided to pull vegetables from the grassy flats, then use them to create *"the most delicious salad."* 8-bit arcade music plays as we bound up and down between levels, rendering it reminiscent of Q-Bert or Donkey Kong given the colors, action and format. Gravity behaves differently here.

THE VICTOR and THE RESISTANCE (*confrontational, cathartic, and fierce*) join in, taking starts from opposite sides of the aisle. Occasionally, baskets of loose veggies fall from the sky as "bonuses." When grabbed, celebratory sounds ring through the space. I bounce back and forth aisle agnostic as I gather vegetables. I'm focused, and find the competition fun. I return to my seat, now positioned in a jungle grove kitchen and shred a massive amount of cabbage with a paring knife. Our route and destination are displayed on the back of a cushioned headrest in front of me as I work. The captain announces we're en route to Alaska.

"But I thought we're going to California?"

The topographical map isn't familiar to me. Dramatic changes in water levels seem to have flooded most of what I've previously understood as "Alaska." The rise in sea level happens so swiftly, the map will be obsolete when we land.

"Alaska is icy, rugged and relatively untouched. It's the final frontier," a masculine voice declares over a loudspeaker. I'm indifferent to Alaska. I consider California home.

We're about to land. As we descend, the hearing in my left ear decays. Distracted from salad making by partial deafness, THE VICTOR seizes an opportunity to steal a bushel basket of leafy greens from me. I grab a colander and chase him. Once cornered, I promptly take back what's mine.

"Those are mine! Move!" I shout.

"I don't want to be healed!" THE RESISTANCE and THE VICTOR shout in unison from opposite areas of the plane.

THE RESISTANCE admits she's committed to being unhappy. THE VICTOR is willing to shoulder ancestral burden. I don't want either of those things.

I'm mesmerized by the bounty of arugula, avocados, artichokes and fennel in front of me. I'm committed to ensure THE RESISTANCE and THE VICTOR both have nourishing salad. Sharing with them delights me. I continue bouncing back and forth between hemispheres of

56

the plane. THE VICTOR and THE RESISTANCE's affinity for me plummets, but I'm not deterred. We may be competing, but my intentions are to create a team and produce nourishing salad.

An oversized red and white checkered oven mitt passes slowly in front of my face. Moments from touchdown, the game clock is about to expire. I divide the salad into large stainless-steel bowls for tasting and judging. Bowl in hand, I approach the judges, recognizing one as "Death" though the name placard on the table reads "Healer." I curiously chat up the dark being feeling no hesitation, nor fear.

"Do I hear a baby screaming at the back of the plane?"

I'll never know, as the jet engines roar to slow the plane which has just made a textbook landing.] //

⁕

DONKEY KONG: #0450
SHOULDER: #0671, #0775
GAMES: #0448, #0626, #0714, #0724
VEGETABLES: #0563
THE RESISTANCE: #0035
THE VICTOR: #0039

⁕

#0035 - January 9, 2017 @ 04:20 (Montaña Larapata, Peru)
*First recorded nightmare. *

[0035.1 / 0096] [I'm invited to deeply explore the sensation of fear. I'm dropped on the upper floor of a familiar house. It's dark. I'm forced to my knees on a mattress on the floor. Am I blind? Was I just blindfolded? I'm stripped naked by multiple sets of hands. The sequence repeats.]

[0035.2 / 0097] [I grab what I think is a brass tube on a headboard. I'm coerced by a captor to masturbate with my right hand. My dick feels abnormally large, thick and solidly straight. Surprised, I glance down and see a mangled mass of flesh. I look away and all feels normal. I look down and my eyes witness corporeal horror. The lube the captor forces on me to grease up my cock is chunky, coagulated and has the consistency of sticky millet.

"I'll make this pleasurable," I assure myself, but get frustrated when pain and heat from friction override my ability to orgasm.

I know that downstairs on a well-lit back porch a dying body bleeds out. Someone pushed another out an upstairs window. A wormhole opens in a wall and collapses reality. The scene abruptly halts. Ephemerally I ponder,

"What don't I want to see? Am I not ready?"]

[0035.3 / 0098] [Bacchanalia erupts rowdily through a group. I'm in the hell panel of Bosch's "Garden of Earthly Delights." I'm repeatedly tortured and dismembered, with increasing brutality.]

. . .

[0035.4 / 0099] [I awaken in a desert spacescape. Non-conforming shapes are incomprehensible and seem otherworldly and irrational. The only thing I can make sense of is here, tallow wax candles are commoditized, scarce and highly prized. I enter a dusty sick house for lepers. After exchanging a few social niceties, I become singularly interested in finding THE HEALER. He's popular. I find him on the floor in a cantina. His face is disfigured. He's paraplegic, but scurries about quickly on his hands, dragging his legs behind. As I watch him interact, I suspect he may be drunk. He's missing an eye, and his face is so grotesquely contorted my usual assessment process fails.

I introduce myself. We chat briefly before he breaks away and barrels full speed toward a wooden platform with a five-foot-tall terracotta vase on top. The cataclysmic impact sends the vase flying from the table. It collides with an adobe wall and shatters into powdery red fragments. THE HEALER suffers head wounds. Blood profusely coats his face. I see his pearly white teeth flood with red as heaves and screams,

"I WANTED TO SUFFER!"

He climbs up and looks out a round hole in the clay wall. Blood dripping from his chin, he reaches for a ram's horn and raises it to his lips, trumpeting a tone joyously received by an outside gathering of children who dance the Maypole at the base of the wall.

THE HEALER drops the horn and flings mean spirited energy towards me from his eyes. He traverses the cantina, then violently slams the rickety door to his sleeping room. THE CHEF stands in front of the door with arms crossed. Looking down his nose at me he says,

"He's not to be disturbed."

I find his word choice ironic. THE CHEF places two large mangos with thick rinds on the nearest window sill. Their usable life is limited. They'll soon spoil due to the intense heat. When sliced, their insides look like cantaloupes.

It's socially acceptable for people to publicly play out personal dramas at the cantina. THE SIREN enters and sits. From a high platform behind a dusty curtain, THE OTHER SIREN and THE HIATUS (*observant, contemplative, and judgmental*) descend, assisted by wires and harnesses. They're coated in a film of grey dust. Handprints and mouth marks on their bodies give telltale clues they've just had sex. Once on the ground, they snort a brown powder off each other's shoulders and passionately kiss. THE SIREN simply observes her partner and her twin sister. Fanfare and revelry supersede humiliation.

On another stage, a pair perform acro-yoga postures in the center of a large, well defined circle. A different group of four enters to *"play out their pictures."* They wear ornate Arabian garb. A woman in the quartet is tossed high in the air, her legs straight and toes pointed vertically. When caught by the base trio, I notice the flyer is THE RESISTANCE. She waves at me, inviting me to the stage to share in a "cornflake community circle." Upon sitting a shunt is plunged in by back as another arm wraps at the elbow around my neck, choking me.

"You're being bled so a woman on the other side of the circle can receive a critical transfusion. It's for the shared good. Don't resist," a male voice informs.

I see gritty purple brown blood flow into the tube, infused and thickened with cornmeal before emptying into a rubber bladder.

A woman shouts, *"DON'T MAKE THE HEALER A DEMAGOGUE!"* as I'm grabbed by three shadow beings, one at left, center, and right. I squint and in a startled moment blurt,

"I don't want to be heard!"

I open my eyes. Two blue flame candles hover in front of me. A strong gust of wind blows them out. Chords of liberated dissonance strike with fortissimo on stringed instruments when the candles light themselves. This repeats on a loop. Each iteration leaves my breath quickened until the scene decays.]

. . .

[0035.5 / 0100] [I'm face down on the pavement behind the tailpipe of an idling car. Its left turn signal blinks. The car turns right and drives off, leaving me in the dark.] //

✲✲

Maj. = *20- THE HEALER: #0037*
DESERT: #0700, #0735, #0795
BLURT: #0465
BLOOD: #0699, #0701, #0723, #0732
NIGHTMARE: #0406, #0518, #0519, #0764
THE SIREN: #0045
THE HIATUS: #0053
THE RESISTANCE: #0082
THE CHEF: #0365

✲✲

#0036 - January 13, 2018 @ 02:00 (Montaña Larapata, Peru)

[0036.1 / 0101] [Odd violence. I concurrently watch an evening broadcast news program, while being featured in B-roll for one of the segments. Civil unrest and uprising results from a political scandal. A cameraman stands behind me and another unknown man as we hunker down together at the bottom of a paved concrete hill. There are no cars on the road. A chain link fence to the left separates the road from a green field. Trees line our side of the fence. We crouch and cradle pipe bomb guns as we watch a parade of teenage boys of varying ethnicity run down the hill. They rampage towards us with guns raised and blazing. Play by play reporting makes the circumstance feel like an Olympic event, not a social crisis. Expressions on the boys' faces are wild and menacing, making them appear like hyped up knights rushing to battle. A young Black man in a soccer jersey passes me. I turn and shoot him in the back with my pipe bomb gun, and he explodes. An announcer in the background says,
"Let's see that again in an instant replay!"
The scene rewinds and replays in slow motion. Shrapnel punctures and sears through clothing, then burns the young man's flesh. His expression shifts from ecstasy, to surprise, to wincing pain when he notices his limbs blowing apart at the joints.]

[0036.2 / 0102] [I'm with THE GUITARIST outside a house, set in a deep retention basin with a steep green lawn. It's an overcast day. It recently rained. We spend some time talking outside and are eventually compelled to go inside to get a soda. The tri-level home has late 80's decor. A looming sense of stress and threat hangs heavy in the home without a specific source to assign it to.]

[0036.3 / 0103] [We're at a fancy banquet hall seated amongst hundreds of guests gathered to celebrate a Brazilian man and his wife for their *"significant contributions to global culture."* Attendees sport tuxedos, with many wearing crimson toned vests and cumber bunds. THE GUITARIST and I want to sit next to one another, but a tall olive complexed man wedges himself between us. I consider the man handsome. He speaks kindly to us in Portuguese, but neither of us understand, nor are able to respond.]

[0036.4 / 0104] [I'm in a small condo in Brazil with basic amenities. I hide in a bathroom and take a shower. A TV, viewable through the mirrored reflection from the cracked bathroom door, is tuned to a "preview channel." Ads for violent news programs bleed from one to the next. THE WEAVER pops her head through the bathroom door and asks if I want to watch anything in particular, as steam pours out and upward. She answers a knock at the door, then goes out in the hallways to talk to a man. It's obvious she's trying to distract the man to conceal my whereabouts. I don't know who he is, nor why he's looking for me.] //

***

Maj. = 0- THE WEAVER: #0044
Min. = ♣- THE GUITARIST: #0064
VIOLENCE: #0549, #0576, #0768
BRAZIL: #0608
TUXEDOS: #0406
TRI-LEVEL: #0644, #0687, #0759

***

#0037 - January 13, 2018 @ 04:15 (Montaña Larapata, Peru)

[0037.1 / 0105] [I'm in a small suburban home. It's late at night, just prior to first light. I hear THE HEALER having a phone conversation in an adjacent office, intermittently whistling and singing healing icaros. To lead off the agenda he sings one to *"pierce through the veil of the group's illusions."* THE HEALER performs remote healings for those dialed in. I snoop on him, watching him as he works. I'm not supposed to bother him while he's in session. His young daughter sleeps near me on a futon. If I wake her up, THE HEALER will know I've been listening. I curl up on the couch and cover myself with a white Shipibo medicine weaving. All but my left foot is covered by the blanket. Just as I drift off to sleep THE AYURVEDIC removes the cover and wakes me up. I'm momentarily irritated before realizing I've been shoved in a box on the floor in THE HEALER's office.

I sneak out of the box and crawl from the office on hands and knees. Once outside, I gather scattered clothes into a pile and stuff them in a large white Macy's bag with other objects, among them a VHS cassette of the film "Black Sheep." I leave the house and walk through an empty two car garage. The door is fully opened to the driveway where I meet THE DANCER who leans back against a compact car while looking down at her phone. She's recently completed a paper survey form THE CLUB KID (*wild, triggering, and addicted*) asked her to fill out. She's provided answers to questions 48, 49, and 50. She's intentionally left the rest blank. She puts the paper survey on the roof of the car. We get in the car and pull through a fast-food drive thru. I want to post her answers to a public website. I'm more perplexed why she hasn't included a postage stamp on the envelope to mail her responses back, than by how the survey remains on the roof as we drive. As we order I get out, open the trunk and rifle through the Macy's bag. I look past the car down the street and see a cherry picker slowly driving directly at us. A strong thunderstorm trails behind. We'll be run over, then drenched.] //

#0038 - January 13, 2018 @ 05:50 (Montaña Larapata, Peru)

[0038.1 / 0106] [*"Do you hear her song?"*
"She's changed her name twice, but I know who she is."
THE AYURVEDIC asks me about a member of the "temple construction crew" who is also a highly followed public figure and performer. It's January. We've just held a project kickoff meeting and remark it's amazing but odd to start the process so early in the year. We walk down a long, dimly lit corridor towards an exit. We know there is a tremendous amount of work to accomplish in a short few months. We're sure all will complete as scheduled by August since THE MAKER is the lead artist accountable to the sponsoring organization. We walk around outside noticing THE DIPLOMAT's staff has gathered on the roof of an A-Frame house for a group photo. After shifting configuration a few times, THE DIPLOMAT *(calm, inviting, and proactive)* invites me to join them. He suggests we gather on top of a 15-passenger van parked in a nearby lot. Once standing on the roof together, the vehicle instantly blazes down a twisty mountain highway while we snap multiple candid photos. The wind blows our hair back wildly. Our facial skin ripples and waves. It's absurd and hilarious. This team is equal parts love and happiness.
"This is a good memory."] //

#0039 - January 14, 2018 @ 02:05 (Montaña Larapata, Peru)

[0039.1 / 0107] [I run around the inside of a large, well ordered mansion. As I bounce between rooms, I realize the house is home to dozens of playful vaporous spirits. My senses are heightened. I feel exhilaration over danger. I'm expansive, alert, and focused. I'm awake! Randomly placed chocolate bars, all colorfully wrapped, appear on desktops and windows from nowhere with a "poof." Some hang weightless in the air. I grab a king-sized Kit Kat bar, and instantly eat the entire thing. I barely taste it as I continue bolting around the house at increasing speed.

Light inside and outside the house shifts rapidly and fluidly. Light becomes dark. Night becomes day. I believe I'm part of a scavenger hunt surveilled by a dark and potentially malevolent force. I stay cautious and undistracted. I run through a solarium, a garage, an attic, and a series of uniquely decorated rooms.

"It's kind of like the house in 'The Masque of the Red Death,'" I mutter while moving on to collect more chocolate bars.

A narrator begins providing omniscient play-by-play commentary. THE HUMBLE MAN (*seeking, transforming, and curious*), THE FLUTIST (*growing, intelligent, and self-transforming*), and THE VICTOR (*undone, deep feeling, and surrendered*) take positions at various places around the property. I occasionally toss them candy bars I've collected. They develop taste preferences and make special requests for specific niche candies, though fulfilling special requests is **not my priority**. I tend to give them the candy bars I want the least, or most likely will not eat. In all, I collect 11 different varieties of Kit Kats, my favorite being the *"80% Cacao ones."* A single Reese's Peanut Butter Egg is prized as rare by the three. Consuming multiple candy bars leaves me feeling heavy, lethargic and bloated. My pace slows to a stroll.

At the back of the garage, I inspect every cabinet on a gridded wall, each filled with hundreds of drawers. Ghosts behind me provide playful encouragement to remain active. THE HUMBLE MAN, THE FLUTIST and THE VICTOR stand outside the back door awaiting another choco-delivery. Kit Kats remind me of Japan as I cram one after the next in my craw. The taste is amazing, and reeks of reaction.

"I stress eat Kit Kats after challenging conversations."] //

⁂

CHOCOLATE: #0763, #0764, #0775, #0787, #0798
MANSION: #0428, #0431, #0655, #0657, #0710, #0745, #0750
GHOST: #0401, #0461, #0545, #0619, #0687, #0727
THE FLUTIST: #0041
THE VICTOR: #0309
THE HUMBLE MAN: #0787

⁂

#0040 - January 14, 2018 @ 03:30 (Montaña Larapata, Peru)

[0040.1 / 0108] [I'm cast in a CHRISTOPHER GUEST style mock-u-mentary. *"A slapstick comedy with abundant heArt,"* raves Vanity Fair. Core to the story are vignettes centered on the dramatic and fiercely competitive lives of museum curators. A featured gallery team speeds to complete an installation of intricately woven textiles, to beat a competing museum to market. THE LYRICIST (*meek, soulful, and funny*) and THE PSYCHONAUT are hosted artists and stand near a display of their finest works. They've woven musical scores into vibrant tapestries, hung prominently on a stark white wall. They're invited to unveil the spotlight installation of textiles woven by a culturally revered contemporary. Featured pieces are clothes, mostly multi-panel trousers and socks. Fashioned as representations of the letter "N," they follow a standard presentation template size of *"40" square."*

THE HEALER ushers me to another room and selects a costume for me from a black, brass bracketed steamer chest. He passes me two mittens that look like yellow rubber duck hand puppets, along with a large duck head mascot mask. He smiles as he places it over my head. Wearing the costume, I walk through the gallery viewing pastoral scenes woven into wool sweaters displayed among other large tapestries.

Outside, I see ZACHARY QUINTO with a blonde female actor. One is a hero. The other is a villain (*though it's not clear which is which*). A fresh foot of snow has recently fallen on the ground around us. ZACHARY and the woman stand together with a young boy, posing for a family portrait. They glow with happiness.

"Hey You! I got a little house!" ZACHARY yells to me as he offers a friendly wave.

He crouches and dives through a doggy door sized entrance to a tiny snow topped cottage, offset from a much larger neighboring legacy home.

I bypass the cottage and walk into the mansion. I'm immediately taken by its exquisite decoration and opulent ornamentation. Though large, the mansion seems cozy and homey. I could live here. A "noir dressed" woman approaches. *"**Miss Scarlet from 'Clue?'**"* I ponder, considering her classy, hilarious, and perhaps **deadly**. She lights a cigarette to reveal herself as PARKER POSEY *(genius, wit, authentic, and fully expressed)*. She and I saunter through the property scoffing at ourselves as we attempt to generate *"Oscar caliber dialog."* We're so immersed in our repartee; we've forgotten we're filming an improv scene.

Our scene progresses to a velvet chaise lounge where we sip cacao from fine bone china at twilight. We laugh absurdly and continue drinking chocolate. PARKER stands and quickly glides to an antique curio cabinet set just off to the left of a large bay window. The cabinet is softly lit in gold. She draws forth a special heirloom weaving from the case and unfolds it at my eye level to reveal a small portion of *"sacred chocolate."* Breaking the fourth wall, PARKER POSEY says,

"This is in celebration of the rediscovery of your talents. Do not rush it. Be sure you let them figure it out for themselves. This story has many chapters, just like the many movements of this film's score."

I feel seen. I feel deep love flow from her, to, and through me. We gaze at each other as rousing music swells in the background. As we eat the special chocolate, we can see our thoughts and intentions colorfully materialize and swirl upwards from the tops of our heads like spools of energetic thread. The threads feed into a cosmic loom where a lasting mark is made in our panel in the *"tapestry of creation."* We lean towards each other. Our foreheads gently touch and I feel like I've found my way home. We agree our dailies will be fantastic.]
//

⁜

Maj. = 20- THE HEALER: #0045
TAPESTRIES: #0554
BAY WINDOW: #0550
CURIO CABINET: #0579
CACAO: #0573, #0749
MOVIE: #0778

⁜

#0041 - January 14, 2018 @ 05:50 (Montaña Larapata, Peru)

[0041.1 / 0109] [I awaken when I hear THE FLUTIST talking in his sleep at the opposite end of the temple. I rise and walk towards him. He lays on his back. Both his knees are broken, swollen and bent 90 degrees in an anatomically incorrect direction. I gently touch his hyperextended right leg which startles him awake. His eyes spring open and he glares at me wordlessly. Waking him was a mistake. I didn't intend to bother him. The faceless person next to him was the one sleep-talking. Neither of us say anything. A pregnant pause hangs heavy in space until I wake up.] //

⁜

KNEES: #0655
PREGNANT PAUSE: #0759

63

TEMPLE: #0431, #0522, #0526
MISTAKE: #0430, #0562
THE FLUTIST: #0056

⁎⁎

#0042 - January 16, 2018 @ 1:10am (Montaña Larapata, Peru)

[0042.1 / 0110] [I attend a ceremony at a modern cathedral, sharing company with a panoply of familiar essences from the "spirit family" who've gathered to *"embody the true nature."* Dozens in attendance feel familiar, though I don't recognize them. A young masculine expressed female identifying as "the director" calls me up in front of an altar. She asks if I want to be the impromptu lead in a theater production, in which everyone in attendance will participate.

I will be confronted with triggers to smoke out subtly lurking fears I've previously expressed in shared public company. Some may occur as "gotcha's" or "wildcards." From the sanctuary I enter what a fundamentalist would term a "HELL HOUSE." Nightmarish confrontational scenes experienced by others in sacred plant ceremonies have been crudely created with cardboard and streamers in dark rooms along a serpentine path. Passing through an exit, I emerge on the opposite side of the altar. The power goes out. A reserve generator sputters with just enough wattage to cast dim lighting down from overhead. The entire spirit family falls into a trance state, save "the director."

The young woman walks me through a series of corridors and off shooting rooms. I've given opportunities to replay traumatic scenarios from my life. I'm not triggered by the militaristic homophobia, nor the bizarre reconstructions of former office dramas. Occasionally I become mildly sarcastic, mocking,

"Ok I'll play along with this silly game. Are you sure this is all you have on me?"

More than ten floating pictures instantly pop up that I wipe aside like soap bubbles. A moment of interior surprise occurs when I decline eating a plate of writhing mealworms after being told it's the only way I can gain access to the sanctuary. The darkened space pulses with a ghostly white light at floor level that hauntingly permeates a shoulder-to-shoulder row of beings congregated to observe what seems to be *"the cantata of my life."*] //

⁎⁎

FEAR: #0463, #0480, #0649, #0653, #0755
CARDBOARD: #0719, #0734, #0756, #0775, #0780
SANCTUARY: #0628
POWER OUTAGE: #0430

⁎⁎

#0043 - January 16, 2018 @ 03:10 (Montaña Larapata, Peru)

[0043.1 / 0111] [I'm in the Black Rock Desert on a warm morning. It's dry and dusty. Amidst the variety of beings and activities, I trudge toward a semi-truck trailer off in the distance to my left. Each step with my un-tied steel toed boots kicks up tiny clouds of kaolin dust. The wind picks up. A dust storm approaches. I'm to meet up at the trailer with a whiskey swilling rough and tumble woman for a salacious rendezvous. I spot her from roughly 20 paces. She wears a utili-kilt, has a short-cropped rust dyed haircut, and is adorned neck to foot with dozens of tattoos. Some are Latin words, (v e r i t a s printed on her right wrist). Sponge Bob Square Pants is immortalized on her right quadriceps. We connect at the trailer doorway. I think I'm going inside, but she blocks the entrance with her right arm. She takes a drag off a filterless cigarette with the other. She scruffily introduces herself as AMY CUDDY (*supportive, transformational, and scholarly*).

We exchange greetings, hug briefly, and continue through the door. Crossing through, we discover ourselves in an antique store that offers a hodgepodge of goods. Luxury estate sale items are set amongst tables of garage sale trinkets and second-hand memorabilia. After taking a look around together we stand coupled in front of a wooden cabinet with etched glass doors. AMY opens the cabinet, revealing large stacks of heirloom quilts and blankets. After quietly contemplating, she precisely selects two blankets from the middle of a neatly stacked pile, and removes them without upsetting the others. She selects a thick, durable Pendleton blanket. The other is a thin and delicate hand stitched quilt accented with Belgian lace. Both blankets share the same stitched pattern that resemble mallards and swans. She passes them to me. As I hold them, I experience safety and child-like wonder. I hold one to my cheek and react with a slight smile. AMY touches my forearm and says,

"These are so you. Can I buy them for you?"

I agree and accept without hesitation. Across the shop I spot a large black cauldron that begs to go home with us. Inside the cauldron is a freshly baked chocolate chip sponge cake that rests soaking in a shallow pool of sweet condensed milk atop a floral-patterned china plate. I slice off a sizable triangle shaped portion and eat it quickly and joyfully as we celebrate the purchase of the quilts.] //

✱✱

TATTOOS: #0455, #0597, #0644
CHINA: #0422, #0482
ETCHED: #0429, #0610, #0776
CAULDRON: #0604
TRIANGLES: #0559

✱✱

#0044 - January 16, 2018 @ 05:05 (Montaña Larapata, Peru)

[0044.1 / 0112] [I'm with THE CHOCOHOLIC, THE POINT GUARD and THE WEAVER on a daytime excursion. We stop briefly for a meal at a fast-food restaurant. Between gob filled chomps of curly fries, we discuss what we want to do that afternoon. I have a new Polaroid camera that captures five second videos on film. I suggest we go to OZZY OSBOURNE's house to pull a prank on him. We're in agreement, and take a short drive towards his mansion. I'm resolved. The others get cold feet when we arrive on the property. I enter the mansion alone. I wander between rooms and am quite taken by a gallery-like master bathroom. The shower is more than 20 feet long. If I lived here, I'd probably hang out in this room most of the time.

I snap a Polaroid video and place it in the center of a refrigerator door with a small round magnet. I can hear OZZY OSBOURNE react with annoyance and confusion, from his car, miles away from the house. He can sense when the smallest detail is out of order on premises. At the bottom of a long spiral staircase, a male who feels familiar to me pops out from a sidewall suggesting I photograph OZZY OSBOURNE's daughter while she sleeps naked.

"Ick. No." I'm disgusted by the notion.

The house's many windows flood the space with daylight. The inside of the house is lit by natural light sources 80% of the time. I take a second Polaroid video of vintage cars in the garage and put it in my jacket pocket. OZZY OSBOURNE's almost home. I move quickly towards the back door, waking up just before I get outside.] //

⁂

Maj. = 0- THE WEAVER: #0066
OZZY OSBOURNE: #0175
VINTAGE: #0670, #0770
THE POINT GUARD: #0288
THE CHOCOHOLIC: #0353

⁂

#0045 - January 17, 2018 @ 4:55am (Montaña Larapata, Peru)

[0045.1 / 0113] [I'm at a former San Francisco residence in the Lower Haight. THE COSMIC WHITE HEART (*playful monk, expressive, and tricky*) joins me for a slumber party in my bedroom. Our interactions are comedic and playful. He appreciates my invitation to spend the night, and is emotionally moved. I learn he lived here for many years during his childhood and is overwhelmed by the opportunity to reconnect to the building. He regales me with stories of his family inhabiting the entire floor for years, paying in trade for three times the space I now spend over half my income on for a single room. THE COSMIC WHITE HEART's comments are tender, reflective and sober. While offered with tones of joy, they're seasoned with dashes of nostalgic sadness. We hug heart to heart when he stops speaking until we're both full.]

[0045.2 / 0114] [I'm in an empty parking lot. I'm seated in a circle of people who share their prior night's dreams. Discussion flows effortlessly from one person through the next. Each insight offered occurs as a perfect "bolt on" to the prior share and sets the platform for the next. It's a sunny day. We enjoy the opportunity to share outside under a welcoming blue sky with happily dolloped whipped cream clouds. THE WHITE RABBIT sits next to me. I'm attracted to him. At the root of the attraction is a firmly held belief: *"He's an embodied avatar of my soul's guide."*
The circle disbands. I ask THE WHITE RABBIT if he wants to load his luggage in the trunk of my car. His items are scattered around the parking lot. I feel awkward asking him if he wants to ride with me, but I do anyway. We smile at each other. As we pack things up, we pause to soul gaze. Though it's playful and vitalizing, I don't speak about my attraction.
The circle reconvenes. I'm called on to share. I oblige. I leave my body to let something come through the channel to speak. After flying around other universes, I return with no knowledge of what has been spoken through the body. Noting the elapsed time on a small recording device in the center of the circle, I realize the body has spoken uninterrupted for three hours. Whatever was shared moves THE WHITE RABBIT, who locks me in uninter-rupted eye contact while speaking to me gently and tenderly. I pick THE PHYSICIST as the next to share and place the recorder in front of her. The sun promptly sets and the circle is lit by small tea candles that hover inches above each of our heads.]

. . .

[0045.3 / 0115] [I'm in a large nondescript space surrounded by various types of beings. Aliens, angels, sparkling orbs stand out as unique. I'm at an interdimensional travel port. The energy is palpable and uplifting. Beings here have direction. They move with purpose. Best described as "Future Tech" in feel, my attention is snagged by a small basic poster board sign for "Ocean Airlines." Only ticketed clients are aware of the service provider's existence. I follow the small inconspicuous signs placed intentionally below the eye-line of most travelers, breaking convention from traditional marketing tactics.

I get it. It's the result of the merger!" I say excitedly as I walk with other people who have booked a trip with the service.

Once at a service desk, the intake process is rudimentary. I feel like the counter staff knows me. Behind me, rows of high back red cushioned banquet chairs are placed in long rows. Most are empty, but they're prepared for an onslaught of travelers. A few customers sit quietly with tissue paper "now serving" numbers in hand, waiting to be called. Each time a number is called, a customer rises and walks toward a large red velvet curtain which raises and folds in arcs. When my number is called, I don't pass under the curtain, knowing I'll return later for a flight. I ascend an escalator to a standalone doorway. I pass through and enter a restaurant through their side emergency door. The interior is art deco inspired with patterns in black, white and an occasional slosh of red. The tables are round, heavy, and made from oak. Tables are placed at the perimeter of a round room. A single scalloped booth enables every guest a view of the center of the space. I pass through noticing THE SIREN works the floor as a server. I wave at her. She doesn't recognize me. She loathes her job and bemoans her guests. I admire her candor. I turn right and walk swiftly down a staircase, overhearing the head server shhh-ing other members of the team and threatening their jobs if they don't rank and file.]

[0045.4 / 0116] [It's dusk. I'm on the upper floor of Wells Fargo Three in Charlotte, North Carolina. It's been a long, yet highly productive day at the office. THE WHITE RABBIT and THE GARDENER *(aware, accommodating, and gentile)* are coworkers of mine who share a workspace nearby. We're in a playful mood and they're both explicitly flirtatious with me. I don't share a mutual attraction. I glance away briefly. When I look back THE GARDENER has morphed into THE COMBAT MEDIC *(solid, astute, and service oriented)* who dials up the flirting with increasingly provocative suggestions. Again, I glance away. I'm now across the hall where a glass wall separates me from the group. Something caused the spontaneous shift. I don't remember what I've done, but I feel vulnerable, exposed and embarrassed. I've shared something personal which is now public and has gone viral.]

[0045.5 / 0117] [A workgroup sits around a long wooden rectangular table on an exterior patio conference space on a warm sunny day. Atop the table are multiple crystal bowls filled with a unique multicolored bead-like confection the team refers to as "Cacao Candy." An outer sphere of chocolate surrounds a compact hardened pellet. Though the sweet sugary cores can be easily crushed with the teeth, THE WHITE RABBIT constantly spits them out and gathers them in a small saliva-soaked pile on an embroidered cloth napkin. For a gross out *(and to feed my sugar addiction)* I eat the pile.

"Don't you know you're giving away the candy? It's the best part!" I taunt with a laugh and audible jaw crunch.

THE WHITE RABBIT thinks I'm revolting. He continues his remarks to the executive team seated at the table.

At dusk, THE HEALER gives status on a recent phone meeting he had with GORDON RAMSAY. THE HEALER is summarily unimpressed and recommends the firm discontinue future funding of creative endeavors with the celebrity personality. The management team confirms GORDON RAMSAY will be retained until he delivers a keynote at a town hall meeting scheduled for the end of the week. The meeting concludes and the team decides to go out for pizza.

We walk in line, shoulder to shoulder down a bustling and vibrant promenade lined with prominent holographic billboards and rainbow crystal buildings. Seated at a restaurant, open debate about what constitutes *"the best pizza and its proper preparation"* surfaces. THE WHITE RABBIT and I make much innuendo towards one another in *"pizza speak."* I'm genuinely attracted to him. THE WHITE RABBIT turns to the woman to his left. I overhear him whisper in her ear,

"That guy should fuck me."

The unexpected comment startles me, and wakes me up.] //

⁑

Maj. = 20- THE HEALER: #0173
Min. = ◆*- THE WHITE RABBIT: #0072*
GORDON RAMSAY: #0411
PIZZA: #0787
RECTANGULAR TABLES: #0484, #0699, #0787
RAINBOW: #0556, #0587
THE SIREN: #0053

⁑

#0046 - January 18, 2018 @ 06:47 (Pisac, Peru)

[0046.1 / 0118] [*"Remember your voice. Use it for healing. It's a sacred tool."*]

[0046.2 / 0119] [THE IMPRESSIONIST *(free spirited, gregarious, and seeking)* sits on the floor receiving a healing from THE MEDICINE WOMAN *(wise, flat, skillful, and generous)*. THE MEDICINE WOMAN smiles as I enter the room. I feel unsure of myself. THE MEDICINE WOMAN concludes singing an icaro while squatting near THE IMPRESSIONIST. THE IMPRESSIONIST sits straight legged with feet crossed at the ankle. Her arms are at her sides and her eyes are closed. THE MEDICINE WOMAN breathes in to THE IMPRESSIONIST's face, sealing in the medicine with a *"Shoo shoo shoo."*

THE MEDICINE WOMAN looks at me supportively and gestures that she wants me to sing to her. I'm not confident I can give her the healing she wants. I almost don't sing because I believe my voice may harm her. I am at the effect of doubt. A puffy cloud of notional inspiration floats in to sweep out the doubt.

The puffy cloud suggests singing in different keys and pitches provides different healing possibilities. The cloud invites Solfeggio frequencies to resonate one at a time in five-minute intervals. Each rattles different centers of being. ***First the gut, then the heart, the head, then higher.... entire.*** I'm fatigued by the increasingly classroom-like feel of the lesson. The cloud shifts its tutelage by offering a mantra: *"Any healing expression serves the greater good."*

68

A lurker program buried in the posterior tissues of my heart is smoked out and drops to the floor as I repeat the mantra. The wormy slug being emerges with a series of phlegmy coughs,

"IT HAS TO BE...
PERFORMED...
PITCH PERFECT...
TO BE OF...
ANY HEALING VALUE...
SINGING THE...
INCORRECT SONG...
CAN BE TERRIBLY HARMFUL."

It suffers a death rattle before dissolving. THE MEDICINE WOMAN remains a gentle teacher. She lovingly invites me to sing songs for her. Her invitation is non-verbal. She gestures with her hands, moving them from her heart and spreading them towards me, dissolving the illusion of a language barrier. I take a breath and close my eyes. I feel a stock-pile of fear well up in the newly emptied space behind my heart. My mouth opens. I wake up before hearing myself make a sound.] //

⁑

MANTRA: #0423
HEALING: #0733
SINGING: #0618, #0690
BEINGS: #0410, #0474, #0476, #0484, #0593
THE IMPRESSIONIST: #0047

⁑

#0047 - January 19, 2018 @ 05:39 (Pisac, Peru)

[0047.1 / 0120] [An omniscient announcer animatedly speaks, *"Welcome to a mashup of the rational and abstract interactions! Let's explore how super consciousness craters to the non-impeccable, lowest resonant vibration present in a collective agreement! Energetic dips occur in broad strokes when there's a lack of clarity and focus! Luckily for the under practiced, everyone sticks together to share 'The Burden!'"*]

[0047.2 / 0121] [*"Gather up your wellbeing and share it all around." "We are circling, circling togeth-er." "This is family. This is a community."*]

[0047.3 / 0122] [Distraction pervades this group. With a short-term appointment as "The Consciousness" I'm given a tutorial as a bodiless being. I'm shown different circles of entities and shuttled instantly between their polar frequencies to test and build spiritual muscle memory. I discover an infirm body behaves similar to that of an extreme mountaineer:
"A body considered 'collective' can't simply leave a tired left foot behind and allow the heart to summit peaks on its own. The success of a journey is dependent on the ascent of the complete organism."

69

I'm shown abstractions that challenge my patience. In parallel, concurrent experiences of sitting in a circle and climbing mountains are presented to me. Simple linear interactions between body parts and people in the scenario yield arbitrary complexities.

"It's futile and fruitless to attempt stringing together a logical narrative with characters. The small parts do their thing with no awareness of their contribution to 'the greater,'" a bodiless voice whispers.

A sequence results in some intense moments where I feel myself catapulted between the bodies of THE IMPRESSIONIST, THE WARD OF GAIA, THE PANDA, and a body labeled "Joshua." I'm in a heavenly plate spinning act. Those around me coherently meditate as a singular entity would to take steps together to summit a mountain.

As a pure energy body, I understand that the primary objective *(as defined in my current life contract)* reads: "*In any group agreement made, the user commits to an even and balanced distribution between components.*"

While there is verbal dialog among people and body parts, I'm generally not able to intercept, interrupt, nor process the sensational uprisings into a format humans call "words." I move with the intuitive, innate force that harmoniously links *"being."* An occasional word or phrase manifests as a blurt:

"My life contract demands that I'm perpetually in the space of greatest need and highest call."

As "The Consciousness" the Creator charges me to, *"choose immediacy and spontaneity to effortlessly jettison through the path of least resistance."* When I do, travel is instant. Some moments I'm moved inside a body and stare across a void at a being in the body labeled "Joshua." Part of my lesson as a pure energy being is to notice when I begin calling myself "Joshua" and falsely relating to the body as the True "me." When I break from the illusion of a body, I feel swirling sensations that delete my former understanding of Newtonian mechanics and the nature of space time.

My lesson concludes with flashes of microscope images of capillaries that move single red blood cells along one at a time methodically, deliberately and systematically. I'm challenged to hold this micro view while I'm taken to a mountain top to hover above a group of monks floating above the ground in seated meditation.] //

⁎⁎

Min. = ◆- *THE WARD OF GAIA: #0365*
EDUCATION: #0402, #0485, #0754
OUT OF BODY: #0487, #0566, #0573, #0607, #0611
BODIES: #0411, #0474, #0524, #0654, #0725
THE PANDA: #0048

⁎⁎

PART 2 - WANDER

#0048 - #0099

"Run away, go find a lover
Run away, let your heart be your guide
You deserve the deepest of cover
You belong in that home by and by...

You belong among the wildflowers
You belong somewhere close to me
Far away from your trouble and worry
You belong somewhere you feel free."

-Tom Petty

* * *

January 20, 2018 - March 14, 2018

#0048 - January 20, 2018 @ 04:30 (AA Flight 918: Lima, Peru - Miami, FL)

[0048.1 / 0123] [I'm on a flight. Destination unknown. As in prior air travel dreams, the interior of the plane is vast and spacious. I hold space for a group ritual from my seat. I'm preoccupied. I need to shit. I excuse myself, wait in line (*yawning*), use the bathroom, and promptly return to my post. Passengers are physically tethered to one another with foot shackles. Notably, the plane doesn't have seat belts. We encounter periods of strong turbulence that cause us to rise weightlessly then slam abruptly to our seats. The group agreement on board:

"Roll with all disruptions as they arise. Sit with strong determination."

Turbulence intensifies. We're tossed around the cabin like rag dolls.

We chant, *"Om Mani Peme Hung,"* as our bodies collide.

We intend for safe arrival and wrap an energetic blanket of protection around every soul on board. Ritualists are shown a topographical image of a jagged mountain range, projected at the nose of the plane on a giant IMAX screen. Engine power suddenly cuts off and the plane instantly plummets down towards a snowcapped peak, which feeds a roaring river that cuts deep into a valley below.

The flight deck timidly informs the cabin they don't expect any of us to survive. We speed towards imminent collision and certain death. The instant before the plane strikes rock, the engines reengage. The split-second power shift is just enough for the pilots to pull up. We pinch our forearms to prove we're still in our bodies.

I see an advertisement posted in the galley for *"$33 flights to anywhere in the world."* THE NAYSAYER (*challenged, stuck, and joyless*) sits beneath the poster sinisterly giggling under his breath. He broke his protective connection and claims he's responsible for the engine failure. He wants to scare everyone. I cuss him out at full volume until my voice goes mute. I exhaust my anger, and enjoy scolding him publicly. The plane bobs and weaves through a gauntlet of jeweled trees and pristine waterfalls, flanked by jagged and majestic mountains. The big nature visuals are exasperatingly gorgeous. The mood on board is flat and observant.

I'm handed a series of three customs forms and a wooden pen shaped like an adult man's erect penis. As I fill out the forms, one queries,

"Is it your intention to become a shaman? Y/N"

I don't answer the question. My attention instead is drawn to a group of genius children engaged in sacred play under the tutelage of a monk wearing a maroon robe. The monk demonstrates how to conjure up an alien adhesive substance called *"shmek"* from one's chest. The children complete the conjuring, then playfully fling their sticky goop at each other. Silly string glue spills throughout the cabin, making a mess of the space as the monk explains,

"Though 'shmek' has myriad uses, it's generally most effective as a grounding cord enhancer."

Realization: I've failed. I've forgotten I'm their teacher. The monk intervened while I've been distracted by the illusory threat of a plane crash. Frustrated, I lament to THE PANDA (*healing, timid, and strongly intuitive*),

"I'm not smart enough to teach these kids."

She says nothing but smirks at me wallowing in my doubt, and offers a silent invitation to *"stop it"* whenever I choose.] //

⁎⁎

JET: #0540, #0558, #0601, #0671
PENIS: #0563, #0637, #0645, #0647, #0742
MOUNTAINS: #0582, #0683, #0735
ANSWER: #0753, #0775, #0780
THE PANDA: #0056
THE NAYSAYER: #0200

⁎⁎

#0049 - January 22, 2018 @ 03:13 (The Presidio of San Francisco, California)

[0049.1 / 0124] [**Image:** Alien symbols, burned into stone.]
[0049.2 / 0125] [**Message:** *"Remember how to breathe before you fall asleep."*]
[0049.3 / 0126] [**Reaction:** *"MY BODY IS IN REVOLT. S.O.S.!!!"*]
[0049.4 / 0127] [**Warning:** *"FEAR THE FACE OF GOD"* - Reads a bumper sticker in the rear window of a car.]
[0049.5 / 0128] [**Struggle:** I'm in primary school. I score in the lower 10th percentile on a standardized test.] //

⁎⁎

STONE: #0669, #0722
BREATHE: #0532, #0664
SCHOOL: #0703, #0705, #0708
PRIMARY: #0470, #0674

⁎⁎

#0050 - January 24, 2018 @ 05:05 (The Presidio of San Francisco, California)

[0050.1 / 0129] [It's night. I'm inside a county courthouse. The environment is destabilizing and trending towards chaos. THE SEER *(experiential, earthy, and bubbly)* arrives. Her mother is on trial for allegedly dosing a group of minors with psychedelics who recently attended her weekend yoga retreat. I serve in triple capacity as court stenographer, clerk, and bailiff. Pretrial media bias from US Congressional officials *(both the House and Senate)* warrants a possible change of venue to an international tribunal. Spin cycle vitriol and blame pile onto growing public sentiment that precludes the defendant's guilt. Though divided politically, there's consensus among the elected that this woman is a menace. Justice is contorted.

During the punishment phase of the trial, an angel in the body of a beautiful white robed Black man soulfully sings while perched behind a judge who contemplates the woman's fate. The judge reads prepared remarks from a computer screen. I approach the bench to pass him some documents, noting he's paraphrasing the remarks. Words omitted turn from black to grey then auto-translate to Latin. The judge notices me, noticing this. He's been *"got"* by me.] //

⁎⁎

COURT: #0655, #0672, #0726
MEDIA: #0461, #0472, #0538, #0737
ANGEL: #0436, #0474, #0540, #0599, #0800

73

⁎⁎

#0051 - January 25, 2018 @ 00:45 (The Presidio of San Francisco, California)

[0051.1 / 0130] [My phone takes *"very special photos,"* but I don't understand how to hold it to properly use it. Pressure from a user's hand effects image captures. THE CARPENTER is present, along with two young men I don't recognize, yet term *"generous."* The scene decays to abstraction. I'm left moderately anxious in deep dream hyper-reality. Light surrounding me becomes so bright it's terrifying. Is something shining to hide from me?

"I want this to end!" I scream with torrents of light shooting from my eyes and mouth.

My spirit spins with increasing quickness like a pulsar. Reality clicks and refreshes with metronome precision until I awaken.] //

⁎⁎

Maj. = 1- THE CARPENTER: #0069
PHONE: #0401, #0415, #0420, #0422
ABSTRACTION: #0423, #0453, #0536, #0565, #0588
SPIRIT: #0610, #0611, #0654, #0687, #0792

⁎⁎

#0052 - January 25, 2018 @ 04:25 (The Presidio of San Francisco, California)

[0052.1 / 0131] [I'm a teacher. I support a weeklong retreat led by a male facilitator, dressed in Victorian era steampunk fashion (*goggles, top hat, and riveted leather vest*). His face is greased with black and white paint. Attendees select preferred attendance dyads from an a la carte menu at registration. I've been asked to lead a segment on dance and freeform primal movement. I glance at a computer screen to verify enrollments, noticing 114 people are signed up for my module. I think this indicates a good turnout, though quickly realize my session has the lowest prospective attendance across retreat offerings.

I'm relieved to learn THE TEMPLAR (*fiercely feminine, smiley, and welcoming*) is the lead on my event production team.

The dark interior walls of the building are damp like a cave. Attendance is logged on a black slate chalkboard with white chalk hash marks. A massive group breaks out into small groups that I still consider *"large."* I lead a group on one side of the room. Steampunk teacher's group is on the other side. His voice intrigues me. I can hear him speak as I facilitate my session. He delivers content primarily using a slam poem, rap-based form. It's my first time hearing his shtick, though blatantly obvious to me that he's borrowing and rehashing flows from the "Hamilton" soundtrack. Some of my attendees intermittently discharge electricity from their skin while moving through the room.] //

⁎⁎

STEAMPUNK: #0587
GREASE: #0496, #0755
CHALKBOARD: #717
CAVE: #0514

⁎⁎

⁎⁎

#0053 - January 26, 2018 @ 03:50 (The Presidio of San Francisco, California)

[0053.1 / 0132] [I push a cart through a grocery store. I'm searching for *"the perfect"* smoothie ingredients. The market space is open and up fit with earthy, natural wood shelves and crates perfectly appointed for retail displays. The store's offerings are alluringly colored. My movement is speedy. The standard reality frame rate is sped up by ~30%, though all motions and accompanying details still register clearly. I can keep pace. I'm supported by an invisible crew. I don't know who they are, nor why they're helping me. It becomes clear we're filming a live *"man on the street"* commercial for the store. I move through different store aisles pausing to carefully inspect prospective smoothie ingredients. We pair down my selections to the *"three essential best"* items for a new recipe.]

[0053.2 / 0133] [I encounter a teenage woman living alone in a modern and nicely furnished apartment. We have a brief conversation where it's clear that while she's happy, she'd rather live elsewhere.]

[0053.3 / 0134] [Both the conversation with the young woman and the supermarket smoothie ad are simulcast across multiple media platforms. I'm wearing an earpiece. A director's voice cues me to improvise for the rest of the shoot.
"We can always come back," I say when we're unable to immediately find a preferred type of yoghurt. I see a glowing gold crate down a shopping aisle, and walk toward it. Once I draw close, I realize it's full of shimmering dried golden berries. I snag a handful and casually eat them as I continue my smoothie ingredient search. The sweet-tartness of the berries is pleasing. The glands at the back of my mouth liberally squirt saliva to counteract their acidity.
The market is large and labyrinth-like. Numerous ramps and playground slides shuttle shoppers around in a live action manifestation of "Chutes and Ladders."
"Now change the channel and let's do it again," I hear a male voice shout from the side set.
I'm hurried out of frame to the right and huddle beneath a camera tripod until shooting concludes.]

[0053.4 / 0135] [I'm in the collapsed rubble of a damp concrete structure that was formerly a parking deck. The scene feels mysterious. Remaining upright beams support and frame the space like an ESCHER drawing. THE HIATUS (*analytical, and calculating*) and THE SIREN (*emotive, and shy*) have just returned from a big adventure. Per an existing contract they select a cleared parking space to set up an interim camp as their home. I intend to share a friendly conversation with them, but it unexpectedly turns intense and combative. I don't remember the content. They share a lot of wisdom from their recent journey that passes through my ears, but doesn't quite make it to my brain. What they're telling me is important. As it slips from my awareness, I feel increasingly detached and stupid.] //

⁂

ESCHER: #0795
GROCERY STORE: #0523, #0603, #0645, #0741
FRIENDLY: #0459, #0623, #0628, #0640
STUPID: #0587, #0668, #0747

THE HIATUS: #0054
THE SIREN: #1224
⁂

#0054 - January 27, 2018 @ 04:00 (The Presidio of San Francisco, California)

[0054.1 / 0136] [I race THE HIATUS (*smart, soulful, and stoic*) to the basement level food court in the headquarters of our new, prominent Bay Area startup. We're on a break time mission to get dessert. We both eye *"the last"* banana smoothie, topped with whipped cream in a cooler ten paces away. I'm momentarily distracted by a sampler tray of mint chocolate biscotti.

Though we're cofounders, THE HIATUS is the boss. During the last few months, I've been given incrementally fewer complex assignments and responsibility. This gradual erosion of leadership parity illustrates his vote of *"no confidence"* in both my ability and our friendship. He thinks I'm stupid. As we eat our sweets, I remind him prior to our engagement,

"I ran a $65MM technology program," sounding like a petulant child.

THE HIATUS pauses to reflect. Has his opinion of me changed? I know he intends to fire me.

Will he send me off with a kick in the ass and a hefty severance package?

We leave the cafeteria and wind down another corridor to a deeper level of the food court. A crew of teenage soda jerks wearing checkered aprons and paper hats clamor to take our order. The teens laugh and bicker about which of them will serve us.

"Guys, don't take his money, I'm paying," I say flipping THE HIATUS off as he stands at the far end of the counter. I've accepted that I'm going to lose my job as THE HIATUS outlines his perfunctory bullet points:

"1- I only have a $3000 annual budget for you to manage. 2- Your salary expense simply doesn't justify the cost. 3- At least now you can leave with my respect."

My eyes roll. He becomes angry and condescending. He mentally flows the energy of "KNOW IT ALL," in reaction to my dismissal. He won't be receptive to anything else I'll say today. But I still have his back. I care about him. He's my friend.

We've forgotten! Shit! Earlier in the day, a female coworker vanished during a meeting! What will we do?] //

⁂
FOOD COURT: #0726
STARTUP: #0441, #0777
BANANA: #0428, #0756
RESPECT: #0433, #0638, #0656
⁂

#0055 - January 27, 2018 @ 05:30 (The Presidio of San Francisco, California)

[0055.1 / 0137] [I'm at a 1950's era diner, seated in a red pleather upholstered booth, sipping milkshakes with RASHIDA JONES and ROB LOWE. They flirt and kiss each other playfully.

"Why don't you get together?" I ask, taking a sip from my chocolate malt through a peppermint swirl patterned paper straw.

"We're together right now!" They exclaim in unison after a short pause.

Their repartee is so sweet that I cry. They're enveloped by a glowing gold ball that casts a yellow hue throughout the room. A being named "Abigail Bumby" takes a seat next to me, and startles me awake.] //

*⁎⁎

ROB LOWE: #1379
PAPER: #0405, #0450, #0459
SWIRL: #0489, #0735,
1950's: #0752, #0763
GOLD: #0599, #0610, #0659

*⁎⁎

#0056 - January 30, 2018 @ 02:10 (Piaţa Romană - Bucharest, Romania)

[0056.1 / 0138] [I'm outside a concert venue. I don't have a ticket. TOOL performs. Everyone's excited to hear new music, though no new album has been released. I peek in a side exit during a performance of the song, "The Grudge." The music is the same, but the accompanying visuals have been given an elaborate update. A decaying 4D cellular automata swirl of rich orange tones appears at the top left corner of a giant screen and descends behind the band. The predominantly black backdrop is occasionally pierced with intense beams of green light.

I've seen the group perform many times. Each time, the price of a ticket has increased while the show has generally remained the same. I'm not going to pay any more. I'm going to sneak inside. THE THINKER (*fair, deliberate, strong, and loving*) sits by a rear entrance. He's happy right where he is. He can hear the music, occasionally catching a glimpse of the show through a ring of mirrors that surround and face the building interior. He sees me contemplating a break in, and gives me a nod suggesting I go for it. I push my way through a crowd. Once at the front, I'm stopped by an usher who wears an ill-fitting oversized red jacket. As he waves a flashlight, I note his name tag reads, "Daniel." Our eyes meet. I recognize him as a homeless man I regularly see pushing a shopping cart through my neighborhood. "Daniel" is the head of security and wastes no time siphoning off people from the masses who don't have tickets. I'm shuffled with the small group up a staircase, passing THE PANDA who's dropped a bag of Sriracha flavored Pita Chips. I pick them up and put them back in her pack without her knowing. We're corralled in a balcony level box with blackout curtains in the windows. I yawn repeatedly while security admonishes the group.

We're released and ushered across the venue. I lean over a balcony and drop a plastic bag with unknown contents down a deep spiral staircase carved from a single block of stone. We're prodded and lambasted while I complain by screaming out increasing ticket prices and their corresponding years.

"I only paid $16.50 to see them in 1996!"

"Ducky...please man up and pay, or just shut the fuck up!" a familiar voice from below shouts up.

I never see a face, though I'm confident it's THE FLUTIST (*courageous, stern, and musical*) holding me to account.

Our group of line jumpers is guided down a stairwell to the ground floor. A middle-aged man and woman stand at a video kiosk complaining about *"their President."* They're angered this leader will nominate replacements for five seats on the United States Supreme Court. They're inconsolable.

77

"Stuff like this only matters when the majority opinion doesn't conform to yours. RUTH. BADER. GINSBERG. FO-REVAH!" I cackle.

Tricksters and wizards in the group give me high fives. Just before being thrown out, I pause to speak with a young Asian man seated at the bottom of the white marble spiral staircase. He rifles through the bag I dropped from above, taking a new white T-shirt and shoving it in his coat. The high-tech garment reforms the wearer's body to make it look like they have six-pack abs. He asks me if I'm familiar with the word "kismet." The rumble of the bass is loud and distracts me from answering. I'm funneled to an exit door and pass "Daniel" who politely smiles.

"Whoever yelled at me knows me really well," I chuckle, pat him on the shoulder and leave the concert hall.] //

⁂

Min. = ♠- THE THINKER: #0666
TOOL: #0060
DANIEL: #0408
ASIAN MAN: #0434, #0497, #0577, #0724
HOMELESS: #0500, #0527, #0573, #0620, #0726
THE PANDA: #0098
THE FLUTIST: #1412

⁂

#0057 - January 30, 2018 @ 03:50 (Piața Romană - Bucharest, Romania)

[0057.1 / 0139] [I watch a football game where a loaf of white bread is used for the ball.]
[0057.2 / 0140] [A black background shimmers with the outline of gloved hands communicating in American Sign Language.] //

⁂

BLACK: #0764, #0768, #0774
BREAD: #0457, #0489, #0500
HANDS: #0499, #0500, #0521

⁂

#0058 - January 30, 2018 @ 09:30 (Piața Romană - Bucharest, Romania)

[0058.1 / 0141] [Multiple images of penguins sliding around, occasionally drifting beyond the edge of an iceberg and plopping into frigid arctic blue water.]
[0058.2 / 0142] [I install an accessible shower and bathtub at GRANDMA's apartment. She recently turned 99. She's my last living grandparent. She's stern, focused, and fair. She never asks for help, which is why my participation is significant. She attends a class while we work. We eat cereal and cookies while troubleshooting a minor plumbing issue. We believe the installation mitigates her increasing risk of falling injuries. The more we talk, the more our attention turns away from the construction project and to how we can best interview and record her fantastic stories. She's vital and independent. We errantly believe she's fragile and will die any day. It's likely she will outlive all of us.] //

⁂

Maj. = 11- GRANDMA: #0275
TROUBLESHOOT: #0506, #0785
PLUMBING: #0627, #0674
⁂

#0059 - January 31, 2018 @ 11:20 (Piața Romană - Bucharest, Romania)

[0059.1 / 0143] [I fly like a superhero over Caribbean waters, stopping to explore an archipelago. I have a sexual encounter with a different partner on each island. Each partner has intimate knowledge of a single part of my body, brought to connection and arousal through their individual touch and in an order that leaves me feeling empowered, seen, and sensually whole. I climax in each encounter, especially enjoying an interaction where my lover prefers we use a gritty pumice hand scrub for lube. The island crossing adventures are equally open, bright, spacious and breezy. As I depart, I tap "Eros" on the shoulder and say, *"Thank you."* He drowsily acknowledges me, and we write a brief updated contract to bring him out of hibernation and back into my life. He really needed a long nap to recharge after our last agreement was fulfilled.] //

⁂
SEX: #0403, #0431, #0467, #0472
ISLAND: #0479, #0550
EROS: #0524, #0558
FLYING: #0481, #0500, #0561, #0655, #0725, #0786
⁂

#0060 - February 1, 2018 @ 02:00 (Piața Romană - Bucharest, Romania)

[0060.1 / 0144] [I write songs with a band. A camera crew films me for a documentary that profiles our writing process. We're spread around a large dark room with comfortable furniture. I'm in another TOOL dream. MAYNARD KEENAN (*illusive, vulnerable, creative, and deliberate*) and I sit in a medicine circle. We develop a musical motif and grow it into a simple four bar melody inspired by the surrounding mountains. Simple. Elegant. Anti-schmaltz. A Native American man wearing a dingy white T-Shirt and jeans appears next to us. He seems young, but is considered an elder. He's just returned from being out in nature for years. His hair is fashioned in two beautiful, long, and thick black braids that fall down his back to the waistline. We sit silently until he begins singing medicine songs, accompanying himself on an acoustic guitar.

"All heart songs move through me,
Before they're shared with humanity," he sings.

MAYNARD looks at me asking, *"Are you ready to go?"*
I affirm.
He declares to the circle, *"This melody was inspired by 'the organic creature.'"*

" -- _____ _____ ____ ____
-- --_ _ _ _ ____
-- --__ _ _ _ _ _

79

_____--_ _ _ _ _ _ --_."

The song comes through in Morse code and infuses the circle with a blessing. Quietly, the elder contemplates our conjuring. He gently tosses his braids over his shoulders and smiles as he tips his head at us in a partial bow. He accepts the melody and, now blessed, it can transform into a song.

MAYNARD and I dive through an oval shaped cut out in a nearby wall, emerging from the portal into a recording studio where we begin laying down tracks in earnest. We occupy different sound proof rooms. We sing together and harmonize. I'm in a large vacant auditorium on stage wearing headphones, while MAYNARD's room is quaint and hygge. DANNY CAREY (*magician, brooding, and powerful*) enters the auditorium and sits at a table in front of me.

"Brother, I've missed you," he says with a single wave of a hand. He begins eating prepared meats from a sterling silver tray (*sausage, bacon, T-bone steaks*).

The writing process remains fluid and stimulating. *"Let's keep it sacred, not scared"* becomes our playful reminder to one another. MAYNARD constantly "disallows significance" as the creative bubble around the studio is poked by "meaning maker" beings. We walk around while singing. Our paths cross at another oval doorway where guitarist ADAM JONES holds an awkward expression of "side crow" pose until he falls flat on his face. His genius manifests when he works beyond his physical edge. He recreates the yoga pose and holds it interminably while MAYNARD and I sing into a leather thigh high boot held overhead like a boom mic. While crooning through the neck of the oversized shoe we encounter a pulsating brain being that expands the more we sing.

"Don't get wrapped up in, nor attracted to that. ADAM will take care of it," MAYNARD whispers between takes.

The pulsing brain keeps swelling, the more we create. The brain reflects the expanding vitality of the song. It happens even more quickly when we sing a take with the intention of *"giving it all back to the mountains."* It's a simple melody, with contrasting flourishes from thundering drums (*bass drums, toms, but no snare*).

The song gestates. We like it and know others will. Some random fans sneak in to the recording session and observe MAYNARD singing on his right side in the fetal position. He completes the performance segment as we return to separate rooms. The next phase requires more personal space to allow for full embodiment of our unique creative expressions. I writhe around on the floor, hands and feet painfully cramped by tetany, yet this does not deter me from being "sung through." Torrents of light spew from our mouths into microphones. The mountains welcome the continuation of our conversation after a 13-year pause. Unexpected harmonies delight us on playback. The song's sonically odd, and captivating.

ADAM will later generate a stop motion animation video featuring a being made from bovine entrails and shiny black injection molded plastic. The being's movements will mimic my gait.] //

⁂

TOOL: #0075
ADAM JONES: #0953
DANNY CAREY: #0933
MAYNARD KEENAN: #0116
BRAIN: #0441, #0451, #0528, #0559
MORSE CODE: #0485, #0632, #0701

BRAID: #0406, #0419, #0458, #0545
ANIMATION: #0401, #0695, #0761

⁑

#0061 - February 1, 2018 @ 05:44 (Piața Romană - Bucharest, Romania)

[0061.1 / 0145] [I perform magic tricks. My family is a group of traveling actors. I'm mad at my dad. I run around a basement in circles, then find myself crouched on the roof of a car. A voice from the void questions, *"No go to forty smudgings?"* My surroundings are blurry and ambiguous.] //

⁑

TRICKS: #0418, #0431
BASEMENT: #0747, #0773, #0793
VOID: #0678, #0745
AMBIGUITY: #0499, #0566

⁑

#0062 - February 2, 2018 @ 08:23 (Piața Romană - Bucharest, Romania)

[0062.1 / 0146] [I sit in a small bedroom writing a progressive rock album with a group of guys. We complete tracking, mixing and mastering in one, 90-minute session. We relax on a couch together to listen to what we've created. I've written music with DREAM THEATER. I didn't recognize them while we were writing. When I realize this, I lose my space and become a fanboy. I insist we listen to their album "Six Degrees of Inner Turbulence," while profusely referencing "2002."
"That album was central to my existence when I first moved to North Carolina!"
I catch myself in reaction and apologize. I excuse myself from the room. Once outside I feel like I'm in a third world country. Trash stacked everywhere. The smell of burning rubber. Only churches line the streets. I don't go in any of them. I doubt my musical ability, even though I've just collaborated with a generous group of creative geniuses that have impacted my life positively and welcomed my contribution.] //

⁑

DREAM THEATER: #0987
BEDROOM: #0665, #0678, #0682, #0683
RECORDING: #0430, #0478, #0654
TRASH: #0426, #0484, #0597, #0764
DOUBT: #0549, #0611, #060
GENIUS: #0761, #0762

⁑

#0063 - February 2, 2018 @ 14:10 (Piața Romană - Bucharest, Romania)

[0063.1 / 0147] [I'm in an episode of "House Hunters," and escorted to different properties by MARTY MCFLY and DR. EMMETT BROWN. We focus on neighborhoods in suburban New York. We're specifically looking for houses listed at $1.2MM. We're solely oriented on the price point and not an amenity wish list. It's just about finding the best place to park an extra $1.2MM in cash. We're guided by a middle-aged female real estate agent who's a bit bossy and impatient. She takes us through a series of amber golden hued "Cubicle Farm Condos."

"These are office spaces where you can live AND share a gender-neutral bathroom," she boasts.

Most of the prospective buyers have a lot of excess cash, but they're in declining health. "Cubicle Farm Condos" basically means, *"veiled assisted living for body broken work-a-holics in their 30's and 40's."* I decide I don't want to live there, deeply offending the real estate agent. It's her perceived *"top listing."*

A homeless woman across the street, recently discharged from a rehab facility, cries because the state won't let her see her kids until she secures a place to live. It's a cruel impossibility because she doesn't have any money. MARTY, DOC and I offer to help her if she plays along with us and acts like she's rich, while we act like we're broke. As we tour a ground floor unit the homeless woman camps up her embodiment as a person of means. She makes an absurdly low bid of $56,000 on an $800,000 unit, contingent completely on the building management changing the color of the fridge. By some amazing stroke of fortune, the seller accepts the offer and the woman is instantly reunited with her children. As she hugs them, she looks up at us and mouths, *"Thank you."*]

[0063.2 / 0148] [I watch the world premiere of a BEYONCÉ video on television with a group of friends. As the music starts the black and white camera shot begins to slowly pull out to reveal a pair of human male and female reproductive organs mid-sex act. As the pullback continues a girlfriend of mine becomes triggered and says, *"OH MY GAWD I CAN SEE PEEEEEEEN!"*

She buries her face in a pillow frantically laughing, surprised, and grossed out. The video portrays two sweat laden, middle aged, normal statured Caucasian people who seem to have red hair, though not verifiable through the monochrome. After penetrating each other in a multitude of ways they fall apart and away from one another. The man isn't satiated, and in the absence of the woman performs fellatio on himself suspended in midair until he climaxes in his mouth.]

[0063.3 / 0149] [The TV channel changes and our group watches a human-interest documentary generated in real time that profiles a person with a disability moving into a new place. The person struggles to find work as a wheelchair user. People who tune in can make patron contributions to the person that are instantly deposited into a checking account. We each send a few dollars. Public interest and viewership rise swiftly, along with monetary contributions. In under thirty minutes the person has enough cash in hand to buy a new home outright.] //

⁎⁎

BEYONCÉ: #0130
THANK YOU: #0528, #0597, #0719, #0787
MONOCHROME: #0788, #0798
WHEELCHAIR: #0416, #0534

⁎⁎

⁎⁎

#0064 - February 4, 2019 @ 10:23 (Piața Romană - Bucharest, Romania)

[0064.1 / 0150] [I'm at a post office standing behind THE AFFLICTED (*self-defeating, and confused*) who argues with the desk clerk about a missing package. They both speak different languages and don't understand each other. I'm annoyed and begin tapping my foot while crossing my arms. A female cyber-goth pops her head in the door and starts screaming anti-Semitic slurs at us while she wildly laughs. She's wearing an oversized black hoodie, and has a very angular, severe haircut accented by hot pink stripes. She disappears out the door, as though she dared herself to scream at us for the adrenaline hit she'd get from the confrontation.]

[0064.2 / 0151] [THE GUITARIST, THE DRUMMER (*bandmate, co-creator, and essential*) and I sit around a round table after completing a recording session on a H5N "handicorder." We've reproduced a catalog of songs recorded in 2000 with new arrangements and flourishes. We're very happy with the results. We agree simplifying the recording process and equipment favorably impacts the quality of the vocals, though we still consider vocals and lyrics for this project of secondary importance. We're satisfied with the unintended benefits and give one another smiles and high fives to celebrate what we've created. It's been fun to revisit old songs we've written, so many years later.]

[0064.3 / 0152] [A giant orange glitter pumpkin hovers over a glittering sea of miniature pumpkins. They're suspended in space, making small wavy patterns while a genderless voice whispers in the background, *"Take your time."*] //

✳

Min. = ♣- *THE GUITARIST: #0130*
ADRENALINE: #0764
RECORDING: #0430, #0478, #0654
ORANGE: #0657, #0715, #0719
THE DRUMMER: #0404

✳

#0065 - February 5, 2018 @ 07:47 (Piața Romană - Bucharest, Romania)

[0065.1 / 0153] [THE DANCER and I are in a large stone brick town square at night. The stones are a dark slate tone. Light flows from the moon supplemented by fluorescent pollution from an adjacent convenience store and adjoining student bookstore. A big white stylish and sleek neon sign reading "TOASTY'S.TO" shines offensively bright light down on us from above.

We're on a futuristic-medieval college campus. We've been dropped in a large puzzle-labyrinth game as part of an exam, though we don't venture beyond the central square space where we stand. I identify light and dark energies as *"ghosts"* that are trying to *"get"* us. The light energies show up as small, fast paced glowing orbs. Dark energies look like cartoonish black balls with small red slits for eyes surrounded by black flame tentacles. We never have direct interaction with either of these types of entities. They show up like blips on a radar screen in the center of my head, which I see clearly when I close my eyes. LARRY DAVID (*awkward, trickster, and irreverent*) appears in front of us declaring, *"Everyone here has beef with me!"*] //

⁂

Maj. = 2- THE DANCER: #0080
LARRY DAVID: #0145
NEON: #0534, #0615
⁂

#0066 - February 7, 2018 @ 04:00 (Piața Romană - Bucharest, Romania)

[0066.1 / 0154] [The dream takes place at what feels like night. I'm uncertain, because it appears I'm on a giant Hollywood soundstage. Physical buildings, trees, and roads fill the space over where I expect to find thick chalk outlines and white tape marks on the ground. I have a job at a fast-food chicken restaurant. The environment behind the sales counter where my team works is bright and chaotic. People scramble around quickly to fulfill orders. A burst of cold air flows in as an overweight hairy man with a Brooklyn accent leans out his station at a drive thru window to yell aggressively and shake his hand at the car that's decided to park directly outside, disrupting the flow of traffic and interrupting business.]

[0066.2 / 0155] [I'm walking on a grey afternoon at twilight on a street near the restaurant in [0066.1 / 0154]. It feels like a hybridization of Washington Heights, San Francisco, and Black Rock City. I stroll up behind a guy on a street corner who's wearing a stocking cap with a fluffy pom pom on top. I'm instantly attracted to him, though I haven't seen his face, nor shared conversation with him. As I move to his side, I notice it's THE ACTOR (*loving, guided, and sensitive*). He's as cute as I remember him. While we flirt, there's mutual implicit awareness that we're not rekindling a relationship.

As we walk together, we turn a corner that puts us back in the direction of the chicken restaurant. The drive thru and entrance are both located on the second floor, above a series of residential units. At street level to our left stands a simple kiosk with a generic white vinyl sign hung vertically to create a doorway. Even though we have no idea what's inside, or if the dwellers within are selling anything (*much less want or welcome visitors*) THE ACTOR and I decide to enter.

We're greeted by a woman in her 20's who looks like a character from a noir film. A middle-aged man sits behind a simple 6' table. The man is dressed like a Catholic priest. Light emanates from an arched tunnel that runs the length of the space. We're invited to sit down. THE ACTOR and I decide to accept exorcisms from the man and woman. THE ACTOR goes first and seems to have a benign, uneventful experience. He decides to wait for me while I receive mine. The man places his hands on my head and asks a series of three questions to zero in on the type of entity that's inhabited me.

"Where do you live?" He asks.

"San Francisco."

"That's a hot spot. Which neighborhood?"

"Lower Haight."

"Oh, that's a hot bed within a hotspot."

I don't recall his third question, but my answer leaves him in bewilderment. He's astonished I've been able to domicile in such a strong point of possessive attraction for so long. I've attracted an intensely parasitic being.

"How have you been able to remain productive, active and (to use your words) 'generally happy' with this thing wrapped around your insides? This would break most people."

I shrug not knowing any other reality.

"You're fairly strong, but you'll benefit from me taking it out."

Immediately a strong vacuum-like whooshing sensation wells up from the core of my being, accompanied by a sourness in the mouth which overwhelms me. He places a palm on my forehead and calls the entity out as I simultaneously vomit and shit. After this happens, I'm rendered unrecognizable to THE ACTOR, who decides to walk away without any further interaction. I take a moment to get grounded. I stand while rubbing my eyes and yawning, then stumble out the door and onto the street to look for him. He's gone. I feel sad and speed around the soundstage trying to find him. Once I've completely felt the sadness, my motion stops. I feel neutral and stand in place.]

[0066.3 / 0156] [I'm a young boy living in an oversized version of my parent's home. The sizes of the rooms, furniture, and appliances are all exaggerated. I wake up from a nap in the basement. My pulse is quick. I feel a rush of adrenaline.

"There's an entity down here."

"It's not evil, it's just a really bothersome being," a guide whispers behind my right ear.

"I won't be possessed again."

I go up the stairwell and find THE WEAVER in the kitchen next to the island. I tug on her leg from down low and tell her about the being. She shrugs me off, but encourages me to do what I need to do.

I descend back down to the basement. I cross a large carpeted area that is mostly dark. I'm taken by an experience of extreme heaviness and lethargy in my body. I run back up to the main floor and decide to start sleeping upstairs with the rest of my family from now on.]

[0066.4 / 0157] [I omnisciently observe a replay of the earlier drive thru interaction at the fried chicken shop from outside the building. The older aggravated man with the Brooklyn accent leans out of the window and screams obscenities while shaking his fist at a grey four door Mercedes. The car hasn't just blocked the flow of customer traffic, but has also soiled freshly poured squares of concrete sidewalk. Its wheels sink deep into the wet cement and become stuck. While there's a lot of screaming, it's all in vain. The driver abandons the car with the engine running. The insults and threats hurled by the drive thru operator aren't heard.

A sexy Latinx man and THE GYPSY *(coachable, eager, and mystical)* enter the exorcism stand beneath the drive thru, laughing as they flip up the vinyl sign and disappear. From this perspective I can better see the advertisement printed on it. THE ACTOR and I enter moments later. I have a realization. I needed the *(now removed)* entity to guide my spiritual growth. I see the impact that agreement had on a former relationship with THE ACTOR, and how it spurred its eventual end. I observe my exorcism, noticing it takes exquisite skill of the priest to remove the entity. The process exhausts and nearly kills him.] //

Maj. = 0- THE WEAVER: #0069, 10- THE ACTOR: #0109

85

SOUNDSTAGE: #0745, #0753, #0765
CHICKEN: #0567, #0587, #0597, #0749
✢

#0067 - February 7, 2018 @ 4:36am (Piața Romană - Bucharest, Romania)

[0067.1 / 0158] [Two white glowing hippos graze on a savannah at night. Out of nowhere, a hurricane strikes. Though they are large, powerful creatures the hippos are washed away by a great wave. They're swept through a lagoon, around a giant mountain, and out of view.
"Who let the dogs out?" a loud voice from the dark cloudy swirling sky asks.
"We'll leave that to the NFL to answer," a voice with equal boom and volume retorts.] //

✢
VOLUME: #0406, #0519, #0536
MOUNTAINS: #0582, #0683
FOOTBALL: #0477, #0698
WAVE: #0462, #0532
✢

#0068 - February 7, 2018 @ 04:57 (Piața Romană - Bucharest, Romania)

[0068.1 / 0159] [Twin brothers play guitars and sing harmoniously in the dark.
"Everyone's a little down on me...Everyone's a little down."
Their songs are quiet and sad. The sweet and vulnerable expressions are felt equally by both of them. They're aligned and fully participating, channeling as a single, bigger being.] //

✢
TWINS: #0456
FELT: #0489, #0528, #0714
GUITAR: #0618, #0677, #0702
SAD: #0476, #0496, #0515, #0548, #0555
✢

#0069 - February 7, 2018 @ 13:21 (Piața Romană - Bucharest, Romania)

[0069.1 / 0160] [I walk on a narrow cobblestone path with a slight uphill pitch. I'm behind three people *(a male/female couple and a single man)* who walk at a fairly slow pace. They feel deliberate, though a bit labored by the walk. As much as I want to pass them out of mild frustration, I can't. The pathway is blocked by a parked, white 15 passenger van. The couple duck to the left side holding hands, while the single man cuts to the narrower passage at right. Since he's moving a little more quickly, I opt to follow him.
I enter a brownstone building. I pass through the doorway and find myself ascending a long staircase to an exposed brick loft space. The ceilings are easily higher than 30 feet tall. THE REVOLUTIONARY *(grounded, rational, and tenacious)* acknowledges me from across the space, but is fully subscribed by her production tasks. Numerous invisible beings make certain the environment is perfectly lit and the air is treated with the proper concentration of

rose water essence using perfume sprayers. Once the space is set, I understand angels have prepared for a performance by a reincarnation of PRINCE (*fluid, expressive, vulnerable, and soul centric*). PRINCE will sing a new song (*previously unheard by humans*) that will eventually be made available to a global audience.

PRINCE manifests in a soft flash of purple/pink/white/gold light. He grips a single microphone at the center of the room which now has celestial, sparkling white walls. He offers a few opening bars in falsetto and begins dancing around the room. Fully engrossed by the performance, I grab at my pocket for my phone. I want to inconspicuously record him. Each attempt I make results in a fuzzy, diffused capture. Each video I take makes me feel increasingly drunk, which intensifies to such an extent I drop my phone. I forget the melody and lyrics to the new song.]

[0069.2 / 0161] [I'm running a little late for a coffee shop meetup with THE WEAVER and THE CARPENTER. I feel hazy, perhaps hungover from my interactions with PRINCE. When I arrive, I greet THE WEAVER and THE CARPENTER who sit with THE COLONEL (*meticulous, type A, and competitive*) at a cafe table next to a window.

"*Bummer! You just missed 'Greg,'*" they say as a group.

I'm confused. I have no idea who "Greg" is. They continue their conversation and blur out of focus. Attention shifts to my phone where I can see "Greg's" avatar on a map moving toward the local public access TV station. Instead of meeting him there, I rush home via subway as quickly as possible. "Greg" now seems like a dear friend, rather than a stranger. I'm excited to see his interview.

Once home I turn on the TV and tune in to the correct channel. "Greg's" at a fertility clinic about to demonstrate to a world-wide audience "*how to properly impregnate your partner.*" He disrobes then engages in consensual, mechanical sex with a non-binary expressed partner. Once "Greg" ejaculates, the partner expunges the semen into a bed pan. It's weighed and measured for volume, then presented by a doctor to "Greg" in a 500ml Erlenmeyer flask, mostly filled "Greg" holds it up next to his face, smiling in a camera as though he's won Olympic gold.] //

✳

Maj. = 0- THE WEAVER: #0070, 1- THE CARPENTER: #0070
Min. = ♠- THE REVOLUTIONARY: #0189
PRINCE: #0177
COBBLESTONE: #0494, #0527, #0548, #0561, #0767
THE COLONEL: #1049

✳

#0070 - February 9, 2018 @ 08:26 (Piața Romană - Bucharest, Romania)

[0070.1 / 0162] [I observe a billiards table from above. The white cue ball strikes a triangle composed of 15 balls on a green table. The balls scatter to various points around the rectangular table, spilling into the six circular pockets (*four in the corners, two in the center of the longer sides*).]

· · ·

[0070.2 / 0163] [I'm a young boy listening to music with THE WEAVER and THE CARPENTER. We listen to vinyl records on a turntable. The mood is uplifting, playful, and happy. Each time THE CARPENTER removes an LP from the turntable it transforms into a series of three silver compact discs, supplemented with their own paper sleeves for storage. Their transformation surprises me. THE CARPENTER is humored by my response to his "magic" trick. The process repeats after every record we play. I help THE CARPENTER put the CD's in their sleeves. He shows me how to put them away. I feel like I'm helping out. He feels like he's teaching me something.]

[0070.3 / 0164] [I'm inside a school bus that's been converted to a shared living space. I'm preparing for Burning Man with a group of Yoga teachers (BARON BAPTISTE (*spacious, and aloof*), THE SHARED HEART (*abundant, and candid*), THE LIONESS (*driven, and clear*), THE TORCH RUNNER (*strong, and neurotic*), THE OBSERVER (*contemplative, and attentive*), THE EXECUTIVE PRODUCER (*bossy, and sharp*). Curious about what they need to pack, they look to me for guidance. We plan at a square table that seats two per side. We're physically present, but preoccupied with our own priorities. We have to focus. The surrounding environment is supremely chaotic.]

[0070.4 / 0165] [Numerous abstract shapes and colors hang weightlessly in my visual field for a period of time, akin to neon signs in a pea soup fog. A clear image of a white baseball cap with a powder blue bill emerges. A two-inch square patch in the center of the hat displays a magic image of a large pink salmon leaping from a calm lake. The word "FISHING" is sewn at the base of the patch with black thread in bold block capital letters.] //

⁎⁎

Maj. = 0- THE WEAVER: #0075, 1- THE CARPENTER: #0075
BARON BAPTISTE: #0085
BLOCK LETTERS: #0471, #0557, #0558, #0606, #0662, #0704
THE LIONESS: #0124
THE EXECUTIVE PRODUCER: #0145
THE SHARED HEART: #0239
THE OBSERVER: #0282

⁎⁎

#0071 - February 9, 2018 @ 10:06 (Piața Romană - Bucharest, Romania)

[0071.1 / 0166] [I'm in a conference room with THE COACH (*masterful*), THE CREATOR (*full feeling*), and THE CHALLENGER (*open, and accessible*). All are connected visionaries, present to the practice of artful living. We've gathered to discuss the possibility of hosting a *"Conscious Leadership Forum"* in a new, as yet untapped market for their consultancy. Though somewhat intimidated, I'm confident I can productively contribute to the organization.
"Something NEW wants to come THROUGH!" We shout together, then laugh.
THE CREATOR's attention turns inward as she focuses on an unnamed personal priority and exits the room. We're all fine with her departure.
THE COACH and I are joined by an unfamiliar, yet helpful man. The three of us share playful conversation while making laps between the nose and tail on the inside of a 747 airlin-

er. Our job is to inspect and ensure that all passenger seat belts "conform to conscious standards." We don't find any problematic seat belts and declare the plane *"safe for both takeoff and landing."*]

[0071.2 / 0167] [I walk out a screen door from a dimly lit room, out to a stone patio surrounded on all sides by high stone walls and discover a designated break area for restaurant service staff. THE CONNECTOR *(feisty, passionate, dedicated, and dramatic)* shoves pork dumplings and XLB's in her mouth from a discarded white Styrofoam container she found on the ground. I giggle, *"I knew I'd find you here."*]

[0071.3 / 0168] [I enter a jewelry store through a thick glass doorway, looking specifically for a *"ring with an 'O'."* "Ego Me" insists I find a particular exquisite platinum band with an "O" fashioned from diamonds atop the band. "Ephemeral Me" giggles expectantly while compassionately rolling its eyes, as every ring in the display case is, a *"ring with an O."* I don't realize this, and spend eons inspecting thousands of rings. I eventually find one worth purchasing and ask a woman with long, dark, straight hair to ring me up. She's warm and engaging as we complete the sale. Amnesia befalls her as she turns to face me. I'm not recognizable to her.
"We're getting a new shipment today, if you don't find something you like," she states blankly before moving on to another task behind the counter.
A mechanical being arrives in a flash of bright, multi-color light. It identifies itself as a "Sentinel" and talks with the shop owner though I'm not able to hear their conversation. The "Sentinel" abruptly blurts at me in an alien language. It repeats itself, with small subtitles displayed mid-air before me to help me decode the blurt, but I can't decipher them.
The "Sentinel" draws a weapon from a back holster, shoots the shop owner in the head, then disappears as quickly as it arrived.]

[0071.4 / 0169] [I'm at "Gymnastics LTD" in Beavercreek, Ohio. I haven't been here since 1996. The space is much larger than I recall. The skill level coached here is well beyond my experience. Many elite athletes flip, tumble, and vault around with shared focus on next month's Olympic Trials. THE REPEATER *(quick, powerful, and dedicated)* practices his vaults into a large blue foam pit. He's highly skilled, but considered junior to others on the team. He's an amazing competitor, and I consider him a mentor.] //

⁎⁎

Maj. = 4- THE CONNECTOR: #0144
JEWELRY: #0431, #0500
VAULT: #0591
BEAVERCREEK: #0429
THE CREATOR: #0153
THE COACH: #0980

⁎⁎

#0072 - February 10, 2018 @ 07:18 (Piața Romană - Bucharest, Romania)

[0072.1 / 0170] [THE WHITE RABBIT and I agree to meet at a specific place and time for a date. I arrive on time. THE WHITE RABBIT is a no-show. I laugh when I check his social media account. His image has been replaced with a white stick figure .GIF that makes Qi Gong motions on a black background. The stick man smiles. He doesn't see the darkness. His light outshines the dark. In spirit, THE WHITE RABBIT tells me he's in Chiang Mai, Thailand. This brings me happiness. I smile and create Qi Gong motions by myself. Originally, we'd have practiced together. The scene is light, perfect, and beautiful. I feel completely connected to him while engaging the illusion of his absence.] //

⁂

Min. = ◆- *THE WHITE RABBIT: #0115*
ARRIVE: #0527, #0577, #0602, #0623
PERFECT: #0561, #0618, #0653
SOCIAL MEDIA: #0472, #0538

⁂

#0073 - February 11, 2018 @ 07:28 (Piața Romană - Bucharest, Romania)

[0073.1 / 0171] [I consult with the band KORN on a social media campaign. We attempt to deploy a new interactive technology that allows fans to use machine learning to generate song lyrics. The process goes live and five songs immediately filter in, forming a stack ranked list for the band's evaluation. For an unknown reason, the most popular track "_____ PROCESS" has the first word of its title censored. JONATHAN DAVIS is frustrated for a few reasons:

1. He doesn't like surrendering creative control.
2. *"FUCK THE REGULATORS, CENSORSHIP SUCKS."*
3. The way fans want the band to perform is no longer energetically aligned.

It feels stagnant and rehashed. JONATHAN's frustration morphs to anger. He gestures towards a webcam feed where we watch a group of Hispanic men fighting and rioting in the middle of a city street.]

[0073.2 / 0172] [THE CLUB KID (*frenetic, creative, and chaotic*) applies makeup at an oval mirror ringed by soft opaque marquis bulbs. He mocks THE SEXUAL SACRED for desiring fame. In lieu of anger, THE SEXUAL SACRED (*searching, modest, and open*) approaches THE CLUB KID and kisses him. Together they step into a bubble bath, and remain standing. They have sex. THE CLUB KID decides to bottom, turns around and bends toward a circular hole in a wall with small pink square mosaic tiling. Waist to head obscured, THE CLUB KID's groans of pleasure can be heard through the wall, while THE SEXUAL SACRED caringly and deeply penetrates him from behind. THE CLUB KID is unstable. THE SEXUAL SACRED, immature. Their energies pair and make them an aligned match. The scene becomes increasingly kinky.

My attention drifts. I leave the bathroom and wander towards a bedroom with white gold walls. A grand marble desk is set in the center of the room. I open a drawer and remove a large fish bowl filled with cool, crystal clear water. At the bottom are hundreds of solid gold Boba-sized ingots. I fish them out, strain, and dry them a handful at a time. The repetitive activity is deeply soothing and helps me focus.

90

A handsome olive complexed Greek man wearing a white terrycloth robe enters the room. We make eyes while I continue straining gold beads from the bowl, which has now increased in size and become a large saltwater aquarium. We move toward one another to kiss, but avoid one another at the last instant. We remember we're in THE DOMINATRIX's *(controlling, sensual, and attentive)* bedroom. We adjourn to a closet to retrieve the blue and gold blanket that's usually stored in the trunk of my car, here neatly folded and resting alone on its own shelf. We notice 4,376 people watch us on a livestream broadcast.] //

⁂

KORN: #0298
JONATHAN DAVIS: #0303
MOSAIC: #0603, #0618
MARBLE: #0431, #0589
OLIVE: #0541, #0558, #0693, #0717
THE CLUB KID: #0079
THE SEXUAL SACRED: #0301
THE DOMINATRIX: #0367

⁂

#0074 - February 12, 2018 @ 00:46 (Piața Romană - Bucharest, Romania)

[0074.1 / 0173] [I sit on top of a cubicle partition having a telepathic conversation with ANNE FINUCANE *(politically savvy, articulate, and strategic)*. As I'm perched over her shoulder, I pepper her with contemplative questions.
"Can we handle that?"
"No?"
"Do you want to...?"
"Only if..."
This goes on for some time and feels engaged, naturally fluid and effortless; more like play than work. We shape the global economy with a few breaths of strong intention, focused thought, and a brief flurry of keystrokes. We share awareness and mutual respect for how our words are interpreted in strategic conversations.]

[0074.2 / 0174] [I drive with THE AYURVEDIC *(seeker, fun, and feminine)* up a snowy mountain road. A guy careens towards us on a bike, without a helmet on a collision course. The impact will kill him. Glancing over towards THE AYURVEDIC, she keeps her eyes on the road and without emoting says, *"He's an idiot. You can't save him."* As our car collides with the bike, everything fades to white.]

[0074.3 / 0175] [I'm a passenger in a black car with THE BOND TRADER *(enterprising, astute, and proper)*. We drive very quickly to a business dinner on the opposite side of Mexico City. It's dark. The city is exceptionally large. Traffic is dense, fast, and moves with precision. THE BOND TRADER screams in Spanish as a car jumps the median and strikes the right rear quarter panel of our vehicle. We survive the crash. Once we skid to a stop we jump out and run back towards the car that hit us. It explodes, engulfing the woman within, in flames. She screams until her skin burns off. She dies, leaving a charred, mangled corpse.] //

JOSHUA D. LUNDELL

Min. = ♦- *THE AYURVEDIC: #0556*
GLOBAL: #0417, #0436, #0505
PEPPER: #0494, #0532
CORPSE: #0774
THE BOND TRADER: #0092
⁂

#0075 - February 12, 2018 @ 06:28 (Piața Romană - Bucharest, Romania)

[0075.1 / 0176] [THE WEAVER and THE CARPENTER refinish a house. They're both practical and make a good team. They divide up tasks and take on all the work themselves. In the process of finishing the basement they discover a homeless person squatting, who refuses to leave. He insists they've unlawfully taken his home. Instead of arguing with the man, they offer him $50,000 to move. He accepts and leaves without any hesitation.]

[0075.2 / 0177] [I attend a concert at a big box retail store. It's another TOOL show. This time I'm disinterested and leave before it starts. I'm mildly annoyed with myself for paying to see the same show again.]

[0075.3 / 0178] [I encounter THE TRANSPARENT HEADCASE (*smart, bipolar, and erratic*) living in an abandoned warehouse. His energy is scattered and frenetic. He shows me around his home, which he's made in a massive tree that has a giant cartoon bubble bite gorged from the trunk. I assume the bite to be fresh, and made by a huge creature as I watch sawdust drop lightly like snow all around. We swing on vines to ever higher platforms, but I wake up before I get to see the inside of the house.]

[0075.4 / 0179] [I hang out with my best friend THE CONFIDANT (*candid, brotherly, and funny*) at a seminar with a wild card topic. A large mass of high vibe beings swarm in to attend. THE CONFIDANT taps me on the shoulder saying, *"Yo dude...isn't that him?"* He points at an attractive, sexy, virile guy named "Brad." "Brad" and I soul gaze from across the meeting hall until he winks at me. I walk up to him and kiss him. We hold hands, looking for an inconspicuous place behind an elevator where I subsequently give him a blowjob.] //

⁂
Maj. = 0- THE WEAVER: #0076, 1- THE CARPENTER: 0080, 16- THE CONFIDANT: #0217
TOOL: #0520
ANNOYED: #0621, #0687, #0726, #0731
BLOWJOB: #0653, #0736, #0748
MASSIVE: #463, #0468, #0476
⁂

⁂

#0076 - February 13, 2018 @ 06:56 (Piața Romană - Bucharest, Romania)

[0076.1 / 0180] [I'm at a modern spa, tiled in abundant blue and white mosaic. Water gently runs over the surface of a tall wall and down to a large common pool. THE FLIRT (*funny, sexual, and playful*) and I engage in a game of cat and mouse throughout the complex. He pursues me. I lead him on. I'm attracted to his husband and express it openly.
"I want to fuck your husband."
"Forget it! I'm here. THE BANKER's *at the other house,"* THE FLIRT breathily exclaims as he backs me into a corner.
He lunges, intending to kiss me.]

[0076.2 / 0181] [I watch a stylized and polished Olympic athlete biography segment that introduces the favored competitor in a demonstration sport. "Snow Skating" combines artistic aspects of figure skating with the adrenaline rush of downhill skiing. The athlete profiled is a bald, non-binary being competing for the People's Republic of China. Slow motion footage of snow powder cutting up around their body as they dip into a spiral-like maneuver (*wearing an all-white uniform emblazoned with sparkly crystals, sequins and white goggles*) artfully tells the origin story of this being's journey through self-transcendence. American TV viewers (THE WEAVER included) don't like this competitor and *"BOO"* at the screen with impunity.
"But I like her!" I exclaim, instantly realizing I've projected my concept of gender on this being.] //

✵

Maj. = 0- THE WEAVER: #0080
CHINESE: #0475, #0522
BLUE: #0544, #0545
WHITE: #0526
POOL: #0538
THE FLIRT: #0557
THE BANKER: #0887

✵

#0077 - February 14, 2018 @ 08:18 (Piața Romană - Bucharest, Romania)

[0077.1 / 0182] [I teach yoga at a vast airport terminal. The large and orderly group of students gathered moves with the impeccability of a military parade. The group is innately open and eager to learn "Bird of Paradise" pose. We take our time, incrementally creating poses that integrate the spine and relax the hips. We place attention on the feet for balance and stability. A swell of cheers erupts as a wave of yogis begin standing tall in their expressions. As one rises, it inspires another to take flight. It's playful, beautiful, and humbling to witness undulating transformation, a breath at a time.]

[0077.2 / 0183] [I'm at sea, floating on a raft between two battleships. One is North Korean, the other South Korean. My raft bobs in a neutral zone, which if breached by either ship will result in fiery conflict. My role is to exchange prisoners of war, held captive by each side. Their safety is paramount, and I'm to keep the activity and outcomes covert, though sensationalizing airplanes for major media outlets buzz about overhead. I'm considered a treasonous rescuer by both sides, though I'm neutral to their judgement. My agreement is with the water, which has asked me to,

"Be balanced and surf when waves are made."

Instead of focusing on the POW exchange, the broadcast airplane chooses to repeatedly run an ad in local markets to incite "Global Masturbation." As night falls, I use the flashlight feature on my phone to illuminate the dark space between ships and communicate in Morse code. The flashes of light reveal both sides have nuclear submarines trolling directly beneath their battleships. Each believes they have the tactical edge over their opponent. They're not present to the stalemate. I move one POW at a time from beneath a thundering wall of water, across the ocean surface and eventually to safety on their nation's maritime vessel. The scene remains calm, though cautiously elevated.

Once all hostages have been exchanged, both sides are satisfied. The ships turn and depart in opposite directions, eventually fading from view. I'm left behind, floating on my yellow safety raft alone in the dark.] //

⁎⁎

YELLOW: #0512, #0532
AIRPORT: #0433, #0447, #0448
YOGA: #0627, #0654, #0682, #0701
ALONE: #0406, #0436, #0476, #0622, #0687

⁎⁎

#0078 - February 15, 2018 @ 10:35 (Piața Romană - Bucharest, Romania)

[0078.1 / 0184] [I try on outfits at a thrift store, perpetually walking a catwalk lined by clamoring photographers. The experience is a fabulous and deeply personal show for an audience of one: **Me.**] //

⁎⁎

CATWALK: #0404, #0620, #0757, #0765
FASHION: #0425
PHOTOGRAPHER: #0436, #0648, #0762

⁎⁎

#0079 - February 15, 2018 @ 14:50 (Piața Romană - Bucharest, Romania)

[0079.1 / 0185] [I socialize with friends on a weekend afternoon. We walk across a vast parking lot at an amusement park. Even though the parking lot is basically empty we've purposefully parked as far away from the entrance as possible. We enjoy the walk. Our excitement increases as we near the gates. We hear the playful screams of people riding a large rollercoaster off in the distance. The screams grow louder the closer we get to the ride. A glowing white neon lined "Handicap Limo" pulls up next to me. In the center of the vehicle is a rotunda-esque dome where THE CLUB KID (*creative, spontaneous, and unique*) and KELLY CLARKSON (*performer, winner, and mother*) pop up and invite me to take the *"fast track"* with them to the roller coaster at the back of the park. I decline. The glowing limo is for people who aren't able to walk. THE CLUB KID and KELLY CLARKSON first try to peer pressure me into taking a ride, then they resort to rationalizing their own misuse of conveyance.

"You really don't have a reason not to."

"It's here now, Honey...you may as well use it while you can!"

"Fuck off."

The glowing white wireframe limo disappears on its monorail track in a soft flash of white light.]

[0079.2 / 0186] [THE CLUB KID readies a listed luxury residence for a private showing. His prospects are an upper class gay married couple, both of whom are buffed and manicured. I fly up and out of the property, ascending high in the air before looking down at the municipal grid that glimmers like a computer motherboard. The city is affluent and lush with large trees and abundant public green space. After moments of flight, I touch down on a faraway hilltop next to an electrical transformer, surrounded by chain link fences and razor wire. It's comparatively grey, rocky, and lifeless. I rest for a few moments with my back to one of the corners of the transformer facing away from the city. It's cloudy overhead.

"Is that the Charlotte, NC skyline?"

I leap upward and orient towards town, honing in on an estate property with a rooftop terrace that boasts two large square formations of Cypress and Japanese maple trees planted side by side. Large red flowers sporadically pockmark topiary maze walls of lush green. In an instant I arrive at the house and land between the green squares. I let myself into the house by opening an invisible door in the center of a large plate glass window. THE CLUB KID shows the property to the same clients. I duck into a family room, leaping over the back of a large leather couch. I land in a seat next to a woman with an asymmetrical bob haircut who watches TV while cuddled cozily beneath a sateen blanket. The blanket is pulled up over her nose, obscuring most of her face.

"Where's Kelly?"

"Hey...psst...I'm right here. It's the weird '2002' me," the woman on the couch says revealing her face.

I don't recognize her, but we give each other a nod with an understanding smile. We exchange high fives then turn towards the TV. I'm not interested in the program being screened. I retreat into my head and contemplate the floor plan for my dream home. As I jump out of my body into daydream, within dream, within dream, a wish list begins taking shape:

+ *I want a large open loft.*

+ *A stately dining room.*

+ *A hip/fun space with lots of natural light.*

+ *Exposed brick wherever possible.*

I second guess the blend of styles, but remember it's my dream home. It doesn't matter if anyone else ever sees it. Being in it makes me feel good.] //

⁎⁎

ROLLER COASTER: #0438, #0479, #0529, #0557

LUXURY: #0444, #0493, #0580

CHAIN LINK: #0521, #0578, #0614, #0724, #0737

THE CLUB KID: #0103

⁎⁎

#0080 - February 16, 2018 @ 07:35 (Piața Romană - Bucharest, Romania)

[0080.1 / 0187] [THE DANCER and I are teenagers in a large home we term "Grandma's House." It's a shady, cool evening, but confusing and odd. The light transitions from lighter to darker, as fast traveling clouds block the sun.

"God's messing around with settings on some dimmer switches again."

We've been left alone to keep an eye on each other. "Grandma's House" has wide, tall wooden staircases and large gathering spaces with comfortable large pieces of furniture on which to lounge. We walk out onto a large screen porch at the front of the house, where we meet a neighbor girl who wants to hang out. Initially, we don't trust her. We talk amongst ourselves for a moment, ultimately deciding we'll invite her inside and teach her how to bake cookies.

THE LAWYER *(deliberate, intellectual, and analytical)* stops through to see what we're doing and then exits without saying anything. As he leaves the scene, it widens and pivots 180 degrees. I observe THE DANCER, the neighbor girl, and I from an alley behind the property. The entire back of the house is exposed, giving it the feel of a giant dollhouse. Intricate stairways give looters passage to the kitchen, who place items stolen from other areas of the home nearby as we remain focused on baking cookies. If aware of the robbery in progress, we don't appear to be bothered by the crime.]

[0080.2 / 0188] [THE PHOTOGRAPHIC MEMORY *(brilliant, bold, and goddess-like)* and I walk and talk between nighttime business meetings on the upper floor of a tall glass skyscraper. We believe we're on the cusp of a technological breakthrough. We're excited that our proposed MVP will eventually revolutionize how computers are deployed to filter, clean, and monitor the global water supply.

Our company's founder is a wealthy Arab venture capitalist. As we continue towards his office, intent on discussing our findings, we hear a "BOOM!" accompanied by a seismic ripple through the floor that causes us to lose our balance. Floor to ceiling exterior windows shatter. We intuitively understand a large commercial jet just struck the building.

"I've got this," THE PHOTOGRAPHIC MEMORY says as she calmly ducks down and traverses the floor, now awash in flame. She walks around a stack of 50-gallon drums on the verge of exploding from the heat and disappears in the inferno. Another female co-worker carrying a stack of loose papers looks at me crying, but continues towards the wall of fire, similarly engulfed and immolated.]

[0080.3 / 0189] [I'm with THE WEAVER and THE CARPENTER walking across a desert. Strong wind kicks up a sandstorm. It's so dusty we can't see our hands in front of our faces. We continue wandering together, though we can't see each other. It's dark, but daytime and oppressively hot. The wind quiets and dust settles. THE CARPENTER walks away from me and THE WEAVER. THE WEAVER looks at me with dusty raccoon eyes left by sweaty cheeks under her goggles. She points at her empty canteen saying, *"Where can I get some more water?"*] //

⁑

Maj. = 0- THE WEAVER: #0089, 1- THE CARPENTER: #0085,
2-THE DANCER: #0088, 5- THE LAWYER: #0123

SKYSCRAPER: #0560, #0745
FIRE: #0748, #0749
WATER: #0755, #0763, #0764
WIND: #0453, #0582, #0786
DUST: #0583, #0760
THE PHOTOGRAPHIC MEMORY: #0422
⁂

#0081 - February 18, 2018 @ 07:44 (Piața Romană - Bucharest, Romania)

[0081.1 / 0190] [Abstract image of a group of children holding hands in a long chain. They wear all red jumpsuits. Viewed from above they look like a strand of red blood cells strewn across a black, glowing microscope slide. They sing hymns and create a barrier between me and a group of men I consider "Conflict Beings." Voices of the children register at high volume and permeate the space. The men express anger and shake their fists, but I can't hear what they're yelling over the children's singing.]

[0081.2 / 0191] [I play kickball in an office environment with a group of pretty, young people. The office building does not have a roof. Many levels of stacked vertical workspaces are marked with x, y, and z-coordinate designations. Am I a Facebook employee? I'm on a team being studied as part of a *"Flow State Achievement"* experiment. I attempt to exit the study and enter an area that has *"Restricted Access."* The security team observing me through a CCTV feed laughs as I fake conversation in Spanish. I speak gibberish but believe I'm communicating clearly with those around me.]

[0081.3 / 0192] [It's nighttime. I work on a team tethered to a tight deadline. I'm responsible for producing a marketing video for a laundry company. I drop the finished product off in person at what occurs as a drab and unremarkable office building. The space is big, open, and clean with flat tone industrial carpeting. A tumbling pit in a far corner is full of large French fry looking lengths of yellow foam. THE TINY TODDLER (*young, and innocent*) plays nearby gathering opaque tape into a large sticky ball for a game she's inventing. I add some tape to the ball as she rolls it by. I return later to review the video and am assisted by a young woman in a tri-colored tracksuit. The delivered video met client expectations, by the agreed deadline.] //

⁂
RED BLOOD: #0648
SPANISH: #0673
ANGER: #0461, #0770
FLOW STATE: #0428, #0446
⁂

#0082 - February 19, 2018 @ 07:40 (Piața Romană - Bucharest, Romania)

[0082.1 / 0193] [THE AGONY (*witty, creative, and fatherly*) and THE ECSTASY (*maturely feminine, nurturing, and deep feeling*) soul gaze. Their eye contact and presence are constant, strong and determined, yet infused with sweet gentility. They psychically transmit the phrase: *"I love you, Baby."*

Their shared vibration rises above the broad low brow collective tone of the internet. Their shift is noted and monitored by a government agency. Eventually their *"I love you, Baby's"* are recorded and distributed to encourage others to *"expand to get closer."*

"I love you, Baby."
"I love you, Baby."
"I love you, Baby."

Appreciation grows and is shared ad infinitum.]

[0082.2 / 0194] [THE CRUNCH *(energetic, optimistic, and flighty)* and I practice yoga in the basement of the Flintstone's home. Cool slate floors. Round, oblong windows. THE RESIS-TANCE *(intense)* and THE COMIC *(masterful, sarcastic, and real-as-fuck)* join us for class. We take turns leading practice. THE CRUNCH becomes distracted during her sequence and spends more time staring out a window than leading.

I offer her feedback after the session. She walks away from me mid-sentence and steps outside. I'm a little upset by this, and mentally label her a bitch. THE COMIC comes over to me and whispers,

"You're not ready. You have to be totally neutral to everyone if you want to lead 'Level 2.'"

I become preoccupied with forthcoming dates for a yearlong immersion I've committed to complete. I have equal interest in completing another program.] //

⁎⁎

I LOVE YOU: #0404, #0617, #0712, #0741, #0767
FEEDBACK: #0461, #0470, #0472, #0603
EQUAL: #0443, #0722
THE COMIC: #0146
THE AGONY: #0805

⁎⁎

#0083 - February 20, 2018 @ 08:20 (Piața Romană - Bucharest, Romania)

[0083.1 / 0195] [I attend a party at a large estate. Grand rooms stretch across multiple floors connected by ornate marble spiral staircases. A giant great room is divided into smaller intimate spaces by 6' accordion dividers. Dozens of playful, cosmetically beautiful guys circulate throughout the fete. We're all hundreds of years old, and have mastered shapeshifting our bodies. We act like teenagers at this retro "Make Out" party.

Everyone raves about how cool the host is for, *"planning a party while his parents are out of town."*

"THE FIDUCIARY? Oh yeah, I know that guy. He's a really great kisser." I lie. I've never met THE FIDUCIARY, nor have I kissed him.

Multiple guys carry Chihuahuas as accessories. I've attended without an accessory pooch. If you pet a dog, it implies a socially appropriate, *"I'm not interested in you."* Though the dogs originally act as landing zones for polite *"declines,"* they become distractions. **The result:** No one connects with anyone else. Attractions remain muddled and unclear.

An olive complexed guy walks up to me. We start making out without exchanging words. I can smell the stink of someone's ass on his mouth. He makes eye contact with me mid-kiss.

98

I wink, implying I know what he's been up to. He gets nervous and fakes needing to take a phone call to retreat from me.

I want to meet the host, but I'm distracted by a dining hall buffet which is dimly lit, with piles of sugary treats (*fudge, and coconut macaroons*). I move through the snack bar without taking anything. I want protein.

I walk through a corridor and wind up in a subterranean dormitory, where I omnisciently observe two young men sharing tender intimacy in a small private room. They're both nude, with exception of calf high crew socks that have three green stripe rings at the top.

I have a bigger appetite for protein now and return to the dormitory dining hall. Placards for nourishing, hearty meals are positioned end-to-end on the stainless-steel counter. A series of platinum charger plates are arranged in domino dot-like patterns. In the center of each round charger rests a tiny, intricate piece of chocolate art. The exquisite detail of items titled "Steak and Potatoes," "Beef Wellington," (*haute art, smaller than a thumbnail*) are viewable with magnifying glasses. I hang out here for a long time, awestruck, and eventually forget about the make out party.

"*Look, but don't touch,*" I'm firmly instructed by a dining hall supervisor.] //

⁂

Maj. = 9- THE FIDUCIARY: #0089
SPIRAL STAIRCASE: #0435, #0441, #0446, #0587
MAKE OUT: #0725, #0778, #0780
PROTEIN: #0481
INTIMACY: #0403, #0534
MAGNIFYING GLASS: #0547

⁂

#0084 - February 22, 2018 @ 06:10 (Piața Romană - Bucharest, Romania)

[0084.1 / 0196] [I've just made a wager with a stereotypical 1980's New York City slumlord. He's grossly overweight and wears a dingy white wife beater (*stained/cigar burns*). His teeth are corroded and yellowed. He wears a cheap white polyester ball cap with a sewn red bill. Though we gamble, I'm not certain of the medium of exchange.

"*I'll raise you a _____ _____.*"

"*I'll see you ____, and raise another half _____.*"

The room we occupy widens to reveal multiple plush couches with pairs of people engaging in mutual oral sex.

I win a round of the game and am awarded, "*Two Bonus Pills.*" The Super begrudgingly extends an arm and brings forth a single palm sized capsule. The oversized pill has a thin brown membrane that squirts and leaks rotting fluid on my hand as he passes it to me. He wants me to share it with the bartender. I ignore him and eat handfuls of sugary popcorn from a 32oz mason jar that crunches like candy and cuts my gums.]

[0084.2 / 0197] [I'm a spy. I'm on a crisp, white, brightly lit promenade boasting a series of very large LED screens splashed with video advertisements. At once, all the screens go white and PATRICK DEMPSEY (*actor, juggler, and attractively nerdy*) walks into the frame to deliver me a special message. The transmission from the massive screen is for my eyes only. Throngs of people around me go about their business, unaware of the conversation being held at high volume between the two of us.]

[0084.3 / 0198] [THE MASSIVE HOMOSEXUAL *(gregarious, intense, and charming)* and I meet casually to discuss business. We haven't spoken in months. He shares the prototype for a new snack food: a bag that instantly creates what a consumer thinks of as they place their hand inside the bag. He's used technology I created to make a lot of money.

"Remember that punch card you and I filled up?" he asks, implying that simply acknowledging his intellectual property theft will restore our relationship. It doesn't work. His business card reads: *"Custom Chip Designer."*]

[0084.4 / 0199] [I'm at an outdoor venue where a union crew installs a concert stage. It's very crowded. Attendees are excited and in a good mood. Cops are in position to keep things orderly. I'm at re-opening celebration for the "EPICENTRE."] //

⁎⁎

TRANSMISSION: #0536, #0559, #0657, #0715
SNACK FOOD: #0416, #0621, #0726
COPS: #0481, #0662
THE MASSIVE HOMOSEXUAL: #0127

⁎⁎

#0085 - February 22, 2018 @ 08:30 (Piaţa Romană - Bucharest, Romania)

[0085.1 / 0200] [THE RENEGADE *(rough, brotherly, and hard charging partier)* swims alone in the ocean at dusk. The water is choppy. He's been stung in the eye by a jellyfish. Instead of considering it an injury he repeats the phrase, *"I have Pink Eye."*]

[0085.2 / 0201] [I teach a yoga class and receive feedback from BARON BAPTISTE *(teacher, mentor, and trickster)*. In another room away from the group, THE CARPENTER *(retiring, loving, and opinionated)* practices. He's not wearing a shirt. The floor of his practice room is covered with sand and candle lit at twilight, while the adjoining room is brightly lit and full of chattering people. He sweats profusely and nurses an injured right wrist. He continues to practice, with deep flowing breath as his guide.

Mid-flow he drops to his knees to take a break. He waves me over and whispers in my ear that he hasn't filled out a liability waiver. He, BARON and I communicate telepathically. BARON notes,

"Oh right, I committed to have a conversation with that guy before class. What are you going to do?"

I blink my eyes and notice I'm in a different yoga studio. Did I just teach a class? If I did, I don't remember any of it. I have amnesia.] //

⁎⁎

Maj. = 1- THE CARPENTER: #0097
BARON BAPTISTE: #0094

100

INJURY: #0451, #0562
CHATTER: #0749, #0795

⁂

#0086 - February 22, 2018 @ 08:55 (Piața Romană - Bucharest, Romania)

[0086.1 / 0202] [A guy stands across from me. I don't recognize him, but he's friendly. He glances at his wrist watch, then looks at me. Casually shrugging his shoulders, he says, *"Soon it'll be time for another beer."*]

[0086.2 / 0203] [A white pencil draws a capital "B," and then a circle around the "B" on a piece of dark blue denim.]

[0086.3 / 0204] [A large pine tree appears in shadow backlit by a grand golden orb of light.]

[0086.4 / 0205] [A stately brown wooden credenza is positioned against a wall. It has highly ornamented and pristinely fashioned curvy beveled drawers. An arm, unattached to a body materializes, opens a drawer, deposits something within, and then carefully closes it before vanishing.] //

⁂

BEER: #0705, #0718
BACKLIT: #0667
FRIENDLY: #0623, #0628
TREE: #0591, #0618

⁂

#0087 - February 24, 2018 @ 07:05 (Piața Romană - Bucharest, Romania)

[0087.1 / 0206] [I sit in the back of a theater. Rows of seats appear in front of me. The stage gets further and further away. The chairs are comfortable and upholstered with red velvet. People pay for performances as they exit. Tickets are dynamically priced, proportional to the range of emotions experienced during the performance. I'm handed a Playbill titled *"Fee'-lings,"* with my accompanying itemized punch list. Each patron's assessment is unique. Some dispute their bill, suggesting that trickery *(special effects and other production values)* distracted them and resulted in a usurious increase to their invoice. I like my list. I agree with the bill. I pay the assessment without hesitation.] //

⁂

RED VELVET: #0402, #0573
TICKET: #0715, #0745
EXIT: #0682, #0708
EMOTIONS: #0548, #0680
THEATER: #0772, #0778

⁂

#0088 - February 25, 2018 @ 04:55 (Piața Romană - Bucharest, Romania
This dream sequence jumps between multiple vignettes

[0088.1 / 0207] [I'm in a commercial retail complex that has deep red and purple upholstered walls. Heavy wood components (*oak, mahogany, cherry*) generate a rooty, earthy decor. My family operates a sushi restaurant that has a large floor-to-ceiling saltwater aquarium tank. I've eaten there many times and want something different today, so I go next door to order "Leftovers" from the vegan buffet. I expect a bowl of mashed potatoes and snow peas. Instead, I'm handed a circular Styrofoam plate boasting a large barbecued skull of some sort with quite a bit of charred meat left clinging to it. Due to the weight of its contents, I hold the plate from underneath and take big bites from the cheeks of the skull.

Across the way a woman in a crop top t-shirt and panties is quarantined by mall security. Their negotiation becomes a bit angry. Eventually the woman agrees to let the security guards place a large body length, translucent pink plastic bag over her head. They flank her and walk her from *"Point A to B"* while restraining her arms. THE DANCER arrives and offers me a piggyback ride to the bathroom. We go up and down many carpeted staircases, passing through many doors, but we never make it there. Along the journey I forget that I need to urinate.]

[0088.2 / 0208] [It's night time, bitterly cold, and snowing outside. I attend a large yoga class held in low light in a nightclub. THE PYRO IN TRAINING (*curvy, voluptuous, and youthful*) enters and begins practice. Waving and calling her name fails to get her attention.

I sit behind a student desk at a high school. A punk rock, misfit girl slaps me hard on the back of the head, then pushes my paper and books from the desk to the floor. She keeps walking, only pausing briefly to turn around and flip me off, while sticking her tongue out. I sarcastically say, *"MULTUMESC!"* as I rub my head.

I walk back to the food court and notice DONALD TRUMP sitting at an elevated round table draped with floor length white linens. He's surrounded by children dressed in bespoke suits, all of whom wear sunglasses. Everyone at their table just returned from the buffet with full plates. I walk directly up to the table and pound my fist on it with an air of familiarity and casualness.

"Hey kids, keep him in line for me, won't ya?"

DONALD is astonished and appalled as I send him a joker's grin while grinding the tip of my index finger into the table like I'm snuffing a cigarette. I maintain eye contact, as he lifts a fork to his mouth about to take a bite of mashed potatoes and green peas.

I initially walk away from the table with confidence, then paranoia floods my veins. I know I'll be followed for the rest of my life because of what I've just done. Believing my phone to be tapped, I toss it in a nearby garbage can.

As I walk down a velvet lined corridor, I see a press junket broadcast on TV from DONALD's buffet table. I overhear him make statements describing his charity as the *"third most generous in the world,"* though no public records corroborate the claim. I consider the shift in his perspective from being the *"best"* and self-downgrading to *"third best"* as a significant win for my influencing skills.] //

*****

Maj. = 2- THE DANCER: #0095
DONALD TRUMP: #0115
MISFIT: #0561

*****

*****

102

#0089 - February 25, 2018 @ 05:20 (Piața Romană - Bucharest, Romania)

[0089.1 / 0209] [I whistle the Oscar Meyer Weiner song while organizing the components of a black Armani tuxedo on a bed. Notably, the bow tie remains in a rectangular box, wrapped in cellophane.]

[0089.2 / 0210] [I sit with THE TINY ROMANIAN (*cute, playful, and curious*), age 4, on a swing suspended from the branch of a giant tree. She's innocent and articulate. She speaks English. Seated on my lap she politely asks if we can swing, *"More slower."*]

[0089.3 / 0211] [I stand in a large gravel parking lot behind an industrial building. A large sacred object has been abandoned. Members of THE ARTIST's (*ecstatic, cathartic, and community oriented*) team work together to determine the most efficient method of its transport to an undisclosed location.]

[0089.4 / 0212] [THE FIDUCIARY teaches his first yoga class at a large aquatics complex. I'm there to support. He introduces the practice to a crowd of beginners and uses note cards to teach, which makes me giggle. I'm both humored and annoyed by his need to *"get it right."*]

[0089.5 / 0213] [THE WEAVER and I are with our dog CHARLEE (*loyal, and playful*) who manifests as a large, shaggy golden retriever. She's a rescue dog. THE WEAVER and I decide to walk her home because she's too scared and anxious to jump up and ride in our car. We walk through a subway tunnel that permits cars to drive through. CHARLEE darts off towards a sea of people walking to their metro trains and disappears. We're unable to find her.]

[0089.6 / 0214] [I walk on a sidewalk that seems as grand and alive as Chicago's Magnificent Mile. I pass by a sandwich board advertising, "YOGA CLASSES! IN DANISH!" Curiously, I enter the building and encounter a playful maze of fast-moving escalators inside the compound.
After a time of going up and down I find myself in front of a very tall help desk staffed by extremely tall/large women sporting beehive hairdos and horn-rimmed glasses. They route calls on a 1950's era long distance switchboard. One woman snaps her fingers at another to get her attention. She needs assistance connecting a customer who wants to enroll in a contract law course to the proper extension.]

[0089.7 / 0215] [I'm inside the aquatics complex. A group of excited women huddle together facing me and take turns holding up round white paddles with groups of three black block letters printed on them. *"BPU! GHI! XYZ! QQP!"* This continues until their cheers become so loud and raucous that I wake up.] //

Maj. = 0- THE WEAVER: #0098, 9- THE FIDUCIARY: #0119
CHARLEE: #0429
HORN: #0600
AQUATICS: #0453
THE ARTIST: #0838
⁂

#0090 - February 26, 2018 @ 07:30 (Piața Romană - Bucharest, Romania)

[0090.1 / 0216] [I'm in a long industrial kitchen with art deco floors and pistachio green, ceramic countertops. An impeccably dressed woman stands next to a man wearing a chef's apron and hat, leaning in to smell aromas and taste flavored steam rising from a large stew pot being gently warmed from beneath by a specially tailored series of gas flames, intended to *"maximize ingredient integration."*

They take turns savoring the fare, each uniquely excited and enamored by the experience of tasting the pot's contents. They make conversation in French and occasionally shoot me an inclusive glance. I feign understanding what they say by offering compliant and friendly nods with my eyes cast slightly downward.

The woman offers me a bowl from the pot along with a spoon and a smile. The dish is a "Boeuf Ragout" and has a rich purplish red color. Its texture is velvety and nourishing. At first taste it's seasoned to perfection with a pepperiness that's new to my palate. My immediate impulse is to share it with a new male friend who appears next to me in the kitchen, seemingly out of thin air. The ragout has a voice of its own that beckons, *"Share Me."*

⁂
PISTACHIO: #0472, #0511, #0545
FRENCH: #0461, #0683
SAVOR: #0483, #0736
PURPLE: #0548, #0595
INDUSTRIAL: #0450, #0520
⁂

#0091 - February 27, 2018 @ 06:40 (Piața Romană - Bucharest, Romania)

[0091.1 / 0217] [I'm on the lower deck of a large yacht. The space is dimly lit and appears to be a large storage basement set with rows of 6' foldable tables. The name "Mary" is familiar, though I'm uncertain if I'm looking for a woman, or if that's the name of the vessel. Through round portholes I see a large freighter pass nearby in the opposite direction.] //

⁂
YACHT: #0468, #0628, #0667, #0747
MARY: #0622
6': #0429, #0500, #0722
⁂

#0092 - February 27, 2018 @ 08:07 (Piața Romană - Bucharest, Romania)

[0092.1 / 0218] [THE BOND TRADER *(proper, polite, and etiquette adherent)* wants to help a teenage boy find a bathroom. The bathroom is in the basement and when they arrive at the door, they discover it's locked. The boy's about to shit his pants. THE BOND TRADER asks me for the key. I have it, but refuse to give it to him.

"Everyone has to take their own path."

The teenage boy starts practicing yoga asana, and then as though time skips like a needle on a record, I observe him advance in age and through various stages of development. Each eye blink changes the channel and moves linear time ahead by a year. I witness him fall into addiction and move through recovery, multiple times.

A red banner with white letters scrolls across my visual screen: *"UPDATE!>>>>_____. _____._____."*

The teenage boy is no longer a male, now identifies as *"gender fucked,"* and lives in a squalid basement apartment. Newsprint soaked in urine and soiled with feces is strewn about the floor. The being uses a black and white checkerboard textured dildo to penetrate itself in various new unhealed bloody holes created through self-administered surgeries. Its hair is long and wispy; the color and quality of pink cotton candy. Its face is messily smeared with pink eye shadow and lipstick. It maintains uninterrupted eye contact with me as it welcomes concurrent penetration from numerous anonymous sexual partners.

"I'm a Pleasure Junkie," it breathily moans as it orgasms.] //

**

BLINK: #0526
DILDO: #0418
KEY: #0540
COTTON CANDY: #0534
THE BOND TRADER: #1026

**

#0093 - February 28, 2018 @ 06:39 (Piața Romană - Bucharest, Romania)
Three overlapping narratives sporadically pivot:

1. *Two kids on a scavenger hunt.*
2. *A transgendered student (who initially manifests as a Black male teen) is harassed.*
3. *A village square scene full of amplified immature masculine energy.*

[0093.1 / 0219] [PIVOT to 2) I step in to defend the black teen who has now shapeshifted into a full bodied, voluptuous, manicured woman sporting a long elegantly braided weave. Her bullies seek a bounty of 15,000 gold coins for capturing a wanted figure.
"What do you want with her?" I ask, extending my right arm, hand palm up.
"You mean HIM?!" A bully taunts and then pushes me.
"You need to ask HER!"]

[0093.2 / 0220] [PIVOT to 1) I stand with the two kids who are "Peace Pawns." I hold a blue rectangular ticket. In a blink, we're in the back seat of a 1930's Ford driving up a snowy hill away from the village square in scene 3. *"Give this to Mommy,"* I say to the kids in a broken elementary version of their native language (*Hungarian?*) as I hand them the ticket.]

[0093.3 / 0221] [PIVOT to 2) I'm in a school office in a verbal altercation with the mother of one of the bullies. She calls herself a yoga teacher. I call her a, *"bigot masquerading as a guru."* I pick her up by the neck and pants, and toss her against the wall, intent on injuring her.]

[0093.4 / 0222] [PIVOT to 3) I'm in the village square participating in a physical fitness drill. A man stands behind me and extends my hands forward by pulling on my wrists. He's a huge being, perhaps three times my size. Across the plaza a muscular, military looking man (*camouflage pants, no shirt*) locks his eyes on me like a bull about to charge. The game is to "High Ten" each other at tremendous speed, like two rams charging and locking horns. I know if he makes contact with me the impact will shatter both of my wrists. I leave my body and drop through the floor out of range as the shirtless soldier flies by overhead.]

[0093.5 / 0223] [PIVOT to 2) I practice yoga asana with hundreds of people outside. The bully bigot guru mother assists. While she still insists she's a yoga expert, she refuses to support me as I practice. She bounds up and away without touching me and moves to another student. I sense she's about to sue me for throwing her against the wall.]

[0093.6 / 0224] [PIVOT to 3) I'm back in the town square. The soldier who charged at me in the drill now gently lays on top of me. He's penetrated aggressively from behind by a large man, who I assume was the supportive coach who stood behind me.
"Do you like that, Bull?" I whisper softly in his ear, then gently kiss his cheek.
The action behind him grows in intensity. The soldier becomes increasingly open and

vulnerable with each successive thrust. In a blend of pleasure and pain, he weeps. I dry his tears, console, caress, and reassure him. He's pulled up and away from me and mounted upside down on a large pommel horse-like device where he's fucked senseless. He's out of reach and I simply watch.]

[0093.7 / 0225] [PIVOT to 1) The 1930's Ford drives through the village and passes by the local pub. I want to leave the kids to go drinking with soldiers, who speak Czech and Hungarian. I know this decision would not only endanger the children, but would not bode favorably for me. I stay in the car.] //

✲
✲✲

HUNT: #0541, #0644, #0800
VILLAGE: #0531, #0578, #0764
SNOW: #0401, #0511, #0526
CZECH: #0765

✲
✲✲

#0094 - March 4, 2018 @ 07:21 (Clapham Common - London, England)

[0094.1 / 0226] [It's night. The energy is dark, thick, and erotic. THE TRAIL RUNNER (*svelte, passionate, and strong*) and I have sex repeatedly. It's electric, limbic, and primal. Sweat drips profusely from our bodies. We're both equally attracted to one another.]

[0094.2 / 0227] [I'm in China, attending yoga training with BARON BAPTISTE. So many people attend the training event, the venue moves to the Birds Nest in Beijing. The arena is fashioned from concrete and from the inside looks as though construction was never fully completed. It feels bombed out and dilapidated.

No assigned spaces nor declared call times are issued prior to the meeting day, resulting in long registration wait times for attendees. I'm shown a mental image of a colorfully highlighted process flow diagram that points to multiple critical path efficiency maximizers that can be integrated prior to future events to avoid similar queue "log jams." "Batch Processing" by group letter is selected as an interim solution to move people along.]

[0094.3 / 0228] [Four of us are seated behind one another like members of a bobsled team. We slide together single file down a long scaffold lined passage. Each time we cross under a rectangular scaffold we pick up additional speed. The top bar of the next scaffolding gateway inches closer to our heads. We crash at the bottom at full speed.]

[0094.4 / 0229] [I'm lost at night in a Chinese city. I walk to a gas station for a snack, surprised when I discover all food items are labeled in both Mandarin and English.]

[0094.5 / 0230] [I'm in a crowded diner. The tablecloths are red and white checkered patterned. Looks like a mass of summer picnic tables. All the service staff are Chinese. THE

FEELER *(insular, motherly, and depressed)* sits at a table and asks me if I want to be in a photo. We agree to leave at a specific time so we can attend THE CONCIERGE's *(masterful, available, and grounded)* lecture at the conference.]

[0094.6 / 0231] [I'm by the waterfront. It's lit by orange and red plumes of flame. I observe three giant hot air balloons emerge slowly from the water, then rise effortlessly skyward. I'm astonished and take multiple photographs of the ascending balloons. *"Where did you get that?"* a pair of white tourists *(middle aged man and woman)* ask me, pointing curiously at my camera.]

[0094.7 / 0232] [I'm on a runaway mine train that races hundreds of feet above the city street. As I whiz about, I check the time and realize that based on where I am, there's no way I'll make it to the seminar on time as promised.] //

⁎⁎

Min. = ♣- *THE FEELER: #0338*
BARON BAPTISTE: #0144
SEX: #0558, #0561, #0647, #0650, #0653
CONFERENCE: #0499, #0529, #0530, #0531
ENGLISH: #0405, #0477, #0578
THE CONCIERGE: #0303

⁎⁎

#0095 - March 5, 2018 @ 05:37 (Brussels, Belgium)

[0095.1 / 0233] [I'm at a pub with THE DANCER. We've been drinking all day. I need to break the seal. A female security guard manages the bathroom line and won't let me by. I need to learn a password to gain entry. I offer to buy a man ahead of me a coffee to teach me the word.
"Ah, the 'ol BHQ,' eh?" I hear the security guard shout from across the space as the man assists me.
The scene is dark and tense. The struggle with the security guard seems totally unnecessary.] //

⁎⁎

Maj. = 2- THE DANCER: #0112
DRINKING: #0405, #0428, #0585, #0615
COFFEE: #0472, #0527, #0528, #0554, #0581
UNNECESSARY: #0511, #0731, #0743, #0757

⁎⁎

#0096 - March 6, 2018 @ 02:28 (Padova-Veneto, Italy)

[0096.1 / 0234] [Riding on a train with family.]
[0096.2 / 0235] [My boyfriend's boyfriend?]
[0096.3 / 0236] [Cats.]
[0096.4 / 0237] [Signing a series of two-day contracts.] //

⁂
CATS: #0516, #0581, #0596, #0791
CONTRACTS: #0423, #0441, #0544, #0562
TRAIN: #0401, #0436, #0490
⁂

#0097 - March 7, 2018 @ 08:53 (Zurich, Switzerland)

[0097.1 / 0238] [THE MARATHONER *(sturdy, consistent, and self-authoring)* and I compete for business. Our customer is a man whose face changes. He's most recognizable to me when he takes the guise of THE RICH MAN *(entrepreneurial, humorous, and gentlemanly)*. We sell him blocks of emails and negotiate contracts in a cubicle farm. The atmosphere is alive, exhilarating, and good humored. I overhear THE CARPENTER take a conference call through the partition beyond THE RICH MAN's desk. We're offered burritos while negotiations progress. THE CONDUCTOR *(open, curt, and authentic)* enters wearing suspenders, quickly shifting my interest from business deals to sex. He and I don't have any physical interaction. I fantasize about taking him into the bathroom and tearing his clothes off. He and I had great sex together on a few occasions a lifetime ago in a scintillating dream within a dream. Hot shit. I cum in my pants.] //

⁂
Maj. = 1- THE CARPENTER: #0112
BURRITO: #0613
NEGOTIATIONS: #0500
FANTASIZE: #0526
THE MARATHONER: #0382
THE CONDUCTOR: #0481
⁂

#0098 - March 8, 2018 @ 06:21 (Zurich, Switzerland)

[0098.1 / 0239] [I'm en route to my wedding. I've agreed to marry both THE HEALED WOMAN *(bright, connected, and joyful)* and an overweight version of THE MAKER *(maturing, artistic, and anxious)*. I walk up a twisting mountain path, surrounded by tall amber grass swaying gently in a breeze. It's sunny. At the top of a hill, well-manicured grass surrounds a flat concrete surface. A quaint cobblestone church with gothic windows and a pointed steeple encasing a bell tower sits at the center. I recognize this place as THE LUTHERAN PASTOR's *(sober, committed, and service oriented)* church.

I enter the narthex and proceed to the sanctuary where the wedding will be held later that day. THE PANDA enters after me with a guitar and amplifier and begins to warm up for her performance. She's calm and happy. Groups of people use black tape to create a square on the floor. It's quite large and its lines are drawn at equal distances parallel from top to bottom. Off to the side a second smaller square is constructed in a similar manner. It's unclear if this is intended to help set up rows of chairs or tables, but the teams proceed methodically with focus and precision.

I decide I don't want to get married because if we'd divorce, I would lose half of my bank stock. Instead of moving ahead with a prenuptial agreement I offer to send THE HEALED WOMAN to a training program. She accepts. THE WEAVER is aggravated by my actions, but renders no comment. THE MAKER stands at a pub table staring off in space and drinking a lager. I pat him on the back to get his attention, thank him for considering plural marriage, and then I leave the church. As soon as I step on to the cobblestone lanai the church is attacked by a group of soldiers who shoot arrows upon their approach.]

[0098.2 / 0240] [Abstract spinning shapes. Orange / Red / Brown Zoetrope.] //

⁑

Maj. = 0- THE WEAVER: #0104
WEDDING: #0548, #0611, #0666, #0793, #0798
COBBLESTONE: #0494, #0527, #0548, #0561, #0767
THE MAKER: #1031

⁑

#0099 - March 14, 2018 @ 01:59 (San Francisco, California)

[0099.1 / 0241] [A large group of people assembled in a line perform back bending yoga poses together. It feels like a new morning. White and gold light pours through spaces in the "wheel tunnel" created by the row of bodies. Practitioners are cast in shadow. A non-distinct voice in the background seems to cue and guide the experience. It's warm, hospitable, loving and vulnerable. This group celebrates being *"a cohesive unit."*] //

⁑

WARM: #0433, #0445, #0472, #0481
VULNERABLE: #0404, #0558, #0634
MORNING: #0726, #0746, #0775, #0789
CELEBRATE: #0451, #0520, #0548, #0549, #0615

⁑

PART 3 - ROOT DOWN

#0100 - #0172

3.1 - THE BOOK OF PISCES - {[0100 / 0242] - [0137 / 0321]}
3.2 - THE BOOK OF URSA MAJOR - {[0138 / 0322] - [0172 / 00409]}

"Here we are
Running circles, around around around around
When nothing's right, just close your eyes
Close your eyes and you're gone...
Nothing gonna get me in my world."

-Beck

* * *

March 15, 2018 - May 19, 2018

⚜

#0100 - March 15, 2018 @ 02:48 (San Francisco, California)

[0100.1 / 0242] [I'm in an office/shopping mall setting with a group of similarly aged male and female coworkers who I know, but do not recognize by face. We gather and walk together to a restaurant, passing through many dimly lit spa rooms boasting infinity pools. We wade through them chest deep as we talk about "Bitcoin." We've each been issued a "Bitcoin," roughly the diameter of a condom, made of plastic, with similar icons on a translucent central disc similar to what one would find on a first-generation iPod. When pressed in the center, the disc gently lights up with soft white light.

The group stops to listen to a shyster give an inspirational speech, extolling the values "Bitcoin." We're on the fifth floor of a building. I open a nearby closet and take a few handfuls of "Bitcoins" and stuff them in my pockets while no one watches. Some "Bitcoins" I've taken are black. Others are white. THE QUEEN OF ENGLAND enters and remarks, *"the house isn't messy enough."* She's aware of my thieving.

Later, while riding with the group on a school bus, one falls from my pocket and draws attention from other passengers. Not wanting to be discovered as a thief I throw all the remaining "Bitcoins" out the bus window. As I do this, I overhear my cohorts celebrating. This new economic tool will eliminate the need for central banks.

"You only transact with yourself. It's genius!" One exclaims.

It sounds fishy and half baked, though if successful it'll be the everlasting gobstopper product equivalent that will disrupt the global financial services industry.] //

⚜

THE QUEEN OF ENGLAND: #0181
INFINITY: #0583
CONDOM: #0587
COINS: #0701, #0788

⚜

#0101 - March 15, 2018 @ 04:28 (San Francisco, California)

[0101.1 / 0243] [*"HELP! Spare this childhood home!"* A news headline pleads. I think I'm in Charlotte, NC but I'm incorrect. I'm outside a house I've previously visited in dreams; a modern, tri-level home with large open rooms. The owners of the home are elderly and ailing. What was once a lush residential lot is now a droll commercial space. The interior of the house remains warm, alive and inviting though the outside is gray, flat, and hard concrete. I leave my body inside and wander between rooms as a spirit, remembering some time ago I really wanted to own this home. STANLEY THE DOG, a chocolate Labrador, wanders in and out, not paying me any attention. The daughter of the owners finds me in one of the bedrooms. She's not bothered, nor surprised by my presence.

"This used to be my room," I declare while going on to describe the former position of bunk beds along now white walls that were once occupied by me and my brother.

I look for furniture scuffs and stains on the paint but don't find any. The home has been remodeled several times since I lived there.] //

CONCRETE: #0542, #0473, #0474, #0484
LUSH: #0550, #0786
REMODEL: #0435, #0678
⁂

#0102 - March 16, 2018 @ 05:20 (San Francisco, California)

[0102.1 / 0244] [I attend a gala, speaking with IVANKA TRUMP and JARED KUSHNER. Sadness flows from them. The environment becomes loud and chaotic as JARED rushes away to greet the President. I whisper in IVANKA's ear, *'I want to teach your dad yoga.'*]

[0102.2 / 0245] [THE CHILD is a baby. She competes in a "Junior Ninja Warrior" jungle gym contest. She squeals with delight as she moves from obstacle to obstacle, language skills oscillating between exacting exchanges with her spotter below and baby babble. She has no fear of falling. A muscular adult male stands just behind her with arms outstretched. Additional support is given from beneath by spontaneously materializing foam landing mats.]

[0102.3 / 0246] [I swim at night with a group of young men. It's flirty, sexy, and feels taboo. Perhaps we've broken into the city pool after hours. I realize in my blind desire to get in the pool and play, I've left my cell phone in my pocket. I scramble out of the pool. When I retrieve the phone from my pocket to inspect it, I'm relieved and delighted the thing still functions.] //

⁂
Maj. = 3- THE CHILD: #0146
FEAR: #0463, #0480, #0649, #0653, #0654
SCRAMBLE: #0718
⁂

#0103 - March 18, 2018 @ 03:30 (San Francisco, California)

[0103.1 / 0247] [I'm in a large off-white, gray artist loft. THE CLUB KID and I flirt while contemplating an installation. His energy is frenetic and chaotic. It's turning me on. We advance through other rooms. The intensity builds. I grab him and bend him over a table. We're both clothed. My crotch presses against his ass. I decide I want to fuck him, and believe it'll calm him down. I pull out my cock and start teasing him. As I grip the base of the shaft, I notice a small skin tear. It's not bleeding, but there's an open barrier.
"Just wear a condom and fuck me already!!!" he shouts.
I decide I'd rather not have sex and put my dick back in my pants.] //

⁂
GRAY: #0540, #0543, #0695
FRENETIC: #0508, #0566, #0659
THE CLUB KID: #0672
⁂

#0104 - March 18, 2018 @ 05:22 (San Francisco, California)

[0104.1 / 0248] [I'm with a group of people walking outside at night. It's foggy and cold. Lots of clouds in the sky. We're on our way to the spa. The path is illuminated by giant transmuting cloud advertisements. A cloud lights up and instantly changes form, to a flashing word presented in regal black letters: **T H _ _ _ _ _**. The crispness of the font is remarkable. I'm awed by the magnificence of this advertising method. There's no waste. It's temporary. *Illuminating! Effective!*

We make our way to a large lodge with a cafeteria. Group consensus is we want pizza for dinner, but a single young woman decides to go her own direction, selecting a chicken sandwich with cheese and mustard on wheat bread. I walk to a point of purchase kiosk offering half liter glass bottles of milk. Half are white milk, the other half chocolate milk. I grab a bottle of chocolate milk, twist off the cap and chug it. The group sits together at large round wooden tables. I take a seat. THE WEAVER says pointedly,

"Are you going to pay for that?"

"You can pay whenever you want. You don't have to prove you're part of this group."

I sit and sip milk while everyone else waits for the pizza to arrive.] //

⁎⁎

Maj. = 0- THE WEAVER: #0112
WHEAT: #0678
MILK: #0405, #0790
WOODEN TABLE: #0649, #0682, #0779

⁎⁎

#0105 - March 18, 2018 @ 06:00 (San Francisco, California)

[0105.1 / 0249] [I stare up at the sky observing a rainbow. I take its photograph and it multiplies into two rainbows. A crowd of people watch the phenomenon and converse.

"A triple!" "A quad?" "Have you ever seen...one, two, three, four, five, six, SEVEN...SEVEN rainbows!?"

The sky fills with colorful ribbons of prismatic light. Likely many more than seven rainbows shine down overhead, but I'm too stimulated to properly count.] //

⁎⁎

RAINBOW: #0556, #0587
SEVEN: #0757, #0762, #0791, #0798
ABOVE: #0654, #0655, #0657, #0714, #0718, #0731

⁎⁎

#0106 - March 20, 2018 @ 06:00 (San Francisco, California)

[0106.1 / 0250] [I attend a party in a multipurpose building. My friends THE M&A ATTORNEY *(cerebral, assuring, and exact)* and THE RENAISSANCE MAN *(frenetic, creative, and fluidly masculine)* host the event at their flat. They share a combined role as "Safety Marshal." I walk down a long corridor to a room with a refrigerator. I look inside and find tall neatly spaced stacks of food in glowing rectangular containers. I don't take any of the food, instead picking up a metal bolt the size of my index finger from a shelf, then closing the door. I walk to a balcony and drop the metal bolt over the edge into a group of revelers below obscured by darkness. It causes a disruption. I can hear people arguing and blaming one another. THE M&A ATTORNEY and THE RENAISSANCE MAN spring into action in their shared role.]

[0106.2 / 0251] [I run very quickly through a subway station. I run up an escalator that has downward cycling stairs. I do this a number of times. It feels like I'm swimming up mechanical waterfalls in a video game. I keep my quick pace until I emerge at street level. Once outside, I'm alone in a calm Japanese garden. I stop periodically to witness and enjoy rainbows streaking the stormy sky overhead. I hunt for rainbows, like a child hunts Easter eggs. I take lots of photos. Each time I photograph a rainbow it breaks into more segments. Some parts of the sky hold rainbow fragments, long after I've taken photos.] //

⁎

SAFETY: #0418, #0549
WATERFALL: #0538
EGGS: #0412, #0604
THE M&A ATTORNEY: #0342
THE RENAISSANCE MAN: #0342

⁎

#0107 - March 21, 2018 @ 06:30 (San Francisco, California)

[0107.1 / 0252] [I'm in a dance club with glass walls and an illuminated floor (*colorful square panels, a la 70's discotheque*). I engage in a "dance-off" with a large fat man. I twirl more and more quickly. My neck tilts up. As I look towards the ceiling, everything becomes a very, very, bright blur.] //

⁎

TILTS: #0405, #0436
FAT: #0568, #0773
BRIGHT: #0450, #0454, #0523

⁎

#0108 - March 22, 2018 @ 06:45 (San Francisco, California)

[0108.1 / 0253] [I lead a yoga class in a converted factory space with old brick walls. Ample light flows in. The class is full of women. They're all scattered around the space. Among them is THE FELLOW (*analytical, independent, and studious*). Mats are oriented in different directions which makes generating group flow and coherence uniquely challenging. Midway through the class I decide to stop everyone and align them in uniform rows. Initially there's a modicum of confusion and resistance. They were totally happy doing it the way they've always done it.]

[0108.2 / 0254] [Black Jaguar F-Type vehicle drives at night on the highway.]

· · ·

[0108.3 / 0255] [Image of a bulldog.] //

⁂

FACTORY: #0578, #0596
DIRECTIONS: #0512, #0561, #0667, #0732, #0760, #0761
BULLDOG: #0682, #0695, #0726

⁂

#0109 - March 22, 2018 @ 08:05 (San Francisco, California)

[0109.1 / 0256] [I walk with THE ACTOR *(soulful, friendly, and tricky)*. We advance down a long corridor that's part railroad station, part jungle, part corporate plaza. I playfully buzz around him and flirt, but he doesn't respond. We want to eat something. The nearest option is a McDonalds.

A giant segment of a "Golden Arch" visible near the front entryway obscures most of a plate glass window. The "M," must be multiple stories tall. We stand in line, deciding what to order. Each menu item has multiple selection criteria *(combinations of sizes, specialty flavor profiles, etc.)*. The degree of customization is so overwhelming we decide we'd rather not eat any of it.] //

⁂

Maj. = 10- THE ACTOR: #0133
PLAZA: #0560
OVERWHELM: #0455, #0468, #0514, #0556, #0571

⁂

#0110 - March 24, 2018 @ 01:08 (San Francisco, California)

[0110.1 / 0257] [I need to pee. I bow forward. I give my power away. I regroup, generate a tall stance, and begin to sway side to side.] //

⁂

PEE: #0426, #0738
POWER: #0505, #0545, #0554, #0592
SWAY: #0541

⁂

#0111 - March 24, 2018 @ 02:25 (San Francisco, California)

[0111.1 / 0258] [I stand in front of a grandfather clock, staring at it as seconds, minutes, hours, and days pass by. I'm waiting for something to happen. I'm calm and patient.] //

⁂

CLOCK: #0484, #0524, #0533, #0619
WAITING: #0405, #0427, #0751, #0769, #0792
PATIENT: #0615, #0735, #0756, #0788

⁂

#0112 - March 24, 2018 @ 06:21 (San Francisco, California)

[0112.1 / 0259] [I'm on a family vacation with THE WEAVER, THE CARPENTER and THE DANCER. Our ages are unclear, though we interact as a group of close friends. We board a 1950's prop plane staffed by an Italian speaking crew. The crew are well manicured and outfitted in royal blue uniforms. The women wear pillbox hats. The interior is nonsensically large and feels like the lobby of a Las Vegas casino. Over the course of the flight, it becomes clear the crew doesn't know how to get us to our destination. Mid-flight we've decided we want to go to Bali. I exit my body and fly outside to the left of the plane. It's a sunny day over an azure ocean. The water below is pockmarked by chains of small green islands. I fly in front of the cabin and catch the crew arguing over navigation coordinates and map position. I give them the finger. They decide they've finished their job and land the plane in shallow waters off the coast of Spain.
THE DANCER and I walk up a floating jet way, as wide as a ferry. We pass by a few female members of the crew who sit together at small circular tables smoking cigarettes. One table is covered with a pile of $3 bills left as a tip by a recent patron, but the women leave them behind when they depart. I consider taking the money, but I don't.
"I need to go back and get my backpack!"
We're separated from THE WEAVER and THE CARPENTER. I want to cuss out the pilot.
"I'm going to file the worst complaint!" I exclaim to THE DANCER as we backtrack to the plane.
We see THE WEAVER and THE CARPENTER walking toward us, unbothered by the circumstances. They're laughing.] //

✳

Maj. = 0- THE WEAVER: #0114, 1- THE CARPENTER: #0114, 2- THE DANCER: #0114
LAS VEGAS: #0475, #0672, #0716
ITALIAN: #0482, #0635, #0696, #0715

✳

#0113 - March 25, 2018 @ 06:43 (San Francisco, California)

[0113.1 / 0260] [I'm in a dimly lit basement room inside a large postmodern mansion, the upper levels of which have glass walls. THE PAINTER (*feisty, gossipy, and creative*) and THE VAULT MANAGER (*committed, neighborly, and passionate*) own the home. They're horny and playful. Their mood inspires me to jerk off. THE PAINTER pops his head into the downstairs room to check in on me, and leaves me alone to tend to myself. He probably watches me the entire time, but I never look back at the door.]

[0113.2 / 0261] [Random images of various canine breeds.]

[0113.3 / 0262] [I'm an old man walking down a hallway on the C-Suite level of a corporate tower. In a prior life I was an executive at this company. I make conversation with a similarly aged cohort as we wander past rows of offices. He's the current CEO of the firm. We turn to face his work space (*an open, light and vast suite*). As we enter, I say,

"Wasn't this MICHAEL EISENER's office?"

Slightly annoyed, my companion casually replies, *"No, he was down the hall. Now he's 7.2 miles up,"* pointing an index finger skyward.

I see a clear mental image of an extremely large office tower, and the precise location of EISENER's new rooftop workspace. A young father swims in the executive rooftop pool with his three children. It's uncharacteristically hot and humid at the top.]

[0113.4 / 0263] [*"Do you code?"* MARK ZUCKERBERG asks.

"I used to know PL/SQL. I admire what you created," I respond.

I move very quickly in a futuristic public transport vessel. I'm surrounded by a crowd of young people who make fun of MARK ZUCKERBERG as he and I bob and weave among an intricate lattice of translucent buildings.]

[0113.5 / 0264] [I disembark from a submarine docked at the Port of San Francisco. The water is dark and cold. A makeshift series of wooden boards serve as the exit ramp from the large vessel.

Someone yells, *"BOY, THERE ARE SOME BRILLIANT BRAINS IN TECH!"*

The group exiting the submarine erupts with laughter.] //

⁂

MARK ZUCKERBERG: #0132
HUMID: #0424, #0568
SUBMARINE: #0540
POST MODERN: #0437
THE PAINTER: #0474

⁂

#0114 - March 27, 2018 @ 04:10 (San Francisco, California)

[0114.1 / 0265] [THE MIRROR (*distressed, self-abusing, and manic*) and I flirt in a large condo with floor to ceiling glass overlooking a vast metropolitan web. We engage in a playful game of cat and mouse. His quickened pace slows. He wants to be caught. I corner him. He shoots me *"the look"* over his right shoulder. I charge him and pounce. Still clothed, I playfully hump him from behind as he provocatively shouts out, *"MORE! MORE!"* with a grin.]

[0114.2 / 0266] [THE DANCER and I share art materials and collaborate on a project. We affix precisely trimmed cloth with illuminated cut out letters over a collection of lacquered baubles and green jewels. We intend to present an emerald green representation of the word, "DJIBOUTI" to THE WEAVER and THE CARPENTER as an anniversary gift.]

[0114.3 / 0267] [THE DANCER and I pool our cash to buy a lottery ticket. We celebrate when we learn we've won $9000, and decide to evenly split the proceeds. THE STUDENT (*friendly, eager, and nurturing*) briefly appears, but doesn't actively contribute to our conversation.] //

#0115 - March 27, 2018 @ 07:30 (San Francisco, California)

[0115.1 / 0268] [THE FBI AGENT *(covert, desirous, and intense)* and I share a messy hotel room and bathroom. Pillows and sheets are strewn about. THE FBI AGENT decides to use the bathroom and leaves the door open. Under a blanket on the floor, I find a red notebook under a red ball cap. I decide these things are mine and I toss them under the bed to hide them from her.]

[0115.2 / 0269] [ANNIE WARBUCKS tap dances around on a white marble staircase. She's just been adopted by Daddy Warbucks, who's a bald incarnation of DONALD TRUMP. Someone in a crowd of observers at the cocktail party makes an excessively foul joke about him. The group characterizes the joke as *"ballsy."* The jokester may be murdered. Conversely, the joke could be the thing that softens Daddy Warbucks' hardened heart. An image of skull and crossbones appears over the center of the room.]

[0115.3 / 0270] [It's a bright sunny morning at a wellness retreat center. Different yoga classes occur simultaneously in three different rooms, led by three different instructors. THE PIXIE *(scientific, queer, and rebellious)* leads one. He hesitates before asking a single student to reposition her mat so she'll align with the rest of the class. Her mat is perpendicular to the others. I create a promotional B-roll reel as I wander with a camera from room to room. THE NURSE *(traumatized, yet friendly)* consistently flickers in and out of frame. Two students explicitly state they do not want to be filmed. I exit onto a seaside patio area shaded by a thick white rudder pergola. As I stand in the light and smell the sunny air, THE WHITE RABBIT appears to my left. We practice Qi Gong together with our eyes closed.] //

#0116 - March 29, 2018 @ 05:01 (San Francisco, California)

[0116.1 / 0271] [Most of the dream occurs in a video game maze, reminiscent of the playing field in "Wolfenstein 3D" or "DOOM." Interior walls rise up towards invisible ceilings. It's light. Red brick walls sprayed with graffiti flank a variety of sloping pathways and ramps. Of the many creatures I interact with *(and run from)* I have strong exchanges with Zombies, Dracula, and a cowboy hat wearing MAYNARD KEENAN. While pursued by an unknown assailant, I encounter a very large woman lying on her back on a pneumatic car lift. Her giant hairy belly is exposed. Later, outside the maze I stand on a dusty hillside next to the cowboy.

"*I know who you are,*" I say to him, receiving a slight hat tip from his downcast gaze as an acknowledgment.] //

⁂

MAYNARD KEENAN: #0118
DOOM: #0700
COWBOY: #0476
GRAFFITI: #0452, #0765
HAIRY: #0500

⁂

#0117 - March 30, 2018 @ 04:00 (San Francisco, California)

[0117.1 / 0272] [I wrap up my last day in a corporate office. It's night time. My desk is set among a row of equally sized workspaces. Though this community is seemingly affluent, no one has a budget for basic office supplies *(pens, staplers, etc.)*. They're commoditized in the same way cigarettes would be within a prison. The walls are low and incomplete as the scene begins. I allow coworkers to go under my desk and drawdown on my stockpile of supplies. I was always well prepared for this job. I let my soon-to-be-former coworkers take what they want for no fee. Each time someone leaves, the cubicle walls grow a little taller. One guy gets particularly aggressive and appears to gleefully loot under my desk, laughing sheepishly. I don't recognize him. I tap him on the shoulder and note it's THE BUBBLE *(innovative, quick, and successful)*. He has a full head of hair. I've only known him to be bald. Seeing him in a new way leaves me amused and surprised.

I make my way to the ground level of the big building. I traverse C-Suite executive offices *(all occupied by women)*. A woman from India occupies one. A Japanese woman takes residence in another. I stumble upon CATHY BESSANT *(curt, smart, and unapologetic)* taking a phone call in her office. I overhear her expressing a curious desire to become a yoga teacher. She sees me, raps on her window, and mouths a phrase to me. I'm unable to hear her and continue exiting.

Once I leave the office building, I enter an airport terminal. I stand in motion on a very long, quickly advancing people mover. THE VIKING ELF *(emotive, cocksure, and sensitive)* and his husband THE TECHIE *(available, game, and supportive)* pass me from the opposite direction. I've never met THE TECHIE, but it's apparent he is angry with me. At the end of the people mover, I decide to turn around and follow them, though they've disappeared.

I enter a fast-food restaurant and take a seat at a small brown square table next to two women. We make pleasant conversation and become fast friends. THE VIKING ELF and THE TECHIE approach the table with trays of food. I discover the women are THE TECHIE's mother and sister. After an awkward silence they remain seated at the table. The pregnant pause becomes ever more intense and awkward.

"*We're on our way to _____,*" THE VIKING ELF offers. Mom and sister stay quiet. After another lengthy silence, THE TECHIE clenches his fists, intent on punching me. He winces then surprisingly says,

"*He really let you have it,*" as his face and body relax.

"**He did. He's among the dearest hearts I've ever known. I've missed you both so much.**"

"*He's dear hearted, but sometimes it's blind.*"

"**I'm so happy about what you're building together,**" I say with tearful eyes as symphonic music swells in the background.] //

⁂

Min. = ◆- *THE VIKING ELF: #0152*
CATHY BESSANT: #0171
BLIND: #0600, #0786
SISTER: #0455, #0598, #0635
AWKWARD: #0483, #0540, #0541, #0593, #0647
THE TECHIE: #0394

⁂

#0118 - March 30, 2018 @ 08:15 (San Francisco, California)

[0118.1 / 0273] [I make wine with MAYNARD KEENAN. It's a white. He pours me a glass. I cry as we toast the fruits of our labor.]

[0118.2 / 0274] [It's morning. I teach a yoga class in a refurbished version of the maze from dream [0116.1 / 0271]. Students create backbends. As each rises up, with hearts unfolding I offer quiet encouragement,

"**Soften. Soften your shoulders. Soften. Soften.**"] //

⁂

MAYNARD KEENAN: #0933
WINE: #0428, #0585
SOUL: #0493, #0619
TOAST: #0461, #0487, #0617
MORNING: #0631, #0726, #0746, #0775

⁂

#0119 - April 2, 2018 @ 09:45 (San Francisco, California)

[0119.1 / 0275] [I watch an electric pink sunset on a beach. THE YOGI (*pedagogical, methodical, and earthy*) is about to lead her last class before leaving on a summer tour. She expresses some affinity and excitement towards a male counterpart. She looks at me saying,

"*ESTHER HICKS is going to join us for this one. It's going to be amazing.*"]

[0119.2 / 0276] [A breezy space floods with gold light and hues of pink and orange.]

. . .

[0119.3 / 0277] [I telepathically connect to THE FIDUCIARY. He's in an expression of doubt about his relationship with THE REFLECTION. I know he's simply making up a problem. *"There's no doubt that boy loves you."*] //

⁎⁎

Maj. = 9- THE FIDUCIARY: #0125
PINK: #0775, #0782, #0783, #0784
AMAZING: #0784, #0787
ELECTRIC: #0449
BEACH: #0428
THE REFLECTION: #0125

⁎⁎

#0120 - April 3, 2018 @ 03:00 (San Francisco, California)

[0120.1 / 0278] [THE PHOTOGRAPHER *(creative, funny, and sexy)* and his mother ride on bicycles quickly downhill towards a park.]

[0120.2 / 0279] [I'm in a large house on a hill. I live with many white people in one half of the house, permitted for high volume occupancy. It feels like a housing project. Much later I discover the other half of the house is occupied by an ultra-high net worth African American family. In this reality, white people are oppressed. We collectively come to an awareness that we are government subsidized residents of the *"Gun Control House."* The whites decide to disrupt a fancy event hosted on the wealthy, spacious side of the property. The Whites have a slogan: **"REVEAL THE _____!"** When we get our first glimpse of the mansion, I'm taken by the sight of a large spiral staircase that spills into a giant kitchen. Once we have the attention of the party goers, we screen a slideshow that includes images of 164 children who, *"we on the other side of the house, reject."* The hosts grow aggravated by our outburst, yet keep their composure. A teenage girl complains. The scene continues to escalate. The commotion wakes me up.] //

⁎⁎

BICYCLE: #0475, #0483, #0497, #0718, #0768
AFRICAN AMERICAN: #0421, #0426, #0452, #0455, #0617, #0619, #0629
WEALTH: #0410, #0748
THE PHOTOGRAPHER: #0121

⁎⁎

#0121 - April 3, 2018 @ 06:00 (San Francisco, California)

[0121.1 / 0280] [I'm in a familiar dream state house. I've been here many times before. Oversized rooms with grand ceilings. Early 1980's cabinetry. Brown shaggy carpeting. The main level boasts an inordinately long kitchen. It appears to be mid-morning. The partly sunny sky outside floods muted light through large rectangular windows. Lights are intentionally turned off for efficiency. THE PHOTOGRAPHER *(flirtatious, generous, and emotive)* and a small Frenchman sit across from each other on opposing countertops gently banging their heels on cabinets beneath them as they smize and flirt.

"You have my attention. Call me!" he says scribbling the number 315-317-3155 on my palm in black Sharpie.

As I shove a series of circular wheat crackers in my mouth, I notice a bike lock placed on the dishwasher to prevent the theft of estate glassware.

The wire frames of my glasses bend outwards, as though melted by a blowtorch *(perhaps radiation)*. I walk down the hall to a solarium. Toys are scattered on the floor. I step up on a bench in an octagonal bay window and take in a view of a large man-made lake. I find the experience soothing.] //

☆☆

PALM: #0418, #0547, #0575
EFFICIENCY: #0698
BROWN: #0734, #0735, #0764
DISHWASHER: #0698
LAKE: #0506, #0547
THE PHOTOGRAPHER: #0236

☆☆

#0122 - April 3, 2018 @ 07:37 (San Francisco, California)

[0122.1 / 0281] [I've driven day and night to get to the Canadian border. I'm pretty tired, then get a surge of energy when I realize I don't have my passport. When stopped by border agents I feel sleepy and drunk. The officer's facial features are diffused and softened, making him unrecognizable. I don't want to go all the way home. I've already made the drive. I negotiate with the Border Patrol officer. Mid-exchange he takes a call from a woman with a strong Brooklyn accent. I ask her three times to, *"leave well enough alone,"* and further tell her, *"I have the situation under control."* She remains insistent on helping me and the guard.

"I've asked you three times. I was calm. Then I was annoyed. Now I'm angry."] //

☆☆

GUARD: #0549, #0705, #0787
ACCENT: #0427, #0545, #0672, #0699
SLEEPY: #0557, #0667

☆☆

#0123 - April 4, 2018 @ 06:33 (San Francisco, California)

[0123.1 / 0282] [THE LAWYER *(articulate, sharp, and cut throat)*, a young woman *(grounded, clear, and boundary oriented)* and I share a square shaped single-story house. An interior garden composed of concentric topiary squares increases in height from the center outward. The woman is a houseguest. A misunderstanding about a check she wrote in the amount of $100 occurs. The two zeroes in the check indicate two values in a string of digits that compose a secret code...*to what, we don't know.* A pepperoni pizza in a box rests on the nearby coffee table.] //

☆☆

Maj. = 5- THE LAWYER: #0149
ZERO: #0483

$100: #0406, #0467, #0482
SECRET CODE: #0461, #0484, #0485

⁂

#0124 - April 6, 2018 @ 06:50 (San Francisco, California)

[0124.1 / 0283] [I'm a large apartment that feels like a ranch style house. I'm in the process of moving boxes around. As I unpack I either don't want, nor have use for their contents. A few friends and neighbors pop in and out, but none of them stay for too long. It feels like I'm in my early 20's. Eagerness and electricity fill the air. My friend THE FILM PRODUCER (*soulful, guided, and loving*) arrives with another young woman. They want to change their clothes. I turn away to give them some privacy as they fully disrobe while giggling. I catch a glimpse of THE FILM PRODUCER's ass in the mirror. THE C-SUITE (*exact, candid, and good humored*) and I then sift through a couple of remaining boxes on the front lawn. The mood is light and curious. Neither of us are attached to anything in the boxes. We're fully engaged in our conversation.]

[0124.2 / 0284] [THE C-SUITE and I sit side by side in a classroom. CLEVE JONES (*revolutionary, social, and wizard-like*) is our teacher. He has long silver hair and stands in front of a black chalkboard ready to administer a lesson. I don't think he remembers me from FRANK ROBINSON's funeral, but as he makes eye contact with me, he smiles and says,
"Hey You, it's been a minute."
The classroom pivots 90 degrees. CLEVE walks by THE C-SUITE's desk to retrieve a course syllabus upon which she scribbles notes. She writes quickly as he snatches the document from her.]

[0124.3 / 0285] [We're on a class field trip to THE LIONESS's (*exuberant, direct, and influential*) grandmother's mansion. On the bus ride I contemplate how to ask THE C-SUITE for a job at her new start up. It lightly snows as we arrive at the carriage house. The scene is wintery and idyllic. I'm absorbed by the warm toned decor which makes the stately property occur as cozy and "hygge." Colors of red and gold "bespeckle" the space. Heavy rich wood furniture adorned with mirrored and crystal baubles simultaneously ground the room and twinkle possibility by scattering prismatic shards of light. Sitting on a bench seat in a breakfast nook, set adjacent to cream toned rectangular windows I talk flirtatiously with two young men about how attractive THE FILM PRODUCER is.
I'm handed a clay mug full of hot cider. I stand and move next to a door where I gaze towards roaring flames in a large hearth. A young woman walks in and shakes my hand. She claims to know me, but I fail to recognize her. It seems she missed the bus earlier. She expects to spend the night with us at the mansion. There are no rooms available, but accommodations will be made to include her.] //

⁂

FRANK ROBINSON: #0264
CRYSTAL: #0526, #0531, #0556, #0595, #0597
HEARTH: #0554, #0746
PIVOT: #0436, #0465, #0544, #0609, #0717

RED: #0720, #0725, #0732, #0755
THE FILM PRODUCER: #0322
THE LIONESS: #0375
THE C-SUITE: #0563
⁎⁎

#0125 - April 7, 2018 @ 01:36 (San Francisco, California)

[0125.1 / 0286] [In a retail environment that is equal parts "Best Buy" and "Wonka-Vision" *(sterile, white, and untouchable)*, an associate makes conversation with me as I take note of a peculiar novel fixture suspended from the ceiling. It looks like a series of rocket boosters mounted to a square platform in a grid, nine cylinders in all with one accordion like square/rectangle *(which from another perspective could also be a cylinder)*. Though they appear harmonious, I'm not able to comprehend the device's higher dimensional geometry. As I stand beneath it, the device springs to life with a sputter and a pulse, its white cylinders expand and extend towards me like fabric covered springs. The device's agenda seems to press me towards the center of a platform beneath the square component. It swiftly and repeatedly drops towards the ground from overhead like a mallet, pulverizing anything beneath. I further discern the device components share consciousness. It senses my changes in direction and attempts to crush me, though I'm able to maneuver away from certain death in the nick of time.
"WOW, that thing almost ended me!"
"Thank you for testing the 'device,'" the sales associate offers with little fanfare, leaving me confused by what's happened.]

[0125.2 / 0287] [I float a few hundred feet away from a bridge that connects futuristic skyscrapers. I can't discern how high up I am. I can't see the ground below *(if there is one)*. It appears dusky, with hues of gold, pink, and purple complementing uncountable and brilliantly illuminated office and residence windows. The dwellings seem similar to what one would find on the USS Enterprise, or on a building from the show, "The Expanse." As I hover, I notice a barrage of people running across the sky decks, all well-dressed professionals on the move from "A to B." I notice they're being ushered, no... CHASED! A commercialized application of the device that nearly crushed me seems to be effective at its job, squashing and snuffing out those who are slowest and most resistant. It's been put in service by the corporation to, *"clean house."*]

[0125.3 / 0288] [I'm in a white and pristine gallery space, with interior walls that curve and bend like a skate park. On the tips of various convex points are small baubles and ornamental statues of bunny rabbits within eggs. Some are crystal. Some are gold. Some are exquisitely painted. I contemplate the bunnies, which seem to be intentionally placed for a scavenger hunt. Upon inspection, I note the inscriptions on their bases contain extreme vulgarities and profanity. A young person could easily read said phrases, but would not understand the content. I encounter many of these objects, unplanned, as I wander through the gallery.]

. . .

[0125.4 / 0289] [I blink and awaken in an industrial kitchen with parquet floors. All major appliances and refrigeration units are suspended in air, 18 inches above the floor. The space is being deep cleaned. Matted hair, dinge and water damage are all exposed and removed. I peek inside a refrigerator and find a box of bones decaying. The words, **"OLD SELF?"** are scribbled crudely across the top of the box. Another box contains photos of childhood memories. As I keep looking deeper within the fridge, I discover more boxes.

I find a single, large bone fragment (*the lower jaw of a horse or cow*) lodged tightly under the leg of a table. I'm unable to shimmy it free.

I have a moment of complaint declaring, *"I DON'T WANT ANY PRESENTS!"* then launch into a detailed story about why and how, *"I have worked my way AWAY from _____ (unrecalled)."*

No one listens to me complain. It's reactive nonsense.]

[0125.5 / 0290] [I'm less than 12" tall. I might be in "Pee Wee's Playhouse." The energy of the space is humorous. I sit on an oversized sofa that can talk. I'm a participant in a fun game that is being watched by a "Big Brother"-like audience. THE PUBLIC MEDIUM (*clear, fairy-like, and pure*) takes in a stray Chihuahua as a pet, then decides immediately to release it. The dog returns on its own, and THE PUBLIC MEDIUM accepts it as a family member. This annoys THE FIDUCIARY and THE REFLECTION who sit together on a recliner, embracing. I stand behind the recliner as a voyeur. THE PUBLIC MEDIUM exits. The dog sits by my feet. I heave it over the top of the recliner and into the laps of THE FIDUCIARY and THE REFLECTION, to wild acclaim from the audience.]

[0125.6 / 0291] [THE NEUTRAL GUIDE (*objective, calm, and expansive*) facilitates a healing circle. Everyone wears white. A non-binary person with Down Syndrome expresses authentic joy and happiness, and stands a few people over to my right. Our collective attention moves to this being. We all smile. THE NEUTRAL GUIDE gently clasps the outside of the person's folded, prayerful hands. She begins gently flowing light through her and into this willing body. The recipient becomes engulfed in a brilliant ball of golden white light that radiates out in a pressure wave through the ring. I'm cogent enough to keep myself grounded and protected as an ecstatic sensation permeates the entirety of my being. I feel intensely strong downward pressure as the white light continues to flood in and through. I experience some flashes of fear transform to exhilaration as my body slips in to complete paralysis. The pressure and intensity of light both continue to amplify. I take in as much light as I can allow. The more I let in, the more I feel, and the deeper the paralysis becomes. I'm unsure if I'm asleep or awake as I'm awash in profound visual and emotional sensations. I'm a spirit.

"Relax and receive," a supportive voice reminds us. I wake up exhausted.] //

✦✦

Maj. = 9- *THE FIDUCIARY: #0148*, 18- *THE PUBLIC MEDIUM: #0159*
Min. = ♥- *THE NEUTRAL GUIDE: #0199*
GALLERY: #0414, #0421, #0496, #0523, #0540, #0567, #0792
DOWN SYNDROME: #0450
APPLAUSE: #0458, #0612
THE REFLECTION: #0159

✦✦

#0126 - April 7, 2018 @ 06:00 (San Francisco, California)

[0126.1 / 0292] [I'm seated in the audience of a children's television show hosted by SHAUN WHITE *(world class, masterful, and philanthropic)*. The set is decorated like a circus tent with grand swaths of red, purple, and brown cloth tied back with golden rope. SHAUN leads a group counting exercise. White block letter subtitles hang three dimensionally mid-air. "FIVE-wvw!" "FOUR-wuw!" The counting games continue as I exit through a doorway and find myself in a familiar, dirty old house that has a bit of a fratty feel, with tumbling mats scattered across cheap industrial office carpet lined floors.

I'm involved in a game. A cute, playful young guy comes down a narrow stairway and wants to participate. I make a pass at him. He ducks away and out of sight. My attention moves to a large vacuum tube hanging from the ceiling that sucks up vast volumes of dried beans, small stones and pebbles from piles on the other side of the room. The sound created by the device and the debris is tremendous. The overarching objective of the game is unclear, but I remain willing to play. The little fairy boy reappears as a trickster. He and I play *"cat and mouse,"* chasing one another through a variety of different areas of the dirty house.]

[0126.2 / 0293] [THE ARMY ANGEL *(patriotic, friendly, and sexy)* and a mysterious woman talk about going to Romania to start over and seek *"new opportunities in a land of hidden miracles."* They take residence in a long row house with a five-story open floor plan. THE ARMY ANGEL and the woman go shopping at the mall, while I bounce between observing them and exploring their home. Within the home, I wander into a conservatory with a black and white checkerboard floor, enclosed by large arching panes of beveled glass. I proceed to a greenhouse where a large cement trough sits in the center of the space. Attached atop the trough rests a clear rubber tube attached to a 50-gallon drum, which acts as a siphon and repository.

I feel water descend in my pelvis, followed by a strong urge to urinate. I piss in the trough, so much the volume startles me. The pipe connecting the trough to the drum becomes dislodged and spills urine all over the tile floor. THE LOGICIAN *(stoic, resolute, and motherly)* enters, noticing the mess on the floor. She moves quickly to clean the room with a mop, then slides the trough to a corner. Sunlight exposes a layer of dried, caked shit on the interior surface of the trough. She simply acknowledges the mess and scrubs it clean by hand. Her demeanor remains positive though on occasion I hear her curse her young sons' names playfully under her breath. I simply observe from a few feet away, and slightly up from the floor.]
//

✱
✱✱

FRAT HOUSE: #0650
VACUUM: #0433, #0520, #0523, #0615, #0734
50 GALLON DRUM: #0518
PELVIS: #0480, #0770
THE LOGICIAN: #0401
✱
✱✱

#0127 - April 7, 2018 @ 10:15 (San Francisco, California)

[0127.1 / 0294] [I'm on a high wire bridge suspended over a large body of water. THE MASSIVE HOMOSEXUAL *(gregarious, flirtatious, and spirited)* flanks me at left. A bossy, loud mouthed woman I don't know walks to my right. She and THE MASSIVE HOMOSEXUAL appear to be friends. We traverse the steel wire side step, one hand-over-hand movement at a time. Midway across the expanse, the woman begins to pass me random objects. I experience some frustration and struggle as I attempt to keep stride while juggling more objects. While gripping a pair of my glasses, a visage of JESUS CHRIST embossed in gold, and a 10-year-old flip phone (*RAZR*), I throw an elbow up and over the top guide wire. I start issuing the woman stern complaints as we begin to slide down the zip line and into a boat house docked at the shoreline. She doesn't hear me.

At the boat house, a press conference proceeds where NFL players vote on amendments to the rules of the game. I break into the conversation with a non-game related question which creates confusion among the debating players. They take down a suggestion I make regarding commentator audio, then begin changing NFL standards in nonsensical broad stroke ways.]

[0127.2 / 0295] [It's October. I'm in the garage of a large dirty house, offering to assist with clean up while a party rages inside. I'm a guest at the "birthday themed" party, though it's not actually anyone's birthday. THE JESTER (*friendly, sarcastic, and witty*) hosts the event at his home which is full of quirky (*and creaky*) characters. I find a stockpile of tequila in a storage closet. Another closet has a makeshift drum kit with a sign on the throne that invites me to sit down and play. A table in the dining room can seat "*36 and FOUR.*" Perhaps the party is being thrown in my honor?

"Really? That's generally not something I'd do, nor want."] //

⁎⁎

Min. = ◆- THE JESTER: #0163
JESUS: #0183
DRUM: #0477, #0518, #0577
GUIDE: #0401, #0446, #0461

⁎⁎

#0128 - April 8, 2018 @ 05:42 (San Francisco, California)

[0128.1 / 0296] [I'm at the "FSD mansion" at night. A large semi-truck is parked out front. A group of students prepare for a gala. The property feels neutral like a classroom. Ornate topiaries and gold statues are placed around the entire perimeter of the property. I take numerous photographs of these "*FSD installations*" and text them to THE GONG MASTER (*radiant, musical, and brotherly*). A pair of young brothers play a piano, surprising me with their cooperation while their parents argue in front of large, lit mansion windows.

THE CARPENTER and I share a heart-to-heart conversation. THE WEAVER is party to the conversation, but not physically present. A sexy "*black and white*" 1920's film woman in a crushed velvet dress relaxes on a plush couch in the atrium of the mansion. The scene pulls back from first to third person revealing a wider, omniscient perspective. Along an interior wall of the gala space (*like a dining hall at Hogwarts with chandeliers of hovering families of candles*) are large strings of digits representing bank account numbers and corresponding names of principal donors that scroll like a stock market ticker. Names on the donor wall are legible if an entity is current with their pledges. Names of donors who are not yet neutral enough to "*part with it all*" remain blurred out in fuzzy white fairy light. A portion of my hear- to-heart with THE CARPENTER relates to this phenomenon.

"Here, you sign up for the privilege of giving up everything. Donated funds are accessible by anyone for any purpose."
THE CARPENTER and I begin a conversation with THE WORLDBRIDGER (*candid, demanding, and soulful*) during which THE CARPENTER asks for assistance with meditation. THE WORLDBRIDGER looks at THE CARPENTER with care and places a hand on his shoulder. He says, *"You have a little orange and blue 'Tide Pod' hovering just above your shoulder. You can get rid of it by 'running green' for two weeks."* THE CARPENTER understands and accepts the contract. I'm proud THE CARPENTER asked for help.] //

⁂

Maj. = 0 -THE WEAVER: #0130, 1- THE CARPENTER: #0130,
7- THE WORLDBRIDGER: #0143
STOCK: #0518, #0584, #0700, #0748, #0756
HOVERING: #0572, #0573, #0717
PIANO: #0612, #0618, #0668, #0747
THE GONG MASTER: #0862

⁂

#0129 - April 9, 2018 @ 06:12 (San Francisco, California)

[0129.1 / 0297] [THE PILOT (*high sensation seeking, revealed, and welcoming*) and I play video games. Our interactions are playful and blur to abstraction. Nearby, a Tupperware container filled with leftovers from a barbecue chicken dish sits alone on a countertop. The chicken floats, spoiling in a bath of excess room temperature sauce. Even with this knowledge, a group of shadowy beings converge and decide to eat.]

[0129.2 / 0298] [I'm seated across a conference table from the US Speaker of the House PAUL RYAN. I hurl criticism at him with increasing volume. Among other things I furiously spout, I chide, *"You're an embarrassment to our alma mater!"* Exasperated and hollowed out to sadness from anger, I go outside to a snowy courtyard without my coat. I call THE LOBBYIST (*direct, no nonsense, and sharp*) then cross my arms and shiver as I wait for him to answer.]

[0129.3 / 0299] [Kids ice skate on a pond in Minnesota.]

[0129.4 / 0300] [I wipe away tears as my children board a blue double decker train and head off on their first day of school. It's not clear if I'm their mother or father.] //

⁂

Maj. = 6- THE PILOT: #0179, 17- THE LOBBYIST: #0139
MOTHER: #0406, #0452, #0463, #0467
FIRST DAY: #0775
COURTYARD: #0428, #0435, #0446, #0461, #0521, #0611
CHICKEN: #0597, #0749

⁂

JOSHUA D. LUNDELL

#0130 - April 10, 2018 @ 05:30 (San Francisco, California)

[0130.1 / 0301] [I find stacks of random antique alien artifacts at THE WEAVER and THE CARPENTER's house.]

[0130.2 / 0302] [I pass a caramel complexion BEYONCÉ. She's joined with her similarly skin toned children and her partner "Justin." They play together on a beach. I watch them for a few moments before cupping my mouth with a hand and saying,
"Wow. You have a beautiful family."]

[0130.3 / 0303] [A scraggly blonde hair ne'er-do-well teen jumps on to the bumper and through the open back window of a school bus. The kid seated behind me says, *"This isn't going to end well."* The teen walks to the front of the bus *(while in motion)*. The bus driver is a woman. She holds up her right arm in a backwards "L" to block the teen from grabbing the wheel. Another kid grabs the teen by the pony tail and flings him off the bus. As we drive by, we see the boy has fashioned a weapon from five haphazardly conjoined vertical wooden planks. The weapon doesn't seem half as menacing as the look on the boy's face.]

[0130.4 / 0304] [I wander around a San Francisco style row house looking for an umbrella, a Nalgene water bottle, and a few other miscellaneous objects. A cleaning crew has just bristled through the space, and I'm unable to find anything. THE GUITARIST plays an Ibanez JEM in a corner of a room. We don't communicate. He's immersed in his expression.] //

✲✲

Maj. = 0- THE WEAVER: #0134, 1- THE CARPENTER: #0139
Min. = ♣- THE GUITARIST: #0168
BEYONCÉ: #0147
SCHOOL BUS: #0477, #0481, #0528, #0534, #0540
UMBRELLA: #0728
EXPRESSION: #0418, #0497, #0767, #0796

✲✲

#0131 - April 11, 2018 @ 04:45 (San Francisco, California)

[0131.1 / 0305] [The Dutch Prince's flag *(orange, white and blue)* hangs vertically from the side of 30 Rockefeller Center at night. At the top of the building, a TV show wraps filming. A woman has just gotten engaged. A camera crew zooms in on a single gracious tear slowly dripping down her cheek. A marketing team scrambles through stills from the capture that can be used later to promote the limited series. Disinterested in the show, I help teams of four, seated around white square tables, select additional team members. I give one team of men an advantage by slipping small deli call numbers under a glass of water. DR. ZOIDBERG and THE CONSULTANT *(aggressive, flippant, and loud)* are on the team.] //

✲✲

FOUR: #0513, #0538, #0548, #0554, #0556, #0575, #0585

130

DELI CALL NUMBER: #0464, #0481, #0485, #0508
FLAG: #0676, #0718, #0725
⁑

#0132 - April 12, 2018 @ 05:26 (San Francisco, California)

[0132.1 / 0306] [I'm at a resort area, under construction. Multiple narratives occur in tandem. In select moments I observe MARK ZUCKERBERG (*aloof, manipulative, autocratic*), from the side. I occasionally drift inside his body to view the build site from his perspective. Drywall is placed by day laborers. Some people paint. Others set rocks in pavement that will eventually become a cobblestone path. The secret service provides property security. MARK is under investigation by the FBI. SNAP (*Food Stamps Program*) has been a target of massive fraud through Facebook. MARK is handed an itinerary and a folio of train tickets. His forthcoming journey will take two days, ending precisely at the intended destination at **18:11:00**.

In a cabana across the courtyard, a group of men have sex. One male participant appears to be tortured, but laughs as his body is repeatedly struck. He's laid on a propped up wooden table. Wooden dowels are drilled through the flesh and muscle just below each shoulder joint, pinning him down. Similarly, dowels penetrate his inner thighs passing between his hamstrings and femurs. He's surrounded by a variety of screens (*flat panels, phones, holograms*) with blurry images of men masturbating, which arouse him. He has a tiny penis.

I turn my head and reality flattens into a Polaroid picture, which I hold in my right hand. Upon inspection, the image features a steampunk clad man sporting a brown moustache, firmly upturned and twisted with beeswax. His hair is wild and wavy. His arms are crossed, with hands towards shoulders. One hand holds a pistol, which he wants noticed based on the continuous small flicking movements he makes with his wrist.

"DONOVAN FROM THE TEMPLE" is crudely scribbled at the bottom of the Polaroid in black marker. I don't recognize the name, but the face is familiar.] //

⁑
MARK ZUCKERBERG: #0295
MOUSTACHE: #0458
FBI: #0562
IMAGE: #0402, #0408, #0459, #0460
FLESH: #0693, #0760
⁑

#0133 - April 14, 2018 @ 06:55 (San Francisco, California)

[0133.1 / 0307] [I've purchased a multi-unit building and intend to turn it into a music performance venue. It needs refurbishment. The current tenants are supportive of my vision. There's a small stage on the second floor. The rooftop would make a marvelous outdoor theater. The place has a LOT of potential. We don't need a liquor license. There's no bar.]

[0133.2 / 0308] [A revival service is held on a gravel lot on Noe Hill on a Sunday morning. Chairs are set in parliamentary rows across from a stage in the center, where a performance is planned. THE ACTOR is an usher. He hands me a program. I scan it looking for his phone number, which is obviously not included. On the way out I glance at the sign-in sheet with a similar intention, met with the same result. Later, while walking down Market Street I pass him again. He's hand in hand with a tall man named "Ben." THE ACTOR winks at me as they get in a car and drive away.]

[0133.3 / 0309] [In the basement of a condo, I try to persuade my female roommate to paint the kitchen walls four different shades of blue.
"Do I sound convincing? You can tell me if my tone isn't."] //

⁎⁎

Maj. = 10- THE ACTOR: #0139
POTENTIAL: #0467, #0468, #0621
PHONE NUMBER: #0445, #0666, #0698, #0710
GRAVEL: #0447, #0477, #0489, #0545, #0655, #0665, #0755

⁎⁎

#0134 - April 15, 2018 @ 06:10 (San Francisco, California)

[0134.1 / 0310] [I'm the lead in a Broadway show. Mid-song I'm passed a prop the size of a soap bar that reads, "Defying Gravity" in a swooping, feminine font. I have such a strong complaint about the prop's construction I leave the stage to discuss with the production manager who quickly dismisses me saying,
"Don't be bothered. The prop master is from a traveling production company."
He exits.]

[0134.2 / 0311] [I find myself in a train station two floors below street level. The space is awash in milky soft white light. Various pedestals and abstractions double as presentation easels, displaying works of modern art. THE WEAVER joins me underground. We wander from piece to piece observing, contemplating, and responding. I take note of an airport terminal that feels irrationally placed within the underground train station. THE ORACLE (*channel, divine feminine, and vulnerable*) sits nearby in a postmodern high back chair *"visual texting"* a strong, mature masculine contemporary. THE WEAVER and I wander upwards to a high ceiling space similar to St. Pancras Station. A series of four large banners hang vertically from the rafters displaying dynamic works composed of complex patterns of inter-woven ellipses constructed in an alien medium.

THE CHARLATAN (*trickster, challenger, and catty*) appears behind us and hands us each a small square cardboard calling card, which identifies him as *"the artist."* A similar pattern of ellipses is printed in black and white on the obverse of the card. THE CORD CUTTER (*wizard*) appears and challenges THE CHARLATAN, who additionally exclaims, *"I DID THE SET DESIGN TOO!"*

He charges THE CORD CUTTER, tackling him upward towards the roof. THE WEAVER gasps and disappears. I'm startled for a moment when I see the quarreling pair stall out at rafter level and tumble toward the ground. I breathe a sigh of relief only after I see them land together on a dusty cushioned couch some distance away.]

· · ·

[0134.3 / 0312] [THE EXPAT *(friend, lover, soul guide)* and I lay together on a large comfortable couch flooded by soft, warm, golden light. We tenderly embrace, falling softly in towards each other chest to chest. We wear square cut swimsuits. The gentle contact made by the skin of our bare torsos results in us giggling uncontrollably and giving one another the occasional flirty finger poke to the side ribs. It's nourishing, restorative, and playfully sacred. His mostly naked body turns me on.] //

⁂

Maj. = 0 - THE WEAVER: #0139
CARDBOARD: #0719, #0734, #0756, #0775, #0780
SOAP: #0401, #0693, #0714, #0791
PEDESTAL: #0414, #0540
THE CORD CUTTER: #0143
THE EXPAT: #0204
THE ORACLE: #0360
THE CHARLATAN: #1118

⁂

#0135 - April 16, 2018 @ 04:30 (San Francisco, California)

[0135.1 / 0313] [Image of THE SOOTHSAYER *(receptive, connected, healer, spirit channel, and Holy)*.]

[0135.2 / 0314] [I'm in a garden courtyard in the black of night. Nearby a mysterious character I assume to be a teenage boy wears a hoodie and dark colors head to toe. Though in silhouette, I'm able to see the being using white headphones while looking at a small screen. I seem to have the support of other invisible entities to follow the shadowy character up a cement sidewalk lined with well-manicured bushes. Some of the time my feet are on the ground, while other moments I float and fly. The shadowy teen disappears and I'm left in an experience of fear. I turn around to see a series of floating green-white doors lightly bobbing up and down at the far end of the courtyard. I'm curious what will be revealed when they integrate into a final configuration and unlock. My skin erupts in goosebumps as a wave of tension passes through my bubble.] //

⁂

HOODIE: #0427, #0436, #0462, #0535, #0575, #0667
INVISIBLE: #0601, #0641, #0664, #0762, #0786
UNLOCK: #0472
THE SOOTHSAYER: #0542

⁂

#0136 - April 18, 2018 @ 06:48 (San Francisco, California)

[0136.1 / 0315] [**PLAGIARISM!**]

. . .

[0136.2 / 0316] [A clinical psychologist informs me my optimal learning conditions are linked to playing video games, *"outside in nature."*]

[0136.3 / 0317] [I receive educational content through a Wi-Fi transponder installed in my brain. The classroom is silent. We dutifully inspect slides under microscopes, while receiving telepathic tutelage as a supplement. THE STRATEGIST (*extroverted, collaborative, and hard edged*) may be the teacher. I'm not sure. A full storyline is absent, but it seems I'm in the process of being expelled from the school.] //

⁎⁎

NATURE: #0786
TELEPATHIC: #0437, #0484, #0529, #0610
STORY: #0404, #0435, #0441
LEARNING: #0437

⁎⁎

#0137 - April 19, 2018 @ 06:48 (San Francisco, California)

[0137.1 / 0318] [I clean out a closet while flirting with THE HABERDASHER (*entrepreneurial, charming, and attractive*).]

[0137.2 / 0319] [I run a footrace on a banked, indoor track.]

[0137.3 / 0320] [I attend the same ROB ZOMBIE concert twice. Each time I arrive, the band plays the song "Superbeast."]

[0137.4 / 0321] [People take turns going up to a dispenser and filling small glasses with a gray liquid, which quickly spins and then firms up into a steel wool-like substance. Everyone eats it like cotton candy.] //

⁎⁎

ROB ZOMBIE: #0256
RUNNING: #0406, #0433, #0475, #0476
COTTON CANDY: #0534
DISPENSE: #0462, #0564

⁎⁎

⁂ 3.2 - THE BOOK OF URSA MAJOR: 0138-0172 ⁂

#0138 - April 21, 2018 @ 03:18 (San Francisco, California)

[0138.1 / 0322] [I lead a yoga class for a large group in a spacious room.] //

⁂

LEAD: #0586, #0592, #0593, #0597
LARGE: #0620, #0625, #0628, #0633, 0634, #0635
SPACIOUS: #0577

⁂

#0139 - April 22, 2018 @ 05:48 (San Francisco, California)

[0139.1 / 0323] [I attend a prayer service in a room with a rich dark wood interior. It feels like a church, but unconventional. I go to a basement level kitchen where I find a large refrigerator. I make whipped cream pies on round paper plates whispering, *"mandala archetype"* to myself on repeat. I eat a few of the pies ravenously, suggesting to myself I don't want to be caught *(but I actually do)*.]

[0139.2 / 0324] [I receive a care package in the US mail from THE LOBBYIST. It contains multiple pairs of "METRO MILE" branded underwear and a series of four photographs of THE LOBBYIST, THE ACTOR and I frolicking in a city crosswalk. I invite THE CARPENTER over to take a look. He appears over my shoulder, takes a brief inquisitive glance at the photos, and in his accepting and matter of fact way says, *"That's pretty neat, Son."*
THE WEAVER sits at an adjacent table compiling VIP lanyards for a Jamiroquai concert *(an event to celebrate freedom, future funk, and connection)*. THE WEAVER is meticulous and debates the quality of her work by extensively studying the top left corner seams of each set of credentials. She has some doubt they'll pass quality assurance, and won't even be seen by concert security staff. THE CARPENTER dismisses the doubt and moves on to another project in the garage.] //

⁂

Maj. = 0- THE WEAVER: #0147, 1- THE CARPENTER: #0168,
10- THE ACTOR: #0167, 17- THE LOBBYIST: #0200
MANDALA: #0470, #0624
LANYARD: #0772
QUALITY: #0404, #0412, #0422, #0513, #0621, #0764

⁂

#0140 - April 23, 2018 @ 04:10 (Park City, Utah)

[0140.1 / 0325] [A friend of mine recognizes a man he considers famous sitting at a nearby cafe table. I encourage my friend to go talk to him. He does. The man dismisses my friend by placing a broken umbrella on the table and suggests my friend go have it repaired for him.
"No way," I say as I stand up and run across the room, pick up the umbrella and fling it forcefully towards the face of the celebrity.

He's burly, unshaven and wears a fedora. He says nothing to me post face strike and begins harmonically whistling a song, which I find musically unusual, magical, and alien. I decide he's a cool, creative being. He and I leave the cafe, get in a car and drive backwards down a busy street at incredible speed while his odd whistling persists.]

[0140.2 / 0326] [I walk through a public bathroom where numerous couples pair off and have sex in a row of stalls. I move quickly through the area. My cell phone camera activates while in my pocket, snapping a burst of blurry pornographic photos. Upon later review by a friend, I claim none of them are of me. Because the images exist on my device, my claims are doubted. Photos on my phone show numerous faceless, contorted, predominantly male bodies fucking.]

[0140.3 / 0327] [We're at a training program for 25 people and one attendee is absent. Their vacant space is highlighted by a white square pillow under a soft downward flow of gold light. I think I know who the missing person is and am surprised when someone unexpected enters the room and sits on the pillow.]

[0140.4 / 0328] [Two 19-year-old women suggestively dance in front of a man with a carnival backdrop behind them. They rip open their corsets and giggle as they reveal their breastless chests. I feel embarrassed for them. They could be my daughters.]

[0140.5 / 0329] [I'm in the passenger seat of a car driven by a frantic female driver. She has beautiful sleeve tattoos from her shoulders to fingertips. Her driving is erratic and jolting. I feel unsafe. We arrive at the destination late. She requests that we take multiple "Boomerang" photos on a very old smartphone to prove to her family that she checked into rehab. Geotags on the photo will confirm this as a "fact." I find it odd that in every photo I take, every other person in the image appears to hold an oversized cardboard printout of the tattooed driver's face.] //

*
**
BACKWARDS: #0455, #0563, #0690, #0726, #0771
CAFE: #0468, #0483, #0532, #0673
ERRATIC: #0760, #0769
*
**

#0141 - April 23, 2018 @ 06:03 (Park City, Utah)
* Dream state manifested with such clarity I did not realize I was sleeping. *

[0141.1 / 0330] [A general decline in mood from confidence, through concern, to terror emerges. I anticipate being stabbed. I'm in a room where I attempt to write things down, but I forget them before my hand makes it to the paper with a pen. The only method useful to recall things here is forced repetition. Among the numerous incantations, spells, and prayers spoken to me by guides and angels the only one I remember is, *"invite the: 'VOWEL SWING*

CAVAZZO,'" uttered to me matter of fact (*and in passing*) by a tall man. The unique timbre of his voice is memorable.

My guide tells me, *"to hear his voice properly you have to experience sound in five dimensions."* I experience it as "Quadra-tonal" with each component layered in with a distinct effect. What does the "VOWEL SWING CAVAZZO" conjure? I have no idea. **shrug**]

[0141.2 / 0331] [I stand on a bridge by a young man overlooking a river next to an urban center that looks like Zurich, Switzerland. I use the spell. Gray clouds swirl overhead as a Charybdis-like whirlpool forms in the middle of the river. A large flock of black birds fly over the river. Harnessing telekinesis, the young man directs the birds to fly directly into the whirlpool on command. The birds behave like atomic donkeys. As the birds descend through the surface of the water in a spade formation, I stand in admiration, alertness (*and mild trepidation*) to the young man's ability to influence. I extend my hand in friendship. He clasps mine without hesitation. We duck below the bridge together and disappear.]

[0141.3 / 0332] [I'm in an industrial treehouse spread across multiple catwalk-connected levels. THE INVESTMENT BANKER (*intense, methodical, and callous*) hides out on a small platform in the corner of a space with a high ceiling. A small ladder leads to the platform, which she could easily descend but consistently reiterates that she's, *"just not ready."*

THE NURSE appears beside me and suggests repeatedly that her daughter, *"deserves a student!"*

When I ask why, THE NURSE becomes highly agitated and begins screaming, *"THIS IS JUST 'STEP THREE!' THIS IS JUST A 'STEP THREE' MOMENT!"* refusing to hear me when I gently tell her, *"it's not."*] //

⁂

Maj. = 13- THE NURSE: #0142
PLATFORM: #0401, #0430, #0538, #0628, #0713, #0718, #0764
DAUGHTER: #0435, #0436, #0498, #0510, #0667

⁂

#0142 - April 24, 2018 @ 06:12 (Park City, Utah)

[0142.1 / 0333] [I spend significant time cleaning an apartment while THE NURSE teaches a class in a high ceiling industrial space next door. From the many students, I take note of a large man and his petite wife working out together side by side. An alarm promptly sounds at 6:31pm, at which point I offer a quick goodbye to the vacant apartment by saying, **"I'll return after three days of play in New York City."**] //

⁂

Maj. = 13- THE NURSE: #0319
ALARM: #0556, #0558
NEW YORK: #0677, #0710

⁂

#0143 - April 25, 2018 @ 03:08 (Park City, Utah)

[0143.1 / 0334] [*"Tell us about your experience of being 'Hitler,'"* a group of guys asks me in unison while sitting on the floor of a church sanctuary shooting up each other's arms with heroin.

A gang member on the far side of the room sets objects on fire to conceal a crime he's just committed. The fire grows ravenous, intense, and all consuming.

"Can you count all the kitties on the ceiling?" I'm asked in unison by THE KETTLE (*sharp, and defensive*), THE WHISTLE (*whimsical, and airy*), and THE SHAKTI SISTER (*grounded, and available*).

I look up and see an innumerable sea of feline faces suspended upside down. The kitty ears are pointy and undulate in ripples and waves, creating a watery living sfumato-esque quality on the ceiling that pulses with vitality.

"I've committed to support a healing beyond what I can remember. I may not be neutral, therefore unable to serve."

It's apparent I've committed fraud, since so many senior teachers have been called in to resolve the fiery situation that's engulfed the sanctuary. THE WORLDBRIDGER enters and quickly begins laying hands on the heroin addicted men. I step in to assist. THE WORLD-BRIDGER shoots me a strong glance as I hear him say, *"BACK OFF!"* wordlessly in the center of my head. I'm startled when I'm repelled backward by his energetic bubble and protection. Intense waves of healing follow that further show me I've overstepped my boundaries into unremembered spaces. Once the healing concludes THE WORLDBRIDGER says, *"You have to leave the United States right now."*

I turn away and walk down a familiar staircase in a mansion where I encounter THE CORD CUTTER (*loving, and supportive*).

"What did you say your number was? It says here you're a 6.3. That's way below what's necessary here. I'll need to check that."

He knows I've reported a higher value than accurate as a way of getting premature access to higher order challenges and skills. I spout off a string of nonsense words in response to THE CORD CUTTER's inquiry.

He instantly retorts, *"Maybe try asking that in the form of a question."*

When I comply, he says, *"You're about to embark on a journey of massive self-discovery."*] //

✷

Maj. = 7- THE WORLDBRIDGER: #0313
HEROIN: #0747
JOURNEY: #0411, #0462, #476, #0618, #0674
THE KETTLE: #0587
THE WHISTLE: #0873
THE SHAKTI SISTER: #0938

✷

#0144 - April 26, 2018 @ 03:38 (Park City, Utah)

[0144.1 / 0335] [From side stage I observe JULIE ANDREWS rehearse a world class musical dance number for a new Broadway performance with an understudy in tow. The stage design gives the impression of how Grand Central Station would appear with red velvet carpeted staircases. From a totally different location BARON BAPTISTE, sits at a desk

surrounded by stacks of paper. He holds a megaphone to his mouth and issues JULIE live feedback.
"You could be doing so much more with your life!"
Unsure, JULIE looks at me. I give her a silent nod offering,
"Don't worry, you've got this."
She continues the number. BARON's feedback becomes louder and more confrontational.
"GIVE IT UP JULIE! GIVE UP THE FERRARI! GIVE EVERYTHING UP! JULIE! GIVE! IT! UP!"]

[0144.2 / 0336] [THE SERVANT (*seeking, and heroic*) enters a dirty bachelor pad. The floors are filthy. Dirty dishes are stacked tall in the sink. The space is in a state of general disrepair. My offer to clean is politely acknowledged and refused. THE BREAKS DJ (*creative, and shamanic*) offers to take me to a club. We delay our dancing to wait for THE CONNECTOR who never arrives. The frame pans out to show a house on a hill. Like the back of a doll-house, the rear of the property is exposed. Some of the rooms are lit. Others are dark this particular night. The landlord knows all the tenants, who share and generate appreciation as a community for the watchful, supportive eye he keeps on each of their lives.]

[0144.3 / 0337] [I'm in a long retail space. I decide to stand on a table top as I shop for shoes. Boxes on the table are white and uniform in size. It's a bit exasperating to make a choice since there's nothing on display. I really like a pair of silver fur boots and am delighted when I discover they're on sale for $75. I walk across a few other tables toward the exit door and hop to the floor with my prize under my arm.]

[0144.4 / 0338] [I chat with a cute guy on Grindr who skews younger than I tend to date. He immediately shows up at what was the (*now formerly*) filthy apartment in [0144.2 / 0336]. The space sparkles with cleanliness. As we chat and become better acquainted, he mentions he frequents THE TEACHER's (*skillful, patient, and loving*) yoga classes. Next to the wall is a large six-foot cube which is damp to the touch and acts as a mount for a large industrial transformer. I hold my hand near it to channel some electrical power to the house. My hand gets severely shocked, and I receive an eye shaped burn in the center of my palm.]

[0144.5 / 0339] [THE MODEL (*playful, flirtatious, and open*) stands in the middle of a city street on a blue skied sunny day. She clutches a series of three large gold balloons in her right hand. One is an "N," another an "O," and finally an "E." Cupping her mouth with her left hand she smiles and yells *"NOE!"* loudly asking passersby in the crosswalk. *"Does anyone have that name? 'NOE?'"* The mood is happy and playful. As she spins the balloons reorder above her to read: *"ONE."*] //

⁂
Maj. = 4- THE CONNECTOR: #0235
BARON BAPTISTE: #0357
SHOCK: #0475, #0726, #0768

NOE: #0435
SILVER: #0561, #0573, #0654
LANDLORD: #0529
DATE: #0540, #0554, #0637
THE BREAKS DJ: #0226
THE MODEL: #0456
THE TEACHER: #1403
⁂

#0145 - April 26, 2018 @ 05:24 (Park City, Utah)

[0145.1 / 0340] [I'm in a frenetic waiting room in an urban social worker's office. The sea of desks could just as easily be a call center at a police station. I'm hastily shuffled to a windowless room where a young Black woman attempts to draw blood from my left arm multiple times. She vindictively stabs my arm while grinning and staring me down. She's followed no basic protocols to ensure sterilization.

She grabs my forearm with an ungloved hand while continuing to repeatedly stab downward into the eye of my elbow with increasing force. A glimpse of her dirty fingernails triggers my anxiety response. I stand up, swing my arm, and promptly leave the office by storming angrily down the hallway to log a complaint with the attending physician. When asked if I was wearing my lapel camera at the time of the alleged abuse, I confirm I was not, thus disqualifying me from further administrative support and legal recourse.]

[0145.2 / 0341] [Stacks of quarters line a countertop in a bar. They're set there with the express intention of funding patron trips to the sandwich shop across the street, where they have, *"THE BEST HOAGIES."* LARRY DAVID (*cynical, candid, and awkward*) determines how large a stack of quarters each guy in line gets based on his relative fondness for the joke they tell him.]

[0145.3 / 0342] [THE EXECUTIVE PRODUCER (*growing, controlling, and precise*) gives birth to a newborn baby.] //

⁂
LARRY DAVID: #1101
FINGERNAILS: #0443, #0597
QUARTERS: #0548, #0641, #0747, #0788
BLOOD: #0452, #0467, #0518, #0520, #0521, #0563, #0576, #0648
THE EXECUTIVE PRODUCER: #0154
⁂

#0146 - April 27, 2018 @ 03:40 (Park City, Utah)

[0146.1 / 0343] [A Boston Marathon participant is disqualified from competition mid-race because their right foot takes a single step outside of a marked boundary. The incident is reviewed via slow motion replay. At the end of the tape, it's revealed that as the runner advances down a brown rocky hillside scramble after the infraction, they fall forward and breaks their wrists.]

[0146.2 / 0344] [I paint two large swaths of gold on the interior wall of a basement room with a floor composed of durable mattresses. Duty of care and attention is paid in their routine cleaning. I sit and watch the gold paint dry. The top line has a bluish complementary hue, the one beneath is similarly accented with a red base. THE COMIC (*friendly, contrary, and expressive*) and I use telekinetic powers to consolidate and draw energy through the room. One high frequency orb pops through for a visit. Sending it back out to the world proves exhausting for us. We pause to catch our breath with hands on shins. With a panting, labored breath THE COMIC quips,
"*That light was heavy.*"
The humor diminishes as I hear THE CHILD (*innocent, and gentle*) cry. I'm not able to console her. She tripped and fell into a door face first, hitting her upper front gums on a small brass doorknob.]

[0146.3 / 0345] [Upon their formal discharge from service, Army veterans are offered the opportunity to buy their combat weapon. If purchased, the gun is packaged in a plastic box. One soldier who decides to purchase feels cheated out of the "proper" number of bullets and gold coins packaged in the box with her gun.]

[0146.4 / 0346] [I run a half marathon with a group. We cheat the course by running down a large grassy hill with numerous wavy tiers. At the end of the race, we discover a locker room and shower facility which houses hundreds of race finishers. My attention stays focused on a nude woman with a hairy abdomen as numerous beings shower and prepare for their next events.] //

⁎⁎

Maj. = 3- THE CHILD: #0147
SLOW: #0538, #0543, #0582, #0735
HAIRY ABDOMEN: #0500
GUN: #0460, #0549, #0558, #0659, #0718
THE COMIC: #0148

⁎⁎

#0147 - April 27, 2018 @ 06:09 (Park City, Utah)

[0147.1 / 0347] [THE CHILD plays while repeating the same five-word response each time she's asked a question. THE DANCER gets mildly annoyed by the continuous repetition, but centers herself by appreciating her daughter's practice and precision. THE DANCER occasionally remarks with similar repetition,
"*My daughter is darling. I love her so much.*"]

. . .

[0147.2 / 0348] [A special BEYONCE concert takes place in a theater on a yacht. I file into the multi-thousand seat room with other eager attendees. JAY-Z *(enterprising, proud, and friendly)* sits next to me for a time smiling and anticipating his wife's performance. He's physically smaller than I assumed he would be. The entire venue flip flops and, **now on the "negative" side of the image**, I become aware that this gathering is a joint discussion among black entrepreneurs and venture capitalists. The key topic of the gathering centers on how to pivot public perception of SHELL OIL COMPANY, by leveraging BEYONCÉ's celebrity to drive up customer affinity and *(by extension)* shareholder value. Many articulate beings offer their ideas and context into microphones set at side stage. Small groups of name tag lanyard donning participants gather in their own small group conversations and exit the auditorium.

A little male "bowling pin shaped being" pointedly asks me,

"Where are your friends?"

Instead of answering, I pay him a compliment to which he favorably responds. He has a little pot belly, and wears a white A-frame t-shirt, with ill fitting, saggy tightey-whitey underwear. He's some sort of guard, but easily passed by.

I advance down a narrow corridor to a basement level pool. People come and go individually from a dark room at the opposite end of the pool room. A nude woman casually dries her long brown hair as she walks through the mysterious, steam laden space. A few other people, slathered head to toe in baby oil, leisurely enter and exit. Peeking around the door reveals people having sex labeled with large ink stamps on their buttocks that read: "**HOOKERS.**" An exhausted, olive-complexed muscle man leaves the orgy and dips his foot in the cool pool water while walking towards the exit door.]

[0147.3 / 0349] [A sunset made of bands of color slowly unfolds looking like album art from the TYCHO album, AWAKE. The experience is backed by music from said album, making the environment lush, alive, and vibrant. A plane has crashed in the water next to the yacht. One woman is rescued from the ocean wreckage. Once on deck the woman reveals strong telekinetic ability and hurls those who attempt to assist her, forcefully against a wall.

I receive a text from THE WEAVER who tries to discern my whereabouts. When I enter the auditorium and think I've found her sitting a few rows from where I stand, I find it's actually THE GDMF UNICORN *(wild, attention grabbing, and gregarious)* and it leaves me confused. THE WEAVER and I eventually meet up in a smaller secondary theater as the intro to DREAMGIRLS begins playing.

"I've tried to text you the same thing 25 times," THE WEAVER says as we both grip our Playbills, printed on tissue thin red velvet stock with gold leaf print. The delicate, yet regal presentation draws the eye of the reader into a sensorily immersive experience.

We leave the theater, walk to a lower deck, and enter a prep kitchen. She and I are in the racial minority. We're separated from each other, and the group. I make small talk with a husband and wife who're enrolled to teach yoga to BEYONCÉ and the gathered entrepreneurs. I ask if I can join their team. A woman identifies herself as "Andrea," who asks us to move quickly and, *"get their prayer."*

A drag queen performs a song from DREAMGIRLS. Once complete, BEYONCÉ and her entourage enter and take station behind a buffet counter. They sing an odd hymn that is equally beautiful and unsettling. My phone malfunctions and won't close a social media app, which causes me to fail at delivering on "Andrea's" request. My attempt to film misses most of their prayer. I really wanted to capture the moment for THE WEAVER. Furthermore, I inadvertently missed the experience while fumbling around with a distracting piece of technology.] //

⁑

Maj. = 0- THE WEAVER: #0154, 2- THE DANCER: #0148, 3- THE CHILD: #0154
BEYONCÉ: #0189
JAY-Z: #0974
THE GDMF UNICORN: #1401

⁑

#0148 - April 29, 2018 @ 05:39 (San Francisco, California)

[0148.1 / 0350] [I make cookies in a classroom setting with THE FIDUCIARY. The flour in the current batch isn't fully mixed. As the teacher passes by our workstation, she comments that, *"They're usually more _____."* THE FIDUCIARY leaves.]

[0148.2 / 0351] [I find myself in a lengthy serpentine line at a Dunkin' Donuts. Orders are taken through touchscreens. The one I use malfunctions, and results in me being moved to the back of the line. The entire line becomes out of sorts and a bit disquieted. On my second pass through, an old man standing on a countertop brandishes a knife and threatens the woman immediately ahead of me in line by lopping off the tip of his index finger and pointing the bloody digit at her. Unbothered, I say,
"Dude, put that away."
Once at the front of the line I'm jettisoned to the back again just as I'm about to order. I send a bogus Instagram story to THE DANCER about my experience of the, *'line at McDonalds."* Nearby, a woman plays the harp. Notably the instrument's strings are all red.]

[0148.3 / 0352] [I make out with THE COMIC as we playfully exchange soul gazing, *"I love you's."*] //

⁑

Maj. = 2- THE DANCER: #0154, 9- THE FIDUCIARY: #0159
DONUTS: #0406, #0549, #0564, #0760, #0772
THE COMIC: #0239

⁑

#0149 - April 30, 2018 @ 05:41 (San Francisco, California)

[0149.1 / 0353] [I'm at a big box retailer shopping for a new laptop computer. I want an Apple MacBook Pro. The service team is attentive and friendly. I'm particularly interested in a model that has a black marble maze texture on the outer casing. Though I'm handed a white one for purchase, I actually want a silver or black one. The team assures me I qualify to buy, and they have the item onsite.
The young man and woman duo usher me through a portal to another dimension. We land in a large aircraft hangar. A line has formed where committed customers have their orders fulfilled. An arcane and absurdly complicated purchase process involves recalling

obscure movie trivia, and generating stock responses to randomized Instagram stories while in queue.

Example: *"Mike D. loved this at 8:41am & commented, "GREAT IDEAS!" 4120 people loved this."*

The posting process ultimately determines which products I'm eligible to buy, as well as their dynamically generated price point. My myriad complaints fall on deaf ears. No one cares. I'm particularly frustrated when I learn another woman in line has, *"guaranteed, 'locked in' pricing,"* without having to post anything.

Once I complete the sales process, I'm loaded on a bus with a hundred other people and begin a journey back to San Francisco. As we drive away, I realize we've just been inside a new Apple retail campus.

A New Year's celebration occurs onboard the bus as it winds through green and amber rolling hills. I'm handed a party hat, noise makers, and a sandwich bag filled with confetti. We pull up to a hillside gated community. Our pace slows and a woman on the bus turns to me remarking, *"This is a REALLY nice neighborhood, don'cha think?"* The bus continues to San Francisco and lets us off at a depot adjacent to the bay.

It's a windy and blustery day. With computer boxes under arm everyone rushes into a low vibration grocery store, where a few functional fluorescent lights flicker overhead. Electricity has been routed to a central aisle to illuminate a display wall of sugar filled, colorful boxes which people clamor to buy. I want none of the promoted boxed cereal and walk towards three round apple barrels. The barrels are mostly empty. Three varieties of apple are for sale: *"Honey Crisp," "Smudged," and "KPPs."* All that remains for sale is a single bruised, *"KPP."* I hold the *"KPP"* in my right hand to inspect it. Disclaimer signs prominently displayed make it very clear that this store,

"DOES NOT PROVIDE HOME DELIVERY SERVICE FOR ANY PURCHASE.
NO EXCEPTIONS."]

[0149.2 / 0354] [THE LAWYER lends me a flat screen TV.] //

✱✱

Maj. = 5- THE LAWYER: #0173
APPLE: #0473, #0659, #0701, #0777
CEREAL: #0620, #0790
WINDY: #0472

✱✱

#0150 - May 2, 2018 @ 05:02 (San Francisco, California)

[0150.1 / 0355] [I briskly walk across a sky bridge between two opulent corporate towers. THE VINTNER *(masculine, analytical, and indecisive)* notices me approaching from the opposite direction and waves. He playfully accelerates and shoves me out of the flow of foot traffic for a quick conversation. He pulls out a piece of paper from his suit coat pocket and begins reading,

"I love you, one hundred times."

He repeats this phrase, 100 times. He hands me the paper. I read it back to him, giggling and flirting the entire time. Day shifts to night. The sky bridge descends down through the ground, instantly morphing into a subterranean tunnel at the root of the buildings. THE VINTNER and I say farewell and walk in opposite directions. THE CHEMISTS (*precise, brilliant, and intellectually beyond the pale*) stand at a round cocktail table. I pause with them to celebrate their new research role at a large multinational consultancy. Other unfamiliar characters come and go, offering them similar encouragement.]

[0150.2 / 0356] [I work on a cleaning crew at an amphitheater with a bunch of middle-aged women. We spend ample time discussing where to gather soiled white towels and how to most efficiently transport them to the laundromat. We pile into the same car, after nonsensically exiting an elevator on an upper level of a luxury condominium tower.] //

⁂

100: #0482, #0487, #0557, #0583, #0614, #0618, #0757
CLEANING: #0502, #0671, #0700
NEW JOB: #0681, #0752
AMPHITHEATER: #0515, #0572, #0600, #0628, #0744
THE CHEMISTS: #0982

⁂

#0151 - May 4, 2018 @ 06:05 (San Francisco, California)

[0151.1 / 0357] [I work as a barista in a cafe.]

[0151.2 / 0358] [I'm in a dilapidated mansion that looks similar to the Bates Motel. As I stand on the ground beneath one of the dormers, I dodge dead bodies that roll off the edge of the roof and spin towards me on their groundward descent. The yard is littered with trash and outlined by a chain link fence. I float upward toward the roof as bodies strike the ground with heavy thuds, then roll out of sight.]

[0151.3 / 0359] [I chew off a sizable chunk of tissue from the inside of my right cheek. I spit it in my hand. It looks like a chewed piece of gum. I place it on a slide to observe under a microscope. I'm quickly whisked away by some laboratory technicians to a press conference to discuss, *"the discovery of a new plastic explosive derived specifically from human cheek cells."*]

[0151.4 / 0360] [I enter a house under construction. The ceilings are low. The walls are freshly painted white. It's apparent I've entered the back of the home as I traverse the interior. The front door and driveway are revealed after I move swiftly around a wall to the right. DIANE FEINSTEIN and a young girl sit at a kitchen counter telling jokes.]

[0151.5 / 0361] [I'm at a wedding in Kentucky. THE VICAR (*engaging, fanciful, and alluring*) is the host for the wedding party and distributes gift bags that contain small Ziplock pouches, each with 2.5 round electrolyte tablets. She winks as she hands me mine, which I take as an indication they're actually pressed pills of ecstasy.] //

⁑

DIANE FEINSTEIN: #0271
PLASTIC EXPLOSIVE: #0700
PILLS: #0532
BARISTA: #0789

⁑

#0152 - May 6, 2018 @ 05:05 (San Francisco, California)

[0152.1 / 0362] [THE VIKING ELF is awarded "Student of the Year" on a cruise ship out at sea. He clasps his hands and moves them side to side at ear level victoriously as he approaches a podium to accept the honor.] //

⁑

Min. = ◆- *THE VIKING ELF: #0226*
CRUISE SHIP: #0792
STUDENT: #0549, #0587, #0592, #0620

⁑

#0153 - May 6, 2018 @ 06:53 (San Francisco, California)

[0153.1 / 0363] [THE CREATOR (*clear, vulnerable, and playful*) gives me a hug and tells me she's proud of me. I want to ask her for a job, but I forget. After I blink, I'm in the basement of a large house. A tall, thin woman in a black evening gown tends to an infant that floats naked and face down in a large saltwater fish tank. I work with about a dozen people, some from "Reiki Two" training on creating an improv television show scheduled to air specifically from, "*6:00 to 6:15.*" THE REIKI MASTER (*confrontational, social, and healing*) is the director of the program and sternly moves the group into their appropriate marks. I spend time on set with a friend named "MARK" painting over black and gold basement walls with neutral tones. Though I haven't ventured out of the basement, I know I'm inside an extraordinarily large house.] //

⁑

GOWN: #0407, #0511, #0552, #0614, #0715, #0767
NEUTRAL: #0537, #0559, #0572
DOZEN: #0437, #0483, #0545
THE REIKI MASTER: #0156
THE CREATOR: #0980

⁑

#0154 - May 7, 2018 @ 04:11 (San Francisco, California)

[0154.1 / 0364] [I'm on a raft at sea with LOUIS CK. I console him and say, "*Give it a few years*" as the sea funnels into a serpentine water slide. Household furniture floats alongside us. While I feel genuine concern for his wellbeing, my attention shifts to my pants pocket. I'm worried my phone will get wet and ruined.]

. . .

[0154.2 / 0365] [From the rafters of a warehouse, a powerful woman observes and directs her very large wedding dress to get ratcheted to tension around multiple large spools suspended overhead. Giant crystals in the bodice sparkle brightly and obstruct my view of her taunting and humiliating a gagged and bound, tuxedo wearing HUGH JACKMAN. The dress moves towards him like spider silk from multiple directions, wrapping and spinning him up in a glistening cocoon. He's eventually mummified in a wrapping that sparkles in the light. It feels like it's dawn. All is calm. *"This is normal."*]

[0154.3 / 0366] [A leadership team sprints through an airport terminal. THE EXECUTIVE PRODUCER is uncharacteristically late. We approach a coffee stand together, which is in the process of closing for the day. The crew remains willing to serve us anything we want as they clean up and shut down.]

[0154.4 / 0367] [THE BRAND MANAGER (*skillful, conservative, and persuasive*) discloses his long-term partner's name is "ERIC WHITEMAN," a world-renowned DJ. THE WEAVER and THE BRAND MANAGER discuss why they believe THE DANCER and THE ATHEIST's relationship works.
A circle split vertically down the center by a line has a phrase printed on each hemisphere: *"I PICK UP." "YOU DROP OFF."* The circle floats a few feet in front of them. THE WEAVER points at the large circle split in two that now glows like neon.
Standing outside and alone THE BRAND MANAGER reveals himself to be a Black man who softly mutters to himself,
"He was my first partner."
His family refers to "ERIC" as THE BRAND MANAGER's "friend."]

[0154.5 / 0368] [**Random skips:** DONALD TRUMP, THE CHILD, THE WEAVER, and THE DANCER.] //

⁎⁎

*Maj. = 0- THE WEAVER: #0168, 2- THE DANCER: #0161,
3- THE CHILD: #0193, 8- THE ATHEIST: #0175*
DONALD TRUMP: #0449
WILLING: #0441, #0474
SPIDER: #0653, #0728, #0779
THE BRAND MANAGER: #0245
THE EXECUTIVE PRODUCER: #0156

⁎⁎

#0155 - May 8, 2018 @ 02:52 (San Francisco, California)

[0155.1 / 0369] [I've volunteered to be a hostage. An attractive man otherwise unknown to me seems friendly, supportive, and at his insistence is a *"good confidant."* While he seems nice, I sit with a primal fear that he may snap at any moment and beat me severely. I teach meditation to my fellow prisoners as well as my captors. For many days, many sessions I'm continually treated respectfully though anticipate abuse. I can see myself being repeatedly struck in

147

the face until bloodied and split cheeked, with my teeth broken if the delicate balance is lost. The prison is white walled and well lit; its stately marble columns give the impression of a luxury atelier. My male captor's muscular, hairless legs repeatedly gain my attention as he ascends and descends a vast white marble staircase.] //

⁎

SUPPORTIVE: #0609, #0623, #0689, #0733, #0757, 0771, #0787
TEETH: #0406, #0423, #0500, #0521, #0564, #0606, #0757
RESPECT: #0433, #0527, #0638, #0656
ABUSE: #0718

⁎

#0156 - May 8, 2018 @ 06:18 (San Francisco, California)

[0156.1 / 0370] [THE EXECUTIVE PRODUCER teaches me how to use her brand-new high definition SLR camera. She provides a very thorough overview of the various display functions and features, with explicit focus on the role of light and distance from a subject play in order to capture a frame of, *"Immaculate Impact."* On the front, an arc of tiny almond shaped black buttons adorns the lens like a crown. I count nine equally spaced buttons in the arrangement.]

[0156.2 / 0371] [THE REIKI MASTER *(assertive, sharp, and self-interested)* expresses a desire to hold a group session at the nude beach, remarking that, *"if it's going to happen, he needs to make a reservation ASAP."* A crying child sits next to him at a table, who I glean is his daughter.] //

⁎

CAMERA: #0457, #0473, #0531, #0534
ASAP: #0539, #0668
ALMOND: #0411, #0573
NINE: #0568, #0621, #0755, #0756
THE REIKI MASTER: #0339
THE EXECUTIVE PRODUCER: #0238

⁎

#0157 - May 9, 2018 @ 04:30 (San Francisco, California)

[0157.1 / 0372] [I've purchased a luxury condo which occupies the entire 33rd floor of a modern tower. Floor to ceiling windows all around the perimeter offer brilliant skyline views. The space feels narrow. Unexpectedly, the entire building bends in half sending me toppling feet over my head along with sofas, chairs, and a dining room table. I think I'm going to die as I brace for impact with the ground. I'm certain a large earthquake has caused the disaster.

I survive and roll outside. When I come to a stop I look toward the building and note the structure has filled with yellow foam insulation. I determine that there was no earthquake, and that structural deficiencies in the foundation are the root cause for the collapse. The collapsed tower is the singular structure in a misty mountain region, and not the center post of a bustling urban center as I had perceived from the 33rd floor, just prior to the demolition.]

148

I place a phone call to my family to inform them I've survived the catastrophe. A chain link fence rings the footprint of the building parking lot. No vehicles are visible. I was the only person in the building when it collapsed. THE THEM (*controversial, vocal, and self-identified*) appears to my left and asks,

"Is this your new place?"

They point toward the pile of concrete rubble, broken glass, and twisted metal. We notice an entry point for an alpine coaster with two side-by-side concrete tracks. We each get in our own car and begin to leisurely descend the mountain, making light and humorous conversation as we bob and weave from top to the bottom. I have no concern, nor attachment to, the total loss of what was my short-term home.] //

⁂

EARTHQUAKE: #0674, #0787
TWISTED: #0405, #0655
URBAN: #0473, #0566, #0614, #0620, #0682
REGION: #0772, #0787

⁂

#0158 - May 9, 2019 @ 06:10 (San Francisco, California)

[0158.1 / 0373] [I'm seated in the long front row of desks in a classroom, of which there are two of equal size. We're guided through new content by advanced teachers who are skilled and artful healers. The class is disrupted by two male students of unknown age who disrobe and begin radically contorting their bodies. They scream, moan, and shout as the class is told to hold a healing vibration to support them. Other advanced students run to restrain the possessed naked men against a wall to the far-right side of the classroom. My attention and focus are challenged by their unsettling multi-tone vocalizations, wails, and caterwauling. I remind myself to ground, and in so doing note that my protection symbols instantly update. I feel total support of the school and community during this new period of rapid in-the-moment learning.]

[0158.2 / 0374] [I share a meal with THE GREGARIOUS CONSULTANT (*curious, loving, and uproariously funny*). As we converse, he repeatedly underscores a desire to move to an, *"English speaking country."* We conclude our rendezvous at precisely 10pm. Oddly, it's still bright as midday and I decide it's reasonable to call THE ANGRY SPRITE (*meticulous, erudite, and social*) to hang out. I assume he'll be available since his young sons are asleep and safe. I leave him a voicemail as I walk a narrow path between various gothic cathedrals.

The path bobs and weaves around flying buttresses positioned like zipper teeth when viewed from above. The footprints of neighboring cathedrals are staggered to allow for maximum utility and parcel zoning efficiency. Adjacent parcels have municipal land easements to accommodate trespassing buttresses. It becomes clear the large buildings are not churches, nor monoliths, but rather a sophisticated network of entities that communicate and collaborate like a family of redwood trees.] //

⁂

NARROW: #0481, #0527, #0548, #0559, #0613, #0631
CATHEDRAL: #0535, #0618, #0758, #0772

149

ZIPPER: #0436
THE ANGRY SPRITE: #0235
⁘

#0159 - May 11, 2018 @ 04:50 (San Francisco, California)

[0159.1 / 0375] [I'm on the side of a winding country highway. It's late morning, sunny, blue-skied and dryly warm. An occasional breeze wafts the scent of freshly trimmed grass, making waves in the waist high golden wheat, across fields which seemingly extend forever. The road is one lane, has no shoulder, and is made from stony gravel. A classic 1950's convertible with pistachio green paint, art deco seats, and whitewall tires that was transporting me and my pals (THE LANDSCAPE ARCHITECT, THE FIDUCIARY, THE REFLECTION, and THE PUBLIC MEDIUM) has stalled out. None of us are put off by this. THE PUBLIC MEDIUM scrolls through a haberdashery site on his phone while paying modest attention to an open book in his lap.

THE FIDUCIARY and THE REFLECTION get out of the car, walk to the field and hold each other's wrists hand-over-hand as they face each other and begin to spin. They maintain uninterrupted eye contact and spin quicker and quicker until they lose balance, topple over, and out of view. Odd cat-human purring sounds occasionally are heard between breezy whistles.

THE LANDSCAPE ARCHITECT sits with his back against the door of the car reading from a book of poetry that dynamically generates stanzas based on his prevailing thought. He co-creates with the book, pausing momentarily to supplement the current work with a turn of phrase meant to be, *"exclusive."*

I notice a line of traffic emerge behind the stalled vehicle and attempt to reroute cars to a non-existent, *"other lane."* I ask THE LANDSCAPE ARCHITECT to generate a poetic verse composed primarily of, *"inclusive phrases."* He nods, obliges, and instantly traffic begins to move again. Our stalled, blockage of a car becomes non-solid and holographic, which allows the traffic behind to move through without incident. A person driving through honks his horn at us, screaming aggressively in an unkind tone. He's much larger than me, is missing several teeth, and chews a cigar stump stained red by his diseased and bloody gums. I stand in front of him in a compassionate confrontation. He grins menacingly and bellows in a low dark resonant tone,

"WHO'S MISSING KINDNESS?"

He's a mirror. I'm speaking to a direct reflection of myself.]

[0159.2 / 0376] [My alarm jolts me from sleep. I run out the door to teach a 6am fitness class.]
//

⁘

Maj. = 9- THE FIDUCIARY: #0180, 18- THE PUBLIC MEDIUM: #0169
CONVERTIBLE: #0610, #0698, #0726
POETRY: #0052, #0547, #0662, #0849, #0850, #0969
THE LANDSCAPE ARCHITECT: #0164
THE REFLECTION: #0323
⁘

#0160 - May 12, 2018 @ 06:28 (San Francisco, California)

[0160.1 / 0377] [Abstract impression of a golden lattice, woven from *"infinite gossamer mandalas."* Pulses of light blip through the network like whizzing pachinko balls. Eventually the gold light begins to stratify into wireframes that become the background for dream narrative.]

[0160.2 / 0378] [I'm on a bus tour, but I'm unaware of the path, point of origin, and destination. Light accordion music with French lyrics fill the space at low volume, infusing the environment with a sense of levity and ease. After a time, it becomes clear I'm on a mission to survey brick and mortar locations for new stores. I'm able to find a space that meets all requirements and can immediately accommodate a new tenant. The warehouse space has been taken down to studs, but some leftover pieces of furniture from the prior occupant remain.

"How will I move that large circular rug?" I contemplate, pulling back an edge to reveal a subfloor with sodden, chalky sheetrock that flakes away like feta.

I notice another corner of the space where the floor has been similarly torn up.

Nearby a woman sells single, golf ball sized spheres of lapis lazuli, intended to be strung in strands of beads. Most of them are priced at $295 each. I consider them to be beautiful, yet vastly overpriced. She knows their value and holds her price point steady while I attempt to negotiate. Onlookers speak excitedly under their breath to one another in French. //

⁎⁎

ACCORDION: #0528
FRENCH: #0683, #0695, #0781
GOLF: #0478, #0691
BEADS: #0435

⁎⁎

#0161 - May 13, 2018 @ 05:26 (San Francisco, California)

[0161.1 / 0379] [I'm in a Van Gogh-esque night scene standing around a large cauldron and satisfied as I inspect a leopard pelt that's been dyed silver. The black spots are not colored by the dye, as was expected. Starlight playfully bounces off, causing it to magically shimmer.]

[0161.2 / 0380] [I'm late to an appointment where I'm expected to teach a yoga class in a basement. THE DANCER and I discuss and determine the class started late due to an electronic miscommunication.]

[0161.3 / 0381] [Unclear abstractions of writing cursive scripts on placards for dessert foods, while disrespecting police officers without any context.] //

⁎⁎

Maj. = 2- THE DANCER: #0170
DESSERT: #0406, #0617, #0734, #0775

APPOINTMENT: #0441, #0468, #0496, #0658, #0722
SCRIPT: #0426, #0484, #0614, #0672
⁂

#0162 - May 13, 2018 @ 06:51 (San Francisco, California)

[**0162.1 / 0382**] [I wait at a graffiti tagged bus stop with THE GENIUS, who confidently suggests he's an, *"intellectual and curious trickster."* I alternatively declare myself a *"NEO-LUDDITE."* He yawns and stretches to indicate my comments are elementary and boring. It's night. The bus stop is lit by street lights. The bus never arrives.]

[**0162.2 / 0383**] [I'm in a neighborhood that feels like 8th Ave. North in Fort Dodge, Iowa. When I look around, I realize I'm in the Mission district of San Francisco. Houses have sprawling emerald green lawns, watered by in-ground sprinkler systems that irrigate in artful sequences choreographed to classical music. I turn a corner onto an urban plaza where a production crew films a music video. Camera grips, gaffers, the director, and many others prepare the set for the artist. Across the plaza are bleachers filled with row upon row of fans who film the filming with their camera phones.

I become excited when I realize I've stumbled across DONALD GLOVER creating his next work of genius pop art. I've left my phone at home. DONALD glances up at me, and our eyes meet. I flash him a peace sign with my right hand. He smirks and gives me a wink. I begin to levitate and fly above the city back towards my house. I observe the video being filmed from above using a single long shot. The other actors all hold unique static poses as DONALD dances among them, as though time has stopped. Perhaps he and I are moving together at tremendous speed? I notice all San Francisco street signs (*white background, black block letters*) have the first two letters blurred out with hashtags (##URCH, ##LORES, etc.). This characteristic stays present for the duration of my levitation.]

[**0162.3 / 0384**] [I'm on a bus where I observe rows of shoes. I turn around and discover myself standing in the caboose of a rickety old train. The train chugs, clicks, clangs and occasionally whistles as it rolls along. I paint the caboose walls gold, to cover flaking red paint on the dry rotted wood. I understand a pair of shoes equals a dead body. DONALD GLOVER pops his head in the side door of the train car to check in. I assure him death doesn't bother me. It's a sunny day. Blue sky above. Green hills roll by. I keep painting the walls gold, occasionally wanting to be an extra in the video from [**0162.2 / 0383**], though I know that job would likely kill me and my shoes would be left in the ever-growing row. For now, I'd rather live.] //

⁂
DONALD GLOVER: #0200
IOWA: #0428, #0501, #0776, #0787
DEAD BODIES: #410, #0452, #0466, #0567
SHOES: #0415, #0441, #0445, #0467, #0504, #0653, #0667, #0790
THE GENIUS: #0224
⁂

#0163 - May 14, 2018 @ 04:20 (San Francisco, California)

[**0163.1 / 0385**] [I'm on Buckingham Drive in Charlotte, North Carolina. THE JESTER has a petite girlfriend who boasts a gorgeous head of big frizzy grey hair. It's house cleaning day. We turn up the rugs inside which leaves a thin layer of dust on table surfaces and glass countertops. Numerous bolts of regal fabrics rest on the dining room table. I grab a dirty sock to use as a dust rag. I start to wipe around the fabric bolts but stop when THE JESTER notices my technique. I feel embarrassed.

"I get to run the flagship store in Atlanta for two days," THE JESTER says, suggesting it's a path to prove himself qualified for a large promotion. He continues as we clean, *"We can make ends meet, paying 40% of what I was making. They cut my rate. That's enough talk about freelance consulting."*

We set our cleaning supplies down and walk together to the gallery to contemplate various works of art precisely and lovingly installed on 13-foot solid gold walls. THE JESTER, his girlfriend, and I each keep equal space between us as we silently observe the paintings. A small square table in the center of the room presents a rectangular glass vase that holds a smattering of charred roots and vines assembled into a morbid bouquet.

"Scout's honor," I whisper in the girlfriend's ear, drawing forth from her a small peek of a smile.

THE JESTER and his girlfriend begin whistling in harmony. The whistles suggest they're counting down together from 10 to zero in their unique musical code. As the tones descend in frequency to the beautifully apparent *(and sternum rumbling low)* "zero" I hear a voice say *"FOCUS!"* so loudly between my ears that it jolts me from dreaming to instantly awake and smiling.] //

⁑

Min. = ◆*- THE JESTER: #0188*
GREY HAIR: #0608
GALLERY: #0414, #0421, #0496, #0523, #0540, #0567, #0792
FOCUS: #0468, #0523 #0528, #0676, #0682, #0783
HOUSE CLEANING: #0502, #0671, #0700

⁑

#0164 - May 15, 2018 @ 04:55 (San Francisco, California)

[**0164.1 / 0386**] [THE LANDSCAPE ARCHITECT's on walkabout in a foreign country.]

[**0164.2 / 0387**] [A group of vacationing women decide to go home. They pack up and depart the woodland property a night before scheduled.]

[**0164.3 / 0388**] [Lovers hold hands and ice skate together.]

[**0164.4 / 0389**] [I see a student loan billing statement. The payers don't want me to know their outstanding balance is $1.7MM.] //

⁑

LOVERS: #0607
VACATION: #0701, #0725, #0746, #0775
LOAN: #0698
THE LANDSCAPE ARCHITECT: #0223

⁑

#0165 - May 16, 2018 @ 01:15 (San Francisco, California)

[0165.1 / 0390] [Image of a thin black line segment on a stark white background.]

[0165.2 / 0391] [I practice running energy in a supernatural environment. Other beings and energies are present as I practice. THE NUN may be sitting with the group as a receiver tuned to tones of "Holy Spirit" and "Divine Feminine." The "high frequency" room is considered special by all present.] //

☆☆

Min. = ♦- *THE NUN: #0166*
HIGH FREQUENCY: #0781
SPECIAL: #0405, #0406, #0412, #0472, #0517

☆☆

#0166 - May 16, 2018 @ 04:54 (San Francisco, California)

[0166.1 / 0392] [I enter a gateway to dream state and confirm _____ with *"the other."* THE NUN remains present. I continue to practice running energy and sit in a state of deep meditation. I oscillate in and out of an awareness of my connection to the Creator. I deepen the connection by updating and signing my contract with it.] //

☆☆

Min. = ♦- *THE NUN: #0236*
GATEWAY: #0655
THE OTHER: #0749, #0775, #0777, #0787, #0792, #0798, #0799

☆☆

#0167 - May 16, 2018 @ 06:15 (San Francisco, California)

[0167.1 / 0393] [A dinner party takes place in a small room with a very large black square table. The husband *(head of household)* is seated on a side identified by placard as the *"head of the table."* He swirls a glass of wine without a plate of food in front of him. To his left, his wife and adult daughter dine and make quiet conversation.]

[0167.2 / 0394] [I'm seated at a cafe sipping tea and writing. Up a curvy smooth ramp, I think I see THE ACTOR seated at a table facing away from me. Rather than investigate I return to my task. The scene is well lit. The tone is flat and neutral.]

[0167.3 / 0395] [Seated on the carpeted floor of a tech startup office *(in a basement)*, I spread out a number of storyboard sketches. I'm with similarly aged male and female friends who I experience as *"trendy"* and *"current."* We've come together to author a book. *"What's more interesting? A) A story about diamonds, or B) _____?"*
A binary criteria assessment process goes on for some time. The language in the conversation is structured with the lilt and playfulness of a Dr. Seuss book.] //

⁂

Maj. = 10- THE ACTOR: #0212
DINNER PARTY: #0561, #0724
DIAMONDS: #0472
TRENDY: #0749

⁂

#0168 - May 17, 2018 @ 04:00 (San Francisco, California)

[0168.1 / 0396] [I travel through a subway station with a French film director. We move briskly to a small slot in a wall we discover to be a nondescript doorway and fall backwards one at a time away from a clamoring star struck public who approach us with cameras held like rifles. He and I descend to a lit lower level, but I don't see any readily identifiable light source. The entire area is smooth, shiny, and has the look of an urban skate park. The area by the doorway is just out of reach, slippery, and too steep to claw our way up to exit. From where we stand it looks like we're in the barrel of a cresting concrete wave. The director and I stand casually with hands in pockets and hoodies upturned, making conversation while observing single random objects and mailed packages descend the chute.]

[0168.2 / 0397] [I work as a union laborer, breaking down a set and stage after a large special event. In the process of dismantling a tall series of white rectangular cupboards I spot a cylindrical translucent tub of red Twizzlers candy. I peek to both sides before deciding to stuff my mouth and pockets full of the waxy sugary braids. I attempt to take as much as I can, as inconspicuous as possible. I walk to the staff cafeteria and have a friendly encounter with THE CARPENTER. As I advance through the line, food requests ahead of me are flung at those who've made orders, causing customers to duck and scramble. Splatters and splotches on the wall compel me to adapt my order before I speak. I select dry stock items: Beans, Lentils, flour, wait FLOUR?! *"I've made a mistake,"* I say just before being quickly slogged in the face with a big white **POOF!**]

[0168.3 / 0398] [I'm in the passenger seat of a car driven by THE GUITARIST. We're in a rush and hastily take an exit off the freeway he considers a shortcut. We pass by a residential construction zone where many single-family homes and duplexes have frames composed predominantly of steel plating. It's dusky and THE GUITARIST waxes uncharacteristically philosophical. He makes many remarks that I want to remember and apply to my own life, but he offers a non-sequitur that disrupts my memory: *"This is where they let the kids out to take a dump."* We laugh and drive out of the construction zone.]

[0168.4 / 0399] [I'm in line at customs, where numerous border patrol agents make thorough and paced inspections. Each of my items is removed from my bag and set on separate trays. Among my things is a JFK half dollar and an oversized Sacajawea gold dollar that gleams as the intense fluorescent light from overhead strikes its obverse. I begin the process fully compliant, though this shifts when I realize that my inspected items will not be returned. I slow my pace, and eventually completely stop removing items from my bag. I complain and protest, *"NO! YOU WON'T KEEP MY PHONE!"*]

[0168.5 / 0400] [I'm in drag. I wear white platform boots which match my hip length wig. THE WEAVER approves of my purple vinyl corset.] //

⁂

Maj. = 0- THE WEAVER: #0169, 1- THE CARPENTER: #0169
Min. = ♣- THE GUITARIST: #0274
CONSTRUCTION: #0404, #0405, #0418, #0429, #0437, #0533, #0561
WIG: #0568, #0653, #0708

⁂

#0169 - May 17, 2018 @ 07:44 (San Francisco, California)

[0169.1 / 0401] [I teach a yoga class.]
[0169.2 / 0402] [Numerous concurrent narratives confuse me. I move out of the basement level of a multi-level woodland house. Only a few boxes of my personal belongings are left in the basement, which are randomly scattered around. I've decided to take a road trip with two young women I meet as I move out. We determine that a trip to their parent's house would take eight hours. The car is fully packed and I'm unsure how I'm going to get all my remaining stuff inside. I notice THE WEAVER doing household chores and mowing the lawn. From a box of random objects, I pull a CD out of a paper sleeve and see a title: "DISC 4 - THE BAPTIST FAITH" written across it in black sharpie pen. I recognize the handwriting as THE CARPENTER's. This discovery seems important.

A long basement passage acts as an escape route from the house. I pass THE PUBLIC MEDIUM's bedroom, which has a bed with a live tree for a headboard growing through the wall. The dense winding limbs and greenery are flanked by a wall filled with panels of highly intricate Shipibo icaro medicine weavings. While in the passage I encounter two beings I'm convinced I know as "KIKO" and "CHRIS." I'm confused because I think they're married, but they are not. "CHRIS" is Asian. "KIKO" is Caucasian. They agree I recently met their daughter and put together sets of pressed steel dog tags on neck chains at THE RUBY's *(powerful, rational, and feminine)* home. I give them hugs and sprint towards a door.

I encounter the escape passage "Gatekeeper." He identifies himself by showing me his artist profile on Spotify. He's satisfied his latest release has been streamed 400,000 times on the first day. I expect him to challenge me to leave the house and basement, but he doesn't. The box I'm carrying has a series of notebooks full of musical compositions. I spill out onto a parking lot where the contents of a moving van are emptied onto a curb. Many synthesizers and amplifiers are scattered incoherently around the parking lot. All are out of their cases and exposed. I contemplate taking one, then recall my car is full.

I drive with the two women through an area that feels like the Argentinian steppe. The car winds through the area, ripe with waist-high brown grasses. Estate homes near the road seem significant, though I'm unable to recall their architectural details.] //

⁂

Maj. = 0- THE WEAVER: #0181, 1- THE CARPENTER: #0181,
18- THE PUBLIC MEDIUM: #0176
SYNTHESIZER: #0438, #0515
CURB: #0768
THE RUBY: #0306

⁂

#0170 - May 18, 2018 @ 06:40 (San Francisco, California)

[0170.1 / 0403] [*Soul music plays in the background* I visit a male inmate on death row. I reach through the jail cell bars to hold hands with him. I'm effortlessly pulled through the bars into the cell, then the two of us are instantly transported to the interior of a car. We continue to hold hands as he moves towards me to kiss. We make out for a while. He becomes increasingly aggressive. It begins pleasurably, but I decide I don't want to have sex. He rapes me. I'm not certain of my sex or gender identity in this scene.]

[0170.2 / 0404] [I'm with THE DANCER in the lobby of a Vegas hotel. "CASH ONLY" signs are predominantly displayed as we walk together past a very long unstaffed concierge desk. The walls are a unique teal tone offset by tall cream-colored Corinthian columns. The opposing wall has large dark brocade draperies suspended from a ceiling so high I can't see where it peaks. Another feature of this vintage hotel is its antique store. THE DANCER and I pause momentarily to look in the window, then ultimately decide not to enter.

We spill out onto the strip at night. The roads are very wide and filled with cars driving in both directions. THE DANCER departs and I find myself in the gravel lot of a gas station at sunrise. A beautiful black sports car pulls up to a pump. The gravel beneath the car transforms to pavement as it passes over. THE AESTHETE (candid, somatic, and beauty loving) and THE FASHIONISTA (humorous, committed, and stylish) emerge from the vehicle and open the trunk. They discuss how to best organize bags for their day trip to the beach. We playfully chat as they fuel up the car.]

[0170.3 / 0405] [I'm in an abandoned mall, moving briskly past dilapidated retail spaces. I cross an area which has row on row of dust laden stacks of banquet chairs. They have been out of service for many years. I chew on mouthfuls of white Tic Tac breath mints, crunching and releasing sugar crystals of breath freshening dust across my soft palate. I pass through areas that may have had former lives as car repair shops, taking cues from abandoned auto-lifts and rusty gasoline signs affixed to the walls.]

[0170.4 / 0406] [I find myself entering a theater. I'm handed a playbill and seated on a side of a large square space outlined on the floor with masking tape. A being sits behind me. I'm fairly certain it takes the shape of a large framed woman. She places her hands on my shoulders and neck, which I initially consider odd. I accept that she wants to give me a massage and receive it.]

[0170.5 / 0407] [THE CONTRAST JUNKIE (playful, flirty, and soulful) takes me on a tour of his new rental home. The large building is familiar. I've been here in other dreams. As we walk from floor to floor, I sense that this was (or perhaps still is) THE PHILANTHROPIST's home. We duck back down a hidden staircase to the kitchen where THE CONTRAST JUNKIE confidently declares,

"Six-bedroom house for $5K per month. Pretty good deal!"

While the space is palatial, each room grand and more inviting than the next, I'm particularly taken by an onyx staircase and a unique pool table with black and blue marbled felt.

Large presentations of flowers in grand vases sit atop round marble tables. Small silver speakers, mounted in a rhombus diamond pattern around the perimeter of the room, create an immersive surround sound experience visually observable from the exterior patio of the property.

THE CONTRAST JUNKIE and I bounce between the interior and exterior of the home instantly, multiple times. It's unclear if the sun rises or sets, but light outside is limited. A large tarnished copper avatar of Shiva slowly dances on top of one of the marble tables in one of the home's many atriums.] //

*
**

Maj. = 2- THE DANCER: #0177
SIX: #0534, #0563, #0671, #0672
JAIL: #0406, #0467, #0467, #0724
PERIMETER: #0446, #0520, #0561, #0583, #0669, #0799
(But what does it all mean?)
THE PHILANTHROPIST: #0249
THE AESTHETE: #0384
THE FASHIONISTA: #1228
*
**

#0171 - May 19, 2018 @ 01:30 (San Francisco, California)
This dream did all it could be ignored and forgotten

[0171.1 / 0408] [I ring the doorbell to a penthouse residence. CATHY BESSANT *(authoritative, discerning, and direct)* greets me at the door. She's generously taken me on as an apprentice, but I feel resistance even as she shows me to my new luxury accommodations. I familiarize myself with the home as CATHY begins her daily routine.

She suggests we take breakfast in the restaurant, where upon our entrance she and I are the only two diners in a space set for 100+ guests. A single elevated table behind a velvet rope is where CATHY is accustomed to taking her morning meals. The use of the space seems inefficient and wasteful.

We speak of strategy, cultivable leadership qualities, and a variety of other topics before she swiftly moves to a lectern where dozens of microphones and hands holding recorders thrust towards her through a portal. She calmly and dutifully responds to each query in her preferred sequence.

As I observe her, I feel a sense of compassion and appreciation for her ability to weather the court of public opinion, and the low-level drama that endemically lurks within her enormous global team.

I understand the spacious restaurant and living quarters are essential features that load level the burden commensurate with leading the backend of a worldwide enterprise.] //

*
**
CATHY BESSANT: #0950
OPINION: #0483, #0496, #0754
MICROPHONES: #0416, #0455, #0789
BURDEN: #0531
*
**

#0172 - May 19, 2018 @ 02:56 (San Francisco, California)

[0172.1 / 0409] [*NIGHTMARE* I'm a woman with long straight hair. I discover myself in the backyard of a large single-family home in the middle of the night. I'm covered in blood, so much so that my hair is thick and feels like it's weighed down with a gallon of red paint. The back door of the house is ajar. I hear a stereo system blast music within. All the interior and exterior lights on the house are warmly illuminated. A washer-dryer, microwave, and dishwasher whirr and add to the ambient noise pollution.

I go back inside. I don't know how wretched my actions have been, but I start to remember I've done some really sinister things here. A neighboring family of evangelical revivalists knock on the front door with an exclamatory,

"HELL-OOOOOOOO!"

A husband and wife enter with two teenage sons and a toddler daughter held under the husband's left arm. So engrossed in their proselytizing, they fail to observe I'm covered head to toe in sanguine coagulation. I excuse myself to take a shower, and focus on scrubbing off all the blood from my skin. As I wash, I'm interrupted by intermittent flashes of light, static ohms, and glimpses of me slaughtering and dismembering members of the *(now former)* household. The dead are familiar to me. Perhaps they were my family? The recollections become so strong and visceral I collapse in the shower vomit all over myself.

Still naked and wet from the shower, spots of pink watercolor drip from my body and splatter on the hardwood floors as I walk. The well intending family downstairs will eventually realize what's happened here. To prevent them notifying the authorities, I systematically murder them one at a time. I don't recall how I do it, but I have the sense I treated the God espousing mother in a particularly savage manner. I get a glimpse into each of the five cruel demises. Once I've witnessed myself commit every murder, I fling both arms overhead and scream,

"IT WAS ME! I DID IT! I'M GUILTY!"

Upon acceptance of my culpability, I'm transported from the house to the Roman Colosseum for an evening performance with the souls of the family whose lives I've just ended. The family is seated next to me in a row. Both young men are closeted homosexuals.

"You're gay," I tell them plainly.

They both yawn and are disinterested. I'm not telling them anything they don't already know. The elder of the two winks at me and tells me he, *"has a nine-inch dick."* I'm put off by his proposition because he's under the legal age of consent. Not dissuaded, he ups the ante by espousing tales of prior sexual exploits particularly keen for one where he alleges he was, *"a preferred fuckboy of BARACK OBAMA's."*

The performance becomes audience interactive. We're encouraged to move about the amphitheater to search for artifacts. In an underground maze we find the Holy Grail *(simple, clay, and ordinary)*. The father wants to steal it, specifically because he believes it's made of, *"priceless 100% asbestos."* The surrounding area beneath the Colosseum remains damp, dark and mysterious.] //

⁎⁎

BARACK OBAMA: #1001
NIGHTMARE: #0406, #0518, #0519
MURDER: #0406, #0452, #0467, #0518, #0682, #0724, #0800
DRIP: #0428, #0439, #0461

⁎⁎

⁂

PART 4 - STRANGE BEDFELLOWS

#0173 - #0228

"Stars fading, but I linger on, dear
Still craving your kiss
I longing to linger to dawn, dear
Just saying this
Sweet dreams 'till sunbeams find you
Sweet dreams that leave all your worries behind you
But in your dreams whatever they be
Dream a little dream of me."

-Gus Kahn

* * *

May 19, 2018 - July 4, 2018

⁂

#0173 - May 19, 2018 @ 08:15 (San Francisco, California)

[0173.1 / 0410] [I'm in a ceremony with THE HEALER. I'm served food on a round white paper plate. I'm intoxicated to such an extent that I must sit down as I eat. Nearby in a wood-land area, young men wearing leather harnesses play with and pleasure one another on rows of massage tables. I stumble by a young guy who has passed out on the ground. I pause to ask if he's ok. He gives a barely coherent nod, then plants his face back in the leafy mud.]

[0173.2 / 0411] [I'm drunk and attempting to cook in a condo kitchen on Divisadero Street. THE LAWYER orders Chinese food while I prepare my dinner. THE LAWYER asks me not to drink his bottle of Grand Marnier. He points to a small flask on a shared nightstand between our two twin extra-long beds. The recipe I'm working from requires four table-spoons of oil. I drunkenly misread it as "four cups," an amount I pour liberally into a clear Pyrex dish. I add four tablespoons of balsamic vinegar to the oil, which retracts into hundreds of tiny dark globes and mandalas suspended in the golden amber liquid.

I place a square skillet over a gas burner and pour the disintegrated liquid suspension on it until it overflows the edges. It spills beyond the edge of the pan, off the stove and pools on the floor behind the appliance. I crawl behind the stove onto a gangplank (*wide enough for me to go completely behind the range*) and spend time dutifully mopping up the mess I've made.

Once finished, I drunkenly stumble back to the bedroom and drink a little more as a reward for tidying up. I'm roused from sleep by a ringing phone. THE LAWYER leaves a second message regarding his Grand Marnier. I notice the empty bottle in the trash. I drank it. I go to a convenience store intending to replace it and pass THE PASSIONATE BRAZILIAN (*quiet, sweet, and statuesque*) and his male companion.] //

⁂

Maj. = 5- *THE LAWYER: #0180*, 20- *THE HEALER: #0200*
INTOXICATED: #0748
FOUR: #0498, #0548, #0554, #0556
THE PASSIONATE BRAZILIAN: #0489

⁂

#0174 - May 21, 2018 @ 06:06 (San Francisco, California)

[0174.1 / 0412] [I spend the entire dream undermining JANE KIM, San Francisco City Supervisor in her bid to become Mayor. I'm a regular and vocal dissenter at her public forums. I write strong negative op-eds in the local papers. I'm conscious of the fact I don't know her, nor her legislative record. Another dream within this dream is lost.] //

⁂

WRITE: #0408 #0450, #0453, #0492
LOST: #0636, #0688, #0732, #0759

⁂

#0175 - May 22, 2018 @ 05:44 (San Francisco, California)

[0175.1 / 0413] [Somehow, I've befriended MIKE PATTON *(genius, creative, and quick witted)*. He and I hang out at his giant studio-loft-penthouse. We decide to create something new and, *"as yet unknown to auditory and visual domains."* MIKE works very quickly. When not creating, he becomes agitated and violent. It's night. Dirty clothing and furniture are messily scattered about the loft. I'm a bit overwhelmed by spending time with my childhood hero. I distract myself by texting THE ATHEIST and other friends to confirm I'm actually doing what I think I'm doing. I manage to get grounded and tell MIKE,
"You know, when I was a boy, I saw you climb the rafters and into the stage fan on the Saturday Night Live set. That really inspired me."
He grins appreciatively and calls for "Naomi." A woman enters. It's unclear if she's a friend, a lover, or the compound concierge. The three of us start looking at real estate online and find a spacious ranch property in New England that we each love equally. We make a low-ball offer of $430,000.]

[0175.2 / 0414] [I'm drunk and sit with my butt out the passenger side window of a 1970's model car at a demolition derby. I grip the top of the car and wildly wave my other arm over-head like a bull rider. Many recognizable faces in the crowd ask me to blast OZZY OSBOURNE songs over the track sound system from my phone. I pick songs I'm familiar with, but my selections fall flat with the crowd. I'm particularly excited when I rediscover "Mr. Tinkertrain" and stream it. I glance up with one eye open. My teeth trap my tongue as I attempt to focus and scroll through a list of tracks, in search of "Mama I'm Coming Home."]

[0175.3 / 0415] [Cats knock over a bowl of Gatorade. It spills on the carpet. I notice this from another room, as I'm roused from dream sleep by the smell of cat shit. A pile of odiferous feces on the floor reeks a foot away from my head as I continue sleeping.] //

✲✲

Maj. = 8- THE ATHEIST: #0226
MIKE PATTON: #0989
REAL ESTATE: #0637, #0665
1970: #0635, #0687, #0716

✲✲

#0176 - May 23, 2018 @ 07:02 (San Francisco, California)

[0176.1 / 0416] [I meet a being named "STEVE" from Florida. THE PUBLIC MEDIUM and I both have prurient interests in him. "STEVE" from Florida is large, muscular, and gives us each an endearing, sweaty, musky hug as we stand together on an elevated iron beam. Plat-forms split off at the end of the iron walkway at multiple irrational trans-dimensional angles.]

[0176.2 / 0417] [A chakra anointment ceremony on a college campus commences as students pack up their belongings in front of the student union. Boxes are stacked everywhere. People move in a single file line through a crowded hallway. A female healer suggests planting an, *"anointment of chocolate on the third chakra."* I try to decide whether to wear the blue shirt for "Joe's" wedding, or the custom vest I wore at THE ROBOT and THE RAPTOR's nuptials.] //

⁂

Maj. = 18- THE PUBLIC MEDIUM: #0241
Min. = ♥- *THE ROBOT: #0251,* ♦- *THE RAPTOR: #0306*
FLORIDA: #0566
CHAKRA: #0493, #0586, #0771
STUDENT UNION: #0427

⁂

#0177 - May 24, 2018 @ 03:58 (San Francisco, California)

[0177.1 / 0418] [THE DANCER and I wash bath towels at a laundromat.]

[0177.2 / 0419] [PRINCE performs a new song, clad head to toe in purple velvet. He pauses between songs, offering to polish and remaster his opening act's debut album. He makes this offer while onstage in the round. Members of the opening act are in the crowd, initially taken off guard by the impromptu offer. They decline. Hissing dissent from the crowd surrounds them. PRINCE smirks, leans in to the microphone, and with voice modified with a synthesizer simply says, *"Fuck 'em."* The crowd erupts in applause.]

[0177.3 / 0420] [I wash bundles of small purple towels, then wrap them in plastic film.]

[0177.4 / 0421] ["THE PERFORMER" requests a snack of small gnocchi sized dumplings made from ricotta cheese wrapped in an ultra-thin rice paper film. The film sticks to itself and is rolled into a small dense nugget that takes focus to unpeel and separate before creating the cheese dumplings. My tongue sticks out between my teeth as I try to peel off layers one at a time.] //

⁂

Maj. = 2- THE DANCER: #0186
PRINCE: #0358
PURPLE: #0459, #0481, #0498, #0548
RICE: #0575, #0613

⁂

#0178 - May 25, 2018 @ 01:40 (San Francisco, California)

[0178.1 / 0422] [At 12:40am exactly, I'm awakened by "The Four Founders" who take turns talking through my body.] //

⁂

AWAKE: #0564, #0585, #0649, #0765
BODY: #0781, #0786
EXACT: #0612

⁂

#0179 - May 26, 2018 @ 08:47 (San Francisco, California)

[0179.1 / 0423] [THE KIND HEART and a group of guys stand in a circle in a white room comparing their new colorful soccer kits. Their joint unspoken agreement is: *"Wait for THE PILOT."*] //

⁑

Maj = 6- THE PILOT: #0180, 21-THE KIND HEART: #0181
WAIT: #0401, #0450, #0471

⁑

#0180 - May 28, 2018 @ 02:00 (San Francisco, California)

[0180.1 / 0424] [THE LAWYER surprises me when he returns early from his trip to the Tetons.]

[0180.2 / 0425] [THE FIDUCIARY begins a primary partnership with a conspicuous consumer and goes deeply into debt. I'm annoyed and don't hesitate to verbalize my grievances.]

[0180.3 / 0426] [THE PILOT and I make uninterrupted eye contact as we fill four ovular containers with hot red liquid Jell-O. Two of the vessels have small rectangular slits where the liquid would ordinarily run through and spill on to the floor. We've made preparations where a two-inch layer of Jell-O has already been poured and cooled to prevent this from happening. Our agreement is to fill all the containers with hot liquid at the same time. Our preparation was reasonable, and conformed to "the rules." The fresh hot liquid melts the top layers of solid Jell-O in the two punctured vessels, but no mess results.]

[0180.4 / 0427] [I hold my space as a strong transmission is translated to English in the center of my head: *"THERE ARE 10,000 OF US ON THIS PLANET."* I don't know who they are.] //

⁑

Maj. = 5- THE LAWYER: #0194, 6- THE PILOT: #0181, 9- THE FIDUCIARY: #0181
JELL-O: #0407

⁑

#0181 - May 28, 2018 @ 04:00 (San Francisco, California)
*Supporting detail instantly fades from these vignettes. *

[0181.1 / 0428] [THE KIND HEART and THE PILOT throw a party. Many women attend. Floor plans for condos are presented holographically in small clouds of dark black smoke above numerous round white linen draped cocktail tables. Great interest from the women turns to the contents of a collection of elaborate and detailed journals set on a nearby table.]

. . .

165

[0181.2 / 0429] [THE FIDUCIARY is in an annoying relationship, which transfers to annoyance in our friendship. We stroll down the streets of London at night. He only responds to questions and conversation with single letters of the alphabet. He asks questions in a similar way. *"A?" "B?" "F?" "J?" "Q?"* He complains he has no one hot to fuck. When I say I'd fuck him, he runs away.]

[0181.3 / 0430] [I'm a 10-year-old boy on a tour of Buckingham Palace. I'm with my family. As we descend a grand marble staircase with red velvet carpet, we pass THE QUEEN OF eNGLAND, who pauses as we advance. She wears a white glove on her right hand to keep a buffer between herself and the few hands she shakes. At the bottom of the staircase a gift shop prominently displays a tall rectangular curio cabinet. My attention is drawn to a small square silver frame. I'm surprised to see a thumbprint sized photo of my family within.]

[0181.4 / 0431] [THE WEAVER and I have a conversation as we leisurely cross the street. THE WEAVER and I are not in a rush, but cautious to the possibility of traffic approaching from either direction. The scene occurs as part suburbia, part rural desert highway on a hot sunny day. We discuss THE CARPENTER's wellbeing. He's out of work again, though has his sights set on attending a retreat in Mexico to figure out what he's supposed to do next.] //

⁂

Maj. = 0- THE WEAVER: #0183, 1- THE CARPENTER: #0206, 6- THE PILOT: #0194,
9-THE FIDUCIARY: #0205, 20-THE KIND HEART: # 0232
THE QUEEN OF ENGLAND: #0182
GIFT SHOP: #0428, #0748
RURAL: #0557, #0776

⁂

#0182 - May 28, 2018 @ 05:51 (San Francisco, California)

[0182.1 / 0432] [*Torture and Brutality* A group of teenage friends have stolen a bag of goods from me. Of the five items in the bag, the only one I can recall is a black shower towel. I knock on the door of a housing project apartment, playfully at first, then become increasingly angry. THE GANG BANGER (*immature, incompetent, and hopeless*) opens the door and attempts to distract me. I force my way in and spot my stolen white bag on the counter. After an awkward pause, the group of teens erupts in laughter. It's night time. I begin to sequentially serve the teens severe individual beatings, each more intense and violent than the prior. They don't run, though they could to avoid the impending oppressive pain.

I hit one of the guys so hard his lower jaw dislodges and bursts through his cheek. He winces, but continues laughing with a flap of unsupported skin drooping and gushing blood. His head hangs forward as he leans into the rope I've used to bind his arms behind his back. The beatings escalate. Once sufficiently pummeled, I grab a broom and begin sweeping up what I notice is a very dusty floor. As I move from corners, under tables, to the center of the room I sweep numerous pilfered passports into a pile. I pick one up to review it, noting it's a document (Jordanian) belonging to THE PAGE (*meek, sensitive, and curious*). THE QUEEN OF ENGLAND neutrally observes the entire situation unfold and holds a stoic pose midway up a staircase.] //

⁂
THE QUEEN OF ENGLAND: #0573
GANG: #0712, #0773
PASSPORT: #0765, #0798
⁂

#0183 - May 29, 2018 @ 06:09 (San Francisco, California)

[0183.1 / 0433] [I'm in a giant cathedral full of movie props. I live in this "set dresser's church" which is unnecessarily over furnished. Furniture is stacked atop furniture. The small town where the church is located is extremely poor. Most residents are homeless. Those with homes don't have any furniture in them, which is odd because there's enough in this one house to furnish every other home many times over.

SERJ TANKARIAN, FRANK ZAPPA and I hang out for a while then decide to write a song about JESUS CHRIST on acoustic guitars. After completing the composition, we duck down a narrow back stairwell, climbing over and between stacks of boxes until we arrive in a church buffet line. The three of us each get a tray of food and move together towards a table where a middle-aged woman dressed in 1950's noir wear offers us oversized vitamin pills that have an overpowering and pungent lemon odor. I decline the vitamin. THE WEAVER is running late. She quickly grabs a banana and departs without stopping to talk to us.]

[0183.2 / 0434] [I'm in the desert with DAVID LEE ROTH. He's dressed in a red sequin singlet. He disappears. A black limo drives toward me kicking up a trail of dust. DAVID now wears a black feather boa and leans out the window flailing his arms as he sings loudly. I laugh my ass off at the sight of him rolling by.] //

⁂
Maj. = 0- THE WEAVER: #0187
JESUS: #0541
FEATHER: #0620, #0777
BANANA: #0428, #0756
⁂

#0184 - May 31, 2018 @ 06:37 (San Francisco, California)

[0184.1 / 0435] [I cuddle up with a sexy Czech porn star. We nuzzle each other and discuss having a three-way? Fourway? Manyway? ANYway?]

[0184.2 / 0436] [THE DOCTOR *(flirty, intelligent, and direct)* invites me to his mansion for lunch. He greets me with rapid barrages of words and without pause exclaims,
"Merry Christmas and Happy New Year! Let me find your present. Is it raining out today?"]

[0184.3 / 0437] [I walk to lunch, enjoying a playful conversation with coworkers about our plans for the upcoming weekend.] //

⁑

CZECH: #0765
CHRISTMAS: #0401, #0417, #0556
DOCTOR: #0401, #0484, #0515, #0534, #0542
PORN STAR: #0403, #0671, #0789
THE DOCTOR: #0382

⁑

#0185 - May 31, 2018 @ 09:43 (San Francisco, California)

[0185.1 / 0438] [I'm in a "Burning Man" house with THE GINGER (*goofy, creative, and tactile*). Lots of narrative detail foregone, but the mood is quirky and "misfit-ish."]

[0185.2 / 0439] [I drive what feels like a 1950's Yellow Cab. The car has a heavy steel frame, with dark red bench seats. I'm lost and wander through a reality with no road system. All that can be seen through the windows and front windshield are projections of early cartoons and black and white zoetropes.] //

⁑

LOTS: #0527, #0547, #0556
YELLOW: #0584, #0587, #0598, #0618, #0620, #0649
QUIRKY: #0668, #0682

⁑

#0186 - June 1, 2018 @ 05:11 (San Francisco, California)

[0186.1 / 0440] [It's golden hour at a large seaside amphitheater on the coast of Greece. In a blink, I'm possibly in a twin venue in Dubrovnik, Croatia. A large crowd gathers to celebrate THE DANCER's new choreography. Waves can be heard crashing beyond the venue walls. Wafts of salty air float through on rays of purple, pink and gold light. As twilight nears, dancers who are physical embodiments of Disney characters (*human princes and princesses*) perform special pas de deux. The crowd roars with approval with each successive lift timed to musical crescendos. Cymbals and waves crash in unison. The mood is celebratory, much like a college commencement.]

Dream accompanied by various songs "Karma Police" by Radiohead, "Seaside Rendezvous" by Queen, and "Amongst the Waves" by Pearl Jam.

[0186.2 / 0441] [I attend a formal dinner set in a cobblestone courtyard. Music is performed in an open-air concert hall adjacent to the dinner space. The stage is recessed like an orchestra pit. I occasionally peek over the edge to catch a glimpse of the performers, clutching my highball glass of sparkling water with lime. A Black man hands me a greeting card with a photo of AMY SHUMER on it and asks,
"Do you like the Fillmore?"
I assume he's referring to the performance venue, but the inflection in his query points to the neighborhood and cultural district in San Francisco which shares the same name.

When I imagine air particles freezing and thawing around my body on demand, this process gives me the ability to fly. I start slowly, first rising up over the dinner table. Once competent with the skill, I make numerous lyrical swoops, spirals, loops and dives. My joy and playfulness bring lightheartedness and amazement to my contemporaries at dinner. I slowly and deliberately descend head first toward the ground and hover an inch above the stone floor for a few moments. I rotate laterally and reach overhead for a marker. I scribble messily in the corner of a blank page in a dream journal to record the name of THE DANCER's composition. My scribble is illegible. I'm momentarily forlorn at the loss of the work's title. My wristwatch reads 4:01am just before I wake.] //

⁂

Maj. = 2- THE DANCER: #0187
AMY SHUMER: #1363
COURTYARD: #0461, #0521, #0611, #0736
COMPOSITION: #0668, #0784, #0798
LIME: #0767

⁂

#0187 - June 2, 2018 @ 07:30 (San Francisco, California)
*Another dream so fantastically real feeling I was almost unable to distinguish it from sleep. *

[0187.1 / 0442] [Yoga teacher auditions are held in a large, well-lit gymnasium. A large group has gathered. I unroll my mat in one of the entry tunnels and begin to practice as other attendees move in together and around me in group flow. I'm in my practice, connected to what the group is doing, while at the same time enjoying the space I've carved out for myself. Romanian teacher trainee graduates have flown here from Bucharest specifically for this event. Eventually, I join up with the group and lead the training. A cute guy winks at me and takes photographs with an antique camera.]

[0187.2 / 0443] [A fiery guy enters and implodes into an abstract cartoon constellation. A series of images link together vertically from top to bottom. A non-physical guide aids me with some cues on how to interpret it. I witness the man's challenges, successes, practices, priorities all laid out sequentially like a cosmic series of photograph negatives. Impressions of impactful events are carried forward with him as blobs of color, and pockets of shadow. This cryptograph-hieroglyph puzzle leads me to THE DANCER who looks at me, holds up her hand and matter-of-factly states:
"I'm just living my life."
A camera man tears the skin off a roast chicken and eats it, then discards the remaining meat and bones. He enjoys the skin tremendously and savors it. People watching the camera man shift their attention to me and become interested in my dream recording process. I'm willing to give them some insights and demonstrate my habits, but am a bit daunted by having to first walk up a fairly steep hill to retrieve my journal containing my speaker's notes.]

[0187.3 / 0444] [THE WEAVER drives a car. We're in a conversation while the car quickly advances. THE WEAVER requests quiet because traffic comes straight at us from both lanes, and she needs to focus in order to successfully bob and weave through oncoming obstacles. This seems like business as usual. The tone in the car is focused, and not stressed. The quick maneuvering continues until I wake up.] //

⁎⁎

Maj. 0- THE WEAVER: #0203, 2- THE DANCER: # 0189
ROAST: #0477, #0500, #0749
ANTIQUE: #0461, #0501, #0561
PUZZLE: #0448, #0450, #0506

⁎⁎

#0188 - June 3, 2018 @ 06:48 (San Francisco, California)

[**0188.1 / 0445**] [I'm in the kitchen, craving dark chocolate. It's warm in the room and there are five large bars of chocolate on the counter top. I unwrap a portion presented in butcher paper revealing kit-kat bar shaped contents which have become somewhat melty. I break off two rectangular segments, which squish a bit between my fingers when I grab them. I tilt my head awkwardly to let the chocolate goo spill into my mouth. It's bittersweet, dark brown and velvety in texture. I eat a lot of it, but savor it as it slides down my throat and coats it.]

[**0188.2 / 0446**] [THE YIMBY *(rational, objective, and methodical)* and an unidentifiable man who appears to be her partner look at various real estate offerings in an urban neighborhood. They're particularly taken by a multi-level home with a neon green frontage and Day-Glo orange accents. They enter the home. The interior is incomplete. THE YIMBY evolves and becomes an entirely different female being. She and her male partner are joined by another woman. The three of them navigate the dark interior of the unfinished house's lower level, trudging up and down staircases until they empty into an area that upon completion, will be a grand atrium.

In front of the three of them lies an octagonal table which has a strand of white fairy lights shining up from beneath. Adjacent to the table is a cane. The other woman picks up the cane and begins to lay it across the table, creating line segments between lit points that cause it to illuminate in shades of electric blue, green, yellow, peach, and pink. This phenomenon delights her. She begins rapidly moving and repositioning the cane at different angles and in line segments of differing lengths. The colored line segments have a corresponding auditory tone and harmonize when stacked on and blended with other colors. The board seems to be an elaborate game. One particular series of line segments causes an exterior steel shield to completely cover the house, rendering it, *"shuttered and locked down."* A few moments of stunned shock yields to frenetic exasperation. THE YIMBY infers that in order to escape the house, one of the women will have to kill the other.

Many days pass in darkness. Food supplies in the home begin to dwindle. Once exhausted, the three starving real estate prospectors discover a gelatinous rotting dog carcass that becomes their common source of nourishment. The man begins to lose his mind and decides to spend his time jogging in a square formation in the dark. He becomes increasingly detached, insular, and over time completely stops acknowledging the women to process the deep fear and anxiety burning in his gut and chest. One of the women contemplates,

"What if we could just choose to be happy here by ourselves? Isn't this what we really wanted anyway?"

A TV production crew observes from a dark room at many angles, presented on many monitors. One zealous team member seems certain they're going to win an award for this episode.]

[0188.3 / 0447] [THE JESTER and I are at what feels like an airport terminal bus stop, but quickly realize we've been dropped in front of a mall. Out front, many square tables have families of four seated around them. Ads on the outside of the buses pitch a paper folding game the families joyfully play and test. The promotional operation is portable. The product requires minimal training and provides a fun way for families to generate passive income through play. THE JESTER and I are fascinated as we watch the multiple rows of families seamlessly play, sell, then pack up and leave for another destination.

Once alone, THE JESTER and I enter the mall and find ourselves in a partitioned laboratory that feels like a generic office building where a research team genetically modifies dogs. SHAQUILLE O'NEAL is the lead scientist. He's surrounded by myriad modified mutts, some of whom are rather unfortunate looking. We exit the lab out onto a gravel parking lot. White carports are set up on white painted cinder block walls. A picnic nears its end. Multiple open, warm, half full cans of Bud Light lay around, which I collect and empty on a nearby patch of grass. I crush the cans and put them in bags under the table, visibly annoying a drunken reveler. He picks up a red, white, and blue can and yells *"AMERICA!!!"* at me as he pops the top and starts swigging from it.] //

⁂

Min. = ◆- THE JESTER: #0199
FAMILY: #0511, #0524, #0556, #0557, #0573, #0579, #0592
RESEARCH: #0671
DAY GLO: #0657
KIT-KAT: #0481

⁂

#0189 - June 4, 2018 @ 03:30 (San Francisco, California)

[0189.1 / 0448] [I'm on a cul de sac where all the houses butt up against one another. Neighboring buildings are joined by a seam at the front top with wooden fasteners that look like giant Legos. The properties have no side yards. All of the garage doors pull double duty as oversized television screens. It's after hours. All door screens buzz with static white snow, indicating the household within is asleep and not consuming any products. I enter a home and encounter THE REVOLUTIONARY *(friendly, cynical, and strongly opinionated)* in the kitchen. We decide to make some popcorn. I become confused when she rinses the dry corn under a faucet. It begins to pop, no flame required. It's perplexing because the freshly popped corn becomes instantly soggy under the steady stream of water. We laugh at the absurdity and decide we no longer want the snack, leaving a pot of still popping soggy corn in the sink.]

[0189.2 / 0449] [I'm at OPRAH's house where three different shows are concurrently produced.

1. BEYONCE performs in a giant Romanesque pool.
2. World class athletes train in the same pool.
3. A nerdy film director is interviewed about his forthcoming feature.

The shows are produced while OPRAH hosts THE DANCER and me as her houseguests. THE DANCER and OPRAH are very familiar and are quick to make small talk after sharing a cheek kiss and embrace. OPRAH knows me, but can't recall from where.

"Weren't you here when I interviewed Malala Yousufzai?" she asks.

"I'm a scientist, but I've never done any research."

My comment breaks the ice and we giggle. Not only does OPRAH tend to our entertainment, she continues producing television episodes. I wonder how she does it all.

BEYONCÉ performs a new album in its entirety wearing a red evening gown while splashing across the shallow end of the white marble pool. She's flanked by smooth glass waterfalls. OPRAH interviews BEYONCÉ psychically, remarking often on BEYONCÉ's singing which concludes with a final moving note sustained beyond pianos, guitar feedback and the fading crash of cymbals. BEYONCÉ's voice smoothly transitions to quiet and after a brief awestruck pause OPRAH gently whispers, *"Simply amazing,"* directly into a camera. THE WRANGLER *(meticulous, artful, cosmopolitan, and motherly)* assists BEYONCÉ offstage.

The second program finds OPRAH interviewing a team of men in speedos who train for a world class competition. After taking a few comments from various team members, her attention turns to the team's coach. A very specific discussion about their pre-competition diet exposes the rigor and accountability he's established with his athletes. After a detailed rundown of formulas and meal times based on collective body weight calibration, he asks me to describe my favorite post workout recovery meal.

"A red bull and two scoops of green protein powder," I say humorously.

After a moment of laughter, the coach's tone goes deadpan as he seriously states, *"That's the recipe for dementia."*

I need to pee and make my way to the "Back Guest Room" which hides underneath a large divided spiral staircase. I find a small door with a sign that reads;

CAT TOILET.

I crawl through on all fours and discover a pint size powder room, equipped with a tiny sink, mirrors and commode. I attempt to position myself to urinate in the tiny room, but it's just not feasible. I retreat and move to the back yard. I can see directly into the neighboring glass house, as I pee in a still aquifer that looks like a designer infinity pool. A couple of lotus flowers pockmark the surface of the water, and as I relieve myself, I can see the speedo wearing team conditioning together as they run around a large track.

I make my way inside and on the nearest TV I see OPRAH and the nerdy director seated in interview chairs on the corner of Castro Street and Market Street *(adjacent to the Muni station on the north side of the street)*. People pass by without paying them attention. A large online audience produces laughs and gasps which accent the interview conversation.

"You realize no woman will ever be turned on by this...Are you real?" OPRAH asks, inviting laughter from the audience.

A small smirk crosses the nerd's face.

A pregnant pause breeds tension, until the director stands on his chair, raises both hands defiantly and declares, *"Whatever OPRAH, you loved it!"*

A clear wide angle shot pulls back slowly as show credits roll. Music begins to play, and the man takes his seat. He and OPRAH make small talk between themselves. I'm still standing in front of the TV, giddy that OPRAH knows who I am.] //

✩✩

Maj. = 2- THE DANCER: #0193
Min. = ♠- THE REVOLUTIONARY: #0214
BEYONCÉ: #0214
OPRAH: #0225
SMALL: #0475, #0477, #0481, #0481, #0484, #0488
THE WRANGLER: #0217

✩✩

#0190 - June 5, 2018 @ 07:51 (San Francisco, California)

[0190.1 / 0450] [I'm at a sex party at 1351 Folsom Street. I get a couple of blowjobs, but have some difficulty maintaining an erection. The sweatier I become, the more intense the encounters get. Dialog and interpersonal exchanges are detailed yet fleeting. I'm mesmerized by the number of bathrooms in the house and their size. Food orders are taken. Most people wind up eating burritos. Attendees are transgendered, intersex, female and male. Feels a bit like a boarding school when people are shuttled away on buses at the end of the event. I leave feeling confident, but a tad self-conscious.] //

✩✩

CONFIDENT: #0552, #0592, #0637
ERECTION: #0450
ATTENDEES: #0415, #0421, #0457, #0466, #0594

✩✩

#0191 - June 6, 2018 @ 03:53 (San Francisco, California)

[0191.1 / 0451] [I'm in a kitchen mixing salad in stainless steel bowls. A couple of groups work together. Our team's bowl has a collection of small unprepared zucchini, squash and eggplant laying on top of a bed of greens slathered with a white creamy dressing. I find it odd because the salads are meant to be eaten a single bite at a time, and as presented the offering doesn't allow for that possibility.]

[0191.2 / 0452] [I track new music in a studio with my band. Upon playback we remark that the rough guitar mixes are unexpectedly quiet.] //

✩✩

PLAYBACK: #0438, #0463
DRESSING: #0499
QUIET: #0556, #0682, #0747

✩✩

✩✩

#0192 - June 6, 2018 @ 06:35 (San Francisco, California)

[0192.1 / 0453] [A guide entrusts me with knowledge of a special diet that benefits healers. A chaotic and noisy world rants around me. I'm not distracted. I've received the transmission.] //

⁎⁎

KNOWLEDGE: #0482, #0597
DIET: #0541
NOISY: #0540

⁎⁎

#0193 - June 6, 2018 @ 08:44 (San Francisco, California)

[0193.1 / 0454] [THE DANCER has two children; THE CHILD and a baby boy. THE CHILD is five years old. She has a shaved head. She wears a burgundy monk's robe. She places her hands together in front of her chest and says, *"Let us pray."*]

[0193.2 / 0455] [I drive down a country highway, intending to get back home to the city. I get distracted by the quickly moving lines in the fields of uniformly planted trees, bushes, and vines. At some point I realize I've driven off the road into the field, while maintaining my speed. Regardless of which direction I turn, the moving lines appear to run the same way, sort of like how I'd imagine being dropped on a high velocity horizontal PLINKO board (*without ricocheting off of the steel posts*). Eventually I slow, and drive down a steep, winding dirt road. I pass an old farmhouse with a grain elevator on the left. I crest a large hill and a cityscape is revealed with topographic variation similar to San Francisco. The vast number of clock towers in this city seems remarkable to me.]

[0193.3. / 0456] [I hand someone a cylinder of KRAFT Parmesan Cheese.]

[0193.4 / 0457] [I'm on a video conference with my team. THE KANSAN (*former boss, efficient, and retired*) joins late. She laughs and calls herself out while pointing at a scroll-like sign hanging in front of another framed picture on her office wall. The scroll espouses our team values, of which one is "timeliness." Her playfulness makes this a powerful moment.]

[0193.5 / 0458] [THE MEME (*woke, individuated, and marvelous*) enters a school adjacent to the fields of the clock tower city in [0193.2 / 0455]. He's flanked by a hype crew intending to confront both the CEO, and "Director of Education and Marketing" for the school. The confrontation occurs in a gymnasium, with a panel of women executives seated behind a six-foot rectangular table. I float above, observing omnisciently.
THE MEME's questions eventually wear down the Director. As she steps away to a water cooler to get a drink and compose herself, she goes crazy. I swoop down and cast a demon out of her, which causes the shape of her head to distort. Her neck and torso expand and split

apart. It looks gruesome, but the woman appears to be made of rubber and plastic. I scoop up the body and toss it in the lowest drawer of the nearest beige filing cabinet.

THE MEME is relentless in his remaining interrogation of the CEO, who becomes increasingly befuddled by the acuteness and precision of the questions. The CEO surrenders, and without celebrating THE MEME and I retreat down a corridor, well-lit with mostly soft white light. I leap and wrap my legs around him. We gaze at each other for a moment before I lean in to kiss his beautiful dark skin.

When we break the kiss, he's become a scruffy white man who says,
"I'm 60/40 at the moment. Let's hook up tomorrow instead."

The white female CEO morphs into a long-haired Black woman who taps her foot impatiently as she reviews a stack of documents. She's a lawyer. She looks at me and says heavily,
"That depo violated policy."] //

✱✱

Maj. = 2- THE DANCER: #0196, 3- THE CHILD: #0198
PRAY: #0611, #0618
MORPH: #0772, #0778, #0788
CABINET: #0563, #0579, #0606, #0607
COUNTRY: #0575, #0746, #0756, #0762, #0765, #0772
FARMHOUSE: #0557, #0756

✱✱

#0194 - June 7, 2018 @ 08:16 (San Francisco, California)

[0194.1 / 0459] [I'm in a new three-bedroom apartment. Each room feels like it's from a different era, region, and socio-economic American reality. The front entry and gathering space feel like a rustic 1930's cabin.

A knock happens at the door as THE PILOT lets himself in. THE LAWYER enters wearing only a bath towel. THE PILOT demonstrates his newly learned skill: **autofellatio**. This turns THE LAWYER on. He drops the towel and gets on all fours, ready to receive anything THE PILOT will give him.

I exit the apartment and start climbing a tall, dark, and narrow spiral staircase. I plateau in an attic where I observe a woman who looks out a floor to ceiling window at the San Francisco cityscape. While in the attic, I inspect stacks of sweaters and other clothing. On wire racks above the hanging clothes are out of date winter holiday items marked for clearance:

- *A cylinder of chocolate truffles wrapped in a foil print cartoon visage of Santa Claus.*
- *A pair of unicorn socks.*
- *A blue square bag of cinnamon sugar "mini" pop tarts.*

I jam a couple "mini" pop tarts in my mouth, grab the bag, and head back downstairs. New roommates move into the back bedroom.

A woman carries boxes.

A dark-haired man with smooth skin disrobes and walks nude towards a white walled sky lit bathroom.

The bedroom has floor to ceiling glass windows. The couple asks me to look after their infant son, and request I take him to a food court to play his preferred memory game.

175

JOSHUA D. LUNDELL

THE PILOT vehemently insists he join.
He and I take the baby boy out the front door and instantly into a colorful and raucous space with yellow rectangular tables surrounded by red circular stools. We stroll up to a small video game terminal and the baby boy becomes excited. His arms flap and he laughs hysterically. We put some coins in the machine to start the game, and before allowing the baby to touch the screen we carefully place a homeopathic tomato seed paste along his bottom gum line, knowing this will amplify his focus...and ultimately increase his score.] //

***

Maj. = 5 -THE LAWYER: #0204, 6- THE PILOT: #0232
SANTA: #0692, #0696
COINS: #0461, #0472, #0573, #0710
DARK CHOCOLATE: #0513, #0714, #0798
CINNAMON: #0487, #0617, #0759

***

#0195 - June 8, 2018 @ 03:10 (San Francisco, California)

[0195.1 / 0460] [THE HEDONISTS *(partners, crass, and virile)* contemplate the best way to fit square pegs in round holes.] //

***

SQUARE: #0761, #0764, #0795
ROUND: #0431, #0529
CONTEMPLATE: #0610, #0613, #0682
HOLES: #0472, #0533, #0666
THE HEDONISTS: #0802

***

#0196 - June 8, 2018 @ 05:20 (San Francisco, California)

[0196.1 / 0461] [THE DANCER. Japan. Round pegs in square boxes.] //

***

Maj. = 2- THE DANCER: #0200
JAPAN: #0430, #0575, #0594
BOXES: #0498, #0528, #0534, #0538, #0550

***

#0197 - June 11, 2018 @ 05:27 (San Francisco, California)

[0197.1 / 0462] [Mantra: *"Relationships are energy."* I observe myself pass beams of light between various individuals, and eventually groups of beings.] //

***

MANTRA: #0423, #0445, #0649, #0684
INDIVIDUAL: #0443, #0498, #0540

GROUPS: #0409, #0470, #0484, #0498, #0508, #0550
ENERGY: #0554, #0624, #0628, #0654, #0656
RELATIONSHIPS: #0600, #0742
✣

⚒

#0198 - June 12, 2018 @ 07:15 (San Francisco, California)

[0198.1 / 0463] [THE CHILD and I practice counting to 15, twice. We giggle as we draw out the pronunciation of each number. She has four arms, each with five fingers. We're on a catwalk type stairwell in a warehouse painted in olive-yellowish umber tones. THE CHILD is taken from me. I'm unable to find her. I know she's being given surgery to remove two of her arms. I can feel the amputations sting in my body. I feel very sad that I can't help her.]

[0198.2 / 0464] [I walk through a well-lit corridor past a series of white linen covered tables. THE ARCHITECT sits at a table with two older women, one of whom he introduces to me as his mother.] //

⚒

Maj. = 3- THE CHILD: #0222
Min. = ♥- THE ARCHITECT: #0310
SURGERY: #0401, #0660, #0664, #0791

⚒

#0199 - June 12, 2018 @ 08:30 (San Francisco, California)

[0199.1 / 0465] [I stand in the bathroom at THE JESTER's house. I take a selfie wearing only a t-shirt and cowboy boots. My genitals are covered, though most of my legs show. I use my phone to upload it to the internet. I forget about the upload, then begin receiving flirtatious messages from different dating/hookup apps. I don't recall taking the photo. I'm confused. My phone shows me the T-shirt and boots photo, but my profile when viewed from a laptop displays another image that's more familiar to me.]

[0199.2 / 0466] [*"Do you have something to share?"* THE NEUTRAL GUIDE asks as I give her my full attention with uninterrupted eye contact.
I'm in a class with a bunch of people. I'm seated on the floor to the left side of the room. Other students sit at desks. We split into two groups. I'm in one group. The rest of the class forms a line as the other group. We proceed down a hallway until we reach a dark doorway.
"Today's class is a study in Cali-FATE Black."
The class proceeds up a stairway as I'm singled out.
"You'll go below for a pipe making workshop."
Acceptingly, but with a twinge of sarcasm I ask, *"Can I do all of my work from my ninth?"*
I descend a staircase, yet wind up on an upper floor of a building with a spacious, white modern interior. I feel intoxicated and notice an open air pissoir along a wall of workspaces, next to floor-to-ceiling windows. I take aim and begin peeing, but my stream of urine misses its intended target. The more I pee, the less intoxicated I become, so I keep peeing.
A young man I don't recognize patiently waits for 10 minutes at a workstation for a single page of black and white printed materials that reads, "TEST PAGE." A self-service snack

stand with a red warming lamp heats the dregs of lunch's now limp curly fries and onion straws. I fill up a white paper sleeve full of hot crumbs, after sweeping in quickly before a coworker. In a blink I experience Deja vu, and I'm behind the guy I cut in front of in line. I place the last remaining long, flat, over cooked steak fry in a paper sleeve, but I don't eat it.] //

⁎⁎⁎

Min. = ♦- *THE JESTER: #0218,* ♥- *THE NEUTRAL GUIDE: #0537*
TEST: #0452, #0506, #0514, #0568
SLEEVE: #0506, #0746

⁎⁎⁎

#0200 - June 13, 2018 @ 04:15 (San Francisco, California)

[0200.1 / 0467] [It's night time. Pitch black outside. I'm on a sidewalk strolling along the perimeter of a single square block of houses lined by a white picket fence. Nothing beyond the sidewalk is visible. Complete abyss. A male being appears behind me and jogs towards me wearing white tri-striped tube socks, short shorts, and a headband. He sweats profusely. I assume he sings or coaches himself, but realize he snarls and barks in an increasingly alien and unsettling tone.

I cut across the picket fence and dart through oddly still lawns. I sense the man has mutated into something else, but I don't look back to confirm. I enter an average suburban home, and discover myself in a kitchen. A microwave oven turns on by itself, and at the same moment I hear a shriek at the back of the house. THE DANCER emerges wide eyed and mutters under her breath as she nervously pours herself a cup of tea from water heated in the microwave.

"Kundalini is here. Don't try to fool THE HEALER," she says.

I step on to the back porch and find myself on a sheer mountain side at high altitude. THE LOBBYIST, THE ENGINEER (*distant*), and THE NAYSAYER (*vocal*) complete a hike up a steep pass, pausing to rest at the house. The house becomes a gathering space for our group before we depart on an unknown adventure together. DONALD GLOVER briefly stops by, leaving just as quickly as he arrives, disinterested in what we're doing. THE LOBBYIST and THE ENGINEER sarcastically joke with one another. THE NAYSAYER becomes a Black man with a giant bloody scar that runs vertically across the entire left hemisphere of his head. The four of us decide to rest up for our pending trip.

I'm awakened by loud low frequency rumbles that rattle my ribs and viscera. Lying flat on my back I interpret the sounds as interference from unfamiliar energies, and my assumption is they're dark. As I lay on my back I think,

"Wait...this is a dream! Just wake up!"

But I don't wake up and the noises amplify and intensify. I try this a few times, but it seems that I'm awake. I scramble around on my back collecting clear flat discs that are a celestial version of "flameless candles." Soft light radiates from the center of the thin translucent devices. I'm under a bed when I do this.

We gather. I microwave some food to calm THE DANCER down. Loud alien white noises occasionally blast through the space, accompanied by a burst of blinding light. I'm willing to hold space to ground and prepare. People's eyes become strange and distant feeling. My main goal is to let THE HEALER sleep. I notice kiddie training toilets in unexpected places around the house. I need to pee but I don't. One kiddie potty is above a book collection. I don't want to risk the consequences of, *"pissing on knowledge."*

A bodiless voice guides us: *"DON'T SMOKE CIGARETTES."*

THE NAYSAYER pulls out a small vape pipe that unfolds into a hand-held espresso machine. As the overhead voice continues its automated warning, THE NAYSAYER shoots a small stream of hot brown liquid from the pipe-turned-machine into a small paper cup.] //

⁎⁎

Maj. = *2- THE DANCER: #0210, 17- THE LOBBYIST: #0265, 20- THE HEALER: #0225*
CIGARETTE: #0541, #0597, #0681
TRANSLUCENT: #0747
THE ENGINEER: #0463

⁎⁎

#0201 - June 14, 2018 @ 07:10 (San Francisco, California)
*Four discrete scenes run in parallel yet don't share continuity. *

[0201.1 / 0468] [I'm part of a team gathered to produce a yoga video. I arrive on set to discover the job pays $100 and is actually a gay porn shoot. I'm supposed to be the "spit roast" in a three way. THE HILLBILLY is the director and intends to be "the top" in the scene. The other person is not disclosed, but my gut feeling is I wouldn't want to fuck whoever it is. A crowd gathers to watch the shoot. The lights and set are all ready, but I choose not to go through with it.]

[0201.2 / 0469] [I visit with THE FARMHAND and THE POSTMASTER. I don't remember what we talk about. It feels like the room we're sitting in is really high up, like a condo in the sky. Our interaction is sweet and loving.]

[0201.3 / 0470] [I'm on the lawn of a rundown house where a group of gangbangers rush out, weapons drawn. They take aim at me. I move laterally as the field scrolls like a first-person shooter arcade game. As I scroll to the right, the scenery becomes the exterior of an elegant restaurant. I keep shooting what I think is a shotgun indiscriminately at the building. I see people dining at tables next to giant plate glass windows. The bullets don't penetrate the windows. No one is harmed. My presence is barely noticed.]

[0201.4 / 0471] [I'm in a grocery store aisle with vibrant, rich colors. Racks full of auto-graphed jerseys, balls, and other sports paraphernalia (*cataloged and displayed by professional athlete names*) are presented for sale. Players have united to buy back pieces of themselves they believe the league has stolen.] //

⁎⁎

Min. = ♣- *THE HILLBILLY: #0216,* ♥- *THE FARMHAND: #0334,*
♣- *THE POSTMASTER: #0214*
AUTOGRAPH: #0453, #0481, #0772, #0796

⁎⁎

#0202 - June 15, 2018 @ 04:57 (San Francisco, California)

[**0202.1 / 0472**] [PRISON BREAK! I manage to escape an Alcatraz-like structure where rust drips stain the walls. THE BOSNIAN (*sensitive, introverted, and childlike*) attempts a similar escape but as he takes a final step towards the door, he's blocked by two large guards. I watch omnisciently, while floating nearby overhead. A large mural composed of words written in an oily icing substance in real time fades instantly like invisible ink on a large brick wall. The brushstrokes are large and the letters are sloppily (*yet artfully*) visible from the side when the light strikes the piece on a particular, intended moment. I'm not able to decipher the secret message.] //

⁎⁎

MURAL: #0560

OMNISCIENT: #0454, #0535, #0566, #0796

RUST: #0506, #0512, #0535

⁎⁎

#0203 - June 16, 2018 @ 05:28 (San Francisco, California)

[**0203.1 / 0473**] [The mood is sneaky. I'm at a large buffet, in a fast-food concept store where customers are encouraged to sample regionally specific offerings, locally. The kitchen is "in the round." A few human workers serve as "error proofers" among a surrounding crew of robots. Once food is plated for customers, robots vacate their stations.

The food appears free but I feel the need to "sneak" a waffle fry here, and a sandwich there. Something seems significant about a round dirty plate. At a counter, the woman taking my order asks for my full name, but I'm only willing to give her my first.

I move on both the interior and exterior of the buffet ring at the same time, taking swigs of sugary drinks and grabbing samples of the various foods on display. I'm partial to chicken nuggets in this reality. A group of people comment loudly at me from across the dining room.

"*You're going to get _____!*" they exclaim, but I'm unable to hear their last word.

I notice a tween-age boy attempting to steal a Lucite, trapezoidal display box which would ordinarily hold rolls or bagels. I admonish him. A moment passes, and the humiliated boy starts crying. A fat woman with burned skin asks me to have a conversation. Turns out, she's the boy's mother and wasn't sure of what to make of my attempt at disciplining her child.

THE WEAVER and I move towards the exit, each grabbing a powder blue cylinder, the size of a wine bottle, as a parting gift. THE WEAVER opens her cylinder. A wool blanket tumbles from it on to the table. A gust of wind blows the blanket from THE WEAVER's hand as she picks it up.

I feel angry about the wind, for no clear reason.] //

⁎⁎

Maj. = 0- THE WEAVER: #0206

WAFFLE: #0575, #0768

LUCITE: #0406, #0467, #0542, #0544, #0575

WOOL BLANKET: #0684

⁎⁎

#0204 - June 16, 2018 @ 07:43 (San Francisco, California)
*Many deep, concurrent vignettes. I took very detailed notes (in each dream level), only to awaken to a reality where I'm presented with a blank page. I've recalled what I could from the 50+ fast moving threads. *

[0204.1 / 0474] [I write rigorously and precisely in a notebook.]

[0204.2 / 0475] [*"GAH! Linda you always do this to me!"* a blue haired guy who looks like a hybrid of THE BREWMASTER (*social*) and THE EXPAT (*sensuous*) screams in the center of a group. Those standing around look on neutrally. One woman scratches her left elbow with her right hand. She holds a phone in her left.]

[0204.3 / 0476] [THE LAWYER scolds me for leaving lime salted rims on used dinner party glassware overnight. He morphs into THE CAREGIVER (*gregarious, methodical, and fervent*), who then becomes a vibrant cyber goth trans-woman. When I ask her when she'll return, she sternly says,
"WHEN. I'M. BACK." She storms out of the house.
The salt indeed, has ruined my morning coffee, which I sip from a soiled goblet with pink lipstick painted around the unsalted segment of its rim.]

[0204.4 / 0477] [Upon entering a restaurant, an unnamed male friend vacantly looks at me and says, *"This is a shit show."*]

[0204.5 / 0478] [A sad man looks at me and asks, *"Did nobody hear me?"*]

[0204.6 / 0479] [I stumble through a beaded curtain and fall into an abyss. This experience was supposed to scare me, but I feel calm and relaxed as I plummet.]

[0204.7 / 0480] [I'm in a modern dining room, expecting to eat. The dinner table remains unset.]

[0204.8 / 0481] [THE COUTURIER spends time building a ladder out of oversized match sticks as she ascends a blue white glacial peak on a clear skied day. She takes great satisfaction in her achievement. Upon reaching the summit, she looks out across the range of jagged peaks and realizes the friend she intended to visit and toiled to travel for is actually on another far away mountain. The matchstick ladder falls to pieces leaving THE COUTURIER stranded and cold.]

[0204.9 / 0482] [An Asian woman and her cute boyfriend psychically flirt with me as we negotiate a three way.]

[0204.10 / 0483] [I sit in the back seat of a 15-passenger van with a group of graduate students. We laugh and joke. We're taking a trip after finishing our theses.]

[0204.11 / 0484] [I sit on the windowsill of a motorized house on wheels, driven fast down a mountain highway.]

[0204.12 / 0485] [I arrive at a yoga studio late, intending to take a class. My friends and I burn off residual laughter from a shared joke and are *"Shhhh'd"* by the front desk attendant.
"Don't do that. It's childish," I retort.] //

☆☆

Maj. = 5- THE LAWYER: #0219
Min. = ♣- THE COUTURIER: #0229
CYBER: #0563
NOTEBOOK: #0551
THE CAREGIVER: #1025
THE BREWMASTER: #0281

☆☆

#0205 - June 17, 2018 @ 02:10 (San Francisco, California)

[0205.1 / 0486] [I teach a yoga class. The flow is oddly sequenced. I have students reposition themselves in the room. Poses and breathing practices lack group coherence.]

[0205.2 / 0487] [THE FIDUCIARY and I have sex in the back of an Uber en route to the airport. We disrobe and have sex in the TSA line simply for the endorphin rush, though it turns awkward when I go inside him as people look on and cheer. We both laugh at our absurdity. Our bags are pulled for inspection. The TSA agents randomly toss their contents aside as we pull our pants up from around our ankles.

I gather six pairs of underwear from the floor and give the three "cutest" pairs to THE FIDUCIARY. I toss the other three in my duffel before flinging the bag over my shoulder. THE GERMAN (*stoic, data driven, and wry*) observes us scrambling from another security line. He attempts to chat with us, but he's just beyond earshot. We offer friendly waves back while proceeding to our gate.] //

⁑

Maj. = 9- THE FIDUCIARY: #0229
UBER: #0411, #0598, #0719, #0759
UNDERWEAR: #0452, #0453, #0455, #0504, #0558

⁑

#0206 - June 18, 2018 @ 05:26 (San Francisco, California)

[0206.1 / 0488] [I'm roughly 10 years old. I'm part of a large family that takes care of a large house while THE CARPENTER is gone. THE WEAVER is stern and insists we not, *"go in the back room."* I ignore her and burn some incense once in back. The mood is mysterious and a tad suspenseful. We enjoy sandwiches wrapped in butcher paper, while sitting on the floor of the empty back room.

THE ERROR PROOFER (*action oriented, severe, and skeptical*) shows up momentarily and stands tall for three breaths in each corner of the room. His role is unclear. Much more peripheral activity fills the space, but I'm fixated on a paper napkin under framed glass supposedly autographed by "Santa Claus," which I know to be fake. We need to make sure the house is clean before THE CARPENTER returns.] //

⁑

Maj. = 0- THE WEAVER: #0209, 1- THE CARPENTER: #0250
FAKE: #0430, #0454, #0461, #0755
INCENSE: #0486

⁑

#0207 - June 19, 2018 @ 01:10 (San Francisco California)

[0207.1 / 0489] [I hover in a reality where I experience deep intimacy with many. Most of our time is spent silent. No words nor touches are exchanged. I experience it as an, *"expansion of consciousness."*] //

⁂

SILENT: #0537, #0605, #0609, #0746, #0752, #0755, #0788, #0800
NO WORDS: #0762
CONSCIOUSNESS: #0565

⁂

#0208 - June 19, 2018 @ 04:19 (San Francisco, California)

[0208.1 / 0490] [I'm seated in the front "Nose Cone" of a bullet train and can see the track whizz by underneath through a clear floor. I'm seeking someone. I'm compelled to take the train back one stop to look again. Much more here is not fully recalled.

"Should I S_____ him?" A bodiless voice asks.

"Well, only if you float downstairs," another replies.] //

⁂

BULLET TRAIN: #0466
LOOK: #0434, #0442, #0450, #0454
DOWNSTAIRS: #0427, #0459, #0476, #0585, #0628

⁂

#0209 - June 19, 2018 @ 06:04 (San Francisco, California)

[0209.1 / 0491] [I believe I've tapped into an energy stream gathering for this upcoming weekend's PRIDE festivities. I briefly chat with many friends. No deep conversations, simply quick hugs, cheek kisses, and send offs. For a time, I'm at a party at a large gathering space with small dormitory rooms lining the perimeter. Everyone uses phones to scan the crowd for familiar faces. I find one guy particularly interesting and we begin exchanging messages. Based on his liberal sharing of personal photos and videos, I learn he's a filmmaker.

I walk towards him to talk. His black hoodie makes him easy to spot. Once we meet and hug, his face rapidly ages. He oscillates from a twinkish boy, to an old white man with a large port wine stain on half his face, to a middle aged African American man with vitiligo. He introduces himself as "SOWL." We flirt, chat, laugh and make plans to meet up later.

The roof of the building where we stand disappears, revealing a giant moonlit band of solid, yet soft clouds that briskly float by overhead. Time is limited. The phenomenon won't last. I want to take a photo. I yell to THE WEAVER and THE FAIRY GODMOTHER to reach in my bag and toss me my camera, though they don't hear me. "SOWL" and I enjoy the view and forgo the photo.

I have a variety of other flirty interactions, some in dinner party settings, some 1:1 at small yet tall, round top cocktail tables. I spend a fair amount of time talking to an older guy who waits patiently for his partner to arrive. Then, I teach a yoga class in the shower of a gym locker room to a large group of guys. They're all very attractive, and they all want to learn how to do a headstand with no hands.

Most of my friends now trend drunk and amorous. They partner up and quickly retire to their dorm rooms to hook up. A woman places a small paper cube containing eight tiny hexagonal shot glasses on the rim of the box in front of me. I inspect the cube, then look at her and say with partial sincerity,

"This is a fun way to get people to buy shit."] //

Maj. = 0- THE WEAVER: #0214
PORT WINE STAIN: #0415
THE FAIRY GODMOTHER: #0254

#0210 - June 20, 2018 @ 06:00 (San Francisco, California)

[0210.1 / 0492] [I assist two Harvard professors structure and set up activities for two male students. One professor is female, the other is male. I follow the female professor, who in moments resembles THE RETAILER (*persuasive, aware, and timely*), up a paved street to a parking lot covered by a carport. I'm given instructions to write out an elaborate mathematical equation on a blackboard that cascades top left to bottom right like a Gantt chart. I use white chalk. The test will later determine if the two students, one of whom is THE BROKER (*competitive, handsome, and power seeking*), can accurately factorize the equation.

While setting up other elements of the intellectual obstacle course we pass through an aquatics center with multiple Olympic sized swimming pools. I peer over the edge of a pool and see three different sized elephants, which also vary in color and age. The smallest, oldest, albino elephant receives the majority of my attention. All three dutifully march across the bottom of the pool, as though it's their normal daily practice.

I jump in a car with the male professor after paying off a parking ticket. We zip through a major city, quickly passing by a mountainside surrounded by _____ that _____. A block letter neon sign blinks,

GOLGOTHA: THE SITE OF CHRIST'S CRUCIFIXION

and makes a sound like a game show participant elimination buzzer as we zip by. We move too quickly for me to take a picture. The games continue.]

[0210.2 / 0493] [THE DANCER and I ski together on a snowy street. My left foot angles inward, nearly crossing my right. I narrowly avoid a fall. We're competitors in the "Urban Mountain Games."] //

Maj. = 2- THE DANCER: #0214
EQUATION: #0466
CRUCIFIXION: #0615
ZIP: #0438, #0487
THREE: #0495, #0508, #0531, #0540

#0211 - June 20, 2018 @ 08:04 (San Francisco, California)

[0211.1 / 0494] [I'm a senior in college, living in a mostly empty dorm room. The majority of people in my class have signed leases on apartments and houses with groups of friends. I live in "DO RE MI RE DO" Hall which is an official gathering place for dunces and remedial music students. I hold a binder full of astronomy lab practical work that I've completed and intend to submit. I spend time bargaining whether or not I should sell my astronomy text-book back to the bookstore. I don't have any money, but I believe holding on to the book will pay off later. Random friends stop by to chat on the couch. It seems I have on demand access to city amenities, as well as a military flight line and countless airplane hangars.] //

⁎⁎

AMENITIES: #0688
BINDER: #0528, #0788
DORM: #0426, #0427, #0538, #0602, #0606

⁎⁎

#0212 - June 22, 2018 @ 03:48 (San Francisco, California)

[0212.1 / 0495] [I'm a housekeeper in a "Planet of the Apes" reality. The mood is dark. I break into an unlit house with some friends. Out of everything that could be taken from the house I'm transfixed by a remote control for an inordinately large television. My cohorts move quickly through, ransacking what now feels like a palace. I turn on the TV and watch a Top 10 music video countdown, with each presentation preceded by an artist's anecdote. I'm particularly interested in "Video #2" though I'm unable to recall the artist.

I'm a down-tier citizen in this reality, preparing for the multi-entendre intended, "RUN-NING OF THE RACES." I hover over a large four-way intersection and see swarms of grey, red, and white colored dots file quickly and uniformly from four surrounding directions towards the center. It's clear this is a sensationalized media event that our ape overlords find deeply entertaining.]

[0212.2 / 0496] [I'm on the upper level of a mall food court. I briefly chat with THE ACTOR, then talk to THE LANDLORD (*responsive, shady, and intimidated*) who insists he give me his email address: snail@gmail.com. I find this funny, because email has become the new "snail mail" in this reality. He suggests I try, *"Really Strong Water _____,"* but I miss the last word.]

[0212.3 / 0497] [I float down a street lined by very large mansions, stacked tightly side by side. One house has two pairs of Greek letters (*Kappa Alpha / Phi Gamma*) on the exterior mounted vertically on a small square gold plate to the right of the front door. "Phi Gamma" is an LGBTQ safe house identifier. Before I get home, I pass my next-door neighbor's place; a greenhouse with a twisted wrought iron frame. The entire exterior and interior walls are made of glass, making it easy to observe the dwelling's stately interior. No one's home, and the owners rarely (*if ever*) use it. It's marvelous.] //

⁎⁎

Maj. = 10- THE ACTOR: #0224
MARVELOUS: #0452, #0487, #0518
INTERSECTION: #0435, #0472, #0578, #0640
SNAIL: #0535
THE LANDLORD: #0900

⁎⁎

186

#0213 - June 22, 2018 @ 05:37 (San Francisco, California)

[0213.1 / 0498] [I'm in a cafe with long counters. The bar is built from rich mahogany. The shelving and cupboards have brass accents. I hover by the register making small talk with customers as they pay for their orders, but I'm not an employee. I'm known as the, *"regular, friendly ghost."* I argue with the barista after my order is incorrectly fulfilled multiple times.

"YOU ordered granola with tomato!" she scoffs dismissively, insinuating I'm going to pay for something I don't want.

"Are you high?" I shoot back smarmily.

Conflict increases after I make some additional lame threats about how,

"I've gotten other neighbors evicted for less. I can outlast you," just before waking.] //

⁂

TOMATO: #0597

THREATS: #0496, #0718

MULTIPLE: #0401, #0403, #0415, #0417, #0423

⁂

#0214 - June 22, 2018 @ 07:11 (San Francisco, California)

[0214.1 / 0499] [THE POSTMASTER, THE WEAVER, THE DANCER and I sit in a car. THE POSTMASTER is behind the wheel. THE WEAVER is the front passenger. THE DANCER and I are in the back seat. We sit in the driveway of a house on "Home Base Drive" and watch BEYONCÉ slip out the side garage door alone, wearing a frumpy grey sweat suit. She's lived at the house for a while. We know she'll return. She's just been declared the biggest *"STAR"* in the world and must leave quickly before the paparazzi arrive. I excitedly recall her Coachella headline performance. I get choked up, barely able to hold back tears as I talk from the back seat about the HBCU marching band that supported her.

"Your tears must mean you really liked it," THE WEAVER offers in consolation while gently patting my hand.

"You need a fierce mama to get to that level," THE POSTMASTER says, shooting THE WEAVER a smile.]

[0214.2 / 0500] [THE REVOLUTIONARY and I are out briskly walking in the neighborhood. I'm impressed at how fast she can move with a cane. It's become an almost unnecessary accessory. She points at cars in the distance up a winding road that have oversized rectangular windshields. We buy two Rockstar Energy Drinks from our corner store. We open one and leave it on a neighbor's front stoop. We each take a sip off the other one and throw the mostly full can in the trash.] //

⁂

Maj. = 0- THE WEAVER: #0224, 2- THE DANCER: #0223

Min. = ♣- THE POSTMASTER: #0250, ♠- THE REVOLUTIONARY: #0245

BEYONCÉ: #0299

ROCKSTAR: #0669

SIP: #0673, #0718

⁂

#0215 - June 23, 2018 @ 05:05 (San Francisco, California)

[0215.1 / 0501] [I'm inside a house. It's on fire. I'm not certain who's inside with me. Some people are trapped in a room where the fire has been contained. Firefighters want me to trust the blaze is isolated and appeal for me to stay inside, but I don't believe them. I'm family with a band of misfits who do what they have to, to survive. The mood is chaotic and anxious.

THE FAITHFUL ONE (*sweet, optimistic, and expanding*) is brought into the burning building on a hoisted chaise, like a pharaoh. He's celebrated. He's practicing surrender and has agreed to be fucked and filled by forty random men. He throws confetti in my face as the procession moves by. I stay to watch the event.

Later, I look out to a parking lot with a new billboard which reads: HELP US ALL FIND A NEW NEGOTIATED SPACE. In a neighboring lot a massive blank white rectangular billboard commands attention. Its thick black border directs the eye to big black block letters in the center that read: HERE. The billboard advertises a fundraising campaign, but I don't know for the benefit of whom.

I leave the building and am followed by a small cartoon dog. I repeatedly toss an iridescent rainbow-colored stick, which the dog retrieves. His owner and I are friendly and familiar, though he walks a few paces behind me. One toss of the stick sends the cartoon pup out into the street, narrowly avoiding a fatal strike from oncoming traffic.

"I'm an imposter."] //

⁎⁎

LETTERS: #0597, #0606, #0662, #0701
THICK: #0407, #0429, #0493
TRAPPED: #0757
FUCKED: #0710, #0800
THE FAITHFUL ONE: #1322

⁎⁎

#0216 - June 26, 2018 @ 04:57 (San Francisco, California)

[0216.1 / 0502] [The primary actors in this dream paint a wooden bed spread with a rich brown pigment. Two young women help THE HILLBILLY, who insists the finish on white wood "won't dry that dark of a color" after I comment on its initial richness.]

[0216.2 / 0503] [THE PILGRIM (*free spirited, dismissive, and eager*) purchases bags of bread (*rolls and pretzels of various sizes*) and declares, "I don't have an identity."]

[0216.3 / 0504] [I work on a construction site with a few other men. We move a giant scissor lift from point to point. It turns too quickly, jackknifes, and falls towards me. I brace for the impact of being squashed by the immense industrial machine. When it strikes me from behind, I feel my face immediately press into the dirt.

I hear men yelling as I wake up.] //

⁎⁎

Min. = ♣- *THE HILLBILLY: #0344*
LIFT: #0501, #0556, #0561, #0585
THE PILGRIM: #0774

⁎⁎

#0217 - June 27, 2018 @ 05:39 (San Francisco, California)

[0217.1 / 0505] [The narrative focuses on a Frenchman. One moment I'm in his body. In others, I float nearby as an omniscient observer. He's an executive who's been granted a geographic transfer.]

[0217.2 / 0506] [As I look up at the sky, I inspect the moon. I observe a spiral tunnel being pushed up from beneath by large subterranean burrowing machines, giving the surface of the moon a textured, swirled, labyrinthine effect.]

[0217.3 / 0507] [A woman sits in a chair dutifully tuning guitars for a band. A corner turn leads me down a hallway to a red lit room where THE WRANGLER (*firm, persuasive, and endearing*) speaks on the phone with THE CONFIDANT. I'm not able to hear their conversation, but I overhear her say,
"*I'm not sure what we're even talking about.*"
The next turn leads me to a vast mass altar lined with tens of thousands of images each illuminated by a small tea light candle. As I swoop over the altar, I'm stopped by another friendly spirit who shouts to another,
"*Hey get this one's (my) picture for community continuity.*"
It's night time, though quite a bit of ambient light shines up from the candle lit ground below.] //

⁂

Maj. = 16- THE CONFIDANT: #0243
THOUSANDS: #0498, #0507, #0520, #0573, #0788
ALTAR: #0568
THE WRANGLER: #0358

⁂

#0218 - June 27, 2018 @ 06:53 (San Francisco, California)

[0218.1 / 0508] [Mantra: "*Embrace without arms.*"]

[0218.2 / 0509] [Strong image of the South African flag.]

[0218.3 / 0510] [I'm at THE JESTER's home. I ask to rent his guest room, furnished with three twin beds set side by side. He's moved the washer and dryer outside to the back porch. I scratch my calf muscles with toes of the opposite foot until my toenails fall off. The pain is minimal. It just looks gross. Bloody black spots dot my toenail beds. I encounter THE ONE NIGHT STAND (*selective, sexy, and mature*) on the back stoop. We make out.]

[0218.4 / 0511] [I hold a copy of CG Jung's, "Man and His Symbols." The binding has completely disintegrated. I reorder the segments of the book and pass out as I encounter

"JEFF and CHRIS." I wake up in a frenetic and hypersexualized environment that appears to be part private residence and part resort. Gay sex happens all around. I recognize many faces that playfully move from steam rooms, to the pool, to other vanity areas. Everyone asks me if I know the host SHELDON ADELSON. I don't. I encounter THE KINKY MD (*analytical, cold, and flat*).

Throughout our conversation we're approached by multiple guys who begin as one person and shapeshift into others upon request. So much happens I'm not able to process it, and become overwhelmed.] //

✲

Min. = ◆- *THE JESTER: #0429*
SOUTH: #0566, #0660
TOENAIL: #0413
STEAM: #0422, #0648
THE ONE NIGHT STAND: #1030

✲

#0219 - June 28, 2018 @ 01:43 (San Francisco, California)

[0219.1 / 0512] [I'm a "Bro." I'm somewhat dopey, but my muscular body distracts others from this truth. My arms hang heavy with excess muscle. I'm in a posh apartment where THE LAWYER looks through kitchen cupboards in search of pineapple juice. We make small talk and I tell a story about my friends THE TWIRLERS (*lovers, community advocates, and socially masterful*) who make a living throwing dance parties that benefit children's charities. Something about this makes THE LAWYER increasingly angry until his voice pops and he begins to yell. Shocked (*and a bit afraid*), I breathe to get grounded and make the tone of my voice flat and quiet. I acknowledge what I shared triggered him.

I move to a small isolated closet that contains a piano placed against the wall furthest from the door. I hear ANDREW W.K. enter and chat with THE LAWYER. From the other room, ANDREW shouts to me,

"PLAY THE ACCOMPANIMENT TO 'NEVER LET DOWN!'"

I start the song and fail epically less than eight bars in, striking incorrect keys and playing the straightforward song in a bizarre alternative meter. The performance devolves so much that ANDREW starts laughing while singing and asks me to stop playing. He pops his head through the doorway, long hair dangling past his right shoulder and large grin on his face. As we make eyes he says,

"I ALWAYS MAKE YOU DO ALL THE WORK."

He sits next to me at the piano and begins playing. Before the lyrics begin, I pat him on the shoulder and say,

"Cool, I get to shift my focus back to the 'Little Ones.'"] //

✲

Maj. = 5- THE LAWYER: #0233
ANDREW W.K.: #1168
BIZARRE: #0445, #0623
PIANO: #0461, #0612, #0618, #0668, #0747
PINEAPPLE: #0518

✲

#0220 - June 28, 2018 @ 06:17 (San Francisco, California)
Nonlinear dreamscape composed of many concurrent narratives and pictures. *

[0220.1 / 0513] [Much of the focus centers on elementary school standardized testing. AI robots give sixth graders the most attention and track real time results on translucent screens and classroom windows. Students get instant feedback on their exam performance. Feedback consists of an individual assessment, and a group problem solved by pods of 15 to 20 children. Extra credit may be awarded for creativity on a case-by-case basis.

The school is large and industrially vapid on the interior, yet the individual technology is highly advanced and specialized. The group exam is underway, as scheduled. The pods have been tasked with determining the vector-based solution that will derive the minimal amount of sodium chloride necessary to "de-ice" the Eiffel Tower.

The height of the tower is dynamic and different for each group, as is the thickness of the ice on every steel segment. Changes in ambient temperature and humidity over a six-hour period increase complexity of the pod's prospective solution. The model must be universally applicable. Students must also make necessary allowances for gravitational "drip and slip" across the structure's thousands of triangular joints.

Collective brain power sparkles over the student's heads like a matrix of diamonds. Some pods are chaotic and hustle, while others solve the challenge quietly, meticulously, and deliberately.]

[0220.2 / 0514] [I'm transported to a snowy mountain top lodge where a furious father on a snow bike rides towards me yelling,
"YOU TEACHERS JUST MADE MORE WORK FOR ME AND MY PARTNERS!!"
I'm quickly shot back to the school where on an SMS leaderboard another parent comments, *"LOVED THE PARIS PROBLEM! <3 <3 <3."*]

[0220.3 / 0515] [The extra credit opportunity demands students generate a musical stage production that features synchronized cycling on tricycles with thick wheels and tires. Students are coached by ROB SCHNEIDER and other male actors who were formerly famous and now are fat and overly hairy.]

[0220.4 / 0516] [California State Senator SCOTT WEINER flirts with me. I'm slightly confused because he's clean shaven and has bleach blonde hair. We attend a wedding reception at a hotel. I walk vertically up giant white columns and pillars to the ceiling, stepping past shelves of photos and revered family trinkets that tell the story of the couple we're there to support. I spend some time observing the various objects until SCOTT yells at me,
"STRFKR is getting ready to go on!"
As I descend to the ground, wedding reception invitations rain down in a slow motion all around me like paper snow. Each card is inscribed with a Roman numeral. One with an XIII pivots and spins as it drops by my face. When I eventually make it to the floor, SCOTT and I walk to a performance hall where "STRFKR" takes the stage.
"STRFKR" is a DJ in this reality, and not the four-piece electro-rock band I was expecting.]

. . .

[0220.5 / 0517] [Something remains unresolved about the school luge team's practice calendar.] //

⁂

ROMAN: #0615, #0698
PARIS: #0580
MATRIX: #0540, #0628

⁂

#0221 - June 29, 2018 @ 03:00 (San Francisco, California)

[0221 / 0518] [I cook a nutritious meal in the spacious kitchen of a luxury condo in a mixed-use skyscraper. The unit is directly below a penthouse suite, which has grand sweeping glass staircases that spiral up and around the exterior of my condo's floor to ceiling windows in an X shaped pattern.
I contemplate asking my neighbor, an Asian Man in his 50's, to join me for dinner.] //

⁂

PENTHOUSE: #0500, #0767
UNIT: #0474, #0790
DINNER: #0496

⁂

#0222 - June 30, 2018 @ 08:30 (McCordsville, Indiana)

[0222.1 / 0519] [An angel laughs as he whispers in my ear, *"Hold on to Bank of America stock. It'll make you a millionaire, but it'll take a loooong time."*]
[0222.2 / 0520] [I follow KUMA the minpin out the door of a cottage. It's her 17th birthday. She walks down through a small-town square to a large grassy rolling field. A second larger, friendly dog joins her as she begins to bounce through the tall grass.
It's cloudy and gray overhead, but the mood on the ground is playful and lively.]
[0222.3 / 0521] [GRANDPA plays hide and seek with THE CHILD who spills an open can of paint on a stack of inflatable bike tires as she ducks under his workbench.] //

⁂

Maj. = 3- THE CHILD: #0235
Min. = ♥- GRANDPA: #0364
DOG: #0649, #0695, #0759, #0792
WHISPER: #0484, #0499

⁂

#0223 - July 1, 2018 @ 06:15 (McCordsville, Indiana)

[0223.1 / 0522] [THE LANDSCAPE ARCHITECT *(free, experienced, and candid)* stands next to a large vertical funnel of gold energy.]
[0223.2 / 0523] [I rifle through dozens of boxes of pillows.]
[0223.3 / 0524] [Things blur and stall as I move rapidly between realities.]

· · ·

[0223.4 / 0525] [I stand next to a swimming pool at night. The pool is lit with soft blue light. I'm interrogated by two guys I don't know. It feels like I'm a character in a gangster movie. I swallow an "anti-truth" pill that will help me hold my cover. It'll prevent the goons from using my words against me. They threaten me with mutated, dog-like beings on chains that gnash their teeth: *CHOMP*BARK*CHOMP*. The interrogation turns to blackmail.

THE DANCER appears for a moment on the periphery. I've discovered a teleportation device that functions by using, *"trans dimensional overlay technology."* Sharks in the swimming pool leap through the portal, disappearing at one end and emerging mutated and distorted upon their return. They become increasingly disfigured as they repeatedly leap back and forth through the portal.] //

⁂

Maj. = *2- THE DANCER: #0227*
FUNNEL: #0615, #0716
MUTATE: #0615

⁂

#0224 - July 1, 2018 @ 08:16 (McCordsville, Indiana)

[0224.1 / 0526] [I walk through a familiar airport terminal intending to board an overnight international flight. The environment is frenetic. I become obsessed with an empty bottle on the floor. As I look up the terminal becomes a train in motion.

A lot of boring travel follows as I slump in a seat with a palm on my right cheek.]

[0224.2 / 0527] [I walk by a classroom. The power is out. It's warm inside the building. THE ACTOR sits in a desk chair, bound and gagged by THE GENIUS. They playfully banter as THE GENIUS tightens the restraints.

I continue to another auditorium and attend a lecture on, *"BDSM in the workplace."* I'm enrolled in a class taught by THE WEAVER, who's recently become a tenured faculty member at the University. I've skipped her class today because I want to hear *(and ogle)* the scheduled BDSM lecturer. I take a seat. The lights go down. THE WEAVER walks out on stage to give the lecture as a substitute.

The hot man isn't there.]

[0224.3 / 0528] [I'm below deck on a commercial freighter. I walk toward a single large wooden crate. The box is branded with a list of names in small black block letters. A series of three asterisks in a line are burned beneath the final name. I stand at the box inspecting the list, but don't find my name.] //

⁂

Maj. = *0- THE WEAVER: #0230, 10- THE ACTOR: #0259*
BDSM: #0552, #0717
INTERNATIONAL: #0700, #0798
THE GENIUS: #0238

⁂

#0225 - July 2, 2018 @ 04:35 (McCordsville, Indiana)

[0225.1 / 0529] [OPRAH buys her friends G_____.]

[0225.2 / 0530] [JULIA STILES makes a scene in public by laughing uncontrollably.]

[0225.3 / 0531] [A collection of small yellow dots converge to a central point on a beige wall grid. They generate a dynamic 3D topographical map.]

[0225.4 / 0532] [THE HEALER works diligently at a desk at the end of a row in a vast cubicle farm. Office walls are bare. Minimal decor. A cork board near his desk has neatly arranged rows of business cards. He's used a red push pin to secure my Wachovia Bank, Finance Consultant Card from 2005 in the top right corner of the board.] //

Maj. = 20- THE HEALER: #0365
OPRAH: #0346
3D: #0404, #0644, #0717, #0720
BEIGE: #0412

#0226 - July 2, 2018 @ 07:43 (McCordsville, Indiana)

[0226.1 / 0533] [I float over a large field.]

[0226.2 / 0534] [THE ATHEIST and I hover around a bathroom after attending a business seminar. I give him a hard time and insist, *"It's rude to take a shit here."*]

[0226.3 / 0535] [Hawaii and other breezy island travel.]

[0226.4 / 0536] [THE VIKING ELF playfully disrobes me. We have sex while discussing the purchase of his second property.]

[0226.5 / 0537] [I'm at THE BREAKS DJ's loft apartment, leaping from one stack of cardboard boxes to another. The descent is sharp and steep. A crude steel pipe railing can be grabbed to prevent a fall.]

[0226.6 / 0538] [I admire THE MIDWIFE *(connected, supportive, and candid)* for her work as a death doula and her other embodied valances.]

[0226.7 / 0539] [A series of three teams race. At each checkpoint the slowest person on each team is eliminated. An Asian woman gets cut from our team at the conclusion of the current segment.]

[0226.8 / 0540] [It's twilight. The air smells of summer. A waitress buses the table while I sit with a friend. She pours us each another glass of the expensive happy hour wine. After finishing the wine, we playfully wrestle out of the bar and on to the parking lot.

"Two glasses of wine cost $35? Happy Hour?!" I exclaim to my friend.

"Well, if anyone would enjoy the novelty of THAT, it'd be YOU," my cohort retorts.] //

Maj. = 8- THE ATHEIST: #0228
Min. = ♦- THE VIKING ELF: #0394
HAPPY: #0422, #0527, #0672, #0750, #0751
SUMMER: #0540, #0618, #0627, #0687
THE BREAKS DJ: #0441
THE MIDWIFE: #0905

#0227 - July 3, 2018 @ 08:11 (Beavercreek, Ohio)

[0227.1 / 0541] [*"We lost Donatella!"*
A voice exclaims. Stiletto heels click as someone walks across a floor, indicating a key corporate sponsorship has been revoked.]

[0227.2 / 0542] [I stand on a beach for a moment before THE DANCER and I share a rental car for our trip to summer school.] //

⁎⁎

Maj. = 2- THE DANCER: #0231
VOICE: #0423, #0435, #0454
CAR: #0579, #0581, #0582

⁎⁎

#0228 - July 4, 2018 @ 07:42 (Beavercreek, Ohio)

[0228.1 / 0543] [Rambunctiously active dream. I run experiments using a "hugging machine" with THE ATHEIST in a gymnasium at night. I jump between realities like flipping through TV channels until I wake up.] //

⁎⁎

Maj. = 8- THE ATHEIST: #0274
GYMNASIUM: #0415, #0416, #0430, #0537, #0575
HUG: #0767, #0777, #0782

⁎⁎

⁂

PART 5 - HABIT FORMING

#0229 - #0299

5.1 - THE BOOK OF CANCER - {[0229 / 0544] - [0241 / 0571]}
5.2 - THE BOOK OF LEO - {[0242 / 0572] - [0273 / 0686]}
5.3 - THE BOOK OF BOÖTES - {[0277 / 0687] - [0299 / 0731]}

"...and then you say well,
like children that dare each other on things...
How far out could you get?
What could you take?
What dimension of being lost,
of abandonment of your power,
what dimension of that could you stand?

You would ask yourself because you know
that you would eventually wake up.
Then you would get more and more adventurous.
Finally, you would dream...where you are now.
You would dream the dream of living
the life you are actually living today.

That would be the infinite multiplicity of choices you would have."

-Alan Watts

* * *

July 6, 2018 - September 13, 2018

⚜

#0229 - July 6, 2018 @ 04:19 (San Francisco, California)

[0229.1 / 0544] [THE COUTURIER and I meet TINA TURNER for lunch at a restaurant. The dining room is designed to look like a recessed inverted pyramid, its many steps and tiers inspired by Incan architecture. TINA is incognito. Her hair is covered by a pink scarf, eyes hidden behind large round sunglasses. We're seated in the center of the room at a conspicuous table. THE FIDUCIARY enters, leans over a brass railing, and waves down to us. TINA excuses herself to use the powder room and never returns. THE COUTURIER and I second guess our restaurant choice, realizing this very public place was not the optimal venue for a wildly popular person who leads a deeply private life. Later, I send TINA an email from my phone lamenting her son's recent suicide.] //

⚜

Maj. = 9- THE FIDUCIARY: #0323
Min. = ♣- THE COUTURIER: #0343
TINA TURNER: #0781
SUICIDE: #0538, #0787

⚜

#0230 - July 6, 2018 @ 05:17 (San Francisco, California)

[0230.1 / 0545] [I'm a session player reviewing a wall of instruments at a music store. I riff on a powder blue 4-string bass guitar. I look past a dusty case of effects pedals and see a vintage "Ducky Wah Wah" displayed upright and listed for $600. With the bass thrown over my shoulder I begin playing the intro lick to "Hey Man Nice Shot" by Filter. I walk out of the store, down the street, and into the woods. I walk up to an oak curio cabinet and peek through the glass. I see two tiny pickles. One is gold. The other is painted like the United States flag. THE WEAVER appears next to me and we admire the tiny sculptures. The bass guitar evolves into a classic 6-string Fender Stratocaster electric guitar. I play a few riffs from the song "Rocket" by The Smashing Pumpkins as I saunter deeper into the woods. *"Boy, it's dark outside."*] //

⚜

Maj. = 0- THE WEAVER: #0235
UNITED STATES: #0472, #0556, #0755
BASS: #0431, #0554, #0580, #0618, #0666, #0692, #0757
WOODS: #0622, #0648, #0686, #0799

⚜

#0231 - July 7, 2018 @ 07:28 (San Francisco, California)

[0231.1 / 0546] [I seamlessly (*and repeatedly*) shift between sleep and wakefulness.]
[0231.2 / 0547] [THE PUBLIC SERVANT (*fun loving, curious, and playful*) lends me her tube of sunscreen. I apply it liberally to my face and neck. We're outside. THE HOUSEWIFE

(motherly, grounded, and family centered) stands next to a truck wearing an apron she designed and sewed. The truck is large, has four doors, and is painted gunmetal grey. It's parked in the driveway of a large three-story house. The main level, garage included, is composed completely of thick transparent glass. The home within is orderly and tidy. A large open kitchen is stocked and ready for use.

Once inside the kitchen, THE DANCER entrusts me with her tiny white pet ferret. It's small enough to rest on the tip of my finger. The ferret leaps off my index finger and darts through a sink filled with dirty dishes. It scrambles across a countertop, then leaps into the air. A set of microscopic wings emerge on its back and flap wildly to help it float gently to the ground.]

[0231.3 / 0548] [I use the bathroom. I perform autofellatio on myself while standing. I experiment with my posture for a bit, not prioritizing the pleasurable sensation in my genitals, but the feeling of spaciousness in my thoracic spine. My back body feels free and renewed.]

[0231.4 / 0549] [I'm in a train station commuting from "A to B." My outbound journey is delayed by a purple train that pages an absent passenger. The trains are modern, tidy, and silent. The pathways between platforms are rubberized and beige. The purple train departs and I wake up.] //

*
**

Maj. = 2- THE DANCER: #0235
SUNSCREEN: #0462, #0560
BEIGE: #0412
TIDY: #0672
*
**

#0232 - July 8, 2018 @ 06:23 (San Francisco, California)

[0232.1 / 0550] [THE KIND HEART, THE PILOT, and I engage in witty banter. We laugh while cruising hook-up apps on our phones, commenting sarcastically at times on profile content we find droll or basic. A young tattooed woman hits on me via an app. We invite her over to play in the sauna. I sneak out the fire escape and greet her at a large, etched glass door. It's night. Soon thereafter, the young woman and I meet the guys in a cedar lined hot house. THE PILOT snaps a multitude of candid photos with his telescopic lensed camera. As I disrobe, I reveal additional layers of sports gear. In total I remove eight pairs of shoes before I find myself nude and enveloped by eucalyptus scented water vapor. We all laugh at the absurdity of the scene until I wake up.] //

*
**

Maj. = 6- THE PILOT: #0246, 21- THE KIND HEART: #0492
FIRE ESCAPE: #0767
EUCALYPTUS: #0424
EIGHT: #0483, #0498, #0541, #0711
*
**

#0233 - July 9, 2018 @ 05:49 (San Francisco, California)

[0233.1 / 0551] [THE LAWYER, THE EPICUREAN and I all run shoulder to shoulder on an indoor track while making casual conversation. It's decided that we'll take a trip to Montreal. I leave them to make my way through a large crowd of men walking in the opposite direction. I arrive at an apartment building, and once inside descend to my large recessed living space beneath a catwalk and settle in. I hear the door open above, and as I look up, I see a hot guy I'd noticed on the street, enter. I whistle at him to get his attention. He holds a stack of autographed books under his arm, which he intends to sell.

Sitting on the couch and looking out, we watch the weather outside turn grey and rainy. Roads begin to flood. The crowd outside sloshes through rising choppy water, all appearing to enjoy it. The flood is expected. The guy and I laugh when the couch becomes a bed. We get quiet and move toward a shadowy corner of the room when we see a pair of "Route Security" officers with ticket books in hand walk toward the window. The apartment floods.]

[0233.2 / 0552] [Two films run concurrently:

1. A tome about a new legal precedent.
2. A man threatens a woman who disagrees with his point of view.]

[0233.3 / 0553] [I'm in an industrial kitchen learning the secret to making "Red Velvet Cozonac" from a genius baker. We hover above a thick crimson river that bends around giant steel pipes, like a lazy river raft ride. He's quick to point out the correct consistency for the batter. He also teaches me, *"how to know to pull from the starter when the right number of grey spots emerge."* There are many other tools in "his manual" he is eager to share.] //

⁎⁎

Maj. = 05- THE LAWYER: #0235
Min. = ❤*- THE EPICUREAN: #0331*
FLOOD: #0416, #0425, #0446, #0455, #0583, #0607, #0715, #0780
CATWALK: #0404, #0620, #0757, #0765, #0773

⁎⁎

#0234 - July 11, 2018 @ 05:55 (San Francisco, California)

[0234.1 / 0554] [I have a series of in-depth conversations with three men who seem familiar, but who I don't know. The first I completely forget. The second is with THE POWER PLAYER *(songful, longing, and quiet).* Most of our conversation is non-verbal and pleasant. The third is with JOSH HOMME *(musical, bad boy, and rough & tumble badass).* He sits next to me at a bar and is insistent we know each other.

"Like, we were either brothers or lovers in a former life."

"For sure, uhhhh yeeeah! We should jam some time," I affirm, feeling like I've just been reunited with a long-lost sibling as we laugh and enjoy getting reacquainted.]

· · ·

[0234.2 / 0555] [I'm behind the bar, working. A man and woman come in and ask a bunch of questions about the menu.

"We sell two types of gas here: SWEET and SOUR."

"OK...I want 20 of them," the woman says without specifying which of the options she prefers.

I don't ask her to clarify. The man places his index finger to his chin. The woman rolls her eyes at his sustained muteness. They're not familiar faces. I want them to leave.] //

⁂

SOUR: #0500

SWEET: #0528

MENU: #0581, #0726, #0775

INDEX FINGER: #0455, #0787

QUESTIONS: #0542, #0547, #0670, #0753

THE POWER PLAYER: #0236

⁂

#0235 - July 12, 2018 @ 04:11 (San Francisco, California)

[0235.1 / 0556] [THE LAWYER takes a phone call in an adjacent room discussing the details of a new client's case. In the course of discussion, he realizes he's made a large procedural mistake that could cost him a favorable ruling, and may put him at risk of a malpractice suit.]

[0234.2 / 0557] [It's night time and cloudy outside. I sit in the back seat of a van. I have really bad gas and I can't contain my laughter as I fart uncontrollably. THE CONNECTOR sits in the front seat and laughs too as she rolls down the window to air out the acrid cabin. The van bobs and weaves very quickly around tight corners in a parking lot. The van proceeds down a mountain highway until we arrive at a fishing dock. LAYNE STAYLEY sits at the end, swinging his right leg and whistling as he fishes off the end of the pier. He's calm and incognito. He's about to die again. I touch him on the shoulder and give him a compliment on his singing voice before continuing on my way.]

[0235.3 / 0558] [THE ANGRY SPRITE *(tricky, fun loving, and fatigued)* and I stand on the sidelines of a soccer field watching one of his young sons play. As the game escalates, THE ANGRY SPRITE leans over to me saying,

*"What hurts the most (**and wasn't expected**) is when someone you love so much talks back when you try to guide them."*

When I express confusion, he points towards his son who's just scored a goal.]

[0235.4 / 0559] [THE DANCER, THE WEAVER, and I are in a park with steep concrete sidewalks. I take candid photos of THE CHILD, who's naked, about six years old, and only wearing roller skates. It's innocent, playful and free. She begins to roll backwards down a hill. THE WEAVER swoops in to grab her little arm just before she falls off an edge, and

down to what would have resulted in a serious injury. We collectively breathe a sigh of relief.]
//

⁎⁎

Maj. = 0- THE WEAVER: #0237, 2- THE DANCER: #0236, 3- THE CHILD: #0274,
4- THE CONNECTOR: #0316, 5- THE LAWYER: #0263
DOCK: #0506, #0547, #0628, #0648, #0687
ROLLER SKATES: #0544, #0561
THE ANGRY SPRITE: #0484

⁎⁎

#0236 - July 13, 2018 @ 04:51 (Phoenicia, New York)

[0236.1 / 0560] [The mood is fairly dark and brooding. I'm in a room surrounded by a bunch of people I want to date and fuck. One by one I have conversations with each of them, ensuring our agreements and intentions are clear. A few people stretch their bodies, as though they're warming up for a workout. A couple of guys are so into it they drool.

THE DANCER and I take a golf cart-like vehicle down the service entry of a large private residence. She's disquieted when we pass a guy she believes is homeless. I reassure her that he's not. He's a tenant. She'd still rather double back to confirm he's ok. It becomes clear THE PHOTOGRAPHER (*effusive, soulful, and generous*) owns this multi-level house, that at one time (*in another dream*) I was really intent on buying. I encounter him on a spiral staircase and thank him for his hospitality. His parents and extended family are all in the process of moving in. The home radiates with love and humor. From the basement I trudge up a winding staircase to a glass window penthouse.

On the path, I encounter THE NUN and THE POWER PLAYER (*strong, virile, and focused*) yet share no memorable verbal interactions. They both simply go about their lives. I enter a salon with a black and white checkered floor. The walls are stone. The windows are gothic stained-glass illuminations. It appears to be a _____ room, though each time I enter and exit, the furnishings change.

I find a scooter with a severed human head attached to the handlebars and use it to glide up multiple flights of steps. The song "Para Noir" plays at moderate volume in the background. I sing along with the morose, defeated lyricist:

"Fuck you, because I loved you."
"Fuck you, for loving you too."
"I don't need a reason to hate you the way, I do."

I enter a dark room filled with people who look for a gathering place, yet are unaware they're already gathered. A wireframe model on display made of green lasers and bright green thread hangs suspended in mid-air in the center of the room.

"Why do you all insist on meeting at the temple? You already have this big open space where you could meet right now!"] //

⁎⁎

Maj. = 2- THE DANCER: #0240
Min. = ◆- THE NUN: #0378
HUMOR: #0434, #0540, #0547, #0573, #0719

CHECKERED: #0414, #0511
WORKOUT: #0682

⁎⁎

#0237 - July 15, 2018 @ 04:45 (Phoenicia, New York)

[0237.1 / 0561] [I talk to THE FRATERNITY MAN (*suffering, good willed, and spirited*) through the organic walls of a giant amniotic sac he's taken as his primary residence. The sac is filled with warm bloody liquid, which regulates his core body temperature. Through the wall he shares the only four photos he's uploaded to Facebook. They reflect the key moments in a cruel lifetime of advancing disfigurement. THE ORATOR (*engaged, accommodating, and galvanizing*) passes us and talks to us from the "secondary face" in the back of his head. It peeks through hair that hides it, almost teasing it has its own "coming out" process to follow. The second face shows itself off as the body walks away.]

[0237.2 / 0562] [ALEX JONES and a blonde woman snort a shitload of cocaine. I admonish the woman, not for the drug use, but for choosing to do it with ALEX JONES. I'm shown a future photo of her where she appears haggard, then another where she's dead. A female coworker who successfully moonlights as a stripper tells her to, *"Stay away from that shit."* The partying woman recently experienced some professional success.]

[0237.3 / 0563] [I sit on a bus with THE SPOTTED DOG (*fit, funny, and helpful*) and a couple of other people. A voice from the dark end of the bus gives me unsolicited feedback about how I teach yoga. Turns out the mystery voice is THE WEAVER. I'm really annoyed she remains hidden and she won't just tell me to my face.] //

⁎⁎

Maj. = 0- THE WEAVER: #0247
FACEBOOK: #0665, #0785, #0795
COCAINE: #0595, #0669

⁎⁎

#0238 - July 19, 2018 @ 05:30 (Phoenicia, New York)

[0238.1 / 0564] [THE WRITER (*dramatic, simplifying, and seeking*) drives around in a red BMW Isetta, at night. I ride along as his passenger. Vertical neon signs indicate we're in a city in Japan, likely Tokyo or Osaka. We stop intermittently to check out various lofts for rent. I have access to virtually any urban home I want.]

[0238.2 / 0565] [I collide with THE GENIUS at a "House of Daphne" sex party. He wears a purple leather harness and rocks a smoking hot genderfucked look.]

[0238.3 / 0566] [THE EXECUTIVE PRODUCER makes conversation in an elevator with her best friend (*a large man*) who embarrasses her. He attempts to diffuse the awkwardness by wrestling with her. A crowd gathers to watch as the action spills from the elevator out into a lobby. The play becomes increasingly aggressive and violent. He begins smashing her head on the floor. I don't like this. I feel nauseous and have to move away from the scene. A group of children in a nearby room help me by laying out yoga mats in orderly rows.] //

⁜

HARNESS: #0682, #0726, #0769
DIFFUSE: #0423, #0649, #0669
THE EXECUTIVE PRODUCER: #0974
THE GENIUS: #0442

⁜

#0239 - July 20, 2018 @ 03:57 (Phoenicia, New York)

[0239.1 / 0567] [THE SHARED HEART places her dirty bare foot in my face because I, *"have that thing Aries' have around personal space."* THE TEAM LEADER (*scattered, trusting, and loud*) takes a double pigeon pose. She experiences a huge physical and emotional catharsis. THE COMIC taps her on the shoulder and tells her that's her last scheduled "showy" release for a while. I compete for team members as they pass through a doorway. I have a male partner and we recruit a female who is skeptical of both of us.]

[0239.2 / 0568] [I've just knocked on the door of a house where THE ALCOHOLIC (*honest, committed, and flattering*) lives. She doesn't answer. Subtext emerges. Her bank account has been zeroed out by a phone scam.]

[0239.3 / 0569] [I observe a lesbian couple working multiple jobs to make ends meet. They live in San Francisco. One is a dog walker who wants to do something nice for her partner. I watch their narrative unfold like a brief uplifting human interest story played at the tail end of the evening news. I'm left with a dose of optimism about humanity.] //

⁜

OPTIMISM: #0550
DOSE: #0566, #0613, #0664
HUMANITY: #0591, #0620, #0718
THE ALCOHOLIC: #0348
THE SHARED HEART: #0485
THE COMIC: #0430

⁜

#0240 - July 25, 2018 @ 06:08 (San Francisco, California)

[0240.1 / 0570] [I interact with a dysfunctional family. Two daughters and I sit in a car, during a rainstorm. The smallest child is behind the driver's seat. The car begins to roll along. We stop. I exit, then confront an abusive father while at work in his corner store. He violently hurls his forehead toward me in an attempt to head-butt me numerous times, but misses. He angrily flings avocados and berries. He's pissed off because I built a house for his family and he feels emasculated. The inside of the house we built is a mostly open concept. I suggest that we collaboratively build an attic next, but only after the foundation and frame are brought up to code.

Later, we drive to the mother's beauty supply store inside and to the back of a deep row house. The building is half below ground. A gravel parking lot slopes upward, obscuring the property's frontage. We drive by and head home without stopping at the store.

Once home we prepare quinoa and pasta for dinner. Single thick spirals of pasta are wrapped around wooden dowels and submerged in boiling water. The mother's method is deeply inefficient. I conclude the mother shouldn't have custody of the kids.

The eldest son discloses doesn't want to confront his abusive dad.

Another child's age on the reality TV show (*cut from the group interaction*) is expressed non-numerically as a dyed "Easter Egg." In the next scene, the child should be an adult, but doesn't age. Linearly, the storyline is nonsense.

THE DANCER makes me aware that "the stock" is up 6.02% in one day to a spot price of $45. I review the jagged upward sloping chart on a computer screen, declare myself a "millionaire," and wake up.] //

⁕⁕

Maj. = 2- THE DANCER: #0259
WOODEN DOWEL: #0557
PASTA: #0627
ROLL: #0513

⁕⁕

#0241 - July 27, 2018 @ 06:10 (San Francisco, California)
Skipping imagery

[0241.1 / 0571] [I'm by a pool. People are gathered. I have a phone and decide not to jump in because I can't put the device down. Many others leap from the edge, soak themselves, and destroy their phones. THE ANESTHESIOLOGIST (*distant, quiet, and alluring*), THE PUBLIC MEDIUM, and THE PSYCHIC (*aware, bombarded, and loving*) stand in a line at the edge of the pool. I speak to each of them individually.] //

⁕⁕

Maj. = 18- THE PUBLIC MEDIUM: #0271
POOL: #0538, #0622, #0629, #0633
SPEAK: #0637, #0742, #0786
SKIP: #0589, #0640, #0724
THE ANESTHESIOLOGIST: #0260

⁕⁕

#0242 - July 30, 2018 @ 06:41 (San Francisco, California)

[0242.1 / 0572] [PAUL MCCARTNEY and I travel by futuristic Muni train to a prominently advertised JANET JACKSON concert. Billboards feature real time text commentary by attendees on social media. I take photos as we swoop along a vast mirror ball slide that feels like a giant silver raging river. Eight people wait on a ticket swap list hoping to attend later. PAUL and I part ways. I exit the train at the top of a pastel lit hill overlooking a cityscape.]

[0242.2 / 0573] [I watch a large virile Black man aggressively fuck a willing submissive male partner. He cums on the guy's face. The previously short bottom guy stands now twice as tall as he was prior to having sex. The Black man looks at me and mutters,
"It's like fucking a ten-year-old...just pound it until it's done."]

[0242.3 / 0574] [I make my way down a buffet table. I make a joke about the importance of always having a tray of canapes ready for guests. My comment is supported by a laugh track.]
//

⚕

PAUL MCCARTNEY: #0332
JANET JACKSON: #0277
PASTEL: #0436, #0561, #0599, #0756, #0767
JOKE: #0776, #0792, #0793

⚕

#0243 - August 3, 2018 @ 02:14 (San Francisco, California)

[0243.1 / 0575] [Mostly a blur, but I recall being in playful conflict with a group of teenage kids. We participate in a large, curated game of "cat and mouse."]

[0243.2 / 0576] [THE CONFIDANT and I solve a puzzle that involves collecting shadow images of peculiar shaped potato chips. We win a bonus when we correctly select the outline of "POTATO CHIP #5."]

[0243.3 / 0577] [I sit atop a series of high shelves and toss items down on teenagers who advance up a series of slow sloped Donkey Kong ramps. I leap upward and fall swiftly head first into an arctic snow bank at night in the middle of a blizzard. I drill down so deeply the kids are unable to find me and give up the pursuit.]

[0243.4 / 0578] [I'm backed into a corner of a subterranean boiler room. As I attempt to ascend a ladder, I'm sprayed down head to toe with "Liquid Rainbow LSD."]

· · ·

[0243.5 / 0579] [I hear a similar story shared between different groups of people. I take note of minor nuances in distortions in each telling, that make sense to the group's hearing, but ultimately move the nature of the story further from...the (T)ruth.] //

⁎⁎⁎

Maj. = 16- THE CONFIDANT: #0259
LSD: #0544, #0566
BLIZZARD: #0401

⁎⁎⁎

#0244 - August 3, 2018 @ 06:31 (San Francisco, California)

[0244.1 / 0580] [Most of the dream is spent building a large aluminum temple in the desert. The foundation is composed of two concrete circles. The interior circle is much smaller than the vast outer ring. A series of intricate curved triangles create a spiral galaxy-like structure. I'm astonished by how quickly the structure emerges, and how the aluminum paneling provides a surface on which beautiful choreographed patterns can be projected. This gives the structure an "anti-gravity" or "gravity defying" quality.]

[0244.2 / 0581] [I wait in line after a MARILYN MANSON concert for an artist meet and greet. I want MARILYN MANSON's autograph. He's absent because his estranged keyboardist "POGO" has taken his chair at the table. Sexual energy shifts the mood of the dream from animated to restless.] //

⁎⁎⁎

MARILYN MANSON: #0379
GALAXY: #0493
ALUMINUM: #0500, #0602

⁎⁎⁎

#0245 - August 4, 2018 @ 07:27 (San Francisco, California)

[0245.1 / 0582] [I watch THE BRAND MANAGER's *(reserved, exact, and highly skilled)* engagement video on YouTube.]

[0245.2 / 0583] [I drive people to the ocean in a wooden car. We leave all electronic technology behind.]

[0245.3 / 0584] [Koi fish in a water filled reed basket eat leaves off the mossy bottom of a flowering plant.]

[0245.4 / 0585] [A father reprimands his kids and later maintains it was the right thing to do.]

[0245.5 / 0586] [Kids play in the snow. Cell phones advertise to the children using their preferred and specialized pronouns.]

[0245.6 / 0587] [A mine train roller coaster runs rapidly up a hill.]

[0245.7 / 0588] [I'm underwater. I follow two giant whales to the edge of the continental shelf to hear their magic whisper just before they descend into the deep. I continue on, in search of a third whale.]

. . .

[0245.8 / 0589] [THE REVOLUTIONARY injects me with heroin. It takes her three sticks to get me high. She jams the syringe deep into my left ankle joint while depressing the plunger. As warm dizziness floods my veins I wake up.] //

⁎⁎

Min. = ♠*- THE REVOLUTIONARY: #0423*
WHALE: #0561
SYRINGE: #0635
ANKLE: #0445, #0452
THE BRAND MANAGER: #1104

⁎⁎

#0246 - August 5, 2018 @ 06:30 (San Francisco, California)

[0246.1 / 0590] [THE PILOT lands a Cessna at Burning Man. I park a car near an orange plastic perimeter fence.]
[0246.2 / 0591] [An inbound storm arrives as I hike down a mountain. Meanwhile, a huge dust storm hits the "Hawaiian Island of San Francisco."]
[0246.3 / 0592] [A basket full of pillows.]
[0246.4 / 0593] [Teams of laborers pack up a fleet of semi-trucks.]
[0246.5 / 0594] [Extremely active dream where >95% of detail instantly vanishes.] //

⁎⁎

Maj. = 6- THE PILOT: #0261
INBOUND: #0756, #0769, #0786
PERIMETER: #0446, #0520, #0561, #0583, #0669, #0799
DUST: #0550, #0583, #0760

⁎⁎

#0247 - August 6, 2018 @ 06:03 (San Francisco, California)

[0247.1 / 0595] [I take a short flight to Washington DC. When I arrive, I head to an office where I spend 40 minutes proving to an admin that I have my paperwork and credentials for a scheduled meeting.]
[0247.2 / 0596] [I see a musical with THE WEAVER.]
[0247.3 / 0597] [Binders in a backpack.]
[0247.4 / 0598] [GAY and KATIE HENDRICKS gather _____.]
[0247.5 / 0599] [A giant space parachute is tested inside a vacuum chamber within a massive grain silo. It appears likely to crash, yet slows moments before impact and gently touches down.] //

⁎⁎

Maj. = 0- THE WEAVER: #0260
GAY HENDRICKS: #0645
CREDENTIALS: #0458, #0634, #0772
MUSICAL: #0404, #0512, #0557, #0578, #0784, #0787, #0794
BACKPACK: #0406, #0461, #0472, #0579, #0592, #0715, #0719, #0735, #0790

⁎⁎

#0248 - August 6, 2018 @ 07:30 (San Francisco, California)

[0248.1 / 0600] [THE IRISHMAN (*witty, slurred, and gritty*) and another man raise a son. They're moving to a new home. The house where they've dwelled for years is packed up and empty. In a side alley, I pick up a backpack and realize it's full of candy and concert credentials strung on bright yellow lanyards. I observe a pair of stuntmen in the process of planning a public spectacle. A miniature scale model outlines their prospective trick. Run of show to ensure flawless execution will happen next week.]

[0248.2 / 0601] [I'm in a vintage shopping mall, with mostly empty stalls. An empty barber chair occupies the space in what at one time was called the "One Seat Salon." I sit down. I look to the next stall and see a table covered with scattered metal figurines. I sense the landlord is attempting to evict the tenant. The tenant is squatting.]

[0248.3 / 0602] [After taking a short flight, I run to catch my connection. I only have a few moments. Acting hastily, I leave my backpack on the prior plane. *"Oh no! I've left my ID and wallet behind! I'm not allowed to backtrack! I'm stuck! Fuck."*]

[0248.4 / 0603] [*Random flashes of lavish scenes:* At the Hearst Castle pool, a woman (CAITYLYN JENNER) pulls her hair back before fully submerging. Elsewhere a young, smooth, muscular man leaps from a claw foot tub and lands naked on a checkerboard tile floor.] //

⁎⁎

MINIATURE: #0472, #0606, #0622, #0667, #0684, #0713, #0746, #0749
MUSCULAR: #0418, #0424, #0450, #0495, #0526, #0534, #0538
FIGURINES: #0508
SALON: #0401, #0518

⁎⁎

#0249 - August 7, 2018 @ 05:30 (San Francisco, California)

[0249.1 / 0604] [I pet a puppy.]

[0249.2 / 0605] [THE ANIMATOR (*innovative, playful, and open*) and I take a walk along the waterfront. When we go under a pier, we see a pair of Bentley limos parked side by side. One is black. The other white. An obese AXL ROSE walks up to the white vehicle and scoffs at us when we ask for a ride. Notably, he jumps in the driver seat. THE ANIMATOR and I walk back to the waterfront, observing the sea level rise and spill over nearby levees. A tornadic vortex of calcified Pompeiian bodies swirl towards us.]

[0249.3 / 0606] [THE LINGUIST (*cultured, mysterious, and deep*) and I drive down a narrow cobblestone road. A row of tall buildings stands to the left. We're en route to a BECK concert. I'm so concerned about hitting the houses on the left-hand side that I strike a string of cars parked on the right shoulder.]

. . .

[0249.4 / 0607] [I'm in my "Dream Kitchen." I've been here before. This time it's clearer. It's partitioned into "light" and "dark" sides with large greenhouse windows along the far side. A ring of Viking burners, ovens, and freezers lead to a large open hearth. A long, elevated community table occupied by family members offers a view of me and my counterparts as we cook. I take a video of us playfully preparing for a giant party. THE PHILANTHROPIST underwrote the construction note for the kitchen.] //

⁎⁎

BECK: #0435
VORTEX: #0479
PUPPY: #0429, #0435, #0467, #0555
THE LINGUIST: #0297
THE ANIMATOR: #0306
THE PHILANTHROPIST: #0655

⁎⁎

#0250 - August 7, 2018 @ 07:50 (San Francisco, California)

[0250.1 / 0608] [Divergent reality. One part portends a civilization equal parts techno-logically advanced and highly specialized; the other post-gold rush, pre-automotive Western America. I arrive at a saloon and make small talk with a woman who runs a restaurant. If you mention them on Instagram, they'll give you free bacon. The woman thinks it's a crafty trick because she's the only person in town who knows, *"what an Insta-gram is."* So, she thinks. I have a smartphone, though I look like a vagrant. I post multiple times about the location, causing the phones of dining patrons placed on tabletops to buzz and blink. This annoys the woman who "Shhh's" me as her guests continue to eat silently at white linen covered tables. I don't care about disrupting the vibe. My priority is to get the free bacon.]

[0250.2 / 0609] [*"Death is a choice, and not a bad one! You get to pick the dimension you want to be in,"* THE POSTMASTER says as he pats me on the back, then walks through a wall of white light. I see him emerge elsewhere on a tractor, driving along a set of railroad tracks. Large fires prevent the train from advancing to the next town. THE POSTMASTER drives along whistling and undeterred.]

[0250.3 / 0610] [THE POSTMASTER, THE CARPENTER and I make lunches on a butcher block countertop. I'm 6 or 7 years old. We decide to make "Brats and Burritos" and pack them in paper bags. THE CARPENTER helps me pack my lunches in the most efficient way. We make jokes about "Gross Squished Burritos."
We get on a mine train roller coaster that begins moving at bullet train speeds. The floor splits and I fall through, catching the end of THE CARPENTER's pant legs which inflate in the seat above from the up draft, and bounce like the body of a "noodle person." It's dark and doomy above, but beneath the track it's cartoonish. Rolling hills and Super Mario Brothers characters skitter around. The tracks are built irrationally high. As the air whips my face, I

contemplate whether or not the design is aerodynamic. Occasionally I fear falling, but trust THE CARPENTER has a hold of me.]

[0250.4 / 0611] [I'm at a performance where the roles flip flop. I'm an audience of one, seated alone on a stage. The performers stand scattered across a series of gymnasium bleachers. School children with guns have a single letter on their T-shirts. They stand in patterns to create the lyrics to the song, "This is America." Three kids are absent in the front row. When the song concludes the set changes instantly to reveal a vast white opaque bowl. I feel uneasy and check the program. The next piece is titled: "THE BATH TUB." I leave the auditorium. As I pass by the door, I see a small console, like a 1980's arcade game that blinks "READY PLAYER ONE" in an old school Namco font. The blinking wakes me up.] //

⋆

Maj. = 1- THE CARPENTER: #0253
Min. = ♣- THE POSTMASTER: #0334
AMERICA: #0421, #0426, #0442, #0452, #0452, #0455, #0472
1980'S: #0402, #0441, #0448, #0752

⋆

#0251 - August 8, 2018 @ 05:42 (San Francisco, California)

[0251.1 / 0612] [I hold a leadership role at "Camp Anachronistic." BASSNECTAR decides to play two parties at the camp, even though he camps elsewhere. He walks up to me. He's slender. His exceptionally dark, long hair hits behind his knees. His eyes are deep, endearing, and kind. He takes to the decks and I can't help but allow my joy to overflow.
"The Biggest DJ in the world is playing at our party! Holy shit!"
I decide I want to quit my camp role to be his roadie. At one point during his set, he stage-dives and then dances among the crowd. THE DELIGHT *(chaotic, helpful, yet reactive)* wants to dance at the Thursday party. Guys at the camp door don't tell her that she doesn't need to ask.
"If you put your focus on the 'Bass Altar' I can play three more hits here tonight than I did in San Leandro," BASSNECTAR shouts at me.
I nod affirmatively and shift my attention to a dark, glowing altar visible to my mind's eye.]

[0251.2 / 0613] [I fake possession and "unload" unwanted energy into a brick.]

[0251.3 / 0614] [Young African kids ask me how I successfully cleared out my _____. I am unable to make up a lie and share a radical truth that I'm a **fake**. DEATH GRIPS premiere a new video on a screen next to us. THE ROBOT is somehow involved, but her role is unclear.] //

⋆

Min. = ♥- THE ROBOT: #0306
BASSNECTAR: #0323

211

TRUTH: #0550, #0719
ROADIE: #0477, #0495, #0702, #0712
⁑

#0252 - August 8, 2018 @ 07:28 (San Francisco, California)

[0252.1 / 0615] [I teach a class how to create Marichyasana *(Bound Sage Pose)*. I take partic-ular interest in a male student named "Joseph" who I've never previously met. I work inten-tionally with specific body cues: *"Flex the feet. Take your left foot to hip distance."* I push him and make him an example for the class. I don't let him hold back. I attempt the demo and surprise myself when I achieve a full fold forward, chest on leg.] //

⁑
TEACH: #0424, #0430, #0431, #0432, #0441, #0450, #0481
MALE STUDENT: #0592
SURPRISE: #0798
⁑

#0253 - August 9, 2018 @ 06:02 (San Francisco, California)

[0253.1 / 0616] [A blurry faced teen hijacks a car. It begins lighthearted, then I realize he's part of a retaliating gang. The car skids around, hydroplaning for a bunch of laps around a track. The burglary turns into some sort of race, but the specific detail fades quickly.]

[0253.2 / 0617] [THE CARPENTER and I sit in a spiral, egg shaped pod-like teleportation device. I have to duck my head under a swerved piece of anodized, textured steel to stand. It's smooth white on the interior and exterior. Something seems significant about family docu-ments I stuff in a binder at the bottom of a box. THE CARPENTER and I are about to take a big trip together.] //

⁑
Maj. = 1- THE CARPENTER: #0260
BLURRY: #0508, #0569, #0656, #0786
DOCUMENTS: #0464, #0796, #0798
⁑

#0254 - August 9, 2018 @ 07:27 (San Francisco, California)

[0254.1 / 0618] [I want to watch a very specific piece of porn involving two men by a pool. I put a query out on "Mental Social Media" and THE FAIRY GODMOTHER *(generous, jovial, and real)* instantly posts a link to the video with a winking emoji to my feed. Turns out the blowjob porn I'm after is actually a video listing for a $6.3MM property. The sex in the ad is hot. I decide to make an offer on the house.]

· · ·

[0254.2 / 0619] [I discuss an upcoming trip to Canada, and have an irrational worry about how dynamic the exchange rate between US and Canadian dollars will be. I contemplate the best use of my cash.]

[0254.3 / 0620] [A green text screen projected on the interior of the passenger window of THE ATTRACTOR's *(light, inquisitive, and service oriented)* truck scrolls flirty text messages that mention I'm needed on a current project.]

[0254.4 / 0621] [I'm supposed to pick up Chinese dumplings for a friend. I forgot my list and stand at the restaurant counter not knowing what to order.] //

✷

LIST: #0665, #0683, #0748, #0780
EXCHANGE: #0403
THE FAIRY GODMOTHER: #0365
THE ATTRACTOR: #0640

✷

#0255 - August 10, 2018 @ 06:23 (San Francisco, California)

[0255.1 / 0622] [*"Puppy wants to play,"* I repeat on a loop in an obnoxious voice. I'm on my knees and wrapped in black lace.]

[0255.2 / 0623] [I'm a day laborer and also work nights at a fast-food restaurant. MIKE PENCE attempts to embezzle from the restaurant. My crew attempts to undermine him by digging a hole in the corner of the room. We could be in a prison, or in a hotel. I'm not certain. What is clear is I don't like MIKE PENCE and I don't recognize him as an authority figure. More detail lost.] //

✷

MIKE PENCE: #1172
PRISON: #0493, #0521, #0614, #0724
DAY LABOR: #0505
FAST FOOD: #0462, #0785

✷

#0256 - August 11, 2018 @ 06:57 (San Francisco, California)

[0256.1 / 0624] [THE PRANKSTER *(youthful, sneaky, and lonely)* is in grade school and stands in line, possibly for a bus. He's switched from one line to another by a teacher, resulting in him being routed to an incorrect home. In a blink, he's a teenager attending, "ROB ZOMBIE HORROR ROCK CAMP." The carnival-like situation boasts games and oddities galore. THE PRANKSTER musters up the courage to hit on a girl who has green skin and is potted like a houseplant in a large terracotta vessel. He offers to water her.]

. . .

[0256.2 / 0625] [An orgy breaks out on the Chicago Marathon course. It becomes a surprisingly oral situation.]

[0256.3 / 0626] [I sit at a restaurant with a plastic table number wedged between two small side-by-side rings atop a stainless-steel post. A voice shouts at me and my date to, *"lay it down!"* We oblige and make adjustments to ensure the cylinder and number do not roll off the round, white linen table.] //

⁎⁎

ROB ZOMBIE: #1099
CYLINDER: #0407, #0602
ADJUSTMENTS: #0527, #0609
TEENAGER: #0460, #0466, #0763
THE PRANKSTER: #1066

⁎⁎

#0257 - August 11, 2018 @ 08:49 (San Francisco, California)

[0257.1 / 0627] [I'm in a gymnastics gym practicing my splits. I wear gym shoes. My back foot is flexed and heel pressed into the wall. My legs feel longer to me than when I'm awake. I'm surprised by how effortless it is to drop in to right, left, and straddle splits. My body feels free and I emanate a lightness that compliments the suppleness of the body.]

[0257.2 / 0628] [I teach a group of women who are extremely chatty. They pause to search for water, mid-practice. I encourage them to return to their mats and breathe when they overly coddle another female student who has reached her physical and emotional edges.]

[0257.3 / 0629] [I wander around the inside of a massive dark convention center with very large LED presentation screens mounted on every wall. The place is swarmed by hundreds of people in bespoke suits. We anticipate the IPO of a new startup. I buy a "Temple 2018" sweatshirt for $65 cash. I pass a soiled cocktail table dirtied by stacks of used plates and napkins. A chocolate eclair wrapper and a crumpled up $1 tip have been left behind for whoever comes through to clean up.] //

⁎⁎

SPLITS: #0452, #0489, #0544, #0634
GYM SHOES: #0504
SOILED: #0516

⁎⁎

#0258 - August 13. 2018 @ 06:56 (San Francisco, California)

[0258.1 / 0630] [A Frenchman prefers downhill skiing as his method of meditation.]

[0258.2 / 0631] [A rock band practices in a suburban home. I try to go inside to watch the rehearsal. I'm stopped by a group of teenagers who block the room and tell me to, *"Stay Out."*] //

⁎⁎

MEDITATION: #0530, #0542
REHEARSAL: #0502, #0520, #0587, #0758
SKIING: #0463

⁂

#0259 - August 14, 2018 @ 05:00 (San Francisco, California)

[0259.1 / 0632] [THE PSYCHIATRIST and I attend a football game at Notre Dame, which he states is his alma mater. This confuses me because I thought he went to Harvard. We sit in seats in the upper ring of the bowl and watch the crowd rapidly fill and empty. Thousands of tiny little dots move much like magnetized iron filings in a Wooly Willy board. We watch this phenomenon for a while, then decide to walk up over the edge of the stadium and vertically down the exterior wall.]

[0259.2 / 0633] [THE DANCER and I stand in line at airport security. The mood is anxious and hurried. We don't share much conversation and spend most of the time buried face first in our phones. A large clear glass speaker I've removed from my bag shatters when it passes through the X-ray machine. I feel sad and want to sue TSA for my foregone hours of future musical enjoyment. I suggest we leave the airport and take an Uber across the country.]

[0259.3 / 0634] [I staff a buffet line serving multiple varieties of bread. I make small talk with a beautiful woman named "Meredith," who's dressed like a noir actress. THE ACTOR is her date. He and I make eye contact. He quickly grabs his tray and leaves.
"What was that about?" "Meredith" asks.
I honestly don't know what to offer and say with a shrug,
"Hey, he's handsome. I'd like to talk to him again sometime."]

[0259.4 / 0635] [THE CONFIDANT has a challenging day at home. He lays back on the couch and tells the kids to do whatever they want. THE DAUGHTER (*opinionated, smart, and persuasive*) disappears quickly. THE SON (*emotive, trusting, and observant*) takes off his clothes and bangs on his chest like Tarzan. The lights go out.] //

⁂

Maj. = 2- THE DANCER: #0273, 10-THE ACTOR: #0305, 16-THE CONFIDANT: # 0358
Min. = ♠- THE PSYCHIATRIST: #0484
SUGGEST: #0532, #0598, #0618, #0735, #0796
IRON: #0405, #0511, #0561, #0727
THE SON & THE DAUGHTER: #0435

⁂

#0260 - August 14, 2018 @ 05:49 (San Francisco, California)

[0260.1 / 0636] [I take detailed notes on a scratch pad until the pen runs out of ink. I realize I'm still dreaming and I haven't actually written anything down. I wake up and scramble to recall major themes. I'm still asleep.]

. . .

[0260.2 / 0637] [THE CARPENTER and I share a casual conversation. THE CHAMPION (*motherly, wise, and complimentary*) passes by, stopping briefly for an introduction. A child with an asymmetrical bob haircut stands next to THE CHAMPION. She gently places her hand on the child's head as we chat. THE CARPENTER is oblivious. This boy has just undergone top surgery to align his body with identity. THE CARPENTER simply sees the person as a girl even as we make more and more obvious cues that indicate the contrary.]

[0260.3 / 0638] [I'm behind giant stage curtains at Burning Man, as evidenced by the grey alkaline dust beneath my booted feet. The curtains are sturdy, durable, and extremely heavy. They're so heavy the sound of the music being performed on the other side is mostly dampened. I close my eyes and see a tiny repeating pattern of microscopic pink triangles. The triangles get larger with the beat and volume of the music. The geometry distracts me as I inquire, *"Have I been dosed with LSD? How will I find my new house?"* I don't receive an answer.]

[0260.4 / 0639] [THE ANESTHESIOLOGIST (*attractive, evaluative, and quick*) and I talk at a round cocktail table. THE WEAVER briefly stops by, apologizing for the interruption, and leaves directions to the new house. Remnants of a bunch of partially eaten pizzas rest in oily cardboard boxes spread around the party space.]

[0260.5 / 0640] [THE BUTCH LESBIAN (*devoted, loyal, and fiercely committed*) and I stand around a red and white checkerboard cloth picnic table. Numerous clear vessels full of water have food submerged within. The water is clear. The food is saturated with liquid but maintains its shape. THE BUTCH LESBIAN pulls out a soggy hamburger on a wet bun and slaps it on my round white paper plate.

Immediately I'm behind the wheel of a driverless car as I begin eating the soggy burger. I override autopilot mode when the car fails to stop at a stop sign before making a left hand turn across multiple lanes of oncoming traffic. I take a couple more bites of the burger, then proceed. I look to the left as I cruise down the suburban highway and still doubt I'll be able to find my way to the new house. I call THE WEAVER who immediately appears in the driver's seat. I teleport to the passenger seat and continue eating the wet burger, even though I'm not certain I actually like it. THE WEAVER drives the rest of the way.] //

⁑

Maj. = 0- THE WEAVER: #0261, 1- THE CARPENTER: #00270
ONCOMING TRAFFIC: #0726
ASYMMETRICAL: #0573
LEFT HAND TURN: #0726
DOUBT: #0549, #0611, #0660

⁑

⁑

#0261 - August 15, 2018 @ 06:53 (San Francisco, California)

[**0261.1 / 0641**] [THE MEDIA TEAM (*energetic, happy, and light*) are kids who hang out in the basement of a house.]

[**0261.2 / 0642**] [I masturbate THE PILOT on the shore of a creek. I serve him a glass of dirty water in a clear tumbler. He doesn't like it and pours it out.]

[**0261.3 / 0643**] [Something about THE WEAVER and "Grandparents."]

[**0261.4 / 0644**] [I observe stages of paper production. Later, I walk around giant stacks of paper packaged for sale.]

[**0261.5 / 0645**] [Image of a bridge and a freeway onramp.]

[**0261.6 / 0646**] [A task takes two hours to accomplish in this generally unclear and syncopated dream segment.] //

⁎⁎

Maj. = 0- THE WEAVER: #0264, 6- THE PILOT: #0266
PAPER: #0561, #0581, #0615, #0645, #0660
FREEWAY: #0573, #0617, #0662, #0712
Oh Hello!
Nice to see you.

⁎⁎

#0262 - August 15, 2018 @ 23:50 (San Francisco, California)

[**0262.1 / 0647**] [I watch an intense red band trailer for a forthcoming film. *"He's half a lifetime away!"* a person screams at a jury box. All other details are lost.] //

⁎⁎

FILM: #0635, #0683, #0725, #0754, #0761
LIFETIME: #0510, #0577, #0606
WATCH: #0413, #0489, #0515, #0525

⁎⁎

#0263 - August 17, 2018 @ 06:45 (San Francisco, California)

[**0263.1 / 0648**] [I enjoy a three-way sexual encounter with THE QUEER (*playful, furry, and flirty*) and another extremely limber guy who can do straddle splits. Notably, a dusty guitar sits on a shelf nearby.

The guy in splits says, *"You lucked out and got TWO for ONE!"*

He's intriguing. His superpower is dynamic hair growth. Every time I look back at him, his hair is a different length and style. It's amazing. Short and cropped. Long. Shiny! Curly! I look away again, and again, simply to see his hair change. The sexual encounter continues through the night.

The next morning THE LAWYER encounters us on his way out the door to work (*where he must arrive before 8am*).

"You three could have been quieter. Your sex noises kept me up all night!" He yells as the door slams.

In a blink the three of us stand naked together in a Roman fountain. In the next blink, we're back where we started. As we leave the house, we notice the bedroom's become bigger.

Dusty shelves along the far end of the unit vertically multiply after we complete our encounter. Some equipment seems to be missing from the gym in the neighboring room.

"Dynamic-Hair-Guy" shares that he runs an improv group. He gives THE QUEER and me an impromptu invitation to a dinner party that night at his place. As we exit the condo building a lesbian neighbor asks if I want to stand in as an acting teacher.

"I can start by being a stand in for, "BRIAN."]

[0263.2 / 0649] [THE QUEER drives a car fast through a day time 8-bit video game scene. I ride along.] //

✶✶

Maj. = 5- THE LAWYER: #0466
HAIR: #0484, #0494, #0497, #0498, #0512, #0532
8-BIT: #0617
THE QUEER: #0697

✶✶

#0264 - August 20, 2018 @ 06:45 (San Francisco, California)

[0264.1 / 0650] [I have an orgy with five guys at FRANK ROBINSON's house. Gravity doesn't have the same effect in this reality. I go into FRANK's house knowing full well he doesn't live there anymore. The interior has significantly changed. The whole place has been modernized. The family who currently occupies it is out of town, though it seems they will be back fairly soon. When I exit, I'm on the panhandle of San Francisco, which has been overdeveloped with a series of row houses, packed tightly together side by side. Many are for sale. One of them has just been put on the market at a bargain price of $8,450,000.]

[0264.2 / 0651] [A woman is buried up to her neck in concrete. THE WEAVER troubleshoots how we might use Gmail functionality to save the woman. It may involve half of a blue green _____.]

[0264.3 / 0652] [I have a yoga fight at an antique store because the teacher is boring and lifeless. I shout, *"GIVE ME SOMETHING!"* at her from the back of the room. I'm in a bad mood. She doesn't oblige...so I get up and storm out.] //

✶✶

Maj. = 0- THE WEAVER: #0273
FRANK ROBINSON: #0394
BORING: #0540, #0662
CONCRETE: #0473, #0474, #0484, #0485

✶✶

#0265 - August 21, 2018 @ 6:30am (San Francisco, California)

[0265.1 / 0653] [I'm with DAVE GROHL hovering above a mass of land owned by his fami-

218

ly. A portion of it has been developed into a golf course. I'm captivated by the undulating pattern of green diamonds that have been cut meticulously into the fairways of this emerald phenomenon. We talk about music and family, laughing often as we sail slowly overhead. We feel like old friends.]

[0265.2 / 0654] [I'm naked, and in a tumbling competition. I leave the apparatus for a moment to sip some water and am admonished by a judge for breaking protocol.]

[0265.3 / 0655] [I'm on a steep downhill ski run in the French Alps, still naked. I race on a yellow unicycle at speeds of 68mph or greater. I take over the event communication system. *"It's cool. I've gone this fast before,"* I say rushing down the lush green mountain side. The speed of my descent unearths primordial fear in other participants.]

[0265.4 / 0656] [THE LOBBYIST and I drive a full car to the airport. Two of the passengers we pick up are guys who've come to town to work a motorcycle convention. We pick them up at the top of a large cobblestone presentation space full of people waving banners. We spiral downward to the main thoroughfare.] //

⁎⁎

Maj. = 17- *THE LOBBYIST: #0279*
DAVE GROHL: #0968
NAKED: #0633, #0641, #0682, #0708, #0717, #0773, #0784

⁎⁎

#0266 - August 22, 2018 @ 05:56 (San Francisco, California)

[0266.1 / 0657] [I hang socks and underwear on a clothesline in a dark room. I'm supposed to use paper clips, but I forget the technique. THE PILOT considers my forgetfulness flirtatious and is simultaneously *(partially)* turned on, and *(partially)* annoyed by my presence.]

[0266.2 / 0658] [I stand over a well, pulling a small washing line with knots tied in to it up from below. Small Polaroid photos are attached to the washing line with images of people and their assigned project roles. "PM," "SME," are scribbled at the bottom of the photos.]

[0266.3 / 0659] [I'm at a MADONNA concert. I've paid extra for a ticket where I can sit onstage directly in front of her podium. I can bi-locate to a seat in front of her sexiest dancers. Smoke rises from the stage.] //

⁎⁎

Maj. = 6- *THE PILOT: #0280*
MADONNA: #0280
SMOKE: #0495, #0541, #0545

⁎⁎

219

#0267 - August 22, 2018 @ 10:46 (San Francisco, California)

[0267.1 / 0660] [I'm at sea in rough water. It's light out. THE LION (*brotherly, talkative, and interested*) hides below deck filming me with a handheld camcorder. We're all wearing rain ponchos. The vessel slams repeatedly into a sharp outcropping of rocks. A large series of waves crest the deck, the last of which sweeps me overboard and in to open water.] //

✺✻

OPEN: #0476, #0518, #0528
SHARP: #0532, #0536, 0538, #0640
BELOW: #0621, #0669, #0698, #0760

✺✻

#0268 - August 23, 2018 @ 06:10 (San Francisco, California)

[0268.1 / 0661] [I inspect a series of art pieces in the desert.]
[0268.2 / 0662] [I walk from the intersection of 31st and Noe across San Francisco. I'm aware this intersection doesn't exist. All of the supporting narrative fades quickly as I wake up.] //

✺✻

ART PIECE: #0536, #0669
WALK: #0561, #0563, #0567, #0575, #0580
FADES: #0433, #0437, #0460, #0514, #0546, #0544, #0557

✺✻

#0269 - August 24, 2018 @ 02:27 (San Francisco, California)

[0269.1 / 0663] [Instagram assigns you a lover based on the things you like. I have a detailed discussion about this service with THE PRETZEL (*striving, penitent, and exhausted*).] //

✺✻

DISCUSSION: #0534, #0543, #0575
PRETZEL: #0513
INSTAGRAM: #0655, #0717

✺✻

#0270 - August 24, 2018 @ 05:35 (San Francisco, California)

[0270.1 / 0664] [Channel 3.]
[0270.2 / 0665] [I'm in a woodland cabin. I enter through a screen door. I offer a "Welcome" incantation to the space. A variety of non-physical beings enter. For a moment I think I may have overdone the spell. I move to the back patio where a number of small effigies have been rigged up with explosives to burn. A couple of fires occur indoors. One large piece in a back room doesn't ignite, which is most likely good because guests are still inside. The atmosphere suggests a party. Artists are chastised and revelers naysay the quality of the bonfires as they stand around with their palms extended towards the flames, warming.
I hold two dice sized cubes made of selenite. I'm given four others that are a darker stone

220

color *(whisky rocks perhaps?)*. It's dusky, and trails of light through the windows surrender to darkness. A few others gather in the room. One of them may be THE CARPENTER, but I'm not certain. I realize the small cubes are actually diamonds. While I'm already rich, the addition of the new four dark cubes greatly expand my estate's wealth. To ground myself and create a space for me to contemplate what to do with these net/new assets, I hide the six objects in a neat stack within a curio cabinet where I believe they are less likely to be noticed or stolen.] //

⁎⁎

Maj. =1- THE CARPENTER: #0273
WEALTH: #0410, #0748
CURIO CABINET: #0579
WHISKEY: #0564, #0692
WELCOME: #0429, #0431, #0664, #0672, #0748, #0756
DICE: #0513, #0798

⁎⁎

#0271 - August 27, 2018 @ 03:50 (Park City, Utah)

[0271.1 / 0666] [A couple I don't know sits on a couch at their home. *"You know it was here,"* the male says to the female. More detail related to their ongoing debate about "the sun" is lost.]

[0271.2 / 0667] [I'm fascinated by a bald guy, who by his nature is unassuming. Musical scores on his piano become increasingly interesting. He writes music performed by globally successful acts like COLDPLAY.]

[0271.3 / 0668] [THE PUBLIC MEDIUM and THE PEDIATRICIAN *(agreeable, honest, and willing)* sit on a log. I sit on the opposite end. We overlook a lagoon at twilight. Weeping willow branches extend over the water and reflect pink and blue hues up to a diamond starred sky overhead. THE PUBLIC MEDIUM wants to eat, but it's too late for me. I want to sleep. As I squint my eyes, I can see THE PEDIATRICIAN's gold creator connection radiating above his head.
"Magic is a chalky, sparkling blue when it's present," THE PEDIATRICIAN says as I drift off to sleep.]

[0271.4 / 0669] [I'm at a media event with DIANE FEINSTEIN where I help her field questions from the crowd. The mood is active and trending aggressive.]

[0271.5 / 0670] [I'm shown a secret artifact that resembles the Arc of the Covenant.]

[0271.6 / 0671] [I'm in a limo parked in a lot outside of a horse racing track at night. I want to organize, pay for, and schedule a social event here a year from now. I realize this will be very expensive. We approach the carriage house in our limo, slowing to talk with a bellhop. THE BOSS quickly exits the car claiming she, *"needs to visit her _____."*]

[0271.7 / 0672] [A guy implies he's been sleeping on the bus and knows, *"what we were up to."* THE INTELLIGENCE OFFICER *(curt, unwavering, and grounded)* and I continue to listen to EDM and pay him little attention.] //

⁕

Maj. = 18- THE PUBLIC MEDIUM: #0378
MAGIC: #0541, #0646
EDM: #0531, #0787
THE INTELLIGENCE OFFICER: #0273
THE BOSS: #0311

⁕

#0272 - August 27, 2018 @ 23:58 (Park City, Utah)

[0272.1 / 0673] [I screen scroll through a combo black and white Instagram feed for a user named "adam.jdl." It's unclear if it's me and another person, or someone else entirely.] //

⁕

SCROLL: #0530, #0589, #0748
BLACK AND WHITE: #0603, #0788, #0798
SCREEN: #0401, #0403, #0422

⁕

#0273 - August 28, 2018 @ 15:25 (Park City, Utah)

[0273.1 / 0674] [It's night time. I'm with THE DANCER in the kitchen nook of a large home. An accident has occurred. We've broken THE WEAVER and THE CARPENTER's wooden kitchen table. Both ends have snapped off of the leaves that extend below the legs of the table. We try our best to fix the damage, but we don't have C-Clamps to hold the pieces after we've glued them. We're overzealous with the glue and upon inspection notice a large amount of excess oozing out and collecting in small white circular pools on the floor.]

[0273.2 / 0675] [I'm in a high foot traffic area in an urban center. A large cube of steel scaffolding surrounds a single red English telephone booth. Unexpectedly, the scaffold collapses, and in doing so rips the steel telephone booth in half from top to bottom. The lines are crisp, and since there's not a lot of debris THE INTELLIGENCE OFFICER *(impatient, naysaying, and self-assured)* and I begin to systematically clean it up. It's not a major incident to us and we make the cleanup process a puzzle to solve.]

[0273.3 / 0676] [THE SOUTHERN BELLE *(gentile, woozy, and flirtatious)* and I share spirited discussion about which of our cars would best accommodate us having sex. We both have hatchback vehicles and the negotiation results in a stalemate. No sex. We're in our 20's.]

. . .

[0273.4 / 0677] [Random images of trains moving extremely fast.] //

⁂

Maj. = 0- THE WEAVER: #0279, 1- THE CARPENTER: #0296, 2- THE DANCER: #0274
BOOTH: #0450, #0563, #0621, #0711
PARALLEL: #0735, #0756, #0759
CRISP: #0482, #0502, #0513
THE INTELLIGENCE OFFICER: #0277
(You're beautiful)

⁂

#0274 - August 28, 2018 @ 05:25 (Park City, Utah)

[0274.1 / 0678] [I riff with THE GUITARIST.]

[0274.2 / 0679] [I walk around the base of a large wooden roller coaster at a popular amusement park.]

[0274.3 / 0680] [I'm on a train. The guy seated in front of me leans back so far it leaves no room for my legs.]

[0274.4 / 0681] [THE ATHEIST's accepted a new job in Singapore. As he fills out customs paperwork, I spend time helping THE DANCER and THE CHILD pack up their belongings for their upcoming relocation.] //

⁂

Maj. = 2- THE DANCER: #0333, 3- THE CHILD: #0275, 8- THE ATHEIST: #0281
Min. = ♣- THE GUITARIST: #0283
ROLLER COASTER: #0479, #0529, #0557, #0696
HELPING: #0620

⁂

#0275 - August 29, 2018 @ 02:44 (Park City, Utah)

[0275.1 / 0682] [I hook up with an older guy. I'm not attracted to him. I want it to be over.]

[0275.2 / 0683] [THE CHILD attends preschool. She stands on an indoor playground and waves at GRANDMA who appears very satisfied.]

[0275.3 / 0684] [I'm aware of only my head in a dark space. One by one, six white terrycloth towels are shoved in my mouth by a pair of gloved hands. A second set of hands firmly grip me by the throat.] //

⁂

Maj. = 3- THE CHILD: #0279, 11- GRANDMA: #0348
THROAT: #0755, #0780, #0782

⁂

⁂

#0276 - August 30, 2018 @ 03:27 (Park City, Utah)

[0276.1 / 0685] [I walk through an empty skyline apartment. It appears sleek and mostly grey. THE PIZZA DELIVERY BOY (*eccentric, talented, and unmotivated*) may live there, but he's not home if he does. The hallways are narrow and the ceilings are very high.]
[0276.2 / 0686] [I encounter a tween-age boy with a mental disorder. He tries to leave when I call his caretaker.] //

⁎⁎⁎

SLEEK: #0436, #0450, #0726
NARROW: #0481, #0527, #0548, #0559, #0613, #0631
EMPTY: #0422, #0431, #0441, #0446, #0476, #0503
THE PIZZA DELIVERY BOY: #0787

⁎⁎⁎

☙ 5.3 - THE BOOK OF BOÖTES: 0277-0299 ☙

#0277 - August 30, 2018 @ 04:55 (Park City, Utah)

[0277.1 / 0687] [I write a musical score. Angels assist me. They suggest I use a new nota-tion composed of three upward swooping arrows to appropriately accent a phrase. The result appears Avant Garde and would not be used on the contemporary grand staff.

I play the composition on an odd and marvelously complex instrument composed of a grid of rich cherry wood blocks suspended in midair. Each of the wooden blocks (2"x4") has a series of tiny golden strings running parallel to the length of the block. When the strings are tapped by my fingers, they produce warm healing tones. The instrument requires multiple players working in unison to generate music. The sounds produced are alien and beautiful.

We bring something special to the world later when we perform on TV.]

[0277.2 / 0688] [I play keyboards in JANET JACKSON's band. During a tracking session I discover the perfect transition for a new song when I accidentally strike a Sus2 chord. The producers are excited by their impromptu decision to secretly record the performance. I can see them working remotely in a studio booth while I perform with the band onstage in Florida.]

[0277.3 / 0689] [I'm in a modern flat at night with a small group of very chic people. An Asian woman guides us to a dark room full of reclining couches. She tells us to, *"Expect a four-to-five-hour experience,"* then tell us quite firmly, *"No sitting on each other's laps!"* THE INTELLI-GENCE OFFICER (*dismissive, cantankerous, and candid*), seated next to me, decides to rest his head on my left shoulder.]

[0277.4 / 0690] [A bat is crucified to the bottom of a shallow wooden dresser drawer. It suffers. We fill a tiny box suspended above its head with single drops of water to keep the creature alive. Once the bat is hydrated, we close the drawer.]

[0277.5 / 0691] [I sit on a set of outdoor bleachers overlooking a small pond. I watch a woman get swallowed whole in slow motion by a giant cartoon "snakefish" from underneath as she swims. I'm distracted by the size, jaggedness, and whiteness of the leviathan's teeth. The woman isn't shredded nor gouged. She simply falls into the giant mouth and disappears.]

[0277.6 / 0692] [I work as a barista at a bright and busy cafe. An odd gentleman wearing glasses and a fedora comes up next to me, places his baby in the microwave for 30 seconds, and then casually walks away. This upsets me and the team. We immediately call the police.

As we wait for them, I hand an old man his special-order pumpkin cookies. No one stops the microwave.] //

☙
MUSIC: #0557, #0559, #0560

225

MICROWAVE: #0470
ASIAN WOMAN: #0436, #0744
FEDORA: #0450, #0579, #0790
THE INTELLIGENCE OFFICER: #1289

⁂

#0278 - August 31, 2018 @ 06:42 (San Francisco, California)

[0278.1 / 0693] [I've committed a murder in a mid-sized suburban family home. I'm a male in my 30's. Post crime, I clean out kitchen cupboards and repackage food. Some of the violence occurred in the garage. I meticulously mop and clean the scene. I deliberately wrap mutilated body parts in plastic and stack them in the trunk of my car. I don't know who I've killed, but it feels calm and almost playful. A couple of old bloodied pillows would be best discarded in a neighbor's garbage bin a few doors down. I dump them and drive home.

When I arrive, a police officer surprises me by jumping up from the back seat of the car. He's suspicious of me. I let him in my house to snoop around. I sit in a rocking chair and watch TV with my legs crossed, curious if he'll find evidence of other crimes in my garage and kitchen cupboards. I've been stealthy and thorough so I feel calm. I don't know what he finds.] //

⁂

SUBURBAN: #0563, #0635, #0672, #0726, #0741, #0768
VIOLENCE: #0549, #0576, #0768
CALM: #0424, #0788
BACK SEAT: #0455, #0579, #0795

⁂

#0279 - September 2, 2018 @ 05:04 (San Francisco, California)

[0279.1 / 0694] [A car drives through a field of chest high amber toned grass. I view it omnisciently from above. THE WEAVER drives the car. Large cow-like creatures are mostly obscured by the high wavy grass. The car barrels across the land quickly but avoids hitting the creatures.]

[0279.2 / 0695] [THE LOBBYIST momentarily unzips the rain flap to his tent. I rush inside. Everything goes dark. I sit on a couch with THE KANGAROO discussing what he, *"really wants out of life."* He draws a cartoonish sketch in black marker of a nude male groin region on a whiteboard.

I hear THE CHILD wake up from her nap downstairs. I go down to check on her, and find her standing on her bed. She smiles and reaches for me saying, *"HUG ME AND GET ME DOWN!"*

When I pick her up, she says, *"SHOW ME HOW TO DO IT! NO, I WILL DO IT!"*

I place her back on the bed and let her climb down on her own.] //

⁂

Maj. = 0- THE WEAVER: #0299, 2- THE CHILD: #0280, 17- THE LOBBYIST: #0304

Min. = ♠- *THE KANGAROO: #0284*
AMBER: #0422, #0423, #0437
WHITEBOARD: #0735
⁂

#0280 - September 3, 2018 @ 02:42 (San Francisco, California)

[0280.1 / 0696] [I'm at home in my parent's house. I'm naked. THE CHILD is coming over to visit and I need to get dressed as quickly as possible. I hear her arrive. I choose to run down a back staircase to get to the garage. I run quickly. She runs up from behind me shouting, *"I'm coming! I'm coming to see you!"*
She startles me when we unexpectedly meet at a doorway and says, *"Oh!"* when she catches a glimpse of my naked body. I quickly pull on some pajamas and say, ***"Please give me four minutes."*** She says, *"OK!"* and runs off.]

[0280.2 / 0697] [I distribute toothbrushes on the deck of a "Fake Ship." MADONNA doesn't want a toothbrush. I've created some sort of public hygiene project to bolster group health. Various decks of the ship are linked by waterslides. MADONNA looks very old. Her skin is haggard from smoking. She looks partied out.]

[0280.3 / 0698] [I have a casual conversation with THE PILOT about sexual kinks. He's my shrink. I've had my fingers up my ass all day. I stick a stinky digit to his nose like a poppers bottle to offer him a smell. At the end of our scheduled hour, I agree with his general assessment of my neuroses.] //

⁂
Maj. = 2- *THE CHILD. #0313, 6- THE PILOT: #0399*
MADONNA: #0481
SHRINK: #0498
KINK: #0541, #0671
STINK: #0484, #0556, #046
HYGIENE: #0668
⁂

#0281 - September 3, 2018 @ 07:00 (San Francisco, California)

[0281.1 / 0699] [I encounter THE BREWMASTER and THE PARKS DIRECTOR (*independent, responsive, and qualified*) walking around on jumping stilts. ***"Did you walk all the way here from LA on those?"*** I ask. *"No, we flew in!"* THE BREWMASTER says with a smile as he raises a stein.]

[0281.2 / 0700] [I wear an Oculus V/R headset and run through a virtual maze, guided by cues given by THE DRAGON TAMER (*savorer, precise, and controlling*). Her directions are deliberate and clear, but I don't trust them after repeatedly running into physical walls which disrupts my game play.]

. . .

[0281.3 / 0701] [I'm back in an office job. The CEO requests a conversation with THE ROCK STAR SPOUSE *(centered, quiet, and grounded)*. He forces her to generate her own video content for an internal training program, while bearing the full burden of production costs. The team considers the CEO's request unfair and absurd.]

[0281.4 / 0702] [People around a conference table eavesdrop on a confidential conversation. I close the door and admonish my coworkers for wanting to create drama. I have very strong opinions about the CEO's performance.]

[0281.5 / 0703] [I'm inside a building driving a car in the dark through an active construction zone. Teams of workers cover small hills with a black substance, over a layer of carpet. Work is in progress the first time we enter. On the second pass through we drive down and across the small rolling hills like character cars in Super Mario Kart.]

[0281.6 / 0704] [The family is in Iowa. While on a video call, they tell me they're taking THE ATHEIST to Ja-Mars for his first pork tenderloin. He doesn't know what to expect.
"No! I want to be there for his first milkshake." I complain.] //

✲

Maj. = 8- THE ATHEIST: #0386
CEO: #0441, #0716, #0799
THE PARKS DIRECTOR: #0717
THE BREWMASTER: #0717

✲

#0282 - September 4, 2018 @ 01:58 (San Francisco, California)

[0282.1 / 0705] [I'm at a summer cottage on a humid, overcast morning. I'm with THE OBSERVER *(informed, paced, and thorough)* and a few other women sharing conversation. I take my erect penis out and begin stretching it. There's no sexual charge towards the women, but they interpret my actions as aggressive and abusive. I explain that I'm performing my daily therapy to conclude healing from Peyronie's Disease. My conduct would be exactly the same at this time of day, regardless of the company I keep. I'm playful with my penis. My focus goes no further than my body. The women move far away from me, leave the house, and walk across a meadow. THE OBSERVER calls the police as I think to myself,
"I must hang around with men too much."] //

✲

THERAPY: #0476, #0487, #0527, #0740
OVERCAST: #0623
PENIS: #0563, #0637, #0645, #0647, #0724
THE OBSERVER: #0712

✲

#0283 - September 4, 2018 @ 04:50 (San Francisco, California)

[0283.1 / 0706] [The majority of this dream takes place in a motel complex in the sky. I recall driving around in search of my building, passing numerous glass frontages and restaurants that seem to all be staffed by the same, single person, dressed in a tuxedo. I stop and eat multiple times, yet I never satiate. Once my plates are cleared, I glance up to discover I'm in a mega-church. Many beings *(in and out of bodies)* are curious about me when I check in for a service. THE HILL *(cautious, loving, and tactile)* greets me and gives me a key to apartment 3-4. I wander the complex interior for a while. It feels a bit like a dormitory and a bit like a Patagonian lodge.

I encounter THE GUITARIST and we decide to create an impromptu performance for the neighbors. His electric guitar doesn't work. He wants to play a song that I don't know and haven't practiced. We might be lovers in this reality. The energy between us is a bit tense. I depart for my room, feeling guilty for cheating on a juice cleanse. I botched it by eating at the end of the fourth day of five. The guilt grows stronger when a group of cute guys arrive. THE HILL has hired them to do a surprise acapella performance of the song "Let's Hear It for The Boy" from Footloose to celebrate my fasting accomplishment.] //

⁂

Min. = ♣- *THE GUITARIST: #0312*
LODGE: #0729, #0751, #0775, #0782
GUILT: #0649
THE HILL: #0404

⁂

#0284 - September 4, 2018 @ 05:59 (San Francisco, California)

[0284.1 / 0707] [It feels like a spring evening at an English cottage. I'm at a house party sitting on a chair across from a large white sectional couch. Guests enter one by one. THE BLUE HAIRED BLOKE *(intoxicated, numb, and sad)* arrives. THE KANGAROO follows behind shortly thereafter and sits on the couch. He promptly falls asleep. I walk stealthily over and startle him by grabbing his shoulder and playfully shouting *"WAKE UP!"*

I have a few odd interactions with another male guest. We seem to find ourselves in each other's personal space in awkward moments. One of them includes sticking his arm through an open window to grab something off a table from which I'm eating. His arm moves repeatedly across my face. He makes conversation with someone outside; blithely unaware he's hitting me in the gob. This interaction remains interesting to me as I eat handfuls of air-dried, triangular nacho cheese corn chips.

I exit the party and have an unclear interaction with the police, while crossing the street with THE CARTOONIST *(expressive, witty, and accomplished)* and another man and woman I don't recognize, yet refer to as "Phil and Kim." At a crosswalk I ask THE CARTOONIST a question, but I'm unable to hear/recall/interpret his answer. He feels sad, almost let down by *(and skeptical of)* me because of the secrets I've shared with him.] //

⁂

Min. = ♠- *THE KANGAROO: #0292*
CROSSWALK: #0472, #0614

SAD: #0622, #0647, #0657
THE CARTOONIST: #0987

⁂

#0285 - September 5, 2018 @ 04:06 (San Francisco, California)

[0285.1 / 0708] [A construction crew builds a skyscraper. THE SKATER *(trendy, cool, and mysterious)* decides to take an intentional fall off the side of the building and is reunited at the bottom with a brother and sister. He doesn't want to make a big deal out of the interaction. **"They've been estranged for a really long time. They each crave their own individual experiences. It's not about rushing for a quick reconciliation simply for the benefit of the family."**
THE SKATER decides he's going to jump again, from the top of the iron scaffolding. His fall is hastened by an unexpected slip of the foot, which sends him tumbling off the edge and cascading headfirst toward the ground. The mood is playful. There is no fear, only exhilaration. His action compels other members of the crew to swan dive head first off the edge, fully understanding this is a totally dangerous thing to do. Shuttle cars await them when they reach the bottom, which expeditiously return the "pavement swan divers" back to the top of the building, like ski lifts or rollercoaster trains.] //

⁂
DIVE: #0607
SCAFFOLD: #0580
HEAD FIRST: #0538
⁂

#0286 - September 5, 2018 @ 06:29 (San Francisco, California)

[0286.1 / 0709] ["OTTERBINE?"]
[0286.2 / 0710] [I attend a gay four way wedding set on a plantation home with a large column lined porch and a vast green lawn peppered with attendees. I pass through the crowd and overhear various conversations and gossip:
"I don't think this is a good thing. We're losing 200 members." "Giving up my last name would be emasculating." "Most of the guys I know who do THAT are femmy bottoms."
Photographs are taken of the four men on the lawn. A banner unfurls and welcomes everyone to the "O'DOO Brothers," nuptials. Each guy has elected to keep the first letter of his former last name, which they concatenate into their new surname. The order of the letters drives further gossipy debate among guests. The guys simply rest joyfully in the new family name they're created for themselves. They are all handsome and uniquely empowered.] //

⁂
BANNER: #0620, #0748, #0796
PORCH: #0547, #0622
EMPOWERED: #0401
⁂

#0287 - September 6, 2018 @ 04:27 (San Francisco, California)

[0287.1 / 0711] [I work with a new, indecipherable, and unfamiliar energy.] //

⁎⁎

ABSTRACT: #0468, #0548, #0580
NEW: #0582, #0586, #0594, #0603, #0611, #0614, #0637
UNFAMILIAR: #0410

⁎⁎

#0288 - September 6, 2018 @ 04:45 (San Francisco, California)

[0288.1 / 0712] [An earthquake rattles the house while THE POINT GUARD sleeps over. We spend time laughing at a _____ in the dark.] //

⁎⁎

EARTHQUAKE: #0674, #0787
THE POINT GUARD: #0351

⁎⁎

#0289 - September 6, 2018 @ 06:00 (San Francisco)

[0289.1 / 0713] ["THIS DREAM UNINTENTIONALLY LEFT BLANK."] //

⁎⁎

THIS DREAM UNINTENTIONALLY LEFT BLANK: #0766

⁎⁎

#0290 - September 7, 2018 @ 04:45 (San Francisco, California)

[0290.1 / 0714] [I'm onstage behind a grand red curtain. Members of a band gather and perform a sound check with their instruments. Some discussion emerges about using the "expensive" guitar picks tonight. Fragments of cheap ones are scattered around the stage like fingernail trimmings. I forgot we're the headliner. I'm confused by the opening act. I watch the grease painted clown face of the current performer set squarely in the center of a TV monitor. A bit of confusion and disagreement about the set list for tonight's performance erupts between band members. A young boy is scheduled to sit in as drummer for tonight's performance. A series of lime green house keys made from hard injection molded plastic are scattered among my cords and guitar pedals. The thunderous sound of distorted guitars wakes me up.] //

⁎⁎

CONFUSION: #0485, #0527, #0537, #0744, #0762, #0775
PLASTIC: #0407, #0427, #0430, #0433, #0461, #0481
OPENING: #0494, #0502, #0508, #0572, #0764, #0774

⁎⁎

#0291 - September 8, 2018 @ 04:46 (San Francisco, California)

[0291.1 / 0715] [It's August. I'm 40 years old. I might be at a bowling alley, then realize we're at THE MOTO's place. THE MOTO (*quiet, rebellious, and strong*) has decided to move to Charlotte, North Carolina with THE SWAB (*quiet, mischievous, and playful*) to start a new life. Many people offer congratulations at their going away party. THE MOTO has chosen to live with THE SWAB and THE TAR HEEL (*somatic, cerebral, and receptive*) in the large compound they recently built. They pass photographs around the circle of guests. I have strong sexual attraction towards both THE MOTO and THE SWAB, but I haven't had a physical encounter with either of them. I feel unsettled, but frisky and playful.

When someone asks, *"What are you going to do with this place?"* THE MOTO huffs, *"I bought it for $600,000, now it's worth $6,000,000. What do you think I'm going to do?"*] //

⁎⁎

GOING AWAY: #0786
CIRCLE: #0431, #0440, #0466, #0473
CONGRATULATIONS: #0429
THE TAR HEEL: #0726

⁎⁎

#0292 - September 8, 2018 @ 05:57 (San Francisco, California)

[0292.1 / 0716] [I'm on a college campus at night. THE KANGAROO and I plan to go on a date tomorrow afternoon. He calls and suggests we delay a day. We postpone. Later as agreed, I pick him up in my car and drive down Maple Street in Oxford, Ohio. I'm sober. He's had a couple of drinks, rendering him "happy drunk" and quite playful. We enter a female dormitory. We break into a room, where a television and stereo remain on to create the illusion that someone's home. We spend some of our date time making techno music and playing synthesizers.

"Don't confuse this with some sort of love story," THE KANGAROO says, becoming a bit more disruptive and sloppier.

"That's fine. We're still going to fuck, yeah? And by the way, love stories aren't short. Let's pick this one up again when we're 70."

We disrobe. I flip upside down and float as we engage in an anti gravity 69. I suck his dick and play with his butt. I'm confused by the absurdity of the situation, but choose to lean into it.

Our overnight encounter concludes. We stand a few feet away from each other. While looking one another up and down we both say in unison,

"I think we did a good job of meeting in the middle."] //

⁎⁎

Min. = ♠- THE KANGAROO: #0314
OHIO: #0429, #0573, #0722
LOVE STORY: #0601

⁎⁎

#0293 - September 9. 2018 @ 05:55 (San Francisco, California)
*This dream had two different vignettes run concurrently. *

[0293.1 / 0717] [1] I find myself in New Orleans. It's swelteringly hot. I observe the scene from two concurrent vantage points. The first, an omniscient view of the city scape, pulled back to see the city sitting well below sea level. A large storm brewing off the coast is likely to submerge the whole thing. On the left it's light, alive and active feeling. To the right of the

232

levy, it's equally as active though the tenor is dark, brooding and calculating. The second vantage point is in first person. I run away from abusive family members who chase me. I rescue a young boy and commit to get him to safety.

A group of female yogis drive up to the two of us in an oversized getaway car. They offer us a ride. I blink and discover myself in a dark room observing a surgery. A bone fragment is removed from the palm side of a wrist. The bone is extracted perpendicular to the direction I anticipate. The wrist is left with two circular wounds the size of dimes. Coagulating, tar colored blood slowly rises and spills across the patient's wrist and on to the operating table.]

[0293.2 / 0718] [2] I'm in Las Vegas. I drive fast down the strip in a car. I cut hard to the left into the parking deck of a new casino adjacent to the PALMS Hotel. I drive upwards in a spiraling motion. At the top of the deck, I'm received by a valet. I'm rushed inside quickly to a concierge. I place a heavy white plastic bag containing wet clothes on the counter. A Shipibo medicine woman stands behind the desk tall, and sweetly grinning. Her demeanor is calm, receptive and accommodating. I don't know her.

"I must get this dried out right now," I say pulling an ornamented alpaca sweater from the bag.

I look closer and notice it's an exceptionally complex pattern made from tiny strands of magnetized gold beads. The medicine woman honors my request. She joyfully handles the garment exclaiming, *"Es Alegria!"* as she holds it up in front of her as a golden ring of light surrounds her.

I'm unsure if it's her aura or simply the ambient light from the marquee. Perhaps they're the same thing. She glows. I feel uplifted and resolved. It seems by surrendering the sweater we've done something that pleases many ancestors.] //

***

WOUND: #0533, #0715, #0723, #0791
TWO. #0792, #0793, #0798, #0799
BROODING: #0496, #0500, #0569
VALET: #0522

***

#0294 - September 10, 2018 @ 02:39 (San Francisco, California)

[0294.1 / 0719] [I watch drag queens perform on television. As I flip through the channels, I notice that channel #2 is the "Gay Channel." I get bored with it and change the station. When the channel flips, everything turns black. When I open my eyes, I find myself driving a car with ZACK DE LE ROCHA riding shotgun. We cruise through decaying urban areas. He used to see a lot of gang violence here. Three other guys ride in the back seat concealed by shadows. Soon I realize we're filming a TV pilot.

"Yo, I don't recognize any of these cars, son" ZACK says to me in his distinctive rap-rock performance voice.

"I'm sorry, Z," I say as I eat a box of three hot cinnamon rolls, covered with gooey white icing.

We roll by a series of parked cars. People tailgate and party around a series of dystopian oil barrel fires.] //

⁂

ZACK DE LA ROCHA: #0334
GAY: #0435, #0467, #0563, #0645, #0653, #0669, #0744
CINNAMON: #0487, #0617, #0759
GOOEY: #0489, #0586

⁂

#0295 - September 10, 2018 @ 04:36 (San Francisco, California)
*Multiple distinct threads in this dream. *

[0295.1 / 0720] [I observe a new Olympic event called "Gymnastics Halfpipe." Athletes perform parkour stunts and bound around a halfpipe covered in tan leather. It feels like floor exercise and vault spliced with skateboarding.]

[0295.2 / 0721] [A Burning Man-like gathering occurs at a Moroccan Castle at night. It has a fairytale feel. The exterior of the castle is decorated like jeweled gingerbread. Overall, the mood is whimsical. A couple of teams have just completed a soccer match. Both teams are owned by MARK ZUCKERBERG, who observes the action from a glass walled room within the upper interior of the castle. He's flanked by two male COO's, one high on crystal meth, the other is crying.

I run up a spiral staircase to their observation deck and note they've destroyed a competitor's product. Tiny precious metal components scatter across the smooth marble floor. I scramble to pick up pieces of the crushed new technology, then charge the drugged-out COO and smack him across the face. I encounter ZUCKERBERG and attempt to take a selfie with him, but he slinks away slyly. He doesn't want his image captured anywhere. I get a psychic download from him that his *"primary index has profound issues"* and that data pulled from *"the system"* is used for nefarious purposes at *"an alarming rate."*

Later, the moth affected COO makes another brief appearance. He attempts to get his wits about him after sustaining the strong blow to the face.] //

⁂

MARK ZUCKERBERG: #0556
SKATEBOARD: #0566, #0763
CRYING: #0456, #0571, #0610, #0759, #0780
CASTLE: #0490, #0750, #0757
Are you paying attention?

⁂

#0296 - September 12, 2018 @ 05:30 (San Francisco, California)

[0296.1 / 0722] [A significant amount of time is spent in pairs, in a group of people doing healing work. More occurs, but what I most recall is sending heart shaped waves of energy from chakra to chakra with my partner. The environment is supportive and feels "Hyper-Real," beyond beauty and reality.]

. . .

[0296.2 / 0723] [I'm with THE CARPENTER. We share company with some neighbors. We sit on a bench with a woman behind us and have a humorous discussion about different types of car engines. THE CARPENTER pop quizzes the neighbor's knowledge.

"That one's a big block!" a female neighbor exclaims and continues, *"and that one is a straight six!"*

Some laughter and teasing ensue. Each time the woman gets an answer correct I notice the sunglasses on THE CARPENTER's face change. It's odd to see his eyes distorted (*black dilated pupils*), but it all remains playful. He feels like a trickster, much like he did when I was a boy.] //

⁎⁎

Maj. = 1- THE CARPENTER: #0300
HEART: #0611, #0618, #0624, #0631, #0655, #0674, #0719
PAIRS: #0459, #0466, #0474, #0500
⁎⁎

#0297 - September 12, 2018 @ 6:45am (San Francisco, California)

[0297.1 / 0724] [I hang out with THE LINGUIST (*kinky, game, and smart*) and THE HUSBAND (*sensitive, endeared, and sweet*). They move to the side of the room to have a private conversation. As they move away, I begin to distrust them. I'm skeptical of what they're talking about, though it doesn't concern me.]

[0297.2 / 0725] [A blurry scene occurs. Many detailed fragments move through quickly. I find myself in a mall cafeteria-like setting, wanting to go to a soup kitchen. THE RESTAURA-TEUR (*hurting, regrouping, and resilient*) waits at a table inside. A young woman wearing an apron asks me to, *"please come back in 20 minutes."*

It's apparent the staff is late, but unclear if the schedule was incorrectly published. Perhaps they're in revolt and unionizing. The young woman shows me around the kitchen, offering me her opinions on why things are, *"so out of whack."*] //

⁎⁎

PRIVATE: #0506, #0527, #0694, #0796
APRON: #0561, #0780
OPINIONS: #0446, #0457, #0476, #0529, #0594, #0717, #0743
THE LINGUIST: #0353
THE HUSBAND: #0353
THE RESTAURATEUR: #0386
⁎⁎

#0298 - September 13, 2018 @ 03:30 (San Francisco, California)

[0298.1 / 0726] [I leave a KORN concert after it finishes. I stand in line at a venue with large Ionian columns. BRIAN WELCH smokes inconspicuously next to a column watching the crowd exit. He flicks the half-smoked cigarette away and quickly rushes inside, and out of view. I look to my right and see THE DANDY (*deep, uniquely expressed, and present*) wearing VIP credentials. He participates as a team interviewee for the current tour and reflects on his job as a roadie. He speaks humorously about his responsibility for many important (*yet seemingly mundane*) daily tasks.

The venue is under construction. The security service changes management companies and uniforms as I stand in line. When I make it to the exit, I'm handed a clipboard and requested to, *"please confirm your full first and last name,"* by a woman expecting a signature. As I hand the clipboard back, she offers me an apology for making me wait and acknowledges I may have missed most of the next show on my calendar.] //

⁎⁎

KORN: #0303
COLUMNS: #0615
VIP: #0568

⁎⁎

#0299 - September 13, 2018 @ 04:35 (San Francisco, California)

[0299.1 / 0727] *["_____ Boy won't give me $.75 to hire a band."]*

[0299.2 / 0728] [BEYONCÉ and I take multiple selfies. None of the photos of us eating pizza can be posted to Instagram.]

[0299.3 / 0729] [*Fear of dating*: Images of people I'm attracted to flash by one at a time. I decide I don't want to date anyone saying, ***"People have their own problems and I'm not interested in dealing with them."***]

[0299.4 / 0730] [I dictate and scribe massive amounts of dream detail multiple times, waking from dreams within dreams...***to begin again***. I collect hundreds of pages on a loop about a ceremony I lead. Pilgrims step forward one at a time to have a golden upside-down crescent moon painted on their foreheads. Additionally, people are photographed with their faces brightly surrounded by a mass of small pink helium balloons. The photographs are gifted to members of the community. THE WEAVER is revered and has been given many of the images by pilgrims over her years assigned to the temple. The mood is warm and playful. She gives me one of her gifted photos, which I deeply appreciate.]

[0299.5 / 0731] [I experience tremendous downward pressure from above on my face and neck. Perhaps I'm being restrained by invisible beings. I attempt to get up but am pushed down to the floor repeatedly. This experience is familiar. I'm not afraid but I exhibit frustration and annoyance as I meditate and attempt to find a way to slip away from this situation until I eventually wake up.] //

⁎⁎

Maj. = 0- THE WEAVER: #0300
BEYONCÉ #0346
PRESSURE: #0403, #0527, #0540, #0607

⁎⁎

PART 6 - CRASH

#0300 - #0367

"...So baby, dry your eyes
Save all the tears you've cried
Oh, that's what dreams are made of
Oh baby, we belong
In a world that must be strong
Oh, that's what dreams are made of
And in the end
On dreams we will depend
'Cause that's what love is made of..."

-Sammy Hagar

* * *

September 14, 2018 - November 16, 2018

JOSHUA D. LUNDELL

⁂

⁂ 6.1 - THE BOOK OF VIRGO: 0300-0331 ⁂

#0300 - September 14, 2018 @ 04:00 (San Francisco, California)

[0300.1 / 0732] [THE WEAVER and THE CARPENTER have a discussion in a minivan. They're parked in a snow-covered driveway during a blizzard. THE CARPENTER's in the driver's seat. THE WEAVER's on the passenger side.]

[0300.2 / 0733] [I shop for jeans in a large department store. The eyelets of my belt have worn out after being pulled through the loops of hundreds of pairs of pants.]

[0300.3 / 0734] [A rotary phone rings. No one answers it.]

[0300.4 / 0735] [An alarm sounds and wakes me up, four seconds before my set alarm actually goes off.] //

⁂
Maj. = 0- THE WEAVER: #0303, 1- THE CARPENTER: #0309
BELT: #0493, #0529, #0534, #0621, #0698
ALARM: #0556, #0558
⁂

#0301 - September 15, 2018 @ 03:23 (Vail, Colorado)

[0301.1 / 0736] [Multiple instances of being forcibly held face down to the bed. I leave my body and run around my hotel room. I stumble around in the dark looking for a light switch. After much searching, I become frustrated. *"If I could just put on some music this would be so much easier,"* I think. I move around the room so much I become disoriented. I worry my teeth are going to fall out.]

[0301.2 / 0737] [I teach yoga in a courtyard at night. A female student jumps on the opposite side of a wrought iron fence and startles me. *"I did not like that,"* I say. A male student reaches into a woven basket, pulls out six small rubber ducks and places them in a triangular formation. After class, I pick up a cell phone left behind by a student. A small sticker on the reverse helps me know it's THE SEXUAL SACRED's (*extroverted, tactile, and light*) device. I'm annoyed the studio only sells coffee, and a carbonated blueberry energy drink. No water.] //

⁂
RUBBER: #0426, #0469, #0615
COFFEE: #0527, #0528, #0554, #0581
DRINK: #0411, #0427, #0428, #0532, #0624
⁂

#0302 - September 15, 2018 @ 07:54 (Vail, Colorado)

[0302.1 / 0738] [This abstract dream explores the concept of deep community. I'm surrounded mostly by women. THE GROOMSMAN (*intellectual, thoughtful, and grounded*) is the only other man present besides me. Some hang out by a swimming pool talking on cell phones. I facilitate an exercise designed to help people *"break through gateways"* and conquer fears. THE ORPHAN, THE MEEK, "Melanie," THE GREEN TARA (*feminine, cunning, and sharp*) and THE GROOMSMAN participate. I cradle THE GREEN TARA's head in my hand and hold her in my arms until she feels complete with her guttural catharsis. Some of them get *"the point."* Others don't. The scene concludes in a long-carpeted room where participants repeatedly run from one end to the other.] //

✵

GATEWAY: #0655
COMPLETE: #0668, #0670, #0698, #0717, #0722
THE GREEN TARA: #0658
THE ORPHAN: #0367
THE MEEK: #0422

✵

#0303 - September 17, 2018 @ 06:30 (San Francisco, California)

[0303.1 / 0739] [THE CONCIERGE (*adept, informed, and helpful*) organizes a house for the band KORN to crash and recover at when their most recent tour concludes. She's precise in organizing ground transportation for them to/from every venue. When they arrive, she gives them philosophical inquiry work. THE WEAVER consoles JONATHAN DAVIS as he talks about his wife's recent suicide.]

[0303.2 / 0740] [I give a short talk about the band THROBBING GRISTLE. Listeners are familiar with GENESIS P.-ORRIDGE's origin story, and the integration of his/her/their wife's characteristics after she left her body. The harrowing tale is received by a deeply attentive and reverent audience.] //

✵

Maj. = 0- THE WEAVER: #0327
KORN: #0372
JONATHAN DAVIS: #0369
TRANSPORTATION: #0554
THE CONCIERGE: #0405

✵

#0304 - September 19, 2018 @ 04:53 (Van Nuys, California)

[0304.1 / 0741] [I walk down an office hallway. On each door under the occupant's nameplate are a short list of *"endorsed emotions."* Little beings walk at knee level in both directions looking for their names, like students hoping to get a part in the school play. *"Endorsed*

Emotions" are unconscious, blind places in the office occupant that need to be awakened and experienced.]

[0304.2 / 0742] [I have a brief verbal interaction with a human-equine hybrid being that refers to itself as "COMPACHA." Onlookers marvel, quietly whispering *"that's the compassion being,"* under their breath to one another. THE LOBBYIST makes a bet with THE WILDERNESS GUIDE. THE WILDERNESS GUIDE loses and must get naked in public while holding only a single, blank, white 8.5"x11" sheet of paper. THE WILDERNESS GUIDE finds the circumstances funny and confidently struts out onto a stage in the center of town with the piece of paper held overhead.]

[0304.3 / 0743] [Lots of fast moving, hyperreal content. So real I don't realize I'm sleeping. It's lost when I wake up...again.] //

✶✶

Maj = 17- THE LOBBYIST: #0317
COMPASSION: #0693
HYBRID: #0456, #0534, #0718
THE WILDERNESS GUIDE: #0321

✶✶

#0305 - September 19, 2018 @ 07:08 (Van Nuys, California)

[0305.1 / 0744] [I drive through a wheat field in a classic car. THE ACTOR owns a house on the acreage and refers to it as, *"the cultural hotbed and creative center of Sonoma County."*]

[0305.2 / 0745] [I walk through a mall with onyx floors. Two guys rapidly photograph me. One has a social media profile that shows a leg dangling in a pool (*screen name: "XXL"*). Another stands in front of a castle. He has floppy hair and rotting teeth. We stand around a table eating softened portions of vegan certified Toblerone as we check each other out. It's flirty and noncommittal.] //

✶✶

Min. = 10- THE ACTOR: #0375
VEGAN: #0698
CLASSIC CAR: #0607

✶✶

#0306 - September 20, 2018 @ 04:37 (Van Nuys, California)

[0306.1 / 0746] [I'm with THE ROBOT and THE RAPTOR in an unfamiliar house. We make props for a real estate flipping show. Random one-off requirements come in via text message. THE ROBOT's ringtone mimics the sound of a dot matrix printer. I'm excited something I've built will be included in the current episode. I've made a fake shelving unit

from balsa wood, but it's faux finish looks sturdier (*like cherry or mahogany*). The speed of requests intensifies causing THE ROBOT to shout,
"EVERY PERSON FOR THEMSELVES!"
I drop what I'm doing and run to the bathroom to pee, tripping over a purple sparkly army boot left in the hall.]

[0306.2 / 0747] [THE ANIMATOR (*magical, meticulous, and abstract*) and I ride in a car driving down a massive highway towards a flooded version of San Francisco. We debate if we'll stay because, *"the water level at Hetch Hetchy is so high this season."* According to health care experts and local CEOs speaking on the radio, *"the next round of funding will bring new jobs we can't yet comprehend."*
It's mid-morning. The air is crisp. The road leading toward the flood is surrounded by dense green trees.]

[0306.3 / 0748] [I attend a very confusing brunch at a modern, high end restaurant. THE RUBY (*firm, scientific, and motherly*) and THE PROFESSOR (*artistic, uplifting, and accomplished*) describe their recent experiences in Spain, though they didn't travel together.
They each take one bite off their expensive plated meal, then shoot a quick glance at a $7 buffet set up across the room. They quickly rise and move to the self-serve station. When they return and resume speaking with me, they begin to bounce up and down on their chairs. The chair cushions are small hump-like mini-trampolines.
"SORRY!" "SORRY!" "Sorry!!" "Sorry?!" "Sorry!" they say in rapid succession as they bounce higher and higher.
Both become stuck in a delayed auditory feedback loop that interrupts their conversational abilities. When the bouncing and apology loop subsides, they both agree to make similar versions of an abstract butterfly through use of a *"mental template."* Both shoot red lasers from their fingertips to cut out the butterflies from credit card sized segments of steel.]
//

✲✲

Min. = ◆- *THE RAPTOR: #0382,* ♥- *THE ROBOT: #0396*
BUFFET: #0549, #0634, #0755, #0759
TRAMPOLINE: #0488, #0606, #0794
EXPENSIVE: #0587
THE ANIMATOR: #0332
THE PROFESSOR: #0614
✲✲

#0307 - September 20, 2018 @ 06:45 (Van Nuys, California)

[0307.1 / 0749] [I attend an urban street fair at night. I recognize THE HUSTLER (*musical, handy, and possessive*) enter, as he walks under a giant red umbrella. His dreadlocks are tied up into a tight ball atop his head. He wears black horn-rimmed sunglasses. I walk up to him to take a selfie and say,
"Hey we should send this to THE GAMER (*ecstatic, commanding, and clear*)." THE HUSTLER agrees.] //

⁜

URBAN: #0566, #0614, #0620, #0682
DREADLOCKS: #0548
HORN: #0532, #0600
THE GAMER: #0494

⁜

#0308 - September 21, 2018 @ 03:45 (Van Nuys, California)

[0308.1 / 0750] [Clear narrative occurs in the dream, but recall doesn't stick. Amusement park. Jack-o-lanterns. I yell at a _____ park employee, then later apologize. The apology is appreciated.] //

⁜

AMUSEMENT: #0438, #0534, #0683, #0769, #0791
NARRATIVE: #0436
APPRECIATE: #0433, #0497, #0503, #0538, #0620, #0681

⁜

#0309 - September 22, 2018 @ 09:03 (Van Nuys, California)

[0309.1 / 0751] [I'm on a weekend getaway with my family. THE CARPENTER asks me to lead the way to find, *"the mint green SUV."* Our rental vehicle is sleek and futuristic looking, and appears to have wheels mounted on large metal bands similar to a tank. I hop in the driver's seat and proceed to plow the vehicle over the highway median into oncoming traffic.]

[0309.2 / 0752] [I remove a pair of new headphones from a small white package. It's a next generation Apple product. The device connects to a phone by a single lit point the same thickness as a former headphone cord. The dongle is magnetized and sticks to various points on the phone.]

[0309.3 / 0753] [I observe a vast mound of trash in a landfill predominantly composed of single use plastics.]

[0309.4 / 0754] [I'm in a wooden mountain retreat setting at dawn. I stand outside of a large cabin on a deck with golden light streaming through large rectangular windows. I stand at the far-right end of a row with other people. THE DALAI LAMA emerges from the doorway flanked by two attendants donning dark orange robes. He offers blessings to our row. He singles me out and I step forward. As I kneel in front of him, he frowns and looks away. I'm not bothered by this. I simply stand up. THE VICTOR steps forward to be blessed and receives THE DALAI LAMA's hand on his forehead. He's also given a sacred splinter of wood.
We file out of the venue in pairs, passing by a highly detailed teak box held by a stone-faced young woman. A strand of prayer flags hangs suspended in front of her. The middle

flag has a Tibetan phrase printed across it. When translated to English it awkwardly uses a *"negative infinitive"* verb: "NO TO _____." I forget the word and the sign's warning.
"Saturday I was sad. Right now, I am so good," I say with tears streaming down my face and my heart burning wildly in my chest.] //

✰

Maj. = 1- THE CARPENTER: #0317
FLAG: #0676, #0718, #725
WARNING; #0611
THE VICTOR: #0393

✰

#0310 - September 23, 2018 @ 06:30 (San Francisco, California)

[0310.1 / 0755] [I'm outside with a group of musically inclined people. There's an absence of sheet music. A guitar sits to the side waiting for *(and seemingly taunting)* us to play it. I pick it up. The first chord I strum after counting off *"one...two...three,"* is incorrect. I blink and awaken in a scene where I flirt and have a sexual encounter with THE ARCHITECT in a booth at a cafe. Coffee is poured at the table while we go at it.]

[0310.2 / 0756] [Signage indicates a paved walkway is under repair. An invisible force shifts large stones to a perpendicular orientation. The construction environment is silent.]

[0310.3 / 0757] [I'm a young boy practicing at a gymnastics gym. I repeatedly tumble into a foam pit. I notice the *"shiny bar"* from where I stand and immediately want to swing giants. A vault is set up with a *"side horse"* orientation. I exclaim, *"We should do long horse!"* as my alarm wakes me up.] //

✰

Min. = ♥- THE ARCHITECT: #0316
FOAM: #0423, #0442, #0466, #0471, #0538, #0563, #0606, #0637
PERPENDICULAR: #0428, #0736

✰

#0311 - September 24, 2018 @ 04:13 (San Francisco, California)

[0311.1 / 0758] [I'm on a business trip to an absurdly large mansion owned by an entertainment mogul. Drones fly around taking surveillance photos of the entire property. Before we enter, THE BOSS gathers the team and says,
"Today is not a blasting day." We all seem to know what that means and nod our heads in agreement.
We enter the property *(which seems to be city blocks long)*. Another vast mansion is housed inside the property we visit. A series of escalators spill up to the ground floor from levels below. As we pass by, I wonder how much this adds to the compound's listing price. A sign outside claimed it's offered at *"market rate."* We enter the private residence which is still incomprehensibly large on the inside. It's so large I attempt to take a vertical panorama shot

with my phone, but can't capture it all. An opulently dressed woman with long black hair nearly catches me in the act. I assume she's the wife of our client as she saunters by deliberately and stoically.

I pass a series of trees with white bath towels hanging from the lowest set of branches. Working class people attend to their maintenance.

I attempt to text my family, *"You won't believe this place!"* but the text fails to go through.

I'm taken by a series of massive brown stone waterfalls, easily 20 feet wide. They zig zag down from the indiscernible peak of the structure's interior.

I pass by a series of eight circular hot tubs with small waterfalls that spill from them to a larger central channel. When viewed from above and when lit they look like representations of the universal icon for "Power." All features are man-made.

A serious mood befalls the space as a vast ceremonial procession begins. Men in bespoke suits file in, in pairs. They walk deliberately and neutrally into the water channel, wetting their suits up to chest level. The husband and wife follow.

Once submerged the overall mood shifts from serious back to light and playful.

"Eh, get a photo of us, yous guys," one of the men yells at us in a thick Jersey accent.] //

⁎⁎

ESCALATOR: #0462, #0493, #0495, #0634
BATH TOWELS: #0800
JERSEY: #0455
THE BOSS: #0563

⁎⁎

#0312 - September 25, 2018 @ 06:56 (San Francisco, California)

[0312.1 / 0759] [I'm in Albania, traveling with a couple of friends. We traverse a long serpentine line until we arrive at a security checkpoint.

I wear a trench coat and have a handgun in my pocket. I slide the clip in and out to occupy my itchy trigger finger. I'm supposed to declare it, but fear if I do so, I'll get shot. The scene is busy feeling and familiar to dream [0025.3 / 0078] where THE GUITARIST and I explore North Korea.

Simple paper leaflets advertise new non-stop routes to Los Angeles. As I snake through the line, I observe a woman bargaining with herself as to whether or not she should confront a man who has just tossed a hot smoker's pipe into a garbage can. We decide that instead of flying we'd rather take a heavy steel gondola to the wintery mountain top where we can tour a large castle in the sky.

It blizzards as we pack ourselves head to foot into the gondola. Only a small rectangular slit allows us to watch our slow travel process up the mountain. The gondola swings and sways wildly with the wind.

Once at the top, we each investigate the castle on our own, without a specific agenda.] //

⁎⁎

Min. = ♣- THE GUITARIST: #0404
GARBAGE: #0597, #0705, #0763
GONDOLA: #0474

⁎⁎

#0313 - September 26, 2018 @ 06:01 (San Francisco, California)

[0313.1 / 0760] [I encounter THE WORLDBRIDGER. He offers me healing, but seems a bit annoyed. He places his hand on my head and says, *"You could use a shakeup. If we go another level deep, you'll experience Lyme Disease."*]

[0313.2 / 0761] [THE CHILD is an infant in a crib. She has spina bifida. A man touches her back to heal her. She rises and walks away.]

[0313.3 / 0762] [I'm a backup singer for NAO, but I don't know any of her songs. The set list is short. One recent performance is at a venue similar to the Warfield in San Francisco. The opening band presents their stage production within the frame of a steel cube. The sides of the cube run up to the edge of the stage. The bottom, front and top are missing. The band is legitimately trapped for the duration of their performance. Our other show occurs in an intimate downstairs cafe.]

[0313.4 / 0763] [I encounter a yoga teacher who leads an Ashtanga class at the request of "John Helmwhast," who remotely updates a Wikipedia page about the practice. "John" doesn't attend the yoga class, even though he requested it.] //

☆☆

Maj. = 3-THE CHILD: #0328, 7- THE WORLDBRIDGER: #0354
BACKUP: #0748, #0752
CUBE: #0416, #0597, #0615, #0640

☆☆

#0314 - September 27, 2018 @ 05:08 (San Francisco, California)

[0314.1 / 0764] [I'm with THE KANGAROO in a cedar sauna at a resort. We're wearing jockstraps. He takes guys in a room alone one by one. I know he's had sex with each of them because he waves the jock strap he collects through the doorway after they complete. It's flirty, light and playful. He and I don't have sex, but we observe each other in the act.]

[0314.2 / 0765] [I'm in a high traffic area, likely a train or subway station. I work with a team to hang three oversized rectangular objects on a brick wall. The wall is painted pristine white. One of the items is an oversized cork board. Groups of people flow by in massive waves.] //

☆☆

Min. = ♠- THE KANGAROO: #0327
JOCKSTRAP: #0494
PRISTINE: #0502, #0531, #0572, #0575

☆☆

#0315 - September 28, 2018 @ 04:25 (San Francisco, California)
*Frenetically paced dream with a sophisticated narrative, but the following images are what stand out as impactful. *

[0315.1 / 0766] [A group of large orange snakes have their fangs crudely cut out. Children play among them. They're doomed. At least one snake still has the ability to deliver multiple fatal bites. The snakes have yellow eyes.]

[0315.2 / 0767] [A group of Navy Seals wait behind a door, just prior to intercepting their target.]

[0315.3 / 0768] [A convoy of RV's helps a guy travel from point-to-point across the country.]

[0315.4 / 0769] [I'm in a black walled room with two other men who fight. I'm a woman. The larger of the two men is aggressive. He has a beard and carries a small blue whip. The smaller man wears a Kevlar suit. He decides to run away from the scene. With his back turned the larger man repeatedly whips him from behind. I slide down a pole as the larger man tracks my movement from roughly 20 feet away. He flings a small ninja star at me. As it approaches, time slows. The blade looks like a swastika, based on my orientation and the spin of the object.] //

✱✱

YELLOW: #0512, #0532, #0556, #0584, #0587
NINJA: #0615
STAR: #0403, #0789
BEARD: #0535, #0718, #0748

✱✱

#0316 - September 28, 2018 @ 06:16 (San Francisco, California)
*Similar punctuated, nonlinear experiences. *

[0316.1 / 0770] [I walk up a staircase and find THE CONNECTOR sick in bed. I spend some time with her and offer her healing. THE CONNECTOR decides to keep working on her current court filing even though she's sick. When I go downstairs, I encounter two naked men in baseball caps eating each other's asses. I stop briefly to observe, offer some gold light, and move on. They're totally absorbed by one another.]

[0316.2 / 0771] [I gently pat THE ARCHITECT on the back. His mother recently passed away. He's sad.]

[0316.3 / 0772] [I invite the Holy Spirit into my body. I experience a brilliant pop of sparkly white light. I see a woman at a counter. As I approach, I recognize her as "MADONNA'S HERO".

"1 W_DDDAL C__S. 2) My M____ is R ____."

She speaks to me but it's unintelligible. While inside my body I repeatedly hear the Spirit say,

"Out with doubt and limiting thoughts. Out with doubt."

My left brain receives a deep cleaning. My right brain expands. I feel disoriented, flushed out, and stupefied.] //

✣

Maj. = 4- THE CONNECTOR: #0321
Min. = ♥- *THE ARCHITECT: #0472*
SICK: #0429, #0785
HOLY SPIRIT: #0610, #0654

✣

#0317 - September 28. 2018 @ 08:04 (San Francisco, California)

[0317.1 / 0773] [An erratic, pock marked skip through dream space. I clean up trash after a large party. I feel like THE RECONCILIATOR *(fully expressed, deep feeling, and reunited)* may have been a guest. THE LOBBYIST's family gathers for photos, pushing stacks of garbage aside to make space for everyone. A surly punk band is on scene.

"THEY DON'T LIKE YOU. DON'T YOU GET IT?!" a young woman screams at me as I try to clean up around the band.

The punks stomp off annoyed with me, but there's no fight. Makeshift tables constructed from wood plates are set on round top faded pastel stools. They look like a single row of dots on a Twister mat.

THE CUDDLER *(clearing, intimate, and still)* and I flirt with each other in the doorway of the garage. We want to make out, but we're too embarrassed to do it in front of "mom." The house is filthy. As I move piles of garbage to the street, I'm shown an image of THE CARPENTER. I'm reminded he constantly cleaned up after me as a kid.

A stack of uneaten pizzas in greasy boxes sit on the sidewalk next to the street. They're not appetizing.

Two books next to the pizzas become interesting when I note both were written by THE ICEMAN, whose encyclopedic knowledge of Aramaic inspires me. The texts are intended for use by a postgraduate audience.] //

✣

Maj. = 1- THE CARPENTER: #0327, 17- THE LOBBYIST: #0321
Min. = ♥- *THE RECONCILIATOR: #0805*
PUNK: #0539
TWISTER: #0770
THE ICEMAN: #0365

✣

#0318 - September 29, 2018 @ 06:24 (San Francisco, California)

[0318.1 / 0774] [I encounter THE ROMANTIC in a steam room. Our eyes meet.
"Would you believe this is my first time in a steam room?" he says with a coy smile.

"What, you mean this one right?" I say winking at him through a nourishing mist of cedar and eucalyptus.] //

⁂

Maj. = 15- THE ROMANTIC: #0319
WINK: #0427, #0499, #0538, #0573, #0677
MIST: #0401, #0535, #0540, #0628

⁂

#0319 - September 30, 2018 @ 05:55 (San Francisco, California)

[0319.1 / 0775] [THE CONVERT and I work together to pour a large vat of carbonated beverage into a long, thick, chilled ice tube that has a layer of mango puree frozen to the sides. THE NURSE is surprised by our success.
"Look, we did it!"]

[0319.2 / 0776] [THE ROMANTIC stops by my grocery store after returning from a trip to Hong Kong. I'm interested in what he's been up to. He buys a candy bar at the register and flirts with me. I'm distracted by his smile, and I lose narrative context.] //

⁂

Maj. = 13 -THE NURSE: #0323, 15- THE ROMANTIC: #0345
KIOSK: #0468, #0498, #0531
THE CONVERT: #0364

⁂

#0320 - October 2, 2018 @ 05:49 (San Francisco, California)

[0320.1 / 0777] [I order an Uber from somewhere on a Chinese mountainside. A huge pickup truck driven by a White man stops. I hop in the back and strap into a jump seat.]

[0320.2 / 0778] [I'm on an evening tour of a castle with friends, perhaps in the same region of China. I drop my phone from a window, hearing it audibly "plunk" into the moat below. I walk down the exterior wall of the castle and into the water to search for the phone. I believe the phone is ruined when I (*underwater and feet stuck to the stone wall*) discover it wedged between the foundation and a large boulder. When I turn it over in my hand, I'm surprised to see it fully operational. It's waterproof and shatterproof.]

[0320.3 / 0779] [I eat a gooey, warm, chocolate granola bar in the backseat of a car. The chocolate bits are shaped like tiny brown cubes. I don't let a bite go to waste. It tastes delicious. I may be a small child.] //

248

#0321 - October 3, 2018 @ 4:31am (San Francisco, California)

[0321.1 / 0780] [I'm at a CrossFit wedding for THE LOBBYIST and THE WILDERNESS GUIDE. The service is non-denominational. The assembled group drops to the floor in unison after a reading to do a set of abdominal crunches.
"I was worried you would fall in love with HIM," THE LOBBYIST says to THE WILDERNESS GUIDE pointing at me as they exchange vows.
I'm left stunned and embarrassed. THE AD EXECUTIVE *(friendly, stylish, and contemporary)* attends with his UK entourage.]

[0321.2 / 0781] [The mood is thick and mysterious in front of a stone castle wall. An extremely large flimsy wooden table sits adjacent to the wall. As we walk around the object THE CONNECTOR excitedly says, "
YOU. SHOULD. STEAL. THIS. BITCH!" I pause and respond pointing at a camera,
"But, there's CCTV."]

[0321.3 / 0782] [My wife is in the hospital for a simple procedure on one of her ovaries that will keep her admitted overnight. Her next day discharge will cause us to miss a scheduled early morning flight to the United Kingdom. Post operation, I want to go visit her in the recovery wing. I'm attacked by an aggressive Kaiser Permanente call center staff member who repeatedly smacks me in the face with a phone receiver while taunting me.]

[0321.4 / 0783] [I open the closet door in my hotel room and look out onto a large front porch during a rainstorm. Water pours in through a six-inch gap between the top of the walls and roof on all sides. Racks of clothes are soaked. From one, I select a "No-Sleeve Sweater" *(new marketing jargon for "vest")*. I debate whether or not to pack a bag as I slip a blazer on. I'm only going to be gone for 72 hours.]

[0321.5 / 0784] [An elaborate switchboard runs behind the walls of the stone hotel. Thick cables run behind the walls between rooms. Palm sized red square buttons can be pressed to activate different room-to-room channels. The numbering convention used to set the board up is an illogical string of integers *(5, 15, 2, 3 ...)*. I spend time attempting to figure out why the channels were numbered in such a way. As I contemplate this, I wake up.] //

⁎⁎
Maj. = 4- THE CONNECTOR: #0340, 17- THE LOBBYIST: #0330
RECOVERY: #0499
FLIMSY: #0607

CALL CENTER: #0573, #0579
THE WILDERNESS GUIDE: #0330
THE AD EXECUTIVE: #1236
⁎⁎

#0322 - October 3, 2018 @ 06:05 (San Francisco, California)

[0322.1 / 0785] [I'm naked with THE FILM PRODUCER. We play arousal games. He holds me close. I get an erection. He starts to jerk me off, then I show him I can blow myself. I pull back quickly when I notice my sister in the bathroom. The door is ajar. She doesn't see us (*though I can see her reflection in the mirror*).]

[0322.2 / 0786] [I attend two different fashion shows in New York City. Something strikes me as odd that one model wears high heels and the rest have furry mascot feet. The catwalk seems galactic, starry, and moves away at increasing speed.]

[0322.3 / 0787] [My apartment is up a small series of stairs. THE TRANSLATOR and her parents are my right-side neighbors. They install a new heavy duty vault door to the front of their unit, much thicker than mine. They're satisfied with the weight and feel of it, though it takes two people to open and close.]

[0322.4 / 0788] [I'm a woman enjoying a spa day with my girls. We all wear simple black one-piece swimsuits. We lay out on lounge chairs and move down a conveyor belt for a four-step treatment that first involves wrapping flat black tubes (*like deflated bike tires*) around our legs. There's supposed to be a flow to this process, but a log jam emerges at the last step and we're mechanically piled on top of one another.]

[0322.5 / 0789] [I'm at a performance hosted by THE PRECIOUS ONE (*overt, expressive, and funny*). The live-action hybridized drag remake of "The Golden Girls" and "Who's the Boss?" is met with favorable acclaim. Between acts, we're entertained by a series of male Cirque Du Soleil performers who create elaborate acrobatic stunts and postures. They flip repeatedly in laid out positions high in the air, then dissolve through the floor like ghosts when they descend.]

[0322.6 / 0790] [I demonstrate how to *"activate amethyst"* while visiting a crystal shop.]

[0322.7 / 0791] [I pass a tall African American man on the street. He wears a suit and sports a black pork pie hat over his long healthy dreadlocks.] //

⁎⁎
Maj. = 19- THE TRANSLATOR: #0369
CRYSTAL: #0526, #0556, #0595, #0597

CIRQUE DU SOLEIL: #0557, #0715
CONVEYOR: #0534, #0621, #0698
THE FILM PRODUCER: #0725
THE PRECIOUS ONE: #1438

✯✯

#0323 - October 3, 2018 @ 07:22 (San Francisco, California)

[0323.1 / 0792] [THE BARKEEP (*romantic, ready, and emptying*) just started a new job as an office accountant. A woman brings an expense report in after business day 2. The monthly books are closed, but the woman insists that the charges be included in the prior reporting period. I scribble in yellow dry erase marker,
"Don't make a fire drill out of this," on THE BARKEEP's cubicle window.]

[0323.2 / 0793] [THE NURSE records herself teaching a class and discusses it. I share the video with our team as THE FIDUCIARY and THE REFLECTION enter our office from an elevator bay behind us. I hug THE NURSE to soothe her but my gesture feels fake.]

[0323.3 / 0794] [A charcoal black bride in a black lace wedding gown walks deliberately around a party greeting guests. I depart and head to the street where I find myself at a rowdy block party with multiple DJ stages.
I duck inside a restaurant and take a seat at an exceptionally long and thin high top bar table. It's occupied by many well-manicured, conspicuously spending gay men. Round platters present large unopened bags of Cool Ranch Doritos for which guests pay an ironically high premium, an absurdly expensive $50 a bag. One bag is open and unconsumed. As we leave, I double back to retrieve it, knowing it will be thrown in the trash. I keep the bag under my coat and out of sight of the other men, who will ridicule me if they find out what I've done. I'll eat them later to spite them.
As I move out onto the street, I pass a pair of Arab male counterparts. They're engaged in a very serious conversation, seated in black steel chairs next to a hotel swimming pool (*lit for night use*). I see them again later in another location. The DJs at the block party spin tracks with low whompy resonance, but they sound like BASSNECTAR copycats. The first saturated drop of a "Heavyweight Sound" hits me in the gut, rattles my ribcage, and blurs my vision. I appreciate the mastery of world caliber sound artists who can alter the waveforms of their compositions in real time to ensure the space and air pressure appropriately balances to the venue acoustics and crowd.] //

✯✯

Maj. = 9- THE FIDUCIARY: #0359, 13- THE NURSE: #0405
BASSNECTAR: #0326
CHARCOAL: #0779
AIR: #0534, #0561
THE BARKEEP: #0377
THE REFLECTION: #0644

✯✯

#0324 - October 4, 2018 @ 04:28 (San Francisco, California)

[0324.1 / 0795] [I work in a fast-paced startup environment that feels like it could be an early stage of Salesforce. It's possible to teleport/bilocate between traditional offices and jungle workspaces partitioned by green shrub walls. Office floors in the jungle are grassy. Miniature rivulets flow into pools and lagoons where meetings and key conversations occur.

I'm in some sort of human resources role. The woman I report to has responsibility for employees "9 to 391," agnostic to role and function. I see a sticky note affixed to the bottom of her computer monitor:

> "I'm having a lady's day. If I don't know how to do something, the young ones do it for me!"

I hear her exclaim with a degree of disbelief and joy as she departs.
I contemplate what it would feel like to be the COO of my own startup.
What would the quality of that be like?
What skills would it demand that as current, I don't possess?

THEN I HAVE A VISION: I see myself as **EMPLOYEE #9** at a new company.

As I walk through the jungle office, I see a series of black and yellow wasps with golden wings crawling along the floors and walls. They're beautiful, and deadly. I mildly worry they'll crawl in my sleep space *(my office)* and sting me while I rest.
A second vision presents a lucrative notion: Learn the current legal process for real estate foreclosure and recreate it to expedite time to market transactions before the next imminent financial crisis.
"I could make a ton of money AND help the economy recover," I think to myself as I continue with my general daily tasks.] //

⁎

JUNGLE: #0615, #0648
BEAUTIFUL: #0774, #0782, #0795
DEGREE: #0422, #0656, #0774

⁑

#0325 - October 5, 2018 @ 05:02 (San Francisco, California)

[0325.1 / 0796] [This is a social dream with a lot of interpersonal interaction. Conversations seem impactful, but I forget most of them. We might be at a bar or club. There seem to be large wooden beams holding up giant plate glass windows.
A little bit of a bro/frat house vibe percolates.
I've lost my purple/pink/white pearl snap tear away blouse. I feel really sad.] //

⁑

SOCIAL: #0559, #0572, #0600, #0607, #0645, #0666
PLATE GLASS WINDOW: #0478
FORGET: #0504, #0570, #0571

⁑

#0326 - October 5, 2018 @ 12:54 (San Francisco, California)

[0326.1 / 0797] [I'm backstage at a BASSNECTAR show. LORIN ASHTON shows a contest winner how he uses his laptops and DJ decks during a performance. Music begins at low volume while he provides the education.
"Hey, I saw you on playa in 2009, right?"
"2008!"
"Oh yeah... Thanks for changing the way I experience 'reality,'" I say as my voice trails off.
I doubt he'll hear me, but he does. He jumps off the stage, walks towards me, then gives me a fist bump and vaporizes. I decide to send him an email suggesting we collaborate when I hear the music begin. Tonight, he's playing an extended set. All the visuals are red. A serpentine line through a cafeteria leads to the auditorium. A woman with a pen knife in her purse gets stopped by security.] //

⁂

LOW VOLUME: #0406, #0519, #0563, #0767
BASSNECTAR: #0431
BUMP: #0500
EMAIL: #0549

⁂

#0327 - October 6, 2018 @ 05:29 (San Francisco, California)

[0327.1 / 0798] [THE KANGAROO teaches a graduate level course. I sit on the floor next to the couch with one knee bent. My right arm is extended, elbow balancing on my right knee cap. The room is softly lit with peach light. The mood is engaging and playful. Students are deeply curious about the content, and connect to his accessible and supportive teaching style.]

[0327.2 / 0799] [I hover behind two German men at an auditorium who wanted to see IMOGEN HEAP perform tonight. They arrived late and missed the concert. Annoyed, one says to the other, *"I'm the one who's out $65."* They wait to use the bathroom in a long line which extends across a vast underground promenade.]

[0327.3 / 0800] [THE CARPENTER stands behind a skillet and makes white rectangular portions of eggs which have the consistency of glass noodles. The first batch he makes are runny and not servable. He contemplates doubling the amount of a stabilizer to firm them up. The Germans arrive and enjoy the eggs. There's a __ in the __. THE WEAVER is there __.] //

⁂

Maj. = 0- THE WEAVER: #0330, 1- THE CARPENTER: #0330
Min. = ♠- THE KANGAROO: #0561
GERMAN: #0417, #0606, #0668
PROMENADE: #0408, #0644, #0777
CONCERT: #0422, #0424, #0477

⁂

253

#0328 - October 7, 2018 @ 04:26 (San Francisco, California)

[0328.1 / 0801] [THE CHILD sits on my lap.]
[0328.2 / 0802] [I attend a dinner party with an escort.]
[0328.3 / 0803] [I attend an awards show. Up and coming Black artists take the stage. A woman wearing a "Red Dot Dress" is among the backup dancers. A large Black man wearing sunglasses says to the dancer, *"You on vacation."*]

[0328.4 / 0804] [I go outside to perform at sunset. A man wearing sunglasses and I extend our right arms towards one another making contact index-finger-to-index-finger, a friendly and semi-covert acknowledgement that we're both aliens.] //

☆☆

Maj. = 3- THE CHILD: #0382
ESCORT: #0550
SUNGLASSES: #0410, #0708, #0731
☆☆

#0329 - October 7, 2018 @ 06:02 (San Francisco, California)

[0329.1 / 0805] [A rainbow abstraction of a manta ray flies over a cityscape at night.]
[0329.2 / 0806] [Playing miniature golf.] //

☆☆

MANTA RAY: #0655
MINIATURE: #0472, #0606, #0622, #0667, #0684, #0713, #0746, #0749
PLAYING: #0750, #0763, #0787, #0788, #0789
☆☆

#0330 - October 8, 2018 @ 02:49 (San Francisco, California)

[0330.1 / 0807] [I attempt to escape from "Grandma's" house through a back window. Dogs chase me. I trip and twist my ankle. THE WEAVER offers me support by providing me a chair. THE CARPENTER doesn't think resting is a good idea. It's golden hour. Autumn sunlight in streaks of violet, pink, peach and gold run across the sky.]

[0330.2 / 0808] [I go to a basement where a series of elaborate oversized cut paper scrapbooks are prominently displayed on a long, heavy wooden rectangular table. Multiple gay couples seated at the table thumb through judging and evaluating photos of men pasted within the books.
"That one. He was a scientist."
"Him? Oh, he was the 'replacement boyfriend.'"
The chatter and response are tongue in cheek. THE LOBBYIST and THE WILDERNESS GUIDE celebrate nearby. I find my private quarters, where a shower has been installed next to the bed, per my request. As I turn it on it soaks the duvet, sheets, pillows and mattress.] //

⁎⁎

Maj. = 0- THE WEAVER: #0335, 1- THE CARPENTER: #0344, 17- THE LOBBYIST: #0336
AUTUMN: #0717
SHOWER: #0488, #0592, #0631, #0709, #0752, #0792
BOYFRIEND: #0430, #0527, #0712, #0726, #0736
THE WILDERNESS GUIDE: #0336

⁎⁎

#0331 - October 8, 2018 @ 04:30 (San Francisco, California)

[0331.1 / 0809] [A group of college aged guys waits for a "Recovery Bus" to take them home after partying. They want me to travel with them, but I take a different route home.]

[0331.2 / 0810] [THE EPICUREAN buys lunch for me when we meet cute at a cafeteria register. The meal would have cost $30, though THE EPICUREAN convinces the cashier to sell it to him for $15. The cafeteria adjoins a large mansion with numerous vast outdoor gathering patios with ample comfortable seating. We gather with others on a marble lanai enshrouded in golden light. A storm approaches. I photograph soft bands of rain clouds as they move briskly across a vast field in our direction. The group takes innumerable photos of nature's spectacular works.] //

⁎⁎

Min. = ♥- THE EPICUREAN: #0744
OUTDOOR: #0401, #0500, #0548
NATURE: #0786
GOLD LIGHT: #0440, #0467, #0481, #0512, #0540, #0547, #0572, #0610, #0709, #0714

⁎⁎

255

#0332 - October 9, 2018 @ 04:26 (San Francisco, California)

[0332.1 / 0811] [I stare at a poster advertising the new Mary Poppins movie, debating if it'll be any good.]

[0332.2 / 0812] [A woman dances alone in a pink dress. THE ANIMATOR *(rebellious, amorous, and flippant)* drives a car excessively fast down a residential street. I yell at him loudly to *"SLOW DOWN!"*]

[0332.3 / 0813] [I party with PAUL MCCARTNEY on an international flight. We gently part ways at the airport. We both enjoy each other's company and linger until the last possible moment. I proceed to wander the airport alone and satisfied.]

[0332.4 / 0814] [I'm at an underground casino. I observe a fool packing a bag full of various length PVC dowels. PVC is the preferred medium of exchange here.]

[0332.5 / 0815] [An alarm sounds. I wake and note the time: 6:50am. I write a detailed journal entry about an "important" dream replete with direct quotes, diagrams, and exquisite exculpatory detail. I wake and realize I've written nothing down. The dream within a dream *(within another dream)* is lost.] //

⚜

PAUL MCCARTNEY: #1268
MARY POPPINS: #1090
NOTHING: #0434, #0473, #0557, #0569, #0763, #0775
RESIDENTIAL: #0613, #0699, #0790
EXQUISITE: #0436, #0552
DIAGRAM: #0405

⚜

#0333 - October 13, 2018 @ 01:22 (San Francisco, California)

[0333.1 / 0816] [I'm frustrated. I'm incommunicado. I'm either an event planner or a Maître D. THE DANCER is on my team. We ready the banquet hall for an event. The simple task of setting up a table becomes unclear and confusing. The length of the table shifts based on where the team moves it. Outside on a grassy lawn, it becomes a cheap six-foot collapsible plastic table. When moved indoors, the table becomes dense, sturdy, and covered with cheap nonsense decorations.
I'm exasperated.
"I have done this thousands of times before. WHY! IS! THIS! SO! CHALLENGING!"
THE DANCER listens but doesn't respond.
We make final preparations by plating salads in a refrigerated walk-in. The guests of

honor tonight are a prestigious heteronormative African American family. The mother and father are glamorously dressed. They have two teenage daughters. One wears a shiny emerald dress. She startles us as she enters through a butler door. I realize I'm in the wealthy side of the home in dream **[0120.2 / 0279]**] //

⁎⁎

Maj. = 2- THE DANCER #0348
CHEAP: #0755
BUTLER: #0513, #0556
GRASSY: #0452, #0472, #0563, #0586, #0655, #0710, #0714, #0717, #0778

⁎⁎

#0334 - October 13, 2018 @ 04:38 (San Francisco, California)

[0334.1 / 0817] [The energy is palpable and revolutionary. Something's going to blow up. ZACK DE LA ROCHA and I convene at the top of an urban hill above a large crowd. We run and leap down a steep paved street. ZACK leads a protest chant into a crowd holding an orange bike tail flag with a clenched fist icon in the center. The image creates a stir and he gets stopped by a young _____.
People are hungry. A line cook, who looks like "Aunt Jemima," serves gumbo to the masses.
Tupperware melts and burns after being left on a nearby stovetop.
I crave frosted cinnamon rolls from a tube, but I don't have an oven to bake them.]

[0334.2 / 0818] [I watch 1930's style newsreels in a cinema. The black and white film showcases a race between a hybrid breed of peacock/ostrich/technoid-like birds that have sharp mirrored blades for tails. They're beautiful and deadly.
I turn to THE POSTMASTER and THE FARMHAND seated behind me and say,
"I love this movie so much."
They're young and on a date. They're cute.] //

⁎⁎

Min. = ♥- THE FARMHAND: #0487, ♣- THE POSTMASTER: #0487
PROTEST: #0640, #0704
HYBRID: #0456, #0534, #0718
BIRDS: #0481, #0489, #0564, #0587

⁎⁎

#0335 - October 13, 2018 @ 6:30am (San Francisco, California)

[0335.1 / 0819] [THE WEAVER stirs a large pot of soup with an irrationally large stick of celery she's sharpened to a point like a pencil. The celery may be spliced with genetically mutated okra.]

[0335.2 / 0820] [Intense flashes of color. Impressions of nonconforming shapes.] //

✻
✻✻

Maj. = 0- THE WEAVER: #0348
PENCIL: #0621
LARGE: #0499, #0500
SOUP: #0597, #0726

✻
✻✻

#0336 - October 14, 2018 @ 05:20 (San Francisco, California)

[0336.1 / 0821] [I attend a wedding held in an arena to celebrate the union of THE LOBBYIST and THE WILDERNESS GUIDE. The ceremony takes place on a stage. Thousands of people attend, including both former BUSH PRESIDENTS. Wandering up the aisle, "George and George" invite me to join them at the concession stand. We make small talk until we reach a counter. We order Polish sausages. I eat mine quickly on the walk back to our seats. I spot another sausage discarded on top of a nearby garbage can. I retrieve it. I eat it.

"Food waste bothers me more than social embarrassment," I mumble with a mouth full as they look at me with revulsion.

I enter the venue as the wedding concludes. Balloons fall from the sky and PHISH plays an all-night concert. The married couple dances on stage with the band.]

[0336.2 / 0822] [I lead a breathing workshop for a large group of *(mostly)* women on a large outdoor field. Some sit in rows of chairs. Others sit on the ground. One female with disheveled, kinky blonde hair who wears thick black rimmed glasses wants to assist me. Half of the group is hidden by a row of hedges and a fence. The right rear of the lawn is empty and feels like the *"Pitied Artist's Stage"* at a music festival.

I wait for those gathered to quiet. I sit myself in the middle of the group and demonstrate alternate nostril breathing. I raise my voice because I don't have a microphone.

A number of people show up to the session late and are admitted without incident.] //

✻
✻✻

Maj. = 17- THE LOBBYIST: #0406
SAUSAGE: #0520, #0624, #0778
BALLOON: #0562, #0618, #0682
LATE: #0773, #0792
THE WILDERNESS GUIDE: #0371

✻
✻✻

#0337 - October 15, 2018 @ 04:54 (San Francisco, California)
*The scenes in this dream flow fluidly and effortlessly one to the next. *

[0337.1 / 0823] [I encounter THE REBEL *(doting, handsome, and thrill seeking)* at a multi-level shopping mall. He attempts a daredevil stunt on a motorcycle, intending to rail slide down multiple levels of escalators. He moves way too quickly and smashes wheels first into a series of clear glass uprights. Massive chunks of glass shatter and cascade beautifully down to lower levels of the structure.

He ditches his bike and takes off his helmet while slowly walking towards me. His ruggedness is sexy. He's got brilliant "Bad Boy" energy. He slips me a scrap of paper with a number scribbled on it, minus a name.

He asks me on a date, and I accept. He never tells me his name.]

[0337.2 / 0824] [THE ADOPTIVE FATHER *(loving, committed, and exhausted)* and I talk in a fenced off backyard at night. He's devastated. He's spent the day crying. He admits he has an opioid addiction. He pops a few OxyContin pills as we talk, then hides his face in his hands. He's shirtless and chiseled. *Is it wrong to get distracted by his hot body while he's in crisis?*

I try to remain neutral and supportive of my friend.

He and THE WILD WEST *(bubbly, sensitive, and trusting)* are getting divorced. THE WILD WEST seeks full custody of the kids. We cry together as we stand around a circular glass table stacking various shapes and lengths of broken glass on top. The table floats. Our hands and forearms get sliced open and bleed profusely as we move around the broken glass.]

[0337.3 / 0825] [I'm on retreat at night on a University campus. THE MIRROR *(loving, tortured, and lonely)* and I flirt and canoodle as we sit in rows with others maniacally laughing at a sunset. We settle in for an overnight rite of passage as another participant demonstrates his ability to shapeshift. He's overly ritualistic in his process, almost obsessive compulsive in his preamble. I disarmingly chide,

"You're just smoke. You aren't even remotely scary. Do something interesting or sit the fuck down."

THE MIRROR and I get bored and leave the ceremony. I convince him to climb the interior of a thorny bush with me. The climb proves to be quite challenging.

An area lit by a spotlight offers a conspicuous place to offer him a blowjob.

He ponders the possibility for a moment, but then chickens out because he doesn't want to get caught.] //

⁎⁎

PILLS: #0532, #0752

BROKEN: #0405, #0518, #0521, #0553, #0562, #0587, #0597

ADDICTION: #0495, #0747, #0748

SPOTLIGHT: #0546

⁎⁎

#0338 - October 16, 2018 @ 06:14 (San Francisco, California)

[0338.1 / 0826] [*"My best day was my last day!"* I exclaim to an alien eyed version of THE FEELER, in reference to my final day of work after 11 years at Bank of America.]

[0338.2 / 0827] [I'm in a softly lit, white walled smoker's lounge. I watch a hot guy get head from his girlfriend who's ducked under a table.

I mouth, *"I want to sit on your dick later,"* to him. He winks at me before his eyes roll back in his head.

His girlfriend continues, notably jealous of my interaction with her partner.] //

*

Min. = ♣- THE FEELER: #0569
BANK OF AMERICA: #0452, #0519, #0718
GIRLFRIEND: #0431, #0645, #0698, #0719

*

#0339 - October 17, 2018 @ 04:15 (San Francisco, California)

[0339.1 / 0828] [I'm with THE REIKI MASTER (*emotive, conspicuous, and restorative*) and a group of other guys. We travel by amusement park tram, rolling along at 5mph. The tracks are made of shiny silver. I extend my hand out and give high fives to people on an invisible train that approaches on parallel tracks heading in the opposite direction. We exit the tram and walk under giant wooden scaffolds, painted rust red.

We're in Mason, Ohio at Kings Island. We inspect the rotting bones of what was once a roller coaster called "The Beast." The tracks are being dismantled, along with the entire amusement park. I feel sad for a moment. I want to ride the back half of the ride. I recall the descending spiral track popping in and out of rickety wooden tunnels. The tracks still stand. The guys run towards the track, and en route mutate into 50' tall men. They cartwheel down the tracks to topple them. They look like giant tumbling Vitruvian Men. The mood is playful and light as we joke, *"WE SLAYED THE BEAST!"*] //

*

BEAST: #0682, #0770
INVISIBLE: #0610, #0641, #0664, #0762, #0786
TRACKS: #0454, #0500, #0526, #0531, #0554, #0580, #0676

*

#0340 - October 17, 2018 @ 06:44 (San Francisco, California)

[0340.1 / 0829] [I attend an EDM concert with THE CONNECTOR. We lounge comfortably in a VIP suite on our half of the venue, but realize all the artists we want to see are slated to perform on the "other side." We're impeccably dressed.

We wait in a security line to change sides. We're pulled from the line and sequestered. We watch an inefficiently slow pat down process, facilitated by a single security guard, create a bottleneck. While detained, we realize that we've misread the event line up and have attended on the wrong day. We're permitted back in line. We decide to stay and endure the arcane security process. I know the nails in my shoes and my car keys will eventually set off the metal detectors.

Two young men stop another young woman a few feet from where THE CONNECTOR and I stand. They harass her, search her coat pockets and leer menacingly. They don't let her enter the venue, which tremendously pisses off THE CONNECTOR.] //

*

Maj. = 4- THE CONNECTOR: #0367
BOTTLE: #0566, #0654, #0663, #0779
(How often do you read between the lines?)
CAR KEYS: #0719

*

#0341 - October 19, 2018 @ 4:02am (San Francisco, California)

[0341.1 / 0830] [I'm under the rotunda at the US Capitol attending a cocktail party. People are dressed fancily in tuxedos, clutching champagne flutes. JUSTICE KAVANAUGH and LINDSAY GRAHAM make fun of MITCH MCCONNELL. They're shocked when I call them out for being impolite.

They say it's, *"just something they've been doing to each other for a looooooooong time."*] //

☆

LINDSAY GRAHAM: #0458
CHAMPAGNE: #0466, #0580, #0786
TUXEDO: #0406
FLUTES: #0786

☆

#0342 - October 19, 2018 @ 05:26 (San Francisco, California)

[0342.1 / 0831] [I stand in a still black field of telephone poles. Each pole has a sturdy gymnasium rope snaking up towards an un-see-able top. Some poles grow apples, as do some ropes. Other poles host beautiful, blossoming, perfectly pink roses. I pull the rope away from the base of a pole sending a few apples tumbling towards the ground. I catch one and begin eating it. THE RENAISSANCE MAN *(fluid, skillful, and neurotic)* appears.

"Apples are fine, but if you touch my roses like that THE M&A ATTORNEY and I will fucking kill you!" He smiles, tone playfully elevated.

"I'm not going to do that. I know you've wanted to keep them perfect this season."

We talk through dates for a new project. We hop in a car together and take a circuitous route to a mountaintop bar where we laugh until we pass out.] //

☆

ROPE: #0561, #0567
ROSES: #0460
PASS OUT: #0520, #0548
THE M&A ATTORNEY: #0701
THE RENAISSANCE MAN: #0867

☆

#0343 - October 19, 2018 @ 07:25 (San Francisco, California)

[0343.1 / 0832] [I ride in a car with THE COUTURIER. We listen to an obnoxiously long pop song. She hates it. *"But this is OUR new song!"*

Song title: **Unknown.** Performer: **"Brand New Maker feat. Skully."**] //

☆

Min. = ♣- THE COUTURIER: #0350
BRAND NEW: #0550
HATE: #0430, #0493, #0749, #0761

☆

#0344 - October 20, 2018 @ 06:17 (San Francisco, California)

[0344.1 / 0833] [THE POOLBOY *(svelte, confident, and effeminate)* gives me a blowjob. It feels good and I enjoy it, but I don't ejaculate.]

[0344.2 / 0834] [I'm in a cab on my way to catch a United Airlines flight. We cross a cloud covered futuristic version of the Golden Gate Bridge that appears to be made from platinum.

The flight takes off in 25 minutes.

I'm likely going to miss it.

THE HILLBILLY calls and asks how far I am from the airport.

"Are you going to make it?"

"No, but it's ok, I have enough points. I'll just catch the next one," I respond while stopped on the bridge.

I get out of the car and hop over the side of the bridge. I find a series of ropes and thick steel chains draped like hair down to the water's surface. Other people climb down around me at different speeds. I may be on a construction crew. I wear overalls and a floppy hat. The chain I'm holding snaps and I fall towards the water.

I don't feel any pain on impact, but know I've died.]

[0344.3 / 0835] [THE CARPENTER stands atop the cab of a white pickup truck. He's just crashed into the San Francisco bay. The truck slowly sinks.

Though quick witted and cleverly enterprising, his best on-the-fly engineering efforts can't save the vehicle.

The truck sinks to the bottom of the bay, never to be seen again.

THE CARPENTER survives and uneventfully walks across the surface of the water back to shore.] //

⁂

Maj.** = **1- THE CARPENTER: #0348

Min. = ♣- THE HILLBILLY: #0485

GOLDEN GATE BRIDGE: #0472

STEEL: #0580, #0597, #0636, #0663, #0666, #0701, #0711, #0732

THE POOLBOY: #0712

⁂

#0345 - October 22, 2018 @ 01:09 (San Francisco, California)

[0345.1 / 0836] [THE ROMANTIC and I flirt playfully for lifetimes. We laugh, ad infinitum.] //

⁂

Maj.** = **15- THE ROMANTIC: #0348

FLIRT: #0420, #0494, #0497, #0498, #0557

LAUGH: #0696, #0715, #0757, #0763, #0770

⁂

#0346 - October 22, 2018 @ 05:51 (San Francisco, California)

[0346.1 / 0837] [Strong women of color return. They sit around a large round wooden table. BEYONCÉ, OPRAH, MAYA ANGELOU, ARETHA FRANKLIN, HARRIET TUBMAN and more sit and talk as DRAKE and P. DIDDY attempt to join the table. The women aren't bothered, but the men's machismo grinds at me. Fan girls appear at the table's side. The men mistake the fan girls for their fans.]

[0346.2 / 0838] [I'm in an abstract geometric cave-hotel-spa. Reality and gravity are askew roughly 15 degrees off what I perceive as "upright." I'm confused that water remains in pools at a slant. Guests use an odd pneumatic platform to enter the pool's "alternate gravity field." I take a turn and once in the water swim a few effortless laps. I don't understand the other forces present here.] //

⁂

ARETHA FRANKLIN: #0467
BEYONCÉ: #0387
OPRAH: #0386
DRAKE: #1355
15: #0533, #0534
SLANT: #0637
EFFORTLESS: #0695

⁂

#0347 - October 22, 2018 @ 06:39 (San Francisco, California)

[0347.1 / 0839] [I watch TV ads for board games accompanied by soupy funky bass. The game boards have swirling graphics.]

[0347.2 / 0840] [I'm kissed on the cheek by a long grey haired male stranger. He simply turns and walks away.]

[0347.3 / 0841] [A gospel choir sings, *"This little light of mine"* repeatedly with soul, spirit, vigor and gusto. It's such a celebration!] //

⁂

FUNK: #0598
STRANGER: #0447
GOSPEL: #0476, #0525

⁂

#0348 - October 22, 2018 @ 07:59 (San Francisco, California)

[0348.1 / 0842] [I'm at home in my room. I fantasize and masturbate while thinking about THE ROMANTIC. A disruption downstairs brings me back to reality.]

. . .

[0348.2 / 0843] [I discover the family spread around a kitchen space. THE DANCER sits at the base of a staircase. THE CARPENTER yells at her from across the room. He's filed her taxes for her again. He's annoyed she's not appreciative, nor listening. THE WEAVER and I tell THE DANCER in unison,

"You're kind of being a bitch," which causes us to chuckle with surprise.

I continue to condescendingly rebuff, *"There might be something for you to look at there."*

THE ALCOHOLIC (*humble, honest, and healing*) enters, delivers the mail, and says,

"Don't shoot me, I'm just the messenger."

She throws up her hands and exits with a laugh. I receive a birthday card from GRANDMA with a small amount of cash and an odd amount of loose change. She's jokingly written,

"Happy Birthday! Enjoy the 'common cents.'"] //

⁙

Maj. = 0- THE WEAVER: #0364, 1- THE CARPENTER: #0353, 2- THE DANCER: #0382,
11- GRANDMA: #0442, 15- THE ROMANTIC: #0360
UNISON: #0526, #0648
LOOSE CHANGE: #0788

⁙

#0349 - October 23, 2018 @ 03:55 (San Francisco, California)
I experience a series of punctuated, abstract images. *

[0349.1 / 0844] [My body itches intensely.]

[0349.2 / 0845] [Storms of deep swirling pink and grey clouds approach, looking like dye dropped in a clear water fish tank.]

[0349.3 / 0846] [Two men lay across each other. One's head is on the other's abdomen. The background is pink, red, black and hellish. They both have thin wooden dowels with spear tips piercing their backs. Both writhe and cry out in agony. I want to help them but a voice very clearly tells me to, *"Let them be."*]

[0349.4 / 0847] [Honeycomb hexagons extend as far as the eye can see, full of unlit cigarettes.]

[0349.5 / 0848] [A popular song lyric is, *"There's sumthin' nasty I wanna do in ya."*] //

⁙
ABDOMEN: #0541
HONEY: #0422, #0493, #0496
LYRIC: #0538
⁙

♣ 6.3 - THE BOOK OF LUPUS: 0349-0367 ♣

#0350 - October 23, 2018 @ 06:14 (San Francisco, California)

[0350.1 / 0849] [I'm at a club where DJs switch over deck duties. A short haired woman takes to the booth. Her black horn rim glasses tease her identity. THE BLACK MADONNA plays a *(slightly)* undercover renegade set. I recognize her, but no one else seems to care. The show is sparsely attended. She winks at me and begins spinning hip hop.

I exit the venue, encounter THE COUTURIER, and tell her where I've just been.

"I love her! I have to go to that show!" She exclaims while entering from where I exited.

A Caucasian man with dreadlocks approaches me on a bike with a wadded up sparkly pink basketball jersey across his lap.

"He wanted you to have this. You can even see the fresh dick print in it he made for you," the cyclist says pointing at a billboard of THE BLACK MADONNA.

"But...I thought...she was a woman?" I say, partially confused. I hold a magnifying glass up to inspect the image on the billboard and see blonde stubble on her face.]

[0350.2 / 0850] [I'm at a picnic where a large bowl of smooth, pale green pistachio flavored pudding is passed among friends.

"So, who's brave enough to actually eat this?"

The challenge is playfully made to all but I'm the only one who risks a spoonful. I love the flavor. It's unexpectedly fluffy and delightful.] //

✲✲

Min. = ♣- THE COUTURIER: #0401
FLAVOR: #0476, #0487, #0693, #0712, #0723
DELIGHT: #0427, #0600, #0787, #0798

✲✲

#0351 - October 24, 2018 @ 05:45 (San Francisco, California)

[0351.1 / 0851] [THE POINT GUARD appears. GREEN FLASH. Narrative lost. I wake up feeling exhausted.] //

✲✲

GREEN: #0422, #0428, #0442, #0472, #0474
EXHAUSTED: #0476, #0654, #0682, #0745, #0785
THE POINT GUARD: #0364

✲✲

#0352 - October 25, 2018 @ 06:27 (San Francisco, California)

*This dream did not want to be remembered. *

[0352.1 / 0852] [*NIGHTMARE* *Extreme Violence* I'm frightened. The scene is suspenseful. I'm chased by a serial killer through a college dormitory. I don't know him, nor why he's after me. Commotion occurs on the back lawn. It's unclear if people hurriedly move out, but piles of belongings pop up in small rectangular groupings.

I hide in a cupboard under the bathroom sink to avoid the monster / killer / whatever it has become. I send the being a stream of gold healing light as I press my face in to my lap.] //

⁎⁎⁎

NIGHTMARE: #0406, #0518, #0519, #0764
HIDE: #0406, #0479, #0566, #0622, #0655
MONSTER: #0490, #0682

⁎⁎⁎

#0353 - October 27, 2018 @ 06:26 (San Francisco, California)

[0353.1 / 0853] [THE HUSBAND (*flirty, social, and suggestive*) and THE LINGUIST (*withdrawn, quiet, and defeated*) have an argument. One of them gets sick and as a result, they cancel their sex party.]

[0353.2 / 0854] [THE GRACE (*feminine, generous, and loving*) picks me up in THE CARPENTER's yellow Corvette after I have dental surgery. I really want to drive the car, but I've had too much nitrous oxide. THE GRACE convinces me it's better to be a backseat driver. I've had substantial cosmetic dentistry to correct the disfigurement suffered from punching myself repeatedly in the face.

I decide to call THE CHOCOHOLIC while in the back seat. I'm not sure if the call goes through.

We stop at a luxury hotel to attend a reception where THE DRAMA QUEEN (*toxic, inactive, and unfriendly*) makes a joke about, "*This guy with...you know...the one with the huuuuuuuuge dick.*" He makes a gesture that looks like he's holding a basketball. He extends his arms towards us while stepping away, implying he's holding a phallus so large it physically lurches him back and away from the group. He tells the joke a few times, insisting we, "*just don't get it*" when our murmured response remains tepid.]

[0353.3 / 0855] [I teach yoga on a boat.

Two realities occur simultaneously: I'm a teacher. I'm a student. When I'm a student I decide to forgo my personal practice to assist other people. Some people jeer and question,

"*Why the fuck would you do that???*"

The rest compliment me excitedly,

"*Wow, that's the most amazing act of service, ever.*"] //

⁎⁎⁎

Maj. = 1- THE CARPENTER: #0358
ASSIST: #0480, #0712, #0729, #0757
DENTAL: #0658
THE CHOCOHOLIC: #0438
THE DRAMA QUEEN: #0925
THE LINGUIST: #0965
THE HUSBAND: #0965

⁎⁎⁎

#0354 - October 27, 2018 @ 15:21pm (San Francisco, California)

[**0354.1** / **0856**] [**DAYDREAM** - I swim in a sea of pink light; my "creator's tone." A sound draws me down from the light to my body where I barf out the words,
"We are MUCH older than that."
I realize I've interrupted THE WORLDBRIDGER as he teaches.
"I'm sorry but that was something that just needed to be voiced."
The comment is acknowledged. The class continues as though no disruption occurred.] //

✦

Maj. = 7- THE WORLDBRIDGER: #0364
PINK: #0511, #0528, #0548, #0568
SORRY: #0614, #0628
DISRUPTION: #0585

✦

#0355 - October 28, 2018 @ 05:15 (San Francisco, California)

[**0355.1** / **0857**] [A dark curly haired "mop top" man wears a white lab coat. We negotiate a deal. For a certain price he offers:
"10 haircuts and all the screwdrivers you can drink."
"I'll take the 10 but you can leave the liquor at home." I counter.
He takes out his shears and begins to cut my hair.
I sit back satisfied and believe I got exactly what I wanted.] //

✦

LIQUOR: #0561, #0732
DEAL: #0771, #0799
SATISFIED: #0579, #0636, #0759
HAIRCUT: #0440, #0485, #0494, #0583, #0658, #0662

✦

#0356 - October 29, 2018 @ 4:00am (San Francisco, California)

[**0356.1** / **0858**] [I place an excessive amount of loose change in a vending machine. Dozens of quarters drop through the slot. When I finish, the machine spits a small green rebate ticket half the width of my thumb from its bottom right corner. Apparently, I have a $20 credit, but no redemption process to follow.] //

✦

CREDIT: #0669, #0683, #0752
THUMB: #0756, #0772, #0777
MACHINE: 0633, #0647, #0774

✦

#0357 - October 29, 2018 @ 07:36 (San Francisco, California)

[**0357.1** / **0859**] [A significant political race concludes. Both parties gather in the same venue to celebrate. A lean and lanky ALFRED E. NEWMAN wins. He sits on the arm of a brown punched leather couch. His opponent sits on the couch. Spirits between them are light and jovial. Neither of them has actually lost anything.

"*I voted for you, Jeff!*'" I say to the seated man as a crowd with cameras gathers around ALFRED, awaiting his first statement as a newly elected government official.]

[0357.2 / 0860] [I play a trivia game with a group of people in front of an audience. I draw a card and realize the set up for the next challenge is fairly elaborate. I briefly consult with BARON BAPTISTE off stage then make a couple of nervous jokes while awaiting direction. The content on the card changes and glows in gold alien script I'm unable to read.] //

⁂

BARON BAPTISTE: #0400
POLITICAL: #0449, #0461, #0667
VOTE: #0527, ##0748
NERVOUS: #0415, #0466, #0659, #0742

⁂

#0358 - October 30, 2018 @ 04:52 (San Francisco, California)

[0358.1 / 0861] [PRINCE steps on stage to perform new music at an underground club. The tiny room throbs with anticipation. We're all gathered as spirits, curious what he's going to call through tonight.]

[0358.2 / 0862] [I wander the hallways of a school after the bell rings.]

[0358.3 / 0863] [THE CONFIDANT and THE WRANGLER watch new episodes of a Family Guy spin off where the protagonists are cats.]

[0358.4 / 0864] [*"You're blanking with your thin brain."*]

[0358.5 / 0865] [The family has an 11pm dinner reservation. Before seating we debate how to best travel to the Olympic Ice Skating Finals. Though I paid for the tickets, I'm fine watching the event here on TV and argue the view from the dining room is likely much better.

A group of students enters and approaches the host stand. They present a gift card, which instantly breaks them up and seats them across multiple tables. Their names are listed at the bottom of the gift card.

Tiny gold print beneath the names denotes the card holders as "seat fillers."]

[0358.6 / 0866] [IMAGE OF A MISSING CAT.]

. . .

[0358.7 / 0867] [I assist a yoga class where a woman practices *"coffee grinder headstands."* She frantically flips her entire body around the origin point of her head. It looks really violent and unsafe, but she doesn't injure herself.

I encourage her to *"be aware of the bodies around her."*

I leave her and attend to another student while her body continues whipping and flailing around in circles.]

[0358.8 / 0868] [I discover myself at the Olympic Ice Skating Finals with my entire family seated down the row from me. We observe a new event: The Trio or "Throuple" skate.

A group competes. One member is an exceptionally large, strong man. The other two are smaller, and their gender identities are not revealed. The hallmark of the performance occurs when the man tosses both teammates in the air at the same time, and catches them like a pair of juggling clubs.

THE CARPENTER exclaims, *"Wow that guy must be at least eight feet tall!"*] //

⁂

Maj. = 1- THE CARPENTER: #0364, 16- THE CONFIDANT: #0435
PRINCE: #0436
UNDERGROUND: #0718, #0748
THROB: #0615
UNSAFE: #0718
THE WRANGLER: #0960

⁂

#0359 - October 30, 2018 @ 06:32 (San Francisco, California)

[0359.1 / 0869] [I sit on a couch in the dark with THE FIDUCIARY. The room is illuminated by the soft white glow of a large TV in a mahogany entertainment center. We flip through channels, finding nothing to watch. We pause at a preview station. I suggest we plug in to an all-day marathon of a program called, "The Lovelies," a spinoff/reprise of "The Golden Girls." Same actors. Same sets. Different theme song.

"Can you believe BETTY WHITE is 90? She looks amazing! And she was smokin' hot back in the day."

Instead of responding with words, he lunges forward and surprises me with a kiss. Our hangout turns into a hook up. I dial things up by unzipping his shorts and pulling out his hard dick. After a brief hesitation, I tenderly blow him.

"I think I need to skip your class tonight," he says while pulling away.

"I didn't know you were planning on coming," I respond a bit puzzled.

"Your 'ASSana' has been amazing lately and I don't want to miss it."]

[0359.2 / 0870] [I blink and the two of us are seated in the lobby of a movie theater. A man and woman who work there think we're sitting on each other's laps (*a flagrant violation of house rules*).

We ignore them and they eventually leave us alone.

THE FIDUCIARY, crying and overwhelmed says, *"I think I just need some time,"* as he pulls up his pants and leaves.] //

269

⁕⁕

Maj. = 9- THE FIDUCIARY: #0420
MOVIE THEATER: #0461, #0544, #0778
CLASS: #0415, #0779, #0781, #0792

⁕⁕

#0360 - October 31, 2018 @ 06:46 (San Francisco, California)
*Of multiple highly engaging dream threads, three stand out. *

[0360.1 / 0871] [1) THE ROMANTIC makes a casual appearance and blows me a kiss.]

[0360.2 / 0872] [2) I'm on a large sailing rig in the middle of an azure blue lagoon. A storm approaches. Dark clouds swirl overhead. Multiple large ghostly, alien tuna fish leap from the water and nearly strike the boat like cannonballs. If they did, their weight and speed would sink the vessel.]

[0360.3 / 0873] [3) I'm about to make an offer on a house. While in the garage, I notice signs for agents who've been showing the property next door. I'm a motivator, teacher and coach being coached from just beyond the property line by THE ORACLE (*divine, feminine, and godmother-like*).
A group of architecture students assess the property without basic measurement tools. They use their knowledge of geometry, and the relative position of the sun (*and shadow*) to generate floor plans. One discouraged pair of students hover by a bush in the backyard picking berries and throwing them forcibly at the ground. I convince them to, *"take a breath and remember how exponents scale."* An infographic hangs midair to provide them with clues.
THE ORACLE approves of my intervention. I appreciate it when she coaches me on my coaching.] //

⁕⁕

Maj. = 15- THE ROMANTIC: #0364
BERRIES: #0487, #0747
GARAGE: #0406, #0479, #0508, #0525
SUN: #0531, #0572, #0575
THE ORACLE: #0376

⁕⁕

#0361 - November 2, 2018 @ 07:21 (San Francisco, California)

[0361.1 / 0874] [I talk to my neighbor ROBIN WILLIAMS through my car window. Our driveways are made of grass.] //

⁕⁕

ROBIN WILLIAMS: #0841
CAR WINDOW: #0731
NEIGHBOR: #0744

⁕⁕

#0362 - November 2, 2018 @ 08:23 (San Francisco, California)

[0362.1 / 0875] [MANTRA: *"If it's to be, it's up to me."*] //

※
MANTRA: #0363
※

#0363 - November 3, 2018 @ 05:12 (San Francisco, California)

[0363.1 / 0876] [*"Heart centered awareness. Heart centered awareness. Heart centered awareness."* A simple mantra repeats while a smiling image of THE DULCE DE LECHE tapping his chest emerges from the center of a cross of white light.]

[0363.2 / 0877] [I lead an inquiry session in a schoolhouse. THE PORTRAIT ARTIST *(friendly, optimistic, and reverent)* stands and asks a question. She's triggered and anxious. The best thing I can do is have her ask her question again. It feels pushy and uncomfortable for me to bring her back to her question. I wrap both of us in a bubble of "compassion light." She runs around the venue attempting to get away. I don't let her go, which upsets many of the other students.] //

※
Min. = ♣- THE DULCE DE LECHE: #0673
MANTRA: #0445, #0498, #0509, #0649, #0684
BUBBLE: #0466, #0487, #0526, #0534
COMPASSION: #0575, #0693
THE PORTRAIT ARTIST: #0770
※

#0364 - November 3, 2018 @ 06:41 (San Francisco, California)
*This nonlinear dream had numerous overlapping elements. *

[0364.1 / 0878] [1] I drive down a major street. I note a boarded-up building, previously home to a large BANK OF AMERICA branch and a CHEVY's Fast Mexican restaurant. Both have permanently closed, which surprises me.]
[0364.2 / 0879] [2] CHEVY CHASE passes me in a hallway and tries to convince me that he's not an asshole. I'm skeptical. Why is he talking to me?]
[0364.3 / 0880] [3] THE CONVERT and her mom sing karaoke in a room down the hall from where I'm scheduled to teach a workshop.]
[0364.4 / 0881] [4] THE ROMANTIC canvases door-to-door in Nevada to get out the vote.]
[0364.5 / 0882] [5] I wash my hands and notice the water has stripped off my purple finger-nail polish.]
[0364.6 / 0883] [6] THE WEAVER and THE CARPENTER have just completed a glass addition to their home. It's beautiful *(and will be easy to vandalize)*. THE CARPENTER asks

me to return his hammer; a makeshift tool composed of a tree branch, stone, and thin yellow twine which crosses and secures the stone with an "X." THE CARPENTER is frustrated THE POINT GUARD was given GRANDPA's knife. THE WEAVER is upset for other reasons.]

[0364.7 / 0884] [7) I drive under an overpass. Cops watch from above.]

[0364.8 / 0885] [8) I run energy while I move around a gathering space. THE WORLD-BRIDGER asks us to alternatively set the room for meditation due to tonight's small count of students. A snaking series of TSA baggage rollers look fun to run at, and slide across. A young woman yells at us to help.

"You're very easy to read," I say dismissively. She shapeshifts into a cyborg and stupefies me. THE WORLDBRIDGER continues to lead meditation in another room.] //

⁕

Maj. = 0- *THE WEAVER: #0368, 1- THE CARPENTER: #0377,*
7- THE WORLDBRIDGER: #0374, 15- THE ROMANTIC: #0370
Min. = ♥- *GRANDPA: #0442*
HAMMER: #0718, #0772
SLIDE: #0544, #0561, #0611
THE POINT GUARD: #0390
THE CONVERT: #0498

⁕

#0365 - November 5, 2018 @ 04:13 (San Francisco, California)

[0365.1 / 0886] [I'm backstage at an LCD SOUNDSYSTEM concert. I've been selected as the opening act. I'm a little nervous. This is the biggest crowd I've ever played for. I find the band remarkable. They're all ancient. They move their own equipment on and off stage. Another group performs their set flooded by red light and black smoke.

I don't recall my performance. When I snap out of my standing trance, I'm at the side stage watching the headlining set *(live streamed to social media)*. The band performs an entirely new, never before heard album from front to back to wild acclaim of the roaring crowd. THE FAIRY GODMOTHER *(clear, strong, empowering, and nurturing)* is the first person to "like" a comment I post referencing the concert.]

[0365.2 / 0887] [I'm in a suburban neighborhood. The streets are covered in snow. THE HEALER and THE WARD OF GAIA have recently purchased a small house on an American outpost for their growing permaculture institute, intended to serve as a guest house for pilgrims and penitents. Current guests play like children, laughing as they throw snowballs at each other in the street. It's lighthearted. Strong wind gusts cause the temperature to plummet. THE WARD OF GAIA remarks on the property's expensive mortgage, which was underwritten by Wells Fargo.

"As much as we're paying them in interest, they should really give US a sign without their name on it for the front lawn," she says somewhat sarcastically.

"They did. It's that tiny little thing at the end of the road" someone else says, pointing to a small white sign with black block letters and a single red stripe at bottom barely visible at far the end of the street.

We step inside for a group conversation. When seated in a circle, THE HEALER reprimands a being who shapeshifts between being THE CHEF and THE ICEMAN, both advanced

272

students from different communities. The being makes gorgeous multicolored tissue paper flowers. Once completed they're placed in a white five-gallon bucket. Intended to be gifts, they presently distract the group. The interior of the room is warmly lit, inviting, and has a soft golden hue.]

[0365.3 / 0888] [I'm with "The Band" in Venice, Italy driving an early 1970's Fiat. The scene outside looks like the set of a Fellini or Antonioni film. The car goes off a bridge with us inside. We laugh when we crash into the water below. Water flows in through open windows, but we aren't bothered. Once fully submerged we simply swim out the open windows. We surface and note the water is only chest deep. Oddly though, the car disappears. We wade through a rainy piazza.

The three of us sit at a square table with THE SWIM COACH (*seeking, motherly, and curious*). THE SWIM COACH sits across from me. A man sits to the right, a woman to the left. THE SWIM COACH proceeds to give the woman a psychic reading using a series of small, white, domino sized paper cards embossed with alien characters. She stacks the cards in a floral pattern. The man is somewhat nervous and surprised by the process, and attempts to make small talk. After sustained silence, THE SWIM COACH uses a small watercolor typewriter to create a scroll which reads: "*THIS SPELL ACTIVATES @ 2PM on MARCH 28, 2019.*" Raindrops fall and smudge the text as I say,

"*Interesting. Your spell activates on my 40th birthday.*"] //

⁑

Maj. = 20- THE HEALER: #0658
Min = ◆- THE WARD OF GAIA: #0693
ANCIENT: #0547, #0548, #0621, #0748
1970's: #0635, #0687, #0716
WATERCOLOR: #0423, #0669
OFF A BRIDGE: #0745
THE FAIRY GODMOTHER: #0444
THE ICEMAN: #0683
THE SWIM COACH: #0938
⁑

#0366 - November 6, 2018 @ 06:13 (San Francisco, California)

[0366.1 / 0889] [I'm in a giant cathedral art gallery. I offer a group of interested people a tour of the property. The panels I've painted are extremely large, the size of two-story houses, which still fit neatly within the grand, softly gold lit space. As I describe my processes, I feel I've given too many secrets away. I've shown them how to produce a texture my pieces are known for. I also spill a truth, "*I've never accepted payment for anything I've produced.*"

As I share this, it makes them more desirous of my work.] //

⁑
ART GALLERY: #0523, #0567
PANELS: #0443, #0794
DESCRIBE: #0623, #0630, #0637
⁑

#0367 - November 6, 2018 @ 07:00 (San Francisco, California)

[0367.1 / 0890] [It's night. I walk down a long hallway in the basement of a house. I'm there to help THE GREEK and THE DOMINATRIX *(newly married, chaotic, and incommunicado)* who avoid talking to each other. They each individually nurture one of their newborn twins. I'm invited to stay overnight in a haunted room. Once I shut the door I don't leave, not even to pee.
   "I'd rather hold it in or piss myself than interact with spirits here."
THE CONNECTOR shows up as a tall blonde haired male version of herself. His/Her skin is brown and smooth. He/She has a very large penis that presses up against my back when He/She gives me a nourishing embrace from behind. A third being joins us to cuddle. Our throuple experiences deep healing on many mind/body/aura levels.
   THE ORPHAN is also on the property. The space she occupies is confusingly bright for night. Together, the four of us set up a series of lightweight cheesecloth mosquito net tents on a manicured putting green, furnished with unique items fashioned from long rusty poles we've rescued from a decaying stack on the side of the house. THE ORPHAN is stoked by our creative use of materials.]

[0367.2 / 0891] [I'm on the set of a movie that's off schedule and over budget. LADY GAGA is the star. After brushing by to kiss me on the cheek LADY GAGA jumps in a car with tinted windows and shuttles off to another set where she stars in another highly anticipated film with the working title: "*LOIS. *"] //

✱✱

Maj. = 4- THE CONNECTOR: #0377
LADY GAGA: #0423
TWINS: #0456
STACK: #0732, #0755
THE ORPHAN: #0470

✱✱

PART 7 - WHISPERS

#0368 - #0556

"Row, row, row your boat.
Gently down the stream.
Merrily, merrily, merrily, merrily,
Life is but a dream."

-American Nursery Rhyme

* * *

November 7, 2018 - March 18, 2019

⚜ **7.1 - THE BOOK OF SCORPIUS: 0368-0391** ⚜

#0368 - November 7, 2018 @ 00:46 (San Francisco, California)

[0368.1 / 0892] [I pose with a group of yogis for a photo on a set of stairs.]

[0368.2 / 0893] [THE WEAVER and I get out of a car and leave an infant buckled into a car seat, in the back. As we move away from the car, I become paranoid the child will be kidnapped, but THE WEAVER assures me all is well because we've acted, *"under cover of dark-ness."* We arrive at our destination (*a Japanese restaurant*), which appears to be open for busi-ness, yet under construction. At front, a rotund African American man in management training deeply struggles while learning to navigate the reservation fulfillment application. Coincidentally, I wrote the software and teach him how to use it as he checks us in. He walks us through the kitchen.

The restaurant has issues with refrigeration. Prepped portions of tiramisu melt and run off the plates, pooling in a soupy mess at the bottom of the cooler. Odder, and perhaps upset-ting, are the rotting bloody pork spines stacked on an aluminum tray next to the wilting desserts. *"I must confess..."* I say staring into the glass case, *"I sure do like the hearts!"* My comment generates nervous laughter from the staff.] //

⚜

Maj. = 0- THE WEAVER: #0371
INFANT: #0456, #0593, #0597
MANAGEMENT: #0685
SOFTWARE: #0468

⚜

#0369 - November 7, 2018 @ 02:07 (San Francisco, California)

[0369.1 / 0894] [THE TRANSLATOR runs energy with me while sitting under a tree. From our eighth chakras, she telepathically shows me, *"You've been this way for 1,000 years."*]

[0369.2 / 0895] [A man in a wheelchair runs me over and leaves me paralyzed. In the moment of our impact, he sweats profusely.]

[0369.3 / 0896] [I walk through a basement awards gallery with JONATHAN DAVIS. *"This was supposed to be our meal ticket,"* he says tapping on an image of the "Take a Look in the Mirror" album cover. *"Instead, it was murderously cruel,"* he continues. I don't ask any questions.] //

⚜

Maj. = 19- THE TRANSLATOR: #0373
JONATHAN DAVIS: #0666

MIRROR: #0429, #0467
1,000: #0514
WHEELCHAIR: #0416, #0534
⁑

#0370 - November 7, 2018 @ 03:11 (San Francisco, California)

[0370.1 / 0897] [THE ROMANTIC meets me for coffee at our modern co-owned cafe. En route to the table he stops to chat with a couple who leave him giddy and reminded of a lover. He sits and places his reading glasses on the table. One lens is round, the other a square. The frames are navy blue with tortoise shell accents. He spins a small black and white top on the table. As we sip coffee, we mutually dote on each other's cable knit sweaters while discussing politics and art. *"I don't like abstract art,"* he says squarely. *"If it doesn't at least look like the thing it's supposed to be, what's the point?"* I wake up twice from this dream and write it down, before actually waking to record it. ***Sneaky bugger. ***] //

⁑

Maj. = 15- THE ROMANTIC: #0423
GLASSES: #0547, #0585
KNIT: #0501, #0780
ART: #0414
⁑

#0371 - November 7, 2018 @ 05:39 (San Francisco, California)

[0371.1 / 0898] [THE ADONIS *(strong, chiseled, and disciplined)* sits next to me on a bed. We both pull covers up to our noses to hide our faces. A dead woman with long hair enters. She's THE ADONIS's girlfriend. The woman's larynx and pharynx have rotted, rendering her unable to speak. He's unable to sign. She's surprised to learn I know sign language.
"If that situation doesn't work out, we should date," I look to THE ADONIS saying as she exits the room.
THE ADONIS doesn't respond.
"It's ok, I'll ask again in six months," I say to break the silence. My heart leaps in my chest as I offer a wink of the eye.]

[0371.2 / 0899] [THE WEAVER blow dries her hair in the bathroom down the hall from my room. I don't have any furniture. A large ball of crumpled up cash sits in the center of the floor. Hip hop music plays in the background. Two similar aged teen boys enter, one through the door, the other through a basement window. One of them is high on meth. Afraid they'll steal my money ball, I hastily pick it up and leave.
I stumble out of the house onto a cobblestone street where I'm almost hit by an approaching car constructed from childlike black and white crayon scribbles. I make my way to a large glass cafeteria supported by log walls. I toss the cash ball on the floor and peel away a few $1's, a $50, some $20's like leaves off a head of lettuce. THE PIXIE enters playing *"computer music"* through a small JBL speaker which I promptly power down. The only exit is a long serpentine ADA compliant ramp.]

· · ·

[0371.3 / 0900] [THE WILDERNESS GUIDE has a girlfriend named "Annie," who THE ADONIS and I both agree is very attractive.] //

⁂

Maj. = 0- THE WEAVER: #0380
Min. = ♠- THE PIXIE: #0450
CRAYON: #0405
SPEAKER: #0406, #0472, #0514
METH: #0748
THE ADONIS: #0379
THE WILDERNESS GUIDE: #0395

⁂

#0372 - November 7, 2018 @ 07:00 (San Francisco, California)

[0372.1 / 0901] [I'm in an airport terminal having an elaborate heart to heart with JAMES MUNKY SHAFFER, a guitarist from the band KORN. This unexpected interaction was carefully curated by a mysterious woman who sits at the end of our row of chairs bouncing a baby on her knee. We blink and find ourselves in a high school gym. MUNKY and I discuss family, evolution, *"being a conscious channel,"* and fame.
"Fame is something you don't want. Take it from someone who knows. IT. OWNS. YOU."
I'm so engrossed by the conversation I forget to blink again to return to the airport terminal. I nearly miss my flight. I charge from the gym out a door, and cross the terminal on foot to my gate. I hand the attendant a yellow validated parking ticket instead of an airline QR code boarding pass. I'm not permitted to board the flight and the gate attendant calls security. It's late at night. The mood remains calm, even though I attempted to breach security.]

[0373.2 / 0902] [I sit behind the reception desk at a yoga studio. I'm surprised when the smiling face of a middle-aged man pops out from behind a vase of flowers.] //

⁂

KORN: #0477
FAME: #0467
HIGH SCHOOL: #0477, #0481, #0540, #0718
PARKING: #0433, #0438, #0441

⁂

#0373 - November 8, 2018 @ 00:28 (San Francisco, California)

[0373.1 / 0903] [Though somewhat abstract, I've looked in a box and discovered Schrödinger's cat. It manifests as a solid gold balloon animal. As I contemplate, *"Why does this thing have infinite lives?"* THE TRANSLATOR appears to my side saying, *"Infinite and one are the same."*] //

⁂

Maj. = 19- THE TRANSLATOR: #0377
BALLOON: #0526, #0618, #0682

INFINITE: #0747
ONE: #0755

⁂

#0374 - November 8, 2018 @ 03:32 (San Francisco, California)

[0374.1 / 0904] [I'm on an ice-covered planet. I need to make a decision quickly to get back to a house and avoid freezing to death. I traverse an icy pond in a blizzard, submerged in near freezing water up to my neck.

THE WORLDBRIDGER guides me toward the aligned path, but I'm enamored with my surroundings and distract myself by taking photographs. Portions of the ice formations are a deep indigo tone, and appear like weightlessly suspended giant blobs of ink. My body quickly dies. I feel warm and woozy. I make my way to the corner of what seems to be a parking lot. I bob on my tippy toes towards the edge, increasingly frustrated as I claw pointlessly at the ice wall. I'm unable to climb out.] //

⁂

Maj. = 7- THE WORLDBRIDGER: #0376
ICE: #0763, #0790, #0795
PARKING LOT: #0441, #0447
BLOBS: #0659

⁂

#0375 - November 8, 2018 @ 07:00 (San Francisco, California)

[0375.1 / 0905] [I walk down the zig zag interior of an aquifer gone dry. I pass THE ACTOR as he takes a walk with his dog "Kuma." I continue on, passing hastily unpacked piles of clothing. I enter a gift shop. The featured toy is a metal monkey holding a disproportionately large magnetic banana.

I leave the display and walk towards THE LIONESS (*ferocious, engaging, and successful*). I give her a hug after she shares she's had a tough day. We cheer each other up by singing karaoke to one another in a bar created from a tunnel of welded RVs.

The mood is uplifting until a super fratty bro donning new J. Crew clothes comes to our tableside. He pours an entire liter of beer across my back and down the right side of my body. I don't initially react, though laughter roars all around me. I make eye contact with a psychotic grin on my face and give the guy grim detail on how I intend to detach his body one part at a time. The room becomes quiet and neutral. He hears my threats and offers to get me a white towel to help clean up the mess he created.] //

⁂

Maj. = 10- THE ACTOR: #0394
GIFT SHOP: #0428, #0748
RV: #0433
Oh, Darling!
TUNNEL: #0521, #0525
THE LIONESS: #1047

⁂

279

#0376 - November 9, 2018 @ 05:10 (San Rafael, California)

[0376.1 / 0906] [I'm on retreat with a group of healers. THE ORACLE (*aware, supportive, and crisp*) and THE WORLDBRIDGER exchange gifts with each other.]

[0376.2 / 0907] [I'm in a top gun jet pilot flight simulator. The experience is active and hectic. The plane wildly jostles around. Small orange square foam pads pop out from the neck of the chair to prevent my cervical spine from snapping. I'm in a competition with a bunch of other cadets. The stakes seem high.]

[0376.3 / 0908] [I'm at an amusement park that feels like Disneyland. I watch a Viking ship ride lumber nonsensically slow as MICKEY MOUSE stands on the bow. He's obscured by a massive spray of colorful booming fireworks.]

[0376.4 / 0909] [THE MASSEUSE (*delicate, skilled, and caring*) invites me to pass through her home. She ascends a staircase and disappears. She's a superhero.]

[0376.5 / 0910] [I'm in a bingo parlor surrounded by elderly people who sell chocolate bars to passersby. I only want to buy one bar. I'm handed $10 worth of chocolate (*equivalent to the entire amount I paid*). I'm given two same sized bars, and one other that is half sized. Only one of the big bars has the *"purple crushed velvet labyrinth wrapping"* that I desired. Initially, I want to give the two silver wrapped ones back. I ultimately decide to keep the chocolate. I open a small box and discover a series of large palm sized fake diamonds. I'm fixated on an oddly thick Ben Franklin half dollar. At first, I think it's made of silver, but upon closer inspection I discover another coin, perhaps made of lead, welded to the reverse. A pair of foreign eyes peer at me vacantly through two melted holes in the half dollar. The coin is effectively worthless (*as are the gemstones in the box*). I put the coin down.
"Who's gonna give us $.44 to help us reach our goal?" an old man shouts.
"Every group has their own family jewels," another old man says, laughing and patting me on the back as he walks away.
THE WORLDBRIDGER receives a healing at the other end of the table. Movement to the left side of his face is restored after having previously been paralyzed.] //

⁎⁎

Maj. = 7 - THE WORLDBRIDGER: #0377
VELVET: #0567, #0573, #0622
JEWELS: #0561
PEER: #0567, #0748

⁎⁎

#0377 - November 10, 2018 @ 05:32 (San Rafael, California)

[0377.1 / 0911] [I'm on a temple construction site. THE TRANSLATOR is present. THE

CONNECTOR accosts me by saying, *"REMEMBER YOUR LINEAGE BITCH, OR THIS THING WON'T GET BUILT."*]

[0377.2 / 0912] [A yoga class starts late. THE BARKEEP *(tired, committed, and wishful)* is asked to substitute, though won't make it to the studio on time. I decide not to volunteer as a last-minute hero and let circumstances remain as they are.]

[0377.3 / 0913] [*"I GOT A TROPHY!"* I triumphantly say as I hold up my third-place award.]

[0377.4 / 0914] [It's the 1950's. I work on a car with THE CARPENTER. We might be siblings. The door that covers the gas cap is missing. We contemplate whether or not it's worth fixing.]

[0377.5 / 0915] [I SELECT A "MILKY WAY" candy bar from a bowl. I unwrap it and jam it entirely into my mouth. The sugary caramel coats my teeth, so sticky it almost uproots some of them from my lower jaw. THE WORLDBRIDGER enters. When people ask him if he'd like a candy bar he says, *"I'm only interested in the Milky Way."* I panic. I've taken the only "Milky Way!" I attempt to vomit up/claw/scrape out my mouth in hope of not being found out as he comes around to give healings. My thinking is too narrow and small. He could give a shit about the candy bar; he's speaking to the big expansive space where our little blue dot of a planet is commingled.] //

⁑

Maj. = 1- THE CARPENTER: #0385, 4- THE CONNECTOR: #0401,
7- THE WORLDBRIDGER: #0379, 19- THE TRANSLATOR: #0586
CARAMEL: #0606
THE BARKEEP: #0646

⁑

#0378 - November 11, 2018 @ 04:52 (San Rafael, California)

[0378.1 / 0916] [I'm in Nairobi, excited to meet THE KENYAN *(mentee, deaf, and courageous)* in person.]

[0378.2 / 0917] [THE PUBLIC MEDIUM turns to me and says, *"Yeah, he was there. I got that healing from THE NUN as well."* I'm not certain who he's referring to but I nod in agreement.]

[0378.3 / 0918] [A stop motion animation film is shot frame by frame on a massive concrete wall full of murals. I overhear the crew describe the process. It's taken an entire week for the artists to paint seven frames. They are not deterred, though I find the production inefficient, heavy handed, and excessive. The camera can only roll down the tracks and snap a frame when all the stills for the sequence are complete. A woman in a skirt sits on the camera tracks occupied with her phone, left hand on her chin. She won't move, so the film crew is hamstrung. She's unwilling to move a scant 18 inches when politely asked. After a protracted pause she decides to leave the space without acknowledging anything going on around her.]

[0378.4 / 0919] [Voice memos I attempted to record earlier in the day unexpectedly show up in my log as a single multi-hour entry in my phone.]

[0378.5 / 0920] [I have radiation burns all over my body. Painful sensations are particularly strong on the outsides of my shins. *"I accept the healing."*] //

⁎⁎

Maj. = 18- THE PUBLIC MEDIUM: #0537
Min. = ◆- THE NUN: #0384
SEVEN: #0757, #0791, #0798
BURNS: #0624, #0638, #0642, #0693, #0717

⁎⁎

#0379 - November 12, 2018 @ 06:59 (San Francisco, California)

[0379.1 / 0921] [I'm in a private residence. I encounter THE ADONIS (*clear eyed, connected, and sexy*) in the shower. We move to an inviting softly gold lit bedroom where he bottoms for me twice, so tender and gentle. We're angels, and we've come together as partners for healing. I rest my sweaty forehead on his smooth, chiseled chest. We say goodbye and I leave. I return to the residence the next day. THE AIR TRAFFIC CONTROLLER (*candid, territorial, and controlling*) answers the door declaring he's THE ADONIS's partner.
"I didn't know THE ADONIS had a partner."]

[0379.2 / 0922] [THE WORLDBRIDGER and I are at a concert hall. He's not remotely interested in the show. I take a seat in an area with round white tables. I'm not supposed to be there. A waiter asks me to leave. I jokingly give the waiter a hard time. He laughs at my jokes as a young woman hands me a ticket to tonight's MARILYN MANSON concert. The mood turns tense and aggressive. People in the crowd push each other.
"Is this supposed to be security?"
"Should WE be worried?"
MARILYN performs covered head to toe in thick white grease paint. He looks like a clown. His arms are four times longer than normal. He leans over the crowd to demonstrate *"how spoooooky"* he is. The crowd isn't impressed with the show. Some whisper, *"Poor Demon. Sweet Demon,"* under their breath as they shake their heads and depart the venue.] //

⁎⁎

Maj. = 7- THE WORLDBRIDGER: #0484
MARILYN MANSON: #1001
SPOOKY: #0678

⁎⁎

282

#0380 - November 14, 2018 @ 05:39 (San Francisco, California)

[0380.1 / 0923] [The broader me (*and older me*) tries to convince a young me (*perhaps three or four years old*) to ride a roller coaster. "Big Me" sits facing "Little Me" as a train advances up the hill. When the lap bar drops it misses "Little Me" entirely and sweeps over "Little Me's" head, offering no restraint. THE WEAVER sits next to "Little Me" for a moment, then winks at "Big Me" and disappears. Looking behind me (*as "Big Me"*) I realize we're on a massive wooden roller coaster called, "The Beast." We crest the hill and descend. "Little Me" is secured to the seat by an invisible force and seems to be fine. The ride concludes. We exit the train. "Big Me" turns into a golden-haired cocker spaniel. My tail wiggles excitedly. We celebrate having done a really good thing. "Doubt," "Fear" and "Exhilaration" are all little ghouls who lift me on their shoulders as I confidently chant, *"I rid the Beast."*] //

⁑

Maj. = 0- THE WEAVER: #0386
THE BEAST: #0682, #0770
CHANT: #0682

⁑

#0381 - November 14, 2018 @ 06:47 (San Francisco, California)

[0381.1 / 0924] [I'm the new guitarist for the band AC/DC. I'm backstage and overhear a man and woman converse about market research and statistics. The man makes a minor power play by suggesting it's, *"his job to know,"* and that the two of them, *"should compare notes."* I blink and find myself at the back of the large outdoor venue, walking with the band down a grassy hill towards the stage. No one in the crowd notices us, nor pays us any attention. We're invisible.

Once we arrive on stage, I notice a portion of the massive canvas sign bearing the group's name is untethered at my corner. It's really important to refasten it as a large crowd begins to gather and move in toward security fences at front. A strong performance is expected. I'm up for the challenge. I've never heard my guitar through such a large set of amplifiers before. I hear electricity crackle as generators power up the house lights. An intro track plays. My body tingles with anticipation. I take a large swallow before I raise my arm, pick in hand ready to strike my first chord.] //

⁑

GRASSY HILL: #0452, #0472, #0586, #0655
LARGE CROWD: #0789
ANTICIPATION: #0552, #0726

⁑

#0382 - November 14, 2018 @ 07:15 (San Francisco, California)

[0382.1 / 0925] [THE RAPTOR is surrounded by a group of old ladies who, *"just LOVE him!"* He's taken them out to a local diner for their weekly breakfast and cigarette shopping excursion.]

. . .

[0382.2 / 0926] [I observe a guy hula hooping on water skis behind a fast-moving speed boat on a lake. A shark lurks in the water behind the boat. I have a phone conversation with THE DANCER as I watch, fairly certain the hula hooping man is going to be swallowed whole. *"Yeah, please just don't tell THE CHILD about the shark,"* she says as our call is cut short.]

[0382.3 / 0927] [I'm confused while looking at social media. I'm shown a "memory" of THE MARATHONER *(optimistic, tenacious, and happy)* and THE DOCTOR *(social, lively, and helpful)* celebrating their 10-year anniversary. They've recently made their relationship public. They would have been together non-publicly for years if the digital reminder is true.] //

✲✲

Maj. = 2- THE DANCER: #0389, 3- THE CHILD: #0386
Min. = ◆- THE RAPTOR: #0396
HOOP: #0418
LOVE: #0463, #0610, #0617, #0637, #0638, #0640, #0678, #0703, #0712, #0721, #0741
THE MARATHONER: #1026
THE DOCTOR: #1026

✲✲

#0383 - November 15, 2018 @ 04:15 (San Francisco, California)

[0383.1 / 0928] [I gather in a warmly lit gallery space at night with other adults. One side of the room is composed of giant windows. Candle lit chandeliers blaze overhead, possibly floating. I attend a speed dating event where participants screen-print custom t-shirts. The screens are mounted around the gallery walls and taken down to produce clothing. The finished shirts serve as conversation starters.

I select a panel with diagonal streaks and a small green heart on the lower left quadrant. When prepped, I discover that the overlaid screen will create a small stick figure boy who holds a green heart in his hands to the left of his body, presenting it as his *"gift to the world."* Two guys come over to see what I'm up to. We flirt for a bit before I point to my t-shirt and say, *"I just printed my side over the left pelvis...is that weird?"*

The more intellectual and academic of the two begins to walk away.

"He passes. He didn't say 'hip bone,'" I overhear him say to the other.

"Oh...I actually printed where the garment wearer's left ilium would fall. It'll accentuate the green heart. It'll 'lub dub' as the wearer walks."

My basic anatomical vocabulary has impressed the academic. Now I have both men's attention.] //

✲✲
GALLERY: #0414, #0421, #0496, #0523, #0567
PELVIS: #0480, #0770
Ooh!
La La!
WEIRD: #0613, #0623, #0698
INTELLECTUAL: #0465, #0668
✲✲

#0384 - November 16, 2018 @ 03:20 (Beavercreek, Ohio)

[0384.1 / 0929] [A flat 2D scene includes characters from "The Simpsons." All lack depth.]

[0384.2 / 0930] [THE DEVOTEE leads a yoga practice. Her assistant wanders the classroom. The assistant makes unnecessarily firm contact with my body. She forces me to the ground and holds me there. I become angry. When class concludes I demand to speak to her in the hallway and give her some strong feedback. The discussion triggers a review of participant waivers and *"hold harmless"* forms to ensure every student has current documents on file.]

[0384.3 / 0931] [I ride bikes with friends down a sidewalk on a warm sunny day. I pass THE DEVOTEE. We briefly stop to talk about our past lives. At the end of our exchange she says, *"Ok, now it's my turn,"* before we saddle up and ride in opposite directions.]

[0384.4 / 0932] [I observe a scene where people throw a wiffleball in slow motion at a shaggy dog named "NICOTINE." When people are struck by the ball they lay down in an orderly line on the grass. The field is maintained by THE PROPERTY MANAGER (*witty, loving, and neurotic*). He and I decide to pay THE AESTHETE (*elevated, stylish, and discerning*) a visit, first walking through a luxurious marble space flooded with warm sun. A light scent of coconut hovers on the breeze.]

[0384.5 / 0933] [*"ARE YOU CURIOUS?"* a large white glowing being asks me. I look behind me and see THE NUN who nods, indicating it's my turn to answer.
"Who have you called up tonight?" An out of body female voice asks.
"My angels of the highest order," I respond without hesitation.
"NOW! YOU! KNOW! LOVE!!" Choirs of angelic voices sing in concert behind me while the light surrounding me intensifies.
I feel nourished, supported and healed unlike anything I've ever previously remembered. It's beautiful. I cry.] //

⁎⁎

Min. = ♠- *THE DEVOTEE: #0390,* ♦- *THE NUN: #0441*
THE SIMPSONS: #1335
STOP: #0669, #0673, #0687
OUT OF BODY: #0487, #0566, #0573, #0607, #0611
THE AESTHETE: #1014

⁎⁎

#0385 - November 16, 2018 @ 17:27 (Beavercreek, Ohio)

[0385.1 / 0934] [I'm at Barry's Bootcamp waiting for a new class called, "FREEDOM." The space is atypical. The interior is simple and austere. Cinder block walls are crudely painted with white primer. The class is led by THE ALPHA (*imposing, virile, and confrontational*). THE CARPENTER attends class with me.

The experience is off brand and disorganized. Students spill over to an annex room where the lights and music don't work and the equipment behaves erratically. My treadmill oscillates between 8 and 13mph, consistently holding me in the "11's" as my feet scramble beneath me. Eventually the machine belt snaps and creeps to a stop.

The class concludes. THE CARPENTER tells a large Caucasian Congressman wearing a suit that he, *"probably won't be coming back."* A female executive enters and acknowledges, *"The 'FREEDOM' class has some bugs that need to be worked out, but it's going to stay on the weekly schedule for now. You're going to have to give this workout up to get to where you want to go. All proceeds from the next class will benefit causes that support veterans."*

THE CARPENTER pauses, grins, looks at the Congressman then says, *"I asked you in 2005, 2008, and here we are in 2018 still tiptoeing around the same conversation."* Multiple camera phones capture his comments. The Congressman pauses to choose his words. Regardless of how he responds it will appear callow and tone-deaf to anyone hearing him speak out of context.

"Sir, in 2005...no one was ready to have this conversation. In 2008, a few of us were, but not nearly enough. In 2018 we've hit a critical mass, and are now finally ready to have a productive dialog on how we can honor, venerate and care for our veterans."

Lightheartedness permeates the crowd, resulting in pockets of laughter. The Congressman and THE CARPENTER know upon playback through a major media outlet the interaction would not be well received by the public. A producer requests, *"Let's go reshoot that exchange with both of you sitting on that couch over there."* THE CARPENTER agrees, and they along with the BARRY's video crew head in a similar direction. They manufacture a more socially appealing version of what was a moving, authentic moment.] //

✳

Maj. = 1- THE CARPENTER: #0389
11: #0643, #0654
SPEAK: #0406, #0430, #0453, #0550, #0637
FREEDOM: #0443, #0615

✳

#0386 - November 17, 2018 @ 04:48 (Beavercreek, Ohio)

[0386.1 / 0935] [A family plays miniature golf. An ornamented sign in German sternly expresses, *"drinking is not permitted on the course."* Some of the men hold steins of beer. THE WEAVER calls to them from the clubhouse asking, *"Does the sign say it's ok to do that, boys?"* It's not, but the boys ignore her and play through.]

[0386.2 / 0936] [I stand on the lawn of a large house under construction. It's dusty outside and darkly cloudy overhead. OPRAH's voice begins to whisper omnisciently as I walk toward an empty garage. Rain begins to fall. The drops hiss like steam as they hit the pavement.]

[0386.3 / 0937] [THE CHILD and I stand next to a Christmas tree cutting small pieces of black nylon rope and putting them in a pile. I melt the frayed ends of the pieces with a lighter. There is some risk the pile will catch fire and melt into a hardened ball. On the TV, a guitarist for a heavy metal band laments the untimely death of a bandmate. During the interview he says, *"Losing my friend was like losing my connection to creativity. Like I lost my connection to God. It was instantly gone, but I still intend to carry on and tour in support of the new album. He'd want it that way, and it will be healing for me."* THE ATHEIST watches this and instantly feels sad. I tell him, *"It's okay to cry."* The conversation occurs in the garage from [0386.2 / 0936], which is now finished, lit, and houses multiple vehicles.]

[0386.4 / 0938] [I'm in a banquet hall where a new team of rising stars is announced one by one by THE RESTAURATEUR *(cathartic, emotive, and rebuilding)*. I leave the banquet hall and walk towards a den where a single desk lamp softly lights the space. I enter the room followed by a senior partner from a law firm. He slams an invoice on the desk and asks me why six specific exercises during a recent deposition didn't go well with his principal client, THE ADOPTIVE MOTHER *(youthful, maturing, and optimistic)*. //

⁂

Maj. = 0- THE WEAVER: #0389, 3- THE CHILD: #0389, 8- THE ATHEIST: #0389
OPRAH: #0467
GOD: #0480, #0550, #0719, #0767, #0792
LAW: #0698, #0701, #0774, #0788

⁂

#0387 - November 17, 2018 @ 07:17 (Beavercreek, Ohio)

[0387.1 / 0939] [* INTERRUPTED. CARBON. MONOXIDE. *]

[0387.2 / 0940] [I make a left out of an office park and see a vast, expansive view of the Golden Gate Bridge. Multiple vibrant and saturated shades of blue water color the San Francisco Bay. It feels like a video game. Small alien craft of various sizes, shapes and colors whizz by at dizzying speeds. I arrive at a small, yet regal law office for a meeting with THE CITY EMPLOYEE *(flirtatious, calm, and playful)*. His assistant walks us to a dimly lit meeting room where we prepare to subpoena BEYONCÉ for tax evasion.] //

⁂

BEYONCÉ: #0638
EXPANSIVE: #0505
REGAL: #0548, #0655, #0713
MEETING ROOM: #0431, #0441, 0461, #0502, #0512, #0640

⁂

#0388 - November 17, 2018 @ 10:12 (Beavercreek, Ohio)

[0388.1 / 0941] [I'm in a BDSM scene where participants dangle bricks on chains from their necks as *"Heavy Jewelry."* Bricks can be chopped into quarters and traded amongst "Doms." Brick size doesn't indicate proportional ownership of "Subs." If a sub splits their brick among four doms, each dom retains 100% ownership. The buyback in dexterity is swapped for heavier duties. Less physical weight carried around the sub's neck implies a greater range in emotional capacity. Most in scene *(regardless of role)* fetishize the sound of a wet saw as it grinds through each negotiated brick.] //

287

⁂

BDSM: #0552, #0717
HEAVY: #0401, #0417, #0461, #0494, #0495, #0500
WET: #0443, #0452, #0459, #0484

⁂

#0389 - November 17, 2018 @ 11:00 (Beavercreek, Ohio)

[0389.1 / 0942] [THE CHILD is six years old. She plays with three other similarly aged children. One teaches her how to slide over the second-floor balcony of the upper level of a single-family home and drop down into a stairwell like landing a ski jump. It feels risky, but THE ATHEIST and THE DANCER are not concerned.]

[0389.2 / 0943] [A brilliant aurora streaks the sky, leaving trails overhead like a long exposure photograph. Milky blues and ethereal green swaths paint the sky.
"A Quad. A Quint? A sextuple halo!?" I exclaim as I count concentric rainbow rings that brighten the sky.
No one seems as excited about this as I am, though I attempt to generate childlike wonder. I go inside, get my phone, and then return outside to take photographs. My initial panorama attempt doesn't work. I jump on a bike and ride way out from my starting vista point at the house. The new phone has a much anticipated *(and highly desired)* "double exposure" mode. While charming and novel, my images of the sky are distorted. There's no way to undo or decouple the images. I'm not sure how the function toggles on/off. I capture a variety of images. Some could be massively appealing and used in major publications. All the images are overlaid with braille subtitles.
The brilliance overhead subsides. The sky darkens. I'm left sad, frustrated, and crying. Tears stream down my face. A small puncture in the phone screen, the size of a bb strike, causes the glass to bevel outward towards me. The glass crunches under my thumb as I push the screen back in. The entire device begins to bend and buckle, as though a small battle ensues within. Bubbles and pockmarks scar the device, which is eventually rendered useless and powers down. My sadness deepens. I don't want to buy another expensive device, even though THE WEAVER and THE CARPENTER appear by my side and offer to get me one.] //

⁂

Maj. = *0- THE WEAVER: #0396, 1- THE CARPENTER: #0403,*
2- THE DANCER: #0392, 3- THE CHILD: #0392, 8- THE ATHEIST: #0422
THUMB: #0482, #0756, #0772
BRAILLE: #0475, #0500, #0632, #0634
DEVICE: #0423, #0430, #0438, #0443, #0477, #0526, #0529

⁂

#0390 - November 18, 2018 @ 08:04 (Beavercreek, Ohio)
*Disparate, chaotic dream threads. *

[0390.1 / 0944] [THE DEVOTEE places her hands on my back. My vision goes blindingly white as I receive an infusion of the Holy Spirit. Then, I discover myself as a student, viewing a student film I've starred in. In the movie, a river flows fast and deep. The water churns and gurgles as I walk along its bank. The edges of the river rapidly erode causing vegetation to drop into the rising chocolate toned water. Perhaps a giant serpent lurks just below the surface on both sides of the river. I flee up a trailhead. When I glance back over my shoulder, I see a crash of blue rhinos. As they draw nearer, I realize they're blue triceratopses.]

[0390.2 / 0945] [I'm in a dimly lit banquet room, searching for my phone. My phone is black. I mistakenly snag one from a table, then realize it's pink. The device isn't mine. I've grabbed it off a table where a newly elected congresswoman of color sits. RASHIDA TLAIB, AYANNA PRESSLEY, ALEXANDRIA OCASIO-CORTEZ are seated at the table with her. They universally believe I'm trying to steal their phones. THE DEVOTEE sits at the table reviewing her notes before delivering the keynote address.]

[0390.3 / 0946] [THE POINT GUARD leaps from the second story bedroom window of a house on a suburban cul de sac. It's night. He runs up a sidewalk to walk with me and a pre-teen African American boy. When we arrive at the end of the sidewalk, we enter a subway station together. The young boy leaps over the turnstile and performs a krump dance to "This is America" facing a series of cameras. THE POINT GUARD waves and jumps behind the performing boy in an attempt to disrupt the scene.]

[0390.4 / 0947] [My vision goes sparkly white, pink, and carnival glass bright when I receive another infusion of Holy Spirit energy from THE DEVOTEE. Intense silver, white, diamond carnival glass light shoots through the back of my body and out the front of my face as I say, *Thank you.*" Light streams from my mouth and eyes until I wake up.] //

☆☆

Min. = ♠- *THE DEVOTEE: #0391*
AYANNA PRESSLEY: #0458
ALEXANDRIA OCASIO-CORTEZ: #0554
CARNIVAL GLASS: #0538, #0746, #0774, #0784
THANK YOU: #0787, #0800
HOLY SPIRIT: #0610, #0654
THE POINT GUARD: #0438

☆☆

#0391 - November 21, 2018 @ 04:33 (San Francisco, California)

[0391.1 / 0948] [*NIGHTMARE* I've made contact with an alien race. THE PRIESTESS *(wayfaring, sensitive, and evolving)* informs me they're malevolent. I'm chased from above as I run through a Zen garden, conference room, and shopping mall. Blue electricity crackles across the ceiling overhead. A young boy runs with me. I hold his hand. The boy and I stop running to use the bathroom.

I lose my phone and keys. The chase continues. The speed increases. THE DEVOTEE offers calming mid-stride guidance, but I'm still racked with fear as we run. I'm jostled out of sleep and take a few moments to catch my breath.] //

⁂

Min. = ♠*- THE DEVOTEE: #0585*
NIGHTMARE: #0406, #0518, #0519
CEILING: #0586, #0637, #0664, #0747, #0774
KEYS: #0493, #0653, #0719, #0747, #0772

⁂

⚜ 7.2 - THE BOOK OF SAGITTARIUS: 0392-0422 ⚜

#0392 - November 21, 2018 @ 07:06 (San Francisco, California)

[0392.1 / 0949] [I'm on assignment for a month in London. I have to stop at the consulate to activate a work permit. I stand in line in a grand hall with black and white checkered parquet floors. The line advances. Six people are ahead of me. I get distracted for a moment. When I look back, I've been moved to a position way far back, likely hundreds of people now ahead. I issue a complaint. When no one hears me, I duck in and out of numerous doors trying to find a shortcut. I nearly get caught in the act, but stealthily move away just before being discovered. This happens a few times.

One option places me in the doorway behind the clerk's window. I look around a back staircase and have a conversation with an elderly Black man who incessantly refers to his friend "AL."

"Is your friend AL JARREAU?" I ask. An answer isn't given. He's simply allowing me access to his stream of consciousness. I surrender and wait in line.

As the line loops up and around, I see THE CHILD swinging on a large U-shaped piece of gym rope above the line assembled below. She's not aware of the line. She's excited and over-stimulated. I'm concerned she's going to fall from the 12'-15' height and crack her skull open. She flips over backwards and tumbles head first toward the floor. I scramble past the line to catch her, narrowing averting a catastrophe. I cradle her in my arms. She begins to cry once her initial shock subsides.

I take her to THE DANCER who sits on a bench on the perimeter of the room. THE DANCER is calm and appreciative. THE FAIRY GODPARENTS sit on either side of THE DANCER.

"Mommy, I'm so sorry that they all died," THE CHILD cries, referring to THE FAIRY GODPARENTS' relatives who died in World War II. THE CHILD feels responsible, but she isn't. Skin peels away from her tender pink cheeks, flaking away like eraser rubbings as I dry her eyes.] //

⁂

Maj. = 2- THE DANCER: #0396, 3- THE CHILD: #0411
LONDON: #0755
12: #0409, #0670, #0712
THE FAIRY GODPARENTS: #0799

⁂

#0393 - November 24, 2018 @ 06:02 (San Francisco, California)

[0393.1 / 0950] [I create a piece of interactive trans-dimensional art. It feels so real, I'm not aware that I'm dreaming. Saturated color and alternative laws of physics apply here (*instant movement between spaces, spatial perspective shifts, etc.*). The mood favors *"gender parity."* Most of the experience is non-liner, irrational, and awkward to attempt to set to words. **It's beyond my vocabulary.** I observe a rendering of a bridge. I can move within it in as few as three dimensions to see the details in the painting. I oscillate toward and away multiple times.

In another scene I observe Keith Harring-ish cartoon outlines of bodies spray painted into a high durability/high traffic gray carpet floor.

In another, graffiti painted walls surround an alley where a cataclysmic throw down occurs between rival bands of heavy metal Asian "B Boys." The stark, unapologetic presence of Chinese government influence is present at the duel.

I'm exposed to a type of music that requires multiple new technologies not yet realized nor available on Earth to replicate particular low resonant frequencies. The music can pick people up and move them around as they listen to it. An angel/alien/DJ offers me a tutorial on how to produce and shape this new music. It's dependent on a small palm sized adapter that links a computer to a non-physical source.

THE PORN STAR (*transforming, purging, and exploring*) makes a cameo. He comments briefly on a work of alien art in a lounge area where images of kids appear projected on a wall. *More occurs here but I'm unable to remember.* Another large-scale art piece is on display in the same room. THE VICTOR has his back to me as he looks at it. The scenario becomes momentarily ambiguous. *Things blur.*

"The output appears G_____ and may be H_____, but all we see is that it's B_____." A group of voices chant.

I bounce quickly between a waterfront property with floor to ceiling windows and the center of a body of water similar to the San Francisco Bay. Multiple nuclear weapons have just detonated. The collective (*from an observation deck*) seems to say telepathically (*and in unison*), "Now that can't be good."] //

⁂

PALM SIZED: #0547, #0575
FLOOR TO CEILING: #0586, #0747
NUCLEAR: #0558
EARTH: #0482, #0571, #0678, #0728
THE PORN STAR: #0789

⁂

#0394 - November 25, 2018 @ 07:36 (Park City, Utah)

[0394.1 / 0951] [I'm in an airport. I've lost my dream journal and a few personal objects that I've "made significant." It's possible to get them back, but the time to recover them would be an hour longer than I have before my flight departs. A woman performs back walkovers near an accelerated walkway. I'm worried I won't get my things back and I feel sad. I'm dressed impeccably in new professional duds. I wear black from head to toe.]

[0394.2 / 0952] [I'm at a NINE INCH NAILS concert. *Yes. This is what I want to spend the next 30 years of my life doing, creating, building,"* I say while watching TRENT REZNOR perform for a large crowd.]

[0394.3 / 0953] [I'm at a buffet with basically no food on it except for French fries and whoopie pies. THE OFFICE ADMIN (*conservative, direct, and hardworking*) is there with THE NINER'S FAN (*sarcastic, witty, and sharp*) and THE POLISH PRINCE (*independent, loyal, and aware*), with whom I casually chat. I grab a treat from a lower freezer drawer. I grab some French fries and place them on a paper plate. I errantly dip one in cocktail sauce thinking it's ketchup. I make the same mistake twice. I gag, then I toss the French fries into a large black garbage can in disgust.]

. . .

[0394.4 / 0954] [It's golden hour. A rocky bay front property with pink exterior walls and a Mediterranean style terracotta tile roof is put on the market. The house is isolated on most sides by water which gives the *"illusion of privacy."* As I pull back and float into the sky, I notice most other nearby parcels are the same. A friend of mine owns the home. He attempts to sell it to me. As light floods the space and bounces actively off the surface of the water I decide not to buy the property and fly away.]

[0394.5 / 0955] [I have a conversation with THE ACTOR at FRANK ROBINSON's old house.]

[0394.6 / 0956] [I have a conversation with THE TECHIE (*accommodating, open, and endeared*), THE VIKING ELF's husband who I've never previously met. THE VIKING ELF is nearby on the other side of a chain link fence keeping to himself, smelling wildflowers growing in the tall green grass. He and I don't interact.]

[0394.7 / 0957] [I'm in a large public transportation depot where people are sucked through giant vacuum tubes at tremendous speeds. As I ride through, a display shows my speed as *"85mph+."* An unknown male friend is my travel companion. He zips through the tube just ahead of me. Though the trip is exciting it feels like it's trending towards danger.]

[0394.8 / 0958] [I sit in lotus position and meditate while someone packs capsules of a white substance behind me. They use my right heel as a scale. Seems to be a drug of some sort. A gallon sized Ziploc bag made darkly opaque by a charcoal looking substance rests on a table. Within the bag are hundreds of black quarter sized discs of comparable size to NECCO wafer candy or water-soluble electrolyte. I telepathically infer that these are powerful new drugs that will breed deep addiction across the masses. It could be something that the government wants, but does not yet possess. Discussions are "hush hush" as I sit and continue meditating.]

[0394.9 / 0959] [A middle aged White man gives a speech on a lawn. I watch from 50 feet away. He messes up his comments multiple times. Each time he starts over the mistake becomes more pronounced and exaggerated. After a few cycles we all laugh, the speech maker included.]

[0394.10 / 0960] [I'm washing in a blue glass shower. The water is hot the way I like it. The glass quickly coats with steam. I hear someone enter, then the silhouette of a woman walks in the bathroom. I'm crouched down enjoying the sensation of the hot water raining down over my neck and back. Water runs forward and off my face. A strong stream pours off the bridge of my nose. I attempt to see who the person is through a small crack in the corner seam where the glass meets. "AMELIA?" I wonder, without getting a verbal response to my question.] //

✣

Maj. = 10- THE ACTOR: #0411
Min. = ◆- THE VIKING ELF: #0429
FRANK ROBINSON: #0435
TRENT REZNOR: #0404
NINE INCH NAILS: #0568
SPEECH: #0492, #0682, #0761
THE NINER'S FAN: #0824
THE POLISH PRINCE: #1233
THE TECHIE: #1205

✣

#0395 - November 26, 2018 @ 05:52 (Park City, Utah)

[0395.1 / 0961] [I'm in a building that doubles as both a political campaign headquarters and a high-volume rental property. The property is on US Capitol Hill. The space is dark, disheveled, and has the permeating funk of a college fraternity house. A bunch of us attempt to sleep on our *"filing cabinet bunk beds."* THE WILDERNESS GUIDE is my roommate. He sleeps on the opposite side of the space. Our sleep is interrupted by the thump and boom of loud party music emanating from an adjacent room. I get up and walk across a filthy Astro-Turf floor, kick away the occasional crumpled beer can and empty plastic liquor bottle, eventually finding my way to a music studio mixing board.
The lead guitar track from "Decadence Dance" screeches as I slap the board in the dark, even after I cut the master and all channel volume levels to zero. I've failed my task. A spooning married couple *(male/female)* shout at me. The volume wildly swings from loud to painful. A woman steps over me. Startled, I grab her leg as she passes me en route to the bathroom. It's the wife of the aggravated couple.]

[0395.2 / 0962] [I'm an executive at an Australian firm. I repeat a mantra as details of the scene unfold. I repeat the mantra until I forget it and with it, all remaining details of the dream.] //

✣

COUPLE: #0417, #0425, #0435, #0460, #0483
FILTHY: #0688
BOOM: #0529

✣

#0396 - November 27, 2018 @ 03:16 (Park City, Utah)

[0396.1 / 0963] [I'm at a coastal bus depot surrounded by a vast mall of souvenir shops and boutique art galleries. The time period is unclear. I pause near a wall at the bottom of a staircase next to a large mosaic constructed from multi-colored Post It notes. A crank at the lower right spins and cycles the "Post It's" on a clear film, like a grade school teacher's overhead projector. The rolling spool in motion animates the "Post It's." I attempt to snap a photo of the phenomenon. People descending the staircase to catch buses interfere with the shot.

Various Christmas and wonderland scenes are among the Post It note animations. "The Grinch" makes a cameo in a swath of Green Post It's. When the exterior windows of the building open, the Post It's flutter and animate like the tiled walls of Japanese subway.

A souvenir shop sells wooden boxes filled with seashells, sand, and a single tropical flower. THE RAPTOR, THE ROBOT and I decide to buy one for a friend because it reminds us of her. We agree it's basically junk but aren't put off by the $65 price tag. The shop has it advertised as the hot item of the season. *"ONLY ONE AVAILABLE PER DAY!"* We spend the money. We realize it's heavy as we pick it up and walk across the parking lot. It'll also cost us more than we paid to ship it to our friend. I gently shake the box and see a bunch of small crustaceans emerge then burrow themselves towards the bottom.]

[0396.2 / 0964] [A group of young men prepare for an outdoor ceremony in a marshy fen-like area on a misty morning. They gather around a 4'x3'x2' glass presentation case which contains a variety of small sacred objects, including feathers. When they depart, I get closer to the case and see an enormous eagle feather prominently displayed on the second of three vertical shelves. I take an eagle feather and place it in my coat pocket.

Later, I replace the feather when THE DANCER and THE WEAVER notice it's gone missing from the case. They don't know I've taken it. They're agitated greater care was not taken in guarding the case after it was set up. When they look away, I simply put the feather back and move along as though nothing happened. I traverse the fen and discover an old school backpack of mine on a grassy hill. The leather base has been altered, with pockets cut into it to hold device chargers and other modern tools. An intricate hexagonal molecular diagram has been lightly laser etched in the leather.]

[0396.3 / 0965] [I'm in a gymnasium concerned that my altar and statue of Brahma have been vandalized by the facility cleaning staff. My gifted eagle feather from UNCLE FRED has been taken. I feel anxious.]

[0396.4 / 0966] [A friend stands in a long line with an unknown destination. He's waited many hours. A parallel line of people heading in the same direction expedites and merges 30 people ahead of my friend. Each person expedited adds 30 minutes of wait time. He feels defeated when he realizes an additional 15 hours has just been added to his queueing time. After another hour it becomes clear people wait for personalized life coaching sessions.

I get in another line that moves quickly toward a hotel ballroom, and bifurcates at a registration table. I realize I'm next to speak with WARREN BUFFETT. My queueing friend is WARREN's #1 fan. I'm interested in having a conversation, but have no clear questions to ask. WARREN BUFFETT peeks his head around a corner and invites me to sit at a table. I wave feverishly to my friend for a few moments. He doesn't understand my cues.

I sit with WARREN. He begins talking as my friend walks from the opposite side of the space towards us. Our interaction is light, engaging and brief. WARREN excuses himself mid-session to go to the bathroom, *"all the way to the ground floor."* I continue the conversation with a stand-in mentor, as my friend finally joins me at the table. When he realizes I've been talking to WARREN and he's been waiting in the incorrect line he howls, "NOOOOOOOOOOOOO!" Security begins a search for MR. BUFFETT who never returns.

Two other people enter. One is a shirtless "Bro-ish" guy who begins bouncing and somersaulting around the room. The conference table where I'm seated morphs into a bed. The "bro" attempts to get in before I halt him.

"Dude...you're cute and all, but I was here first," I say, diffusing his charm and holding my space in the bed. He doesn't distract me. Ultimately, all four of us are ushered out by security.] //

⁎⁎

Maj. = 0- THE WEAVER: #0397, 2- THE DANCER: #0405

Min. = ♥- THE ROBOT: #0405, ♦- THE RAPTOR: #0405

UNCLE FRED: #0501

WARREN BUFFETT: #0587

CUTE: #0527, #0483, #0528, #0711

QUEUE: #0754, #0769

⁎⁎

#0397 - November 28, 2018 @ 04:28 (Park City, Utah)

[0397.1 / 0967] [A group of blue-collar men move a giant piece of furniture with a crane. Their effort is supported by a complex web of ratchet straps rising upward from an open retractable ceiling inside a modern home. Some concern and discussion emerge suggesting the final placement of the piece is incorrect and overstretches the property line. A young Black man with leopard-print-spring-coiled-hair enters and acts as though he owns the place.]

[0397.2 / 0968] [I hide a young refugee woman from the authorities. I smuggle her down an elevator shaft in a skyscraper. While in the building the woman discloses, she's actually a *"young man of equivalent age."* He's wanted by the media. I merge with his body and feel what he feels. I see things from his point of view. He has affinity for a hat, and an emotional attachment to a large fish. Our principal concern prior to exiting the building is to conceal a floral print suitcase that holds all his personal property. The suitcase is easily identifiable.

When we exit the building, he becomes a woman. I tell her we may not survive the final leg of the journey. She's not bothered by this possibility, but expresses concern a male member of the team may blow our cover.

"You can't tell her what's going on. She thinks she's safe...and you certainly CAN NOT TELL THE WEAVER." I forcefully tell the male team member.

"FACK YOU! She'll be caught at the Southern border. Her fingerprints are on the National Electronic Database." He dismissively responds.

He's partially correct. Her country of origin has her prints, but not the outbound homeland security agency.

We travel across a jeweled desert at night on Segways. Some of the journey is observed from the desert's dusty point of view. We succeed when we deliver the woman to a conference room in a legally neutral zone, out of local jurisdictional bounds. She quickly builds affinity with everyone else in the neutral zone, including police officers on both sides of an invisible line.] //

⁎⁎

Maj. = 0- THE WEAVER: #0405

296

BLUE COLLAR: #0461, #0469
REFUGEE: #0614
YOUNG BLACK MAN: #0436
INVISIBLE: #0610, #0641, #0664, #0762, #0786

⁎⁎

#0398 - November 28, 2018 @ 05:45 (Park City, Utah)

[0398.1 / 0969] [*"WWJD." "What would 'J' do?" "WWJD." "WWJD"* chirps around me on infinite repeat. I'm detained or jailed. Image fragments.] //

⁎⁎

FRAGMENT: #0410, #0607, #0662, #0760
IMAGE: #0459, #0460, #0480, #0493

⁎⁎

#0399 - November 29, 2018 @ 05:54 (Park City, Utah)

[0399.1 / 0970] [THE PILOT and I hang out. We get bored and decide to masturbate. I'm attracted to a young long-haired man who lives nearby. Much more occurs. Perhaps some significant social unrest or civil violence roils around us, but I block it out. A relaxed, cohabitated vibe in the space and the energy between the two of us suggests we're about to create some amazing art.] //

⁎⁎

Maj. = 6- THE PILOT: #0486
MASTURBATE: #0654
AMAZING: #0457, #0733, #0774, #0784, #0787

⁎⁎

#0400 - December 1, 2018 @ 6:00 (San Francisco, California)

[0400.1 / 0971] [Lots of scolding in a classroom, or workshop setting. A chaotic situation unfolds in the middle of a teaching feedback session. Two women in a conference room get into a huge altercation. We all assemble around them as a group in a large circle. THE SMOKE SCREEN (*open hearted, growth oriented, and committed*) slouches down in a chair. I coax her into sitting up straight after we share a heated exchange. THE LEGEND (*meek, quiet, and blossoming*) enters the room and has something to clear with the group.

Nearby, THE FBI AGENT (*loud, firm, and challenging*) stands, intent on beginning a different feedback session with another woman (*whom I don't know*) in another circle of equal size. The remarkably intense situation becomes physical between the two women. They've arranged and intended for it to unfold in this way. It's also understood the physical altercation between the two women is, *"the only way to clear out the negative energy, and return the group back to neutral."*

My work is to lead a group conversation, broken down into four-minute intervals, while I receive detailed in the moment coaching from BARON BAPTISTE. I lead THE SURVIVOR (*seeking, injured, yet willing*) through a detailed exercise. BARON positions himself over my left shoulder and whispers.

"OK now this when you would ask this.... blah blah blah blah. Now in this moment you would be well suited to do that...blah blah blah blah."
His coaching cues are direct, specific and enter my ear at a rapid pace. He picks me up by the waist and sets me down in the exact center of the room. Another participant begins to share. I crouch down while listening to them speak. I'm told to stand up and am repeatedly encouraged. When I finally do, I discover wires tightly wound around my feet. As I stand up, it hurts more. The pressure inward is strong. The pain is tremendous. My foot hurts really, really badly. Internally, I beg them to let me put my foot down, but I'm never permitted to do so.
I ask again, and again, and again, *"PLEASE LET ME PUT MY FOOT DOWN."* I'm not allowed.] //

⁎⁎

BARON BAPTISTE: #0482
COAX: #0474
LEFT: #0477, #0480, #0495, #0496
ALLOW: #0401, #0499, #0700, #0701, #0723, #077
THE SMOKE SCREEN #0534
THE FBI AGENT: #0562

⁎⁎

#0401 - December 2, 2018 @ 04:32 (San Francisco, California)

[0401.1 / 0972] [I sit at a lunch table with THE COUTURIER and THE CONNECTOR and describe a dream: I'm one of three people invited to attend THE COUTURIER's wedding. They step into the dream with me and I show them around like a tour guide. I paint out details and scenes like a ghost in Charles Dickens' "A Christmas Carol."
"I assure you; I know all the deets," I say, failing to mention to THE COUTURIER that she forgot to include herself *(the bride)* on the ironclad guest list. Security will not allow her to enter.]

[0401.2 / 0973] [I attend a fancy holiday salon. While there are fine upholstered chairs available, THE EQUESTRIAN *(stylish, petite, and emotive)* and I choose to sit on the floor and have a conversation while leaning on the chairs and propping our heads up with our hands. PRINCESS DIANA is the guest of honor. She sits near us *(though not in a body)*, and hovers like a white mist just above a seat cushion.]

[0401.3 / 0974] [We decide to catch a train during a bitterly cold, blizzardy winter night, ascending multiple levels to the outdoor platform where we wait. I drop my phone and the screen cracks into a gorgeous web of glass shards. A gap in the bottom right corner frosts over on the inside of the screen as liquid within the device is hit with a blast of super-chilled air. I need to make a call. My phone, while a beautiful distraction, is utterly useless.
I wave and walk towards a woman in a heavy parka at the opposite end of the platform. Upon approach I discover it's THE LOGICIAN *(motherly, stern, and resolute)* frustrated her husband THE ORANGE PIG *(jovial, engaging, and direct)* won't call her back. She holds a hand

up to me as she attempts another call. The call goes through. She immediately passes me the phone before speaking to THE ORANGE PIG.

"Say something to him that will snap him out of it!" she begs.

"*You're both reality creators, right? Yes?! Then let's get to work,*" I respond without pause.

Snow swirls around me like soap flakes. We sit on the snowy platform. The phone call is still active. We start meditating. The outbound train passes. We make a benign decision to take a later one.]

[0401.4 / 0975] [I sit facing an optometrist who shines a powerful light in my left eye. The doctor administers an eye exam. My head is restrained from behind. My chin rests in a small groove. My forehead is supported by a narrow cream-colored horizontal steel bar. My eyelids are peeled back. I don't like the sensation.

"No more! You're not going to use this brand of disposable contact lenses anymore!" he exclaims in a moment of surprised discovery.

He executes a microsurgery, peeling multiple layers of adhered contacts from my left iris. My attempts at retreat prove futile. I must simply accept the continued peeling away of layers until all are removed. I resist tremendously. Once complete, he scrapes the whites of my eyes to restore my *"dimmed vision."* I don't understand the doctor has given me an unbelievably generous gift.] //

⁂

Maj. = 4- THE CONNECTOR: #0422
Min. = ♣- THE COUTURIER: #0565
WINTER: #0917, #0952, #1153
WEB: #0876, #0951, #1130
SALON: #0950, #1028, #1145
THE EQUESTRIAN: #0855
THE LOGICIAN: #1149
THE ORANGE PIG: #1155

⁂

#0402 - December 4, 2018 @ 04:45 (San Francisco, California)

[0402.1 / 0976] [I'm in an educational environment. I run away from a man with glasses. We head toward a stage obscured by a grand red velvet curtain. A group of people use an overhead projector to display an image upon the pleated crimson background. Another guy repeatedly screams at me. Someone nearby identifies him as a "Junior Storyteller" for a project scheduled for group discussion and review later in the day.]

[0402.2 / 0977] [A 1980's style sitcom intro plays. Actor names are displayed in bulbous, puffy fonts (*words in white*), while cheesy synth music weaves with baritone and tuba sounds. Each actor in the show is introduced with a freeze frame headshot. THE BLACK KNIGHT (*cheating, lying, and eliminated*) hoists his new wife up and over his shoulder, walks up a staircase towards a bedroom hallway, and flips off a light in the moment the theme music concludes.]

· · ·

299

[0402.3 / 0978] [I work with a female partner on an *"essential language speaking exercise."* I complete the requested activity well under the anticipated time allotted. I swiftly take a seat and yield the floor *(and remaining time)* to my partner.] //

⁂

END STAGE: #0857, #0872, #0880, #0909, #0929
CHEESY: #0840, #0876
CURTAIN: #0896, #0922, #0949, #0969, #1071, #1182

⁂

#0403 - December 4, 2018 @ 06:19 (San Francisco, California)

[0403.1 / 0979] [I sit at a bar enjoying a beer with THE CARPENTER. I receive multiple text messages from porn star KEN RYKER. I shield the screen from THE CARPENTER's view even though he's curious and accepting of my sexuality. I don't want him to see my private conversation. The text exchange becomes increasingly salacious. KEN repeatedly sends me photos of his enormous dick. He pressures me for sex. The messages suggest he and I are in the midst of rekindling a long-term relationship. He wants more intimacy from me, but the only way he knows how to ask is through the use of his body. THE CARPENTER leaves for the restroom. As he disappears, I take an incoming call from KEN.] //

⁂

Maj. = 1- THE CARPENTER: #0405
INTIMACY: #0889
RELATIONSHIP: #0904, #0922, #0961, #0991

⁂

#0404 - December 4, 2018 @ 06:19 (San Francisco, California)

[0404.1 / 0980] [I'm in a house with a variety of artists and musicians discussing the construction of an enormous spherical yin yang-like structure. Blueprints are generated and modified in real time. The bottom is a deep black tone. The top is white. A triangular catwalk extends across the middle. A performance space for rock concerts has been engineered in the white half of the sphere.

TRENT REZNOR gathers around the table with a crew of sound engineers and music producer friends. A firm and active debate among the group about acoustical quality commences. Communications are candid, precise, and meticulous. *"Can we create sound that will permeate the entire structure without the use of any electrical amplification?"* The team births an innovation to achieve this outcome. Complex 3D printed slits will be installed around the edges of the floor. If they function as anticipated they'll cycle vibrational activated air down through the depths of the dark half of the sphere, through a combination office/living spaces and back up through the performance shell.

"We've really created a deep community here. This is amazing," TRENT says plainly.

"Today's modern keyboardist requires no fewer than 10 outlets/power ports." I sarcastically declare in non sequitur. My comment is met with snickering laughter.

TRENT mentions casually that he's gained the story rights for a film he intends to produce entirely from B-roll footage. As we discuss the prospective film, the proposed idea morphs into a musical. THE GUITARIST and THE DRUMMER (*robust, consistent, and steady*) spring immediately to mind as session players for roles in a jazz combo scene in the movie.

TRENT's daughter doesn't show up, but is assumed to be part of the house band. I chat with another guy who appears to be TRENT's singular creative cohort. We discuss the likelihood of taking our creation to *"Broadway."* We're intent on getting our story out to the world in an impactful way. We're excited (*and spiritually lit*) to create something unique and magical together.]

[0404.2 / 0981] [THE HILL (*loving, present, and vulnerable*) enters and wraps her arms around me as we exchange, *"I love you's."*] //

⁂

Min. = ♣- *THE GUITARIST: #0933*
TRENT REZNOR: #0568
SPHERE: #0874, #1039, #1088, #1122
COMMUNITY: #1046, #1058, #1084, #1177
THE DRUMMER: #0468
THE HILL: #0534

⁂

#0405 - December 4, 2018 @ 07:54 (San Francisco, California)

[0405.1 / 0982] [*"I'm going to quit."* I argue with THE WEAVER. *Something about a note I left...* THE WEAVER and THE NURSE seem to be the same person. THE CONCIERGE (*thorough, quick, and available*) is THE WEAVER's friend. Their grandkids play together. THE CONCIERGE has two; a boy and a girl.

THE CARPENTER tilts a chip bag towards me, offering me some. In the midst of the situation's stress, I begin eating jumbo sized Fritos, even though, *"it's a fasting day."* The Fritos are stale, and incredibly hard to chew. They cut the roof of my mouth.

I sit on a couch typing on a computer and mindlessly eating until I remember I've broken my fasting practice. I consider fudging the records in my journal. With only a few minutes left in the day I tell myself this is *"ok."* I close the blinds on the living room windows. It's late and I don't want "the intruders" to see in.]

[0405.2 / 0983] [I'm shown a topographical map of the "English Islands." I easily step over them. I see a place called "West City" where I lived North of, as a boy. The land is uninhabited. I feel like a giant. I walk with a man wearing overalls who whistles. We walk behind his grandchildren until we arrive at a pond. We repeat an odd phrase and toss torn off bits of homemade buttermilk biscuits into the water. It's unclear if we're littering or feeding fish.]

[0405.3 / 0984] [I stand in front of a wall stocked with large smoothie cups.
"I've been waiting for people to optimize their smoothie drinking dollar," A restaurant manager says.
A simple sign, red print on a white background suspended by two thin chains from the

ceiling, illustrates the restaurant's step-by-step burger making process. "**3! THREE! Our burgers have 3 (THREE!) layers!**" The very excited sign reads.]

[0405.4 / 0985] [THE DANCER sells a "Doggie Deodorizer" product that coats the surfaces of a pet's feet with a white powdery substance. She pushes a kitty aside in order to demo the product on a nearby table.]

[0405.5 / 0986] [THE WEAVER and I hug after we compare notes scribbled on construction paper. The notes look like kindergarten crayon art. We acknowledge the tension between us as it's released.]

[0405.6 / 0987] [I'm on the set of a STANLEY KUBRICK film, perhaps "The Shining." It's winter, cold, and the crew is deeply aggravated. They don't like the director. Two female protagonists lead what feels like a Victorian era piece. One of the leads is played by JODIE FOSTER. I pay special attention to the minor detail of a crumpled napkin on the floor. Wallpaper peels from the set walls.
  "This is definitely THE RAPTOR and THE ROBOT's work," I whisper in THE DANCER's ear as set technicians are brought in to create a special twisted iron mount, which is to be used for a single, spiraling shot.] //

⁑

Maj. = 0- THE WEAVER: #0411, 1- THE CARPENTER: #0426,
2- THE DANCER: #0417, 13- THE NURSE: #0416
Min. = ♦- *THE RAPTOR: #0520,* ♥- *THE ROBOT: #0891*
VICTORIAN: #0882, #0970, #0979, #1084
GIANT: #1089, #1096, #1106, #1123
THE CONCIERGE: #0579

⁑

#0406 - December 4, 2018 @ 23:46 (San Francisco, California)

[0406.1 / 0988] [I'm in the library of a grand residence. THE LOBBYIST requests to speak with me privately. Each time we attempt to leave we're interrupted by a floppy haired frat boy who insists on getting THE LOBBYIST's opinion. Eventually we change rooms, find a quiet place to talk, and accept that we won't be able to enjoy dinner alone at the hotel later as originally intended. THE LOBBYIST has experienced a loss of some sort, but has little/no inclination to discuss.
  The occasion is formal. We both wear tuxedos as we sit on stools at the mahogany bar. Skipping dinner by offering dessert, the bartender recommends a single scoop of chocolate ice cream doused in scotch and presented daintily in a low-ball glass. The concoction hardens into a dark cold toffee substance that's hard to chew and sticks to my teeth as I eat.
  A shift change occurs behind the bar. A man taking over for a woman leaves $100.23 on the counter and asks me to make change. THE LOBBYIST and I conclude our conversation and decide it's time to receive the public. As we pass from table to table, I take donuts and other sweets from hors d'oeuvre trays, swallowing them without thinking nor tasting. Cake

donuts. Special petit fours. Croissant braids. **So many unique desserts I've never seen and am determined to sample!** THE LOBBYIST pauses me mid-bite to mention, *"You know you could just order some. They're plentiful."*]

[0406.2 / 0989] [*NIGHTMARE* - I'm outside a large building where war crimes have occurred. Many people have been killed by toxic gas. Across the street stands a familiar house I've been through many times. Now it seems like an asylum. I pass through an apartment in the house that may be occupied by JESSICA FLETCHER *(from "Murder She Wrote")*. I rapidly descend exceptionally steep staircases made of stacked wooden crates. The objective is not to get caught. My goal is to expose the war crimes and human rights atrocities that occurred inside the house.

I step into a child's nursery and realize I'm being tailed by the **witch mother**. The old woman opens the short door, inspecting what's afoot within the room as I hide behind it. I slink down behind the door to avoid her seeing the top of my head. I make it out of the house and loop around the side yard, encountering a garage area where a large Russian man moves a car. He allows me free passage back inside the asylum.

The next lap finds me attempting to break out with other prisoners. Some have facial deformities. Others may be mentally retarded. I have a small speaker in my backpack that plays music at low volume as I attempt to hide from the **witch mother** under a set of stairs. I silence the music just before I'm found.

On the next lap through I'm caught by the **witch mother**. She kicks me hard in the ribs. I'm unable to breathe through the tremendous pain.

In a blink, another jailbreak begins. I escape the asylum and run down a dark city street. A blonde stripper wearing pink vinyl short shorts and Lucite heels screams from behind.] //

⁑

Maj. = 17- THE LOBBYIST: #0446
NIGHTMARE: #0929, #0943, #1047, #1150
ORDER: #0901, #0902, #0915, #0920, #0945, #0978, #1001
RUSSIAN: #0806, #0837, #0878, #0933, #0976

⁑

#0407 - December 5, 2018 @ 03:01 (San Francisco, California)

[0407.1 / 0990] [I attend an awards banquet. *"Get in there now!"* a guy exclaims after hastily giving me instructions. I eat a fruit/gelatin mix from a hand sized clear plastic cylinder. Thick sugary blueberry jam fills the top half of the container. A layer of lemon Jell-O rests on the bottom. I move from outdoors to inside with a small tray of tools that can be used to help people sanitarily distribute programs as they enter the banquet hall. I place the small tray under a table and exit. I encounter a woman and a young girl dressed in white princess gowns anticipating their entrance.] //

⁑

LEMON: #0959
BANQUET HALL: #0929, #0974, #1145
EXIT: #0807, #0820, #0824, #0859, #0883

⁑

#0408 - December 5, 2018 @ 04:25 (San Francisco, California)

[0408.1 / 0991] [I'm in college town. Little mini-store fronts along a wide promenade vie for my attention. I pass by a vendor on a lunch break. I don't think I have enough money for a bacon sandwich I see on a baker's rack. My $4 becomes $12 as I notice two of four $1 bills pulled from my pocket become $5's. I pass a chocolatier and a Planned Parenthood. Both are open for business. An unclear theme emerges regarding a being named "Daniel" who wants something, *"to be a certain way."*]

[0408.2 / 0992] [An old woodblock letterpress stamp of a man's image *(think: dictionary illus-tration)* is prominently displayed like a paperweight on a desk. I recall the dream segment in its entirety before I realize I'm still sleeping. I wake up and write this down. *"There is so much I've forgotten in this rewrite!"* I think as I wake up again to a blank page.] //

✳
BACON: #0863
ATTENTION: #0818, #0847, #0849, #0851, #0852
REALIZE: #0801, #0804, #0827, #0837, #0844
VENDOR: #0862, #0903, #0937
✳

#0409 - December 6, 2018 @ 5:45am (San Francisco, California)

[0409.1 / 0993] [I experience a simple triumph! I lead a group of 12 through wilderness adventure training. My method is termed *"out of the ordinary and unique"* when compared to other facilitators who've previously taken groups of equivalent size on a similar path.] //

✳
12: #1056
SIMILAR: #0805, #0808, #0819, #0825, #0856, #0862, #0872
SIMPLE: #0877, #0897, #0911, #0926, #0969
METHOD: #0850, #1058, #1193, #1200
✳

#0410 - December 6, 2018 @ 05:45 (San Francisco, California)

[0410.1 / 0994] [I'm with a group making holiday decorations out of a vast array of crafting materials. We're in a very large house that has two distinct sides. All of us are "Adult Kids" *...non-actualized, highly immature, and fragmented beings.* The "Adult Kids" half of the property is rowdy, chaotic and ridiculous. The other half is managed by "Mom," which by comparison is balanced and predominantly easeful. Someone complains their decorations are ruined. A composite form left in a bucket full of clear resin has hardened, leaving an ornamental knot frozen in a state of suspended animation. THE CARDINAL *(open, gregarious, and emotionally expressive)* wears dark sunglasses which make him seem unfamiliar and distant. Ordinarily he's so inviting!]

. . .

304

[0410.2 / 0995] [A friend's partner (*a wealthy banker*) recently died. The body rests in the atrium of a fancy hotel near a swimming pool. The deceased's limbs are strung up like a marionette. Guests can pull on the strings to receive a hug from the dead body.]] //

⁂

ATRIUM: #0889, #0899
DEAD: #0919, #1095, #1097, #1127, #1139, #1141, #1167
BUCKET: #0918
THE CARDINAL: #0715

⁂

#0411 - December 7, 2018 @ 02:59 (San Francisco, California)

[0411.1 / 0996] [I've accepted a dinner invitation to GORDON RAMSAY's (*precise, skilled, and candid*) home in the sky. I bring whole grain crackers in a cloth napkin lined woven basket. I also bring a basket of my homemade smoked almonds. GORDON inspects every dish before it's allowed in his home. I see a bunch of guests clad in festive party gear (*furry coats, blinky lights, and silly hats*) all speaking French. THE WEAVER leads a demonstration in the kitchen. She teaches the group how to make crostini. I walk down the hallway and enter a guest bedroom with a mini-fridge. I open the fridge, take a purple can of "Red Bull," and pop the top. As I take my first sip, I notice THE ACTOR is a dinner guest. Initially he appears deeply aggravated by my presence.

"What can you possibly be mad about now? We have different lives. We're even living in completely different bodies now than when we dated," I mouth to him from across the room. He pauses, then invites me to leave the property with him for a drink and conversation. I accept, and forego GORDON's dinner. Over the course of a drink, THE ACTOR and I mend fences. We depart together in an Uber. I book two destinations, but step out of the car after the first leg of the journey. I'm charged for both. The updated app reboots as I receive a text that notifies me THE CHILD has a failing kidney.] //

⁂

Maj. = 0- THE WEAVER: #0429, 3- THE CHILD: #0435, 10- THE ACTOR: #0415
INVITATION: #0803, #0893, #0953, #1197
DRINK: #1120, #1149, #1193
hydrate
KIDNEY: #0821, #0957
DESTINATION: #0888, #0920, #1074

⁂

#0412 - December 8, 2018 @ 05:12 (San Francisco, California)

[0412.1 / 0997] [I have special skills. I work on a production line and am expected to pick up and move 50 eggs at a time. The eggs are white. I color them with a beige-taupe lacquer.

"No, watch...I can do 500," I say moving the painted eggs (*as if by magic*) from the painting station to a series of drying racks.

I'm observed and evaluated by a panel of *"light beings"* as I do this.

Once my work leaves the line each item is precisely inspected for quality.] //

305

⁂

PAINTING: #0821, #0937, #1072, #1130
LACQUER: #1065
QUALITY: #0834, #0853, #0857, #0931, #1090, #1140

⁂

#0413 - December 10, 2018 @ 03:06 (San Francisco, California)

[0413.1 / 0998] [I watch my big toenails heal by falling completely off. *"The government is watching."*] //

⁂

GOVERNMENT: #0959, #0976, #1019, #1055
BIG: #1070, #1073, #1081, #1082, #1182
WATCHING: #0827, #0862, #0905

⁂

#0414 - December 10, 21018 @ 04:30 (San Francisco, California)

[0414.1 / 0999] [I'm in an odd gallery with a black and white checkered floor. I've been here before. The floor smoothly swoops up to create art presentation pedestals. The space feels like it's in another dimension, accented with soft purple *(perhaps ultraviolet)* hues. It's otherworldly. Its full inventory of objects and statues seem hauntingly animated. I stand on the base of a large humanoid sculpture. A man beneath me watches my movement and inquires, *"You're an early riser!? Say Yes! Where's Paul?"* The statue looks down its nose at me from above. I don't answer the man's questions.] //

⁂

PEDESTAL: #0987, #1028
SCULPTURE: #0807, #0818
AVATAR: #0926, #1172

⁂

#0415 - December 10, 2018 @ 06:20 (San Francisco, California)

[0415.1 / 1000] [I'm in a large, familiar public use space. I've been here recently, perhaps I am there concurrently. I move up and down between floors using stairwells.

As I pass through a lobby, I tap THE ACTOR on the right shoulder while he sits on a bench checking his phone. I enter another large gymnasium space where a beginner's yoga class is about to start. Flip charts and markers are set on easels at the front of the room. The space has multiple rows of chairs set up for attendees.

I've lost my shoes, and I realize this only after I've gone back inside the building. A woman with a large, beautiful port wine stain covering the majority of her face assists attendees with the orderly placement of their yoga mats. I casually relay an anecdote about an interesting guy I just met, who had bundles of nerve cells hanging from his face like fiber optic catfish whiskers. Unexpectedly, this generates some nervous laughter from the yogis standing around me.] //

⁂

Maj. = 10- THE ACTOR: #0438
WINE: #0871, #1076, #1191
NERVE: #0874, #0999

⁂

#0416 - December 10, 2018 @ 07:27 (San Francisco, California)

[0416.1 / 1001] [I'm in a different gymnasium space than the prior dream. Another yoga teacher training program is in progress. A teenage boy enrolled in the program named "Justin," has cerebral palsy and uses a wheelchair. He has the support of an attendant, who hangs out nearby but gives "Justin" full autonomy. THE NURSE delivers a personal share at a microphone that stalls out mid-sentence and loses the attention of the group. One trainee becomes so bored she falls asleep. I motion with my arm at THE NURSE to *"wrap it up,"* to which she responds, *"Blah blah blah!"* I pass a table in the dark and fumble through an assortment of sugary snack foods. I see "Justin" and the attendant gather their belongings and depart for the day. Alien music blasts at me from a large black cube on a stage. Small purple lights pulse like nerve synapses and flood a black curtain with rivulets and ripples of light.] //

⁂

Maj. = 13- THE NURSE: #0472
BLAH: #0907
RIPPLES: #0821, #0901, #1083

⁂

#0417 - December 11, 2018 @ 04:37 (San Francisco, California)

[0417.1 / 1002] [I decorate Christmas trees outside, spending a lot of time ornamenting one next to THE DANCER's next door neighbor's home. *"I just want the houses to match the rest of the street,"* I say to a nearby couple who may have met during a similar activity last year. They appear smitten and devoted to growing *"the Love"* between one another. A corollary about the VON TRAPP kids singing on tour in Germany emerges, but details fade quickly.]

[0417.2 / 1003] [I start a new entry level job at an airline. I make simple design recommendations regarding the customer seating process that have a swift, favorable and transformational effect on the business. I become a sought-after internal consultant that quickly ascends to the role of *"highly influential senior executive."* This feels deliberate, timely, and neutral… **"Just a natural unfolding."** I'm in heavy demand across multiple global industries. The prerequisite to work with me is: **"You agree to approach every business problem like a work of art."** My personal artwork (*and time dedicated to such pursuits*) precedes any business conversation, every day.] //

⁂

Maj. = 2- THE DANCER: #0426
NATURAL: #0821, #0907, #0920, #0934, #1062
SENIOR EXECUTIVE: #0891, #0907, #0986

⁂

#0418 - December 12, 2018 @ 06:06 (San Francisco, California)

[0418.1 / 1004] [I'm on a Hollywood Squares style game show. Contestants receive bonus points if they log correct answers to a question, even if they don't speak. A woman with a Mohawk receives her "Third Strike."]

[0418.2 / 1005] [An effeminate male hairstylist entertains in his condo. He centers his expression on being humorously, *"FAAAABULOUS!"* Tonight, he's suction cupped a large pink dildo to the center of a sliding glass door. The conspicuous placement of the object draws laughter from two of his guests. Both are old friends who agree to laugh every time the host pulls a similar stunt.]

[0418.3 / 1006] [I create a small counted cross stitch using a hoop no larger than my palm. *"My hands look like my mother's mother's."*]

[0418.4 / 1007] [A gym is under construction. Muscular "daredevil men" use gymnastic horizontal bar equipment and swing complex acrobatic tricks over a poured concrete slab floor. No safety mats beneath. A makeshift vinyl sign with the location's name is hung by two other male members of the community. The mood is playful, yet focused.] //

⚊

BONUS: #1063
HOOP: #0815, #1137
HUNG: #0815, #0917, #0920
CONSPICUOUS: #0803, #0969, #1086

⚊

#0419 - December 13, 2018 @ 03:45 (San Francisco, California)

[0419.1 / 1008] [Hair Braiding. Gift giving. Making out.] //

⚊

HAIR: #1091 #1130, #1141, #1165, #1185, #1021
GIFT GIVING: #0885
MAKING OUT: #0905, #1143

⚊

#0420 - December 14, 2018 @ 05:03 (San Francisco, California)

[0420.1 / 1009] [THE FIDUCIARY and I flirt while he schedules hook ups on his phone. We're in a house. He's distracted. This scene occurs three times.] //

⚊

Maj. = 9- THE FIDUCIARY: #0502
DISTRACTED: #0853, #0943, #0953, #1038, #1132

PHONE: #0828, #0830, #0844, #0891

⁎⁎

#0421 - December 14, 2018 @ 06:02 (San Francisco, California)

[0421.1 / 1010] [I'm at a swanky gallery that doubles as a cemetery. People sit in rows of chairs on an inside lawn. The majority of attendees are well-to-do African Americans. I'm particularly fascinated by ZOE KRAVITZ, who is immaculately manicured and revered as tonight's guest of honor.] //

⁎⁎
HONOR: #1197
ROWS OF: #0817, #0813, #0907, #0923, #0931, #0932, #0951, #0970, #1139, #1169, #1188
FASCINATED: #0811, #870, #0871, #1008, #1199

⁎⁎

#0422 - December 15, 2018 @ 5:02am (San Francisco, California)

[0422.1 / 1011] [I'm in a 16-bedroom home with my family. I don't recognize many new faces, but I know them. *"Yeah, you don't have to mow your own lawn when you live in a house this big,"* I say to THE ATHEIST as we look out the back windows on to a vast rolling green space.]

[0422.2 / 1012] [I attend a business lunch for 15. A recent team accomplishment makes THE PHOTOGRAPHIC MEMORY *(soulful, guiding, and quick)* so happy she cries. She tackles me in the process of bear hugging me to the left, *"because hearts are closer that way."* I fall backward, land on a chair, and snap my spinal column in half. The host and restaurant staff are confused by what just happened.]

[0422.3 / 1013] [I wander/float in and out of houses in a large hilly city. I'm drawn to shoe stores in a Chinatown neighborhood. THE MEEK is a sales associate in one of the stores. I'm chased out by her boss. *"...But that's my friend!"* she exclaims as I run out the door and ascend in flight up to the left.]

[0422.4 / 1014] [I'm not wearing pants. I urinate in the corner of a carpeted room.]

[0422.5 / 1015] [I'm in San Francisco looking for a new place to live. THE CONNECTOR seeks estate furniture to help her nesting process. She has a nice home. She offers me a room, but I don't commit because, *"it'll be a party house and I have no interest in living with club kids."*]

[0422.6 / 1016] [THE SIXTH DEGREE BLACKBELT *(ferocious, masterful, and clear)* appears and says, *"Honey, I'm single again."*]

. . .

[0422.7 / 1017] [I give remarks at the lectern on a podium. Perhaps I'm standing next to a *person / ...man / ...friend / ...lover / ...partner?* The person stands behind me as we look out together at a vast empty concert hall.]

[0422.8 / 1018] [I'm with yoga teachers in a long amber lit bathing area. Small recessed whirlpools are intended for socializing. I float through space like a waft of steam. I pause behind a person using a phone. Their screen displays the photo of a guy I recently dated. The word "GUEST" appears over his face in an oblong oval shaped banner.] //

⁎⁎

Maj. = *4- THE CONNECTOR: #0429, 8- THE ATHEIST: #0431*
PODIUM: #0944, #1046, #1079
OVAL: #0923
THE MEEK: #0473
THE PHOTOGRAPHIC MEMORY: #1366

⁎⁎

#0423 - December 16, 2018 @ 04:47 (San Francisco, California)

[0423.1 / 1019] [I'm an abstraction. Perhaps I'm on the inside of a body. A subatomic droning mantra repeats: *"Contract to the center to expand out."*]

[0423.2 / 1020] [THE ROMANTIC attempts to decipher a message painted on a scroll in watercolor. He places the scroll on the floor and tries to read it while on hands and knees. The content of the message changes with each attempt. The mood becomes suspenseful. He's supported in his cryptographic quest by a woman, THE REVOLUTIONARY, but she stays diffused on the edge of the scene. He smiles as he works to solve the problem. His teeth are brilliantly white.]

[0423.3 / 1021] [I'm at an amber lit auto body shop. The owners have placed a king-sized bed in the lobby. When I enter, I leap face first towards the mattress. I feel a device in my front pocket crack under the weight of my body as I land. When I pull the device out to inspect the damage, it's smashed in multiple places. The device is an awkward size; larger than a phone, smaller than a tablet. In a robotic voice I repeatedly drone, *"Multiple cracks in the screen. Multiple cracks in the screen. Multiple cracks in the screen."*]

[0423.4 / 1022] [I'm on the set of a TV variety show. A LADY GAGA-like being performs in the middle of a large gold Styrofoam clamshell. I wonder who owns the prop. I want to buy it.] //

⚘

Maj. = 15- THE ROMANTIC: #0506
Min. = ♠- THE REVOLUTIONARY: #0428
LADY GAGA: #0457
KING: #0874, #0925
STYROFOAM: #0944

⚘

#0424 - December 16, 2018 @ 14:15 (San Francisco, California)

[0424.1 / 1023] [I teach a yoga class in a highly humid, heated room that's scented with eucalyptus oil. A muscular man enters and looks for his spongey oversized mat. When he can't find it, he decides to take one that doesn't belong to him. I stop him before he's able to leave and ask him to join the class. I lead the class through a sequence with their eyes closed.

One woman falls and injures her right wrist. She expresses pain, and I tend to her comfort. I sit her on my knee, while I encourage students to stay neutral and in their experience. I console the injured woman as I cue *"inward drishti,"* to the rest of the class. The mood remains calm, the room full of deep flowing respiration.]

· · ·

[0424.2 / 1024] [I'm backstage at a sold-out concert. At the last moment, I'm asked to step in for the lead singer of a popular band. I'm outfitted, mic'd, and marked by a production team. I'm ready to perform. The lights go up.] //

✷✷
OVERSIZED: #0961, #0970, #0988
BACKSTAGE: #0887, #0933, #0948, #0953
SOLD OUT: #1176
POPULAR: #0826, #0852, #0873
✷✷

#0425 - December 17, 2018 @ 03:27 (McCordsville, Indiana)

[0425.1 / 1025] [I observe a manga-like couple engage in conversation in a dusty sun lit room. I'm intrigued by the size of the woman's saucer shaped eyes.]

[0425.2 / 1026] [I camp next to a highway. As I drive tent stakes into the ground, I aggravate a nearby ant hill. Ants flood out and up the cords of the tent, increasing in size as they advance. I attempt a diversion by spraying them with liquid nitrogen aerosol. They pause momentarily. When thawed, their agitation amplifies. I go inside the tent and greet a woman dying in a bed. She's well attended to and comfortable. She asks me to place my hand on a stack of fashion magazines to take an *"artist's oath."* I raise my right hand and tearfully say, *'I'm doing everything I can.'*] //

✷✷
HIGHWAY: #0815, #0887, #0974, #1157
ANT: #1100
DYING: #0935, #0980, #1133
LIQUID: #0874, #0891, #0920, #0926
✷✷

#0426 - December 18, 2018 @ 03:05 (McCordsville, Indiana)

[0426.1 / 1027] [I'm in a dormitory bathroom at night. I have a major urge to pee, and while at a urinal I notice an abundance of ornate pink and blue cursive script scribbled on the walls in marker.]

[0426.2 / 1028] [THE DANCER offers to set me up on a date. She wants to hook me up with her gorgeous African American friend, a dancer that looks like IDRIS ELBA. As she heads out to mow the lawn, she's very clear and direct with me. She wants to ensure I don't hook up with that, *"trashy last season guy. The one that was thrown out of the dance company for faking his ability."* Said guy still socializes with and charms other members of our group. His brown eyes draw attention away from his rubbery smooth Ken Doll crotch. I still feel some attraction to him, but I break eye contact when I notice THE CARPENTER waving at me. He and I are soon to leave on a road trip.] //

⁂

Maj. = 1- THE CARPENTER: #0428, 2- THE DANCER: #0430
IDRIS ELBA: #1123
BROWN EYES: #0805, #0824, #0842, #0849
SCRIPT: #0970, #1101
GORGEOUS: #0852, #0871, #0879, #0888, #0897, #0952

⁂

#0427 - December 18, 2018 @ 04:32 (McCordsville, Indiana)

[0427.1 / 1029] [It's Halloween on a college campus. I could also easily be on a semester at sea. I walk up the back staircase of a ship and make contact with two cute boys wearing sailor hats and speedos. They wink at me then duck into a cabin to hook up. I'm invited to join but I continue climbing a ladder upward.

I get to the top, change my mind, choosing to descend the ladder all the way down to the surface of the ocean. The sailors aren't there. The ship is immense and the dark waters below extend as far as I can see. I pass the sailors as I climb back up. I pass through a doorway. Once at the top I find myself on the top floor of a women's dormitory in a long room filled with bunk beds. Each bunk has a woman sleeping on it.

A tall lanky archer wearing a hood enters and opens fire on the sleeping women. His maniacal grin is accentuated by steel braces. I quickly leave and run downstairs to a basement where a makeshift student union store has been set up. The mood is active and party-like in the store. Dance music plays through a small tinny treble speaker. I'm gifted a tattered XXS t-shirt, as well as a hoodie by a very animated sales associate. She's delighted to give me the shirts because it appears I'm buying a specific combination of household items promoted by the store.

I've picked up a clear plastic pitcher and lemonade powder from a sawdust coated particle board shelf. I mix up some lemonade and drink it from the pitcher while waiting in line. The sales associate flirts with me and breaks out into a dance. I interrupt her by relaying there's an active shooter on the upper floor. Undeterred she says, *"Oh I know him. He's such a nice guy!"* as she continues spinning. The woman ahead of me forgot her wallet. I buy her items for her.] //

⁂

HALLOWEEN: #0902, #0968
WALLET: #0909, #1115, #1187
LEMONADE: #0959
STUDENT UNION: #0920

⁂

#0428 - December 19, 2018 @ 03:27 (Fort Dodge, Iowa)

[0428.1 / 1030] [I'm at THE GODFATHER's *(entrepreneurial, funny, and engaging)* mansion, where I drink lots of water out of different sized containers. I blend beans and chia seeds together with water and notice raisins and circular slices of banana float to the top when I look over the open vessel. I intend to share the concoction with another person.

I'm enrolled in a math class and worried about failing because I can't recall which day the course lecture convenes. I've had this experience many times before. THE CARPENTER enters and we discuss whether or not, *"we need to buy more turkey."* We currently have four birds spinning on a kitchen rotisserie. He tickles my balls through my pants as a joke, but I find this to be really awkward.

I keep drinking water and use a new cup each time I refill. **So. Much. Water.** THE CARPENTER has some preoccupation with how many cups we're dirtying in THE GODFA-THER's kitchen and insists we stay on top of keeping them washed and orderly.

I head outside en route to class and notice I'm between two golden hotels set side by side on a snowy winter morning. The main floor of each has a gift shop. One structure has electric green painted highlights. The other is painted dayglo orange. The paint job is crude. Major drips flow down the walls and pool in the interior courtyard. **Gravity works differently here.** I walk perpendicular to the ground up a green accented hotel staircase. The building exteriors appear to be *"Gothic Inspired."* Brass placards reading: "GREEN HOUSE" and "ORANGE HOUSE" are mounted near the front doors of the buildings.

Painting these sacred spaces may not have been OK'd through the register of historical places. I cross through a doorway and head down the hallway to math class. I've only attended lectures twice this semester and the final is tomorrow. I'm going to get an F. I pass an atrium filled with rows and rows of children's competitive trophies. I'm not excited. I've previously won all of them. Nothing new here.]

[0428.2 / 1031] [I attend a surprise party on the beach. THE REVOLUTIONARY appears, no longer requiring the use of a walker. We're both very excited about this. We dance on the sand and laugh as the sun sets.] //

✯✯

Maj. = 1- **THE CARPENTER: #0429**
Min. = ♠- THE REVOLUTIONARY: #0902
SURPRISE: #0876, #0890, #0895, #0923, #1066
BRASS: #0810, #1039, #1052
SEEDS: #1166

✯✯

#0429 - December 20, 2018 @ 06:55 (Beavercreek, Ohio)

[0429.1 / 1032] [I tour a house recently renovated by THE JESTER. He's updated *"the house we shared in Charlotte, North Carolina."* THE WEAVER and THE CARPENTER take the home tour with us. The fixtures are modern and the interior is contemporary. What was previously *"my room"* has been updated with rich toned wood furniture. Every room is accented with a variety of fixtures made of thick steel chains. My dog CHARLEE runs around the back yard, incarnated as a puppy. The human lot of us are humored by her chasing a cat around. An oversized mirror with the word **"CONGRATULATIONS"** etched on it is positioned to welcome a young woman who's scheduled to move in later today. She's recently gained notoriety as a social media influencer. Her decision to move into the property boosts her views and mentions. The mood is playful and inviting. The entire home has been redone and furnished beautifully.]

. . .

[0429.2 / 1033] [A group of us meet at a woodland wine bar. The interior is similar to a multi-level log cabin. THE CONNECTOR has invited us all together. She informs me she's invited THE VIKING ELF to join us. He comes and goes without saying anything. When I asked her about this she says, *"Oh, he's very sick."* I wouldn't have otherwise known this.]

[0429.3 / 1034] [Back at a party at THE JESTER's house I see a very tall man (6'7" +) with golden hair. I seem to have made his acquaintance in San Francisco, but also from life in Charlotte, NC. When I ask THE JESTER about how he knows the golden-haired man, he says, *"I've known him since he was 16 years old."*]

[0429.4 / 1035] [I demonstrate a backbend with my right leg lifted skyward. While inverted I also demonstrate an "abdominal crunch" for a large group of people. While in the pose, I encourage people to gather around. I know I'm being assessed by a panel on my ability to, *"own and generate a community space, as well as my sentence syntax."* The more essential I can be, the better.] //

⁂

Maj. = 0- THE WEAVER: *#0433*, 1- THE CARPENTER: *#0437*, 4- THE CONNECTOR: *#0518*
Min. = ◆- THE VIKING ELF: *#0919*, ◆- THE JESTER: *#0514*
CHARLEE: #0555
CRUNCH: #0879
PUPPY: #0871, #0997, #1060

⁂

#0430 - December 20, 2018 @ 08:45 (Beavercreek, Ohio)

[0430.1 / 1036] [I dictate a dream on my iPhone. I realize part way through I'm recording over other dreams I have not yet journaled, in error. *"I hate you; I hate you; I hate you!"* I scream repeatedly at the phone, even though I made the mistake. Odd strings of text and techno babble appear on the screen. This indicates the device hears only what it wants to. THE DANCER's on the bed with me and I scream at the top of my lungs.]

[0430.2 / 1037] [Rolling power outages occur at a large public use gymnasium. I teach a yoga class in the brown light. THE COMIC enters and jokingly counts 16 students, then stands awkwardly silent until I acknowledge he wants to speak with me. As I walk towards him, I mistakenly step on a woman's hand who rests in child's pose. I crouch down to offer her healing.]

[0430.3 / 1038] [THE BANDANA (*sexual, inventive, and consistent*) and his tall boyfriend prepare for a drag performance next to an Olympic sized swimming pool. THE DANCER is captivated by the boyfriend's height, amplified by his choice to wear silver platform boots. She rushes over to compliment him like a fangirl.
I pace, deep in thought, until I look down and see I've walked on water to the center of the pool. Once I realize this I crash through the surface of the water into the dark blue below.

The power flickers on and off for a few moments in the aquatics complex while I hover below the surface.]

[0430.4 / 1039] [I'm at a Japanese trade show looking at fake plants with microscopically small lights woven into the plastic leaves. They appear as though the morning sun strikes them. Seems like we're outside and that this product would be psychologically supportive for octogenarians who weather the winter months in retirement homes.] //

⁎⁎

Maj. = 2- THE DANCER: #0431
HATE: # 1059
DARK BLUE: #0820
WINTER: #0952
ERROR: #0879

⁎⁎

#0431 - December 21, 2018 @ 07:08 (Beavercreek, Ohio)

[0431.1 / 1040] [I attend an evening meeting of artists. An attendee who is on point to build a Burning Man temple describes his project. His vain, narcissistic girlfriend enters wearing a gorgeous diamond necklace. She interrupts the meeting and discloses that, *"the temple is being built exclusively so she'll have a place to display jewelry and sell goods at a premium."* This moment of candor causes discord and rancor within the group. I get up and decide to leave the meeting and impending conflict behind. Someone at the temple meeting has experienced a recent tragedy and cries, making the assertion on using the space to sell jewelry that much more egregious.]

[0431.2 / 1041] [BASSNECTAR and I beat match and teach one another live performance tips and tricks.]

[0431.3 / 1042] [I'm in a gorgeous mansion. Marble floors. Very inviting and engaging space. The property's surveillance system is accessible through a phone app. Many people have fun, playful, flirtatious sex in various areas of the house. Everyone is kind, polite and game. I have full agency to decide whether or not I want to join. I decide to take a turn by myself and enter an empty bedroom. I lay on the floor and perform autofellatio until I ejaculate in my throat. THE DANCER catches me at this moment and calls me a *"weirdo,"* but that doesn't stop me from enjoying myself.]

[0431.4 / 1043] [I have a spirited discussion with another guy at a round table regarding, *"how the Blair Witch Project sucked."* **'It was just people walking around in a circle for two hours!'** We reminisce about being members of the Columbia House entertainment subscription service. I only wanted three movies when I took the enrollment deal. I split my membership with a friend and offered him the other two freebie selections. THE ATHEIST believes I've compromised my privacy and have given my rights away based on another

similar experience he had. *"You're welcome to it.   Take it!"* I say waving my right hand at him.]
//

⁎⁎

Maj. = 2- THE DANCER: #0433, 8- THE ATHEIST: #0479
ARTISTS: #0827, #0916, #922, #0987
WITCH: #0805, #0929

⁎⁎

#0432 - December 22, 2018 @ 01:35 (Beavercreek, Ohio)
*The second segment of this dream jolted me out of sleep and was instantly forgotten. *

[0432.1 / 1044] [I teach a yoga class and give cues that specifically call out female teachers in the group. My comments are intended to build camaraderie, but instead it embarrasses them and alienates others. **Total failure.** It feels so awkward I wake up.] //

⁎⁎
TOTAL: #1101, #1125, #1195
YOGA CLASS: #0937, #1004, #1016, #1022, #1040
FEMALE: #1157, #1159, #1167, #1170, #1174
⁎⁎

#0433 - December 22, 2018 @ 06:28 (Beavercreek, Ohio)

[0433.1 / 1045] [I'm abroad, possibly in Romania. I'm at an airport where I pluck odd values of currency *(11, 12, 18, 22, 15, 14, and 9)* from my wallet with an intention of purchasing a meal onboard the flight home. The values seem strange, atypical, and confusing. More occurs, yet quickly fades.]

[0433.2 / 1046] [I attend a comedy show at a large auditorium. I've been invited as the guest of one of the performers who is also a close friend. I hang towards the back right rear of the venue and intend to exit promptly following his performance. Adjacent to the space is a large paved parking lot. I blink and discover myself at the opposite side of the lot standing next to an RV where cheerleaders host a bake sale. Chocolate frosted brownies, cookies, and sweets are presented side by side on plastic trays. A competitive spirit exists between the cheerleaders, but I'm not sure of what they pursue.]

[0433.3 / 1047] [THE WEAVER and I are in conflict at various times. We have a conversation in different rooms of a house, and out of sight from each other. THE DANCER's around. I'm in my pajamas. THE WEAVER runs a vacuum outside. She powers down the appliance, walks over to me and says, *"I appreciate you for being honest. I respect you. The things you shared helped me become aware of things going on in my own body."* We cry together and give one another a long warm embrace.] //

⁎⁎
Maj. = 0- THE WEAVER: #0435, 2- THE DANCER: #0435

317

CLOSE: #1053, #1057, #1075, #1145, #1157
AUDITORIUM: #1130
EMBRACE: #0892, #0953, #0983, #1198
⁂

#0434 - December 22, 2018 @ 07:33 (Beavercreek, Ohio)

[0434.1 / 1048] [I walk down a steep city hill in the rain towards a gas station/convenience store. I'm on the left side. The store is at right. I pass through the door and see THE COCK *(odd, handsome, and flippant)* dressed in a suit and tie, seated in a chair leaning back against the wall, with his eyes over the shoulder of a small Asian man attending the register. I've made the journey to thank THE COCK for getting me reacquainted with my visual art practice.
There's virtually nothing left inside the store. It appears to be closing down.
"Are you guys closing up shop?" I ask.
THE COCK nods affirmatively.
I catch a glimpse of a highly complex tattoo composed of spades and hearts that traverses his throat and neck. I admire the art and ask him where he had the work done. Sort of aloofly, *(yet quintessentially him in his humor)* he glances up towards the fiberglass "drop in" ceiling and simply screams, *"NECKS!"* which makes me laugh.
As I look around, I decide the impending closure doesn't make sense given the store's location at the bottom of a hill next to a major thoroughfare. I spend time contemplating how I would transform the space if I chose to buy it after they vacate.] //

⁂
STEEP: #0982, #1099, #1147, #1190
CLOSING: #0909, #0980
THROAT #0917, #0956
THE COCK: #0653
⁂

#0435 - December 23, 2018 @ 06:30 (Beavercreek, Ohio)

[0435.1 / 1049] [I'm at FRANK ROBINSON's house after a remodel has been completed. It's night. The couple who lives there now are gracious and offer me a tour. I recognize the man as "Patrick McFadden," a highly regarded interior designer. He shares the space with a female counterpart. He's gay. She's a lesbian. They've created a business partnership and household. I look up and tell THE WEAVER to notice the new rooftop courtyard they've built. The entire property has been modernized. We're treated hospitably as we take note of all the enhancements they've made.
THE CHILD is with us, age five. She decides to play by exploring the entire dwelling. She follows a group of puppies and giggles as she chases them up and down the stairs. She makes friends with two little "Elf Boys" who drag strands of beads across the new hardwood floor, much to the annoyance of "Patrick."
THE CONFIDANT negotiates bedtime with both of his kids. I keep the kids occupied with some toys while he leaves to prepare them a snack. I decide it's time to turn the television off and go through a series of gyrations to power down. The process isn't intuitive and moderately frustrating. THE DANCER and THE WEAVER stay in the other room while I futz with the remote. I finally get the TV to power down.

318

THE SON (*sweet, gentile, and reserved*) bangs his head while doing forward rolls on a hardwood floor.

THE DAUGHTER (*independent, witty, and confident*) yells at THE CONFIDANT, *"YOU NEVER DO ANYTHING FOR ME. UGH!"*

I look at THE CONFIDANT and say, *"I guess some things are the same across the board with little girls."*

My comment draws the ire of THE DAUGHTER. Ever angrier, her voice rises loudly in complaint.

I wonder if THE CHILD will be like this when she's 10, then I think, *"Where is THE CHILD?"*

She's followed a puppy up a spiral staircase inside a stone turret. My worry dissolves when I leave my body and float upwards to the turret and find her quietly petting the dog. **Everything is fine.**]

[0435.2 / 1050] [I hold a leather-bound book in my lap. It's the first edition of FRANK ROBINSON's life story. The cover of the book is inlaid with a bas relief map of the earth. Countries he visited while in the Navy are highlighted with gold leaf. It's beautiful. It has the weight and feel of an ancient book of spells. I read it at night, by candle light.]

[0435.3 / 1051] [I float up and out of the turreted addition to FRANK's house and hover over the intersection of *"Noe and 20th."* It's cold and lightly snowing next door. BECK installs a new music studio on the neighboring rooftop. I watch him work and fill with delight.] //

⁂

Maj. = 0- THE WEAVER: #0440, 2- THE DANCER: #0438,
3- THE CHILD: #0441, 16- THE CONFIDANT: #0471
BECK: #0752
FRANK ROBINSON: #0598
ROOFTOP: #0904, #0919, #1025, #1154

⁂

#0436 - December 23, 2018 @ 08:00 (Beavercreek, Ohio)

[0436.1 / 1052] [I fold laundry and realize I've stolen a grey zippered hoodie. I decide to take it back to the yoga studio.]

[0436.2 / 1053] [PRINCE and I play keyboards while sitting across from each other at a long table. We riff and trade licks, melodies, and solos. The jam session yields a variety of new motifs for pop songs. One in particular feels like a *"potential global hit."* *"Is it a song that would break down barriers and bring the world closer together?"* We have a lot of work to do on it, and I invite him to another writing session. He gives me a nod and lifts his hands in prayer as an acknowledgement.]

· · ·

[0436.3 / 1054] [I follow the narrative of a young Black man through various key moments in his life. He's a young woman's friend from the time she's a toddler, through the present. Today's her wedding day. She's a twenty something White woman. As he kneels next to her, her skin darkens to an ebony splendor. He invites her to see something spectacular, offering his hand to help her up from the table where she draped a cloth high back chair with the lengthy train of her gown.

He rises from his knee and walks her to a pastoral field. They're stopped jovially by the wedding party, including her father (*a White man*). The group gathers and faces the same direction viewing a pastel sky that glows blue, purple, pink, and gold. The bride stands alone holding her bouquet. She morphs into a tall, slender Asian woman with a sleek silhouette. She stands serenely in the field basking in golden hour light. Her eyes are closed, neck long and exposed, as her head slowly tilts up and down. Her father believes me to be the wedding photographer and insists that I get some shots of his glorious daughter. I take photos of the bride, then pivot to take photos of the sky and marvel at its exquisite brilliance. My gaze is interrupted as a cyclist nearly hits me. I notice I'm standing in the middle of an asphalt bike path.] //

⁎⁎

PRINCE: #0640
GOLDEN HOUR: #0860
WHITE WOMAN: #0859
PRAYER: #0818, #0879, #0934, #0983, #0992, #1001
ANGEL: #0862, #1170

⁎⁎

#0437 - December 24, 2018 @ 08:46 (Beavercreek, Ohio)

[0437.1 / 1055] [I work as a contractor at the *"Gambrell Foundation."* I gather with others at their mansion where we join a group of people who take a meal in the rathskeller. I actively review grant applications for next week's board meeting. A fun, low key food fight breaks out. We toss dinner rolls at eat other while enjoying our *"playing lunch."*]

[0437.2 / 1056] [THE CARPENTER and I sit on the floor collaborating on a small construction project. We cut out dozens of puck sized wooden hexagons that have an amber golden sheen. Stacks upon stacks of thin hexagon chips are produced. We lay out the hexagons in intricate patterns, mastering a method we've developed where the chips can be layered flatly around the corners of irrationally shaped objects.

We're charged to understand, *"how to fully cover an object in six dimensions."* We also develop and refine a specific vocabulary for the layering process in each dimension beyond the third. I'm intrigued by the broader dimensions but don't yet fully grasp what we're doing in the 4th, 5th, and 6th. I'm still learning how to hold a conversation in those dimensions.

I seek verbalization, but the communication there is all mental/telepathic/vibrational. The geometry is complex and elaborate, and this new learning absolutely fascinates me. We have a lot of fun while creating in an *"inside/outside"* environment. High walls with no roof. Post-modern simplistic architecture. Most of this seems to happen at night in a lab. Much more detail quickly fades as I'm awakened by a scream from another room.] //

320

⁂

Maj. = 1- *THE CARPENTER: #0441*
HEXAGON: #0895
BOARD MEETING: #0936, #1008, #1052, #1061
INTRICATE: #0803, #0830, #1111

⁂

#0438 - December 25, 2018 @ 07:16 (Beavercreek, Ohio)

[0438.1 / 1057] [I begin on one side of an amusement park and quickly move to the other where I meet up with my family. THE CHOCOHOLIC and THE POINT GUARD are with us. I zip quickly back and forth across a parking lot, intending to ride a roller coaster by myself. After enjoying my ride, I notice it's closing time, so I zip back across the park and reunite with the family. THE ACTOR is also at the park, riding rides alone.

I remove a synthesizer from a gig bag and set it up on a table. I spool through an archaic interface and notice the device has collected a number of my previous performances, which I've forgotten about and never reviewed. I select a Brahms piece and in the process of loading the file for playback, THE POINT GUARD comes over and starts pressing buttons on the device. I find this deeply aggravating. I scold him for touching my equipment without asking. He expresses worry when I say, *'I told you not to touch it but you did it anyway."* THE POINT GUARD runs out of the room then returns as a toddler. He sits at the console and starts playing the keyboard though the device is still booting up. THE DANCER motions at me with her arm like a mom saying, *"Just let him play the thing,"* under her breath. I surrender and say, *'Fine."*] //

⁂

Maj. = 2- *THE DANCER: #0441,* 10- *THE ACTOR: #0462*
AMUSEMENT PARK: #0867, #1010, #1047, #1069, #1191
TODDLER: #1108, #1404
THE CHOCOHOLIC: #0678
THE POINT GUARD: #1404

⁂

#0439 - December 26, 2018 @ 08:07 (Beavercreek, Ohio)

[0349.1 / 1058] [I pick up a woman who's been jammed ass first into a white five-gallon bucket on the bottom shelf of a baker's rack. I rush towards an exit door. She starts screaming as shit explodes out of the bucket like a fountain. It lands on my shoulder and drips. The woman's excretory thrust ejects her from the bucket. She plops on the ground and becomes completely covered in an oozy brown pile as I cradle her, still shitting. I set her down on the ground outside. She moans as others tend to her.] //

⁂

FIVE GALLON BUCKET: #0918
FOUNTAIN: #0889, #0974, #1004
EXPLODE: #1025, #1035, #1071, #1137

⁂

#0440 - December 26. 2018 @ 09:24 (Beavercreek, Ohio)
*Rapid flashes of images I don't comprehend. *

[0440.1 / 1059] [From a first-person point of view I watch a set of hands scrub black ink spots from a white quilt over a sink. This isn't my body. I'm lurking.]

[0440.2 / 1060] [I sit in a circle with others. Someone runs a set of hair clippers up the left side of my head, then realizes they don't know how to give me a haircut.]

[0440.3 / 1061] [THE WEAVER enters my bedroom and throws open the curtains. As gold light pours through the windows she says, *"Good thing you woke up. It's 2:20pm."*] //

⁎⁎

Maj. = 0- THE WEAVER: #0443
HAIRCUT: #0819, #1000, #1113, #1146, #1163, #1165
CURTAIN: #0897, #0922, #0949, #0969, #1071, #1182

⁎⁎

#0441 - December 27, 2018 @ 06:17 (Beavercreek, Ohio)
*Multiple dream threads. I wake up disoriented and exhausted, as though I've run a marathon. *

[0441.1 / 1062] [THE DANCER, THE CHILD and I walk to the park on the shoulder of a mountain highway at night. THE DANCER and THE CHILD look for socks and shoes on the ground without the aid of a headlamp. They continue to walk uphill, and as I look to the left; I see a car at the bottom of the mountain driving towards us. Its headlights are on.]

[0441.2 / 1063] [The family wears onesies while having a discussion that devolves into an argument. I believe I'm supposed to teach a class. It's 8am, and I'm relieved to learn that I don't teach until 9:30am. I pet each of the four dogs in the living room on the head, then introduce them to the family one by one. THE BREAKS DJ *(creative, generous, and spontaneous)* sits on a La-Z-Boy recliner and watches. Initially, I forget her name before saying *"Hello"* to her, and take a moment as my brain sifts and sorts through a mental database of pictures and names. THE CARPENTER's opinion is, *"we're all aggravated because we're constipated."* I'm annoyed with him because he's putting his story and assumptions on me and not willing to hear me out.

I receive an email on my phone from THE NUN indicating that I've been scheduled for an appointment with her. THE BREAKS DJ finds this interesting because she understands getting an appointment requires filling out a very detailed intake form. I check the time. It's now 9:16am. I'm likely to be late for class even as I hurry out the door and across a parking lot, leaping into a go cart which is staged and ready to race. 1980's pop star PAUL YOUNG sings in another race car. I find his presence really odd and out of place. I assume someone will be at the yoga studio to open the doors for me, even though I'm already supposed to be there, per contract.]

. . .

[0441.3 / 1064] [I walk down a steel staircase to the basement level of a refurbished brick building. I enter the office of a nascent startup company. The energy is activated and palpable. I set up shop in an empty office and call a meeting as the new *VP of Information Security*. I draw a large audience and begin setting corporate direction, even though I'm not employed there. The CEO and board of directors quickly take note of what I've, and swiftly award me the job and title I made up for myself. A bit of a joke remains between staffers about how, *"there was no information security before he walked in the door."*]

[0441.4 / 1065] [I escape down a spiral staircase in the dark. When I get to the bottom, I run across a parking lot in the dark, lit by large incandescent lights.]

[0441.5 / 1066] [A random group of people laugh and point at me. I feel emotionally flat to the situation.] //

⁎⁎

Maj. = 1- *THE CARPENTER: #0444*, 2- *THE DANCER: #0450*, 3- *THE CHILD: #0442*
Min. = ◆- *THE NUN: #0482*
CONSTIPATED: #1020
SPIRAL: #0890, #0895, #0917, #1069, #1084, #1141, #1159, #1181
THE BREAKS DJ: #1256

⁎⁎

#0442 - December 27, 2018 @ 08:24 (Beavercreek, Ohio)

[0442.1 / 1067] [I grab THE CHILD by the arm to startle her as she peeks around a door. I scoop her up and float her over to GRANDPA, and then to GRANDMA for each of them to nuzzle and kiss her. She giggles as we fly by.]

[0442.2 / 1068] [I'm in a town square in 1960's America. I leave a soda shop and see some friends across the street get into a "Double Wide" Cadillac. Imagine two cars welded together side by side, two tone seafoam green and white, with chrome detailing. THE GENIUS *(short haired)* gets into the car and rolls away, taking up both lanes of a two-lane street. I'm curious what will happen when the car turns right on to a one lane road. It disappears from view before I see what happens.]

[0442.3 / 1069] [An entity hovers above my back as I lay on my stomach on the floor trying to sleep. The energy has a Jamaican-Rasta quality. It taps me on my back. It wants me to turn over and look at it, but I remain on my belly unbothered in a neutrality practice.] //

⁎⁎

Maj. = 3- *THE CHILD: #0450*, 11- *GRANDMA: #0443*
Min. = ♥- *GRANDPA: #0780*
1960's: #0947, #1188
BOTH SIDES: #0952, #0988, #1173

323

THE GENIUS: #0900
⁜

#0443 - December 28, 2018 @ 05:22 (San Francisco, California)

[0443.1 / 1070] [A small spider skitters across the ceiling of a house, outlined in a softer smokey grey shadow. I uneventfully point it out to THE WEAVER and GRANDMA. The spider begins making a clicking sound as it moves. We quickly determine the sound actually originates from a dog's claws dragging along the wood floor. It could just as easily be my fingernails clicking on the glass topped kitchen table where we sit.]

[0443.2 / 1071] [I've been hired to be a _____. THE HOT HEAD (*aggravated, self-important, and unhealthy*) works at the office with a small non-binary child. He expects me to join the two of them. I don't want, nor intend to.
"You're fired!" THE HOT HEAD shouts and points at me while winking, which indicates I'm not actually fired.
The action was a formality to keep the work environment (*and powers that be*) unassuming to my *"assertions of individual freedom."*]

[0443.3 / 1072] [I cross a fenced in back lawn at night. I throw axes at giant sheets of ice, which crack wildly when struck. They shatter. The ice is so clear that it looks like panes of glass. The scene is beautiful and dangerous. Giant chunks of shattered clear matter cascade toward the ground. A large machine flips and resets two panels of ice glass at a time, in methodical rhythm. A smaller device holds a panel that's been divided into equal parts of 16 in a 4x4 grid. Each of the small panels are wet with small water droplets, perhaps a byproduct of the cutting process. I've visited this house before in dream [0231.2 / 0547]. *The main level is completely made of glass.*] //

⁜
Maj. = 0- THE WEAVER: #0444, 11- GRANDMA: #0496
ICE: #0886, #0926, #1016, #1085, #1095
DROPLETS: #0889, #1058
16: #1080
⁜

#0444 - December 28, 2018 @ 07:26 (San Francisco, California)

[0444.1 / 1073] [I'm on a road trip with THE CARPENTER to Colorado in search of property.]

[0444.2 / 1074] [THE FAIRY GODMOTHER and THE WEAVER have a conversation about interior fixtures for a new house. THE WEAVER wants to *"go big."* She's desirous of top shelf goods and luxury design for her retirement estate. She wants to buy, *"all the nice things."* When it comes time to purchase, she gets cold feet. THE FAIRY GODMOTHER and I reassure her, *"You've earned it. Spend it."*] //

✳✳
Maj. = 0- THE WEAVER: #0450, 1-THE CARPENTER: #0474
COLORADO: #0974, #1109, #1176
NEW HOUSE: #0866, #1007
THE FAIRY GODMOTHER: #0556
✳✳

#0445 - December 29, 2018 @ 03:14 (San Francisco, California)

[**0445.1 / 1075**] [*"Be the one who makes the magic!" "We're the ones who make the magic!" "It's our responsibility."* Such is the mantra of my film production company and crew that works diligently on a forthcoming show. We've built a bizarre plywood structure as a prop. THE GOTH (*dark, sensitive, and looming*) helps me move it to the center of a dirt path then runs to a truck and turns the key, already in the ignition. The clunker's engine idles to warm up.
BARBRA STREISAND quickly becomes one of my best friends on set. She and I walk side by side talking until she trips and injures an ankle. I kneel next to her and give her foot some Reiki. My mind drifts as I calm her down. I can't believe I actually have her phone number. I'm not sure if I've saved her as "Barbra?" "Babs?" *...not that it matters much.* It's odd to be so close to someone I've made mythic since I was a boy. Her music and movies shaped my love of performance. BARBRA STREISAND yells at me, arms flapping wildly and humorously from across a field. She's barefoot and needs to find her shoes. Somehow, I've drifted a hundred feet away from her.]

[**0445.2 / 1076**] [I sit next to a guy who plainly states the major events of his life. Though initially intrigued, my interest quickly dwindles to boredom. I find myself daydreaming about how novel it is to be friends with BARBRA.] //

✳✳
BARBRA STREISAND: #0446
MANTRA: #0879
REIKI: #1131
✳✳

#0446 - December 29, 2018 @ 04:39 (San Francisco, California)

[**0446.1 / 1077**] [BARBRA STREISAND returns! We attend a large banquet at her home. From the back side of the property, I take panoramic photos of giant windows which flood light out onto a large U-shaped courtyard that occupies the interior perimeter of the grand estate. A large white gloved staff is strategically scattered across the space to, *"offer unparalleled service to guests."*
I befriend a young girl who acts as my guide around the property. When we emerge from the basement via spiral staircase and empty on to a foyer across the grand ballroom, she injures her foot. I crouch near her to help her up and offer support. A large glass case filled with beautiful baked goods allows team members to grab their preferred snack at their discretion without interrupting the flow of work.
DICK CHENEY stops through, attempting to strike up a conversation with me. I pay him little attention and he promptly leaves. THE LOBBYIST diligently works nearby on his

phone. He collaborates with another teammate who stands next to him. BARBRA is quite particular in her preferences and has strong opinions about the placement of furniture. She wants to ensure the energy and flow of each room is *"just so, and without fuss or clutter."* She likes things simple and streamlined. It's quite fascinating to observe. ***"This is a world class operation."*] //

✵✵

Maj. = 17- THE LOBBYIST: #0451
BARBRA STREISAND: #0559
COURTYARD: #0819, #0830, #1145
U SHAPED: #0813, #1134
STRONG OPINION: #0952, #983, #1063

✵✵

#0447 - December 30, 2018 @ 04:09 (San Francisco, California)

[0447.1 / 1078] [I scoot around a parking lot on my gut, belly, and stomach. The parking lot is full of gravel. A woman follows me. She reprimands me. I approach a stranger and nonchalantly extract their windpipe from their neck. My hand easily punctures their skin and clasps around their trachea. Though gruesome it seems rather uneventful and banal. I keep moving. The parking lot may be next to an apartment complex or nursing home. Maybe it's an airport. Not clear.] //

✵✵

GRAVEL: #0859, #0918, #0974, #1073
PARKING LOT: #0909, #0918, #0964, #0985
GUT: #0891

✵✵

#0448 - December 30, 2018 @ 05:30 (San Francisco, California)

[0448.1 / 1079] [Someone sits next to me solving Sudoku puzzles, but the games incorporate 10's, 11's and 12's. This confuses me. A 1980's music soundtrack plays in the background.]
[0448.2 / 1080] [I'm at an airport standing in front of a partially filled vending machine with old products offered at odd prices. The bags of chips and candy bars appear as a constellation among the grid of steel curls.] //

✵✵

VENDING MACHINE: #0988, #1165
CONSTELLATION: #0963, #1015
GRID: #0804, #0925, #0963, #0989

✵✵

#0449 - January 1, 2019 @ 01:34 (San Francisco, California)

[0449.1 / 1081] [A TV changes channels. Each channel advertises Buick automobiles.]

· · ·

[0449.2 / 1082] [Young people drive cars.]

[0449.3 / 1083] [Young people organize as a group and are duped into joining radical political parties.]

[0449.4 / 1084] [DONALD TRUMP holds a secret meeting with Nazis. The meeting is recorded on black and white 8mm newsreel.]

[0449.5 / 1085] [I suck my own dick a few times. My orgasms are incredibly strong. I like the way my semen tastes and feels as it hits the back of my throat.]

[0449.6 / 1086] [A face on a black and white TV interrogates me by repeatedly asking, *"How can we investigate you!?"*]

[0449.7 / 1087] [I shave my kneecaps smooth with an electric razor.]

[0449.8 / 1088] [Storefront TV _____? *"Keep the mood suspicious, sexy and quick."*] //

⁂

DONALD TRUMP: #0679
POLITICAL: #1024, #1196
SUCK MY OWN DICK: #1058
KNEECAP: #0874, #891

⁂

327

#0450 - January 1, 2019 @ 03:56 (San Francisco, California)

[0450.1 / 1089] [I wake from a dream within a dream.
"Were you having Civil War dreams?" THE DANCER asks.
"They were watching me while I slept."]

[0450.2 / 1090] [A small, muscular white dog rams its head into a door as someone knocks on it from the other side. The door opens. A middle-aged man with Down Syndrome enters wearing a suit, fedora, and carrying a briefcase. He's tasked with presenting a young woman with an award.]

[0450.3 / 1091] [I perform fellatio on myself. I enjoy the sensations radiating from my dick-head out into every nerve cell in my body. When I finish, I look out the window of my room and watch airplanes use a steep San Francisco looking hill as a runway. The planes appear sleek and cartoonish. They fly by in rapid sequence. It's a clear sunny day outside.]

[0450.4 / 1092] [I bound down a puzzle of black 6" x 6" x 4' logs that look like giant Cadbury Flake bars as would a Donkey Kong character. Once at bottom, I'm on the back side of an industrial building, intending to teach a class.

But I'm not speaking right now! How will I do it?

Ok wait...that's right...THE PIXIE knew I was going to be practicing noble silence today, so he's agreed to teach the class for me. I'll go take his class!
I run across a parking lot, noting blue text on all the handicapped parking spaces has been whitewashed over. I pass a shoe shine booth where an anonymous nude male torso sports an erection, its legs spread open, and inviting. The big beautiful phallus demands my attention, but gets none.]

[0450.5 / 1093] [I sit at a table with THE CHILD. THE WEAVER stands nearby styling THE CHILD's hair. THE CHILD is not particularly wild about the half ponytail hairdo THE WEAVER has given her. Long untied hair falls in her face and annoys her as she eats. THE WEAVER tells me to go look at THE CHILD's art on the wall near the door. A single piece of white paper covered in bright red scribbles is scotch taped to the wall. I pick up a brown marker and crudely write the word **RED** across the whole thing.] //

✲⁎⁎

Maj. = 0- THE WEAVER: #0455, 2- THE DANCER: #0461, 3- THE CHILD: #0468
Min. = ♠- THE PIXIE: #0453
MIDDLE: #0916, #0929, #0952, #0954
DREAM WITHIN A DREAM: #0856, #0911

✲⁎⁎

#0451 - January 2, 2019 @ 00:04 (San Francisco, California)

[0451.1 / 1094] [I'm in a hotel room with THE LOBBYIST and a few others. We're there to celebrate the court's certification of THE LOBBYIST's adoption of a newborn baby. We sit scattered across two queen double beds making conversation until THE LOBBYIST mistakenly drops the baby. Its head strikes vertically to the ground. No one seems to be bothered by this. I can't help but think the baby has suffered a severe contusion and worry it will soon die from the traumatic brain injury.] //

⁎⁎

Maj. = 17- THE LOBBYIST: #0463
BABY: #1036, #1055, #1089, #1130, #1157, #1158
INJURY: #0889, #1000, #1034

⁎⁎

#0452 - January 2, 2019 @ 04:03 (San Francisco, California)

[0452.1 / 1095] [I follow a man with a shaved head up a grassy hill in a public park. He wears a black leather jacket with a motorcycle club patch stitched to the back. A black garbage bag is slung over his shoulder. At the top of the hill, he empties the bag and dumps the beaten and bloodied dead body of a man on the ground. From across the park, a woman driving a white car sees us and shakes a purple bag at us from her window.

The man shouts at me to follow him. We run to a dilapidated apartment complex, where at the base of a graffiti painted staircase, we find the dead man's crushed phone. Two teenage African American girls play a *"patty cake"* game with their hands. As we turn to walk up the staircase the woman in the white car pulls up and tosses the purple bag at us. She'd seen signs posted earlier in the week by the *(now)* dead man. She found his lost object and wants to return it. She either isn't aware, or doesn't care that he's dead.

At the top of the stairs, the man and I stand at the end of a long hallway. He tells me to run as fast as I can to the other side. I hesitate. He tells me to trust him. We charge forward together. As we come into contact with the portal at the opposite end, it stretches and expands. A *"pop"* in the membrane-like door catapults us forward through *doorway-upon-doorway-upon-doorway* until I awaken in another vignette.]

[0452.2 / 1096] [A group of mercenaries sleuth out aliens living among humans. A large group of people has gathered in a single file line for assessment. Above the line, a large hologram advertises a new LESLIE JORDAN book about murder, which will soon be made in to a limited TV series for a streaming platform. Of many tests administered to snuff out purported aliens, two if: then criteria are prioritized:

1. *"All men must hold straddle splits with their heels placed on elevated concrete cubes for a minimum of 5 minutes."*
2. *"If a man breaks a sweat while holding the splits, they must urinate on demand."*

IF BOTH CRITERIA ARE MET, it's assumed a man is <u>not</u> an alien. My job is to inspect their under-wear for wet spots. Most of the men struggle deeply.]

[0452.3 / 1097] [I develop a new technology that uses holograms to create multi-dimensional .GIFs during a World's Fair demonstration. I lead project operations from one half of a sports arena. Many of my contemporaries make similar attempts. The collective result is a complex cellular automata-like effect that displays multiple marvelous colorful patterns that rise and decay.]

[0452.4 / 1098] [I slide on my butt on a carpeted floor, but I move across it as though it were made of ice. A celebration to acknowledge the unique contributions of transgender people is underway. THE PHOENIX (*authentic, unapologetic, and appreciative*) is selected for recogni-tion. As I overhear two women in front of me discuss her merit I say, *"Well she was recognized as Bank of America's working mother of the year. She's more than earned this award."* A group of female-to-male hockey players ascends the stage to be recognized. They gather for a photo.] //

⁎⁎

ICE: #0821, #0830, #0842
PUBLIC PARK: #0954
DEAD MAN: #1141
PHOTO: #0944, #0989, #1052

⁎⁎

#0453 - January 2, 2019 @ 06:06 (San Francisco, California)

[0453.1 / 1099] [I'm at a public aquatics center, where I'm employed as a bodyworker/phys-ical therapist. It's going to be a long day. The long rows of stalls are full of clients and I've yet to start work. Gender assignments on the rows are flip flopped today. Men are on the women's side, and vice versa.]

[0453.2 / 1100] [I take part in a social ritual where people autograph each other's underwear. I write, *"$10"* on THE DISNEY PRINCE's (*adventurous, noble, and independent*) left butt cheek. An abstraction occurs. Everyone compresses together tightly, like canned sardines. We find this humorous and giggle. I wind up face to face with THE PIXIE.
"You can't see anything from this close."
"Speak for yourself. I can see just fine."] //

⁎⁎

Min. = ♠- *THE PIXIE: #0574*
FLIP FLOP: #0808, #0936
UNDERWEAR: #0907, #1130
GIGGLE: #0878, #0887, #0921, #1073, #1128

⁎⁎

#0454 - January 2, 2019 @ 07:45 (San Francisco, California)

[0454.1 / 1101] [I observe people making fake moose tracks in the forest. The shape is incorrect and they're nowhere deep enough to pass as legitimate. They look like cartoon dog paws.]

[0454.2 / 1102] [Omnisciently, I sit on a park bench watching transparent people stroll by. I can see through their skin and bone to their essence. A voice behind me whispers in my ear, *"Watch. Keep expanding through the heart."* As I hear this, I see small *"greater than"* signs open from the backs of their hearts and out through the fronts of their chests. The greater the expansion in the heart, the slower the cadence of their walk becomes. The colors are tremendous. The capacity for light and bright leaves me full of wonder and love.] //

⁂

FOREST: #0972, #1140
BRIGHT: #0955, #0957, #0964, #0970, #1003, #1078, #1146
WONDER: #0820, #0821, #0884, #0908, #0956

⁂

#0455 - January 3, 2019 @ 00:08 (San Francisco, California)

[0455.1 / 1103] [I'm on a party bus. The master of ceremonies is a popular African American rapper. He wears a backwards ball cap and basketball jersey, but fails to realize he's not wearing any trousers or underwear. He wonders why he can't get the crowd hyped up, until he looks down and sees his dick flapping around.

Everyone erupts in laughter before we all fall into a cuddle puddle. A middle-aged redhead woman lays to my left, the rapper rests in the fetal position to my right. They take turns trying to tickle me. Their version of tickling involves digging a knuckle of their index finger into my ribs. The woman digs into my left side. I howl in pain. The rapper follows suit by digging into my right side. After a brief pause, they both look at me and simultaneously press their index knuckles firmly on my xiphoid process. The sensation is overwhelming as laughter floods my being from all directions.]

[0455.2 / 1104] [I ride in the back seat of a white SUV. THE WEAVER is the driver. My sister is a KPOP star who sings to me on a cartoon microphone. Little animated star tattoos adorn her cheeks. We slide around wildly across a snowy parking lot. The street surface is icy. THE WEAVER's driving way too fast to be safe, given current conditions. The mood is fairly intense.] //

⁂

Maj. = 0- THE WEAVER: #0459
LAUGHTER: #0929
STAR: #0824, #0846, #0893, #1023, #1053, #1057
RIBS: #1039

⁂

#0456 - January 3, 2019 @ 002:15 (San Francisco, California)

[0456.1 / 1105] [I'm in the basement of a large house, babysitting a boy and girl, both under the age of 10. THE MODEL (*open, strong, and motherly*) enters from a door to the right. She has chocolate pudding spattered across her chin. She holds two infant twins, one of whom is crying. She seems exhausted after spending the day out shopping. To add to the commotion, two brown Dachshund-Labrador hybrids run in from the far end of the room. One of them flies at me playfully with its tongue out and crashes into the new subway tile backsplash behind me. *"OH! GOOD! LORD!"* THE MODEL exclaims. I find this situation so amusing I wake up laughing.] //

⁎⁎
BROWN: #0823, #0860, #0915, #0974
BABYSITTING: #1036
WAKE UP: #1057, #1111, #1116, #1156, #1186
⁎⁎

#0457 - January 3, 2019 @ 03:16 (San Francisco, California)

[0457.1 / 1106] [I'm part of a speaker's panel who discuss how, *"'A Star is Born' is 100% conspiracy and a sham by design."*
"It's so contrived and obvious," I say to the camera, then continue, *"Yes, LADY GAGA is amazing. She is a genius...AND there are clues everywhere. Just look at her documentary '5'2.' Even this panel is a contribution to the joke!"* I rant for some time, though I've seen neither of the films I decry. Attendees feign interest in my opinions.
At an intermission I retreat to a table back stage where I join AMY POEHLER to film an episode of "Bread & Butter is our Bread & Butter," a web series where funny people meet at popular restaurants, order food, crack jokes while eating free bread, then leave before their food arrives.
"Our table is missing the butter. My bread is usually buttered!" I howl.
AMY snorts and demonstrates how to eat *"hard rolls"* in a *"sexy way,"* succeeding in her ploy to get me to laugh harder.
"The only other two to get me to laugh this hard are JENEANE GAROFALO and MAYA RUDOLPH!"
Our antics continue until I wake myself up laughing.] //

⁎⁎
LADY GAGA: #0465
AMY POEHLER: #0530
JOKE: #0830, #0908, #1071
OBVIOUS: #0906, #0926, #1149
⁎⁎

#0458 - January 4, 2019 @ 01:42 (San Francisco, California)

[0458.1 / 1107] [It's my last day of work at the US Senate before my scheduled retirement. Though I have credentials, I'm forced to stand in line for an enhanced security badge. My last day of work wastes away in line. What should be easy and uneventful becomes increasingly frustrating. Once through security I encounter JEFF SESSIONS and call him an **asshole**. LINDSAY GRAHAM rushes to his defense, but before he can say a word, I call them both (*among other things*) *"disgraceful, unaccountable messes."* My tongue lashing leaves him dumbfounded and me surrounded by applause.

"I see what you did there." AYANNA PRESSLEY laughs.

"You did? Oh really?" I retort sarcastically.

I like her braided hair, but I find her handlebar moustache a bit confusing.] //

⁂

JUSTICE: #0932
CONFUSING: #0834, #0933, #1028, #1058
DEFEND: #1028, #1055

⁂

#0459 - January 4, 2019 @ 03:26 (San Francisco, California)

[0459.1 / 1108] [A starched and pressed white dress shirt hangs on a wooden hanger.]

[0459.2 / 1109] [Some drama has recently unfolded in a hotel lobby.]

[0459.3 / 1110] [I hold a wet bottomed brown paper bag that bleeds through. Inside the bag are multiple pairs of freshly severed human arms. I head downstairs to "mom and dad's" dusty basement to stash the bag. I really don't want THE WEAVER to find what's been hidden.]

[0459.4 / 1111] [I get a glimpse behind the steering wheel of a purple pickup truck with an unusually low (*and ineffective*) windshield.]

[0459.5 / 1112] [I pick up a simple, clear stained-glass window that falls apart at the seams. I attempt to put it back together in a wooden frame. A friendly set of hands appear and help me with the repairs.]

[0459.6 / 1113] [Basement beds.]

[0459.7 / 1114] [A voice repeatedly questions, *"Maybe just throw it all away?"*] //

⁂

Maj. = 0- THE WEAVER: #0464
HOTEL LOBBY: #1078, #1166
STAINED GLASS: #0887, #1171
A VOICE: #0978, #0991, #1001, #1024, #1123, #1178

⁂

#0460 - January 5, 2019 @ 03:33 (San Francisco, California)

[0460.1 / 1115] [Most detail quickly fades. I'm left with a lingering image of a tree house that's been torn apart. One entire side of a prefabricated replacement structure is laid out in front of me for assembly. I'm with a couple of people I don't know. Am I a teenager? With boyish curiosity I climb up the structure to see if anyone's home, first shouting up, *"Hey are you ok?"* I think SLASH from Guns 'n Roses or another rock musician lives in the dwelling. My mood is confused and scattered.] //

⁂

TREE HOUSE: #1002
GUNS: #0829, #0874, #0986
SCATTERED: #0809, #0819, #0833, #0842
OK: #0867, #0918, #0953, #1005, #1135, #1192

⁂

#0461 - January 6, 2019 @ 03:36 (San Francisco, California)
*Another multi-fragment dream experience: *

[0461.1 / 1116] [THE BOSTON MARATHONER (*elite, sinewy, and precise*), THE FUNDA-MENTALIST (*upset, un-centered, and deflecting*) and I all meet secretly at night in a courtyard to discuss, *"activities related to financial services practice."* THE BOSTON MARATHONER and THE FUNDAMENTALIST shake hands and exchange pleasantries. THE FUNDAMEN-TALIST is quick to say, *"This does NOT constitute an agreement."*]

[0461.2 / 1117] [I'm definitely an oppressor dickhead in this reality, and I know it. THE DANCER is morbidly obese. We fly around a futuristic cityscape like superheroes. I offer THE DANCER some feedback on her parenting. She dismisses it and roils with anger. Things escalate when I respond in a passive aggressive and condescending tone. *"Look, you're a good mom, but if I can't have an opinion, you're just a bitch. Oh...and by the way, you're really fat."* We're not kind to each other.]

[0461.3 / 1118] [I'm at a movie theater that only screens the film "Ghostbusters." I peek in to see, and witness a group of people enthralled by the penultimate scene where Zuul and Gozer are evaporated by accelerated particle streams from proton backpacks. The film has a consistent draw. The theater has become dependent on the film as its sole revenue stream.
In the lobby, patrons can play an antique amusement game where a motor oil can slowly drips at odd intervals onto what looks like a player piano reel or a computer program punch card. The object of the game is to guide the oil can over the card while the card moves through at different speeds. The more oil that infiltrates the card, the messier it becomes to carry home in one's pocket. Those with high levels of precision and skill leave with an, *"unsullied piece of reusable open-source code."*]

[0461.4 / 1119] [I bend down next to an old hippie "love bus" and find a shiny, brilliant quarter. I notice a line of them leading away from the vehicle. As I inspect them, I note the coins bear the visage of THOMAS EDISON. I pick up more and more quarters and put them in my pockets. I eventually make it to a staircase and discover a pile of the new "Edison Quarters" glistening in the sunlight at its top. When I scoop up a handful, they're less heavy than I expect. They're made of plastic. They're fake and valueless, *"but they sure are shiny!"* All the quarters in my pockets have become plastic...*or were they already?* I dunno. **shrug**]

[0461.5 / 1120] [I'm at a university dining hall at night. Numerous *"delicious looking"* foods are on display. Two items that appeal to me are "Eggnog Brioche French Toast," and "Soylent Burgers." Both are heavily promoted as organic. I see them as lifeless, dead, <u>fake food</u>. I overhear two men talking in the buffet line who quickly go quiet when they notice me listening. They're secret agents. They leave the line, duck into a classroom and covertly review a dossier with a political campaign's media team. The lead investigator confirms, *"Yes, the evidence here is circumspect. It's strong enough to bring down those white-collar criminals. Now let's go get them!"* The group high fives, organizes and moves out to apprehend their targets. As the meeting breaks, I wake up.] //

⁂

Maj. = 2- THE DANCER: #0466
QUARTER: #1044, #1110
WHITE: #0849, #0852, #0859
THE BOSTON MARATHONER: #0777

⁂

⚜ 7.5 - THE BOOK OF CAPRICORNUS: 0462-0489 ⚜

#0462 - January 8, 2019 @ 00:32 (San Francisco, California)

[0462.1 / 1121] [I'm in a bookstore descending an escalator. I wear a black hoodie pulled over my face. I look back over my shoulder and see THE ACTOR who's unexpectedly stone faced and angry. I thought we were on good terms? In this situation, that is clearly not the case. I wave back again just to check and receive no response. As I descend, he leaves my field of vision. At the bottom of the escalator a table is stocked with a bulk supply of sunscreen. Customers can dispense as much or little as they want in custom tubes, similar to condiment pumps at a fast-food restaurant. The branding on the tubes and bulk containers sport mauve and taupe flourishes that softly swirl from the center out into veiny branches. As I pick up a tube a voice whispers, *"It's important to take a journey to the heart."*] //

⚜
Maj. = 10- THE ACTOR: #0687
JOURNEY: #0943, #1109, #1122
ESCALATOR: #0809, #0844, #0865
BULK: #0810, #1155
⚜

#0463 - January 8, 2019 @ 02:08 (San Francisco, California)

[0463.1 / 1122] [I exchange messages with THE LOBBYIST and THE ENGINEER (*distant, rugged, and masculine*) as they aggressively ski down a mountain wearing helmet cameras. They send a link to a live feed of their descent to my phone. When they arrive safely at the bottom, I feel like a proud mother. I leap up to hug THE LOBBYIST, but snare his neck with my legs. I lean in to kiss him on the forehead and intentionally make an awkward comment about my groin being close to his jaw.

We review the footage of their successful run on a television at the lodge. The visuals are stunning. The majority of the route is a tight and fast spiral that dog ears left. They try to convince me to take the next ride, suggesting I would love it. They needle me about my fear of skiing. Upon second playback it looks extremely dangerous. It's something I simply will not do. It's dizzying how fast to the left the course cuts, and how massive the crowd of spectators at right becomes. I know I would crash and injure many people if I make an attempt. I feel glad I don't do it. **It's the safe choice.**] //

⚜
Maj. = 17- THE LOBBYIST: #0935
SKI: #1115
CONVINCE: #0969, #1074, #1120
⚜

#0464 - January 8, 2019 @ 03:26 (San Francisco, California)

[0464.1 / 1123] [Old ladies use flip phones at a nursing home. THE WEAVER repeatedly calls the house landline, which is the same number as her cell number (*save a different final digit*). The house line ends with "4," the cell phone number, "7." I take multiple calls on the house landline. THE WEAVER believes she calls her cell phone. I ask THE WEAVER to repeat the number as she's written them. They match, yet when she attempts to call the cell phone ending with "7," her call routes to the house landline that ends with "4." It becomes frustrating and confusing. I review paper billing statements and a variety of other documents to confirm our understanding that number assignments are correct and to prove the incorrect routing of today's calls.

The old women become grouchy when they receive increasingly cantankerous calls from family members for not having their cell phones turned on. All calls to their cell phones route to the same landline. The old women are barely aware of their phones and their functions. They accept moderate familial harassment and aren't bothered. This is business as usual. They're accustomed to being subjugated, yet revered. It's an awkward energy to sit in. The issue does not resolve.] //

⁑

Maj. = 0- THE WEAVER: #0467
DOCUMENTS: #0806, #0867, #0942
GROUCHY: #1197

⁑

#0465 - January 8, 2019 @ 23:14 (San Francisco, California)

[0465.1 / 1124] [LADY GAGA and her assistant argue with a producer about intellectual property and licensing revenue sharing. The item in dispute is a still frame of hands bound behind someone's back. It was used as a source of inspiration for a recent music video. She pivots to me and asks which of her videos is my favorite. Without thinking I blurt, *"SEXXX Dreams!"* even though I'm not sure if a video was created for that song. I've fibbed to her face.] //

⁑

LADY GAGA: #0475
MUSIC VIDEO: #0891, #0957, #0984
FAVORITE: #0899, #0953, #1061

⁑

#0466 - January 9, 2019 @ 00:45 (San Francisco, California)

[0466.1 / 1125] [I'm with THE DANCER at a futuristic music festival. Attendees use an app with a very engaging, animated, and touch sensitive interface. Performers' names are centered in colorful circles of various sizes that rise from bottom to the top of the screen like champagne bubbles. The size of the circle fluctuates based on the size of the crowd gathered to observe the performance. JUSTIN TIMBERLAKE is slated to perform amongst hundreds of others. Even though he's massively popular, he seems radically out of place in this line up.]

[0466.2 / 1126] [I'm a teenager. I sit at a hospital room table with others. ADOLF HITLER joins us. He interrogates us while searching for a specific object. The object, he insists, *"is sacred and made of gold."* He kicks a dead body in a bag at his feet to intimidate us. Unboth-

337

ered, I crack a joke to break the tension at the table. My joking makes the others nervous. They don't want to get shot. I'm not worried.]

[0466.3 / 1127] [I observe a humorous scene where bullet trains sneak out of their stations like rogue teenagers. They're corralled and returned by the "Engine Authorities." They don't get far down the track. Their reality is limited to two dimensions.]

[0466.4 / 1128] [I take an exam in the hallway of a condo. THE LAWYER reviews my work in progress and brings attention to the bizarre expression I've chosen for an equation. He says my answer is correct, but the method I used to derive the answer will cost me all the credit. A team of people show up at the door to grade the exam in real time. I know a few of the exam assessors, who refuse to talk to me because they're working. One of the assessors produces a small metal box, which when opened reveals a series of items made from precious metals, recessed in dark protective foam. The box has pairs of similar objects at different scales. One big. One smaller. They appear to be highly specific measuring tools that are part of an additional, "pop quiz". Six objects. Six questions to answer.] //

✲✲

Maj. = 2- THE DANCER: #0479, 5- THE LAWYER: #0531
ADOLF HITLER: #1165
CHAMPAGNE: #0803, #0924, #0974
EQUATION: #1050

✲✲

#0467 - January 9, 2019 @ 02:37 (San Francisco, California)

[0467.1 / 1129] [Best I can discern: I'm at a firehouse filled with violent criminals. A story breaks on TV that a bunch of offenders have been rounded up in a sting operation and are on the way to jail. I'm looking to stash the bloody smoothie I've created after systematically blending up a body to conceal evidence of a murder committed by another young man. The young man I'm protecting is a former child star who prominently rose to fame after a chance interaction on a morning TV program - {While penned up in a Lucite cage like a puppy at a mall pet store he was reunited with his mother and instantly awarded a lucrative movie deal. His current estimated net worth is $100MM.}- Right before getting caught in the firehouse he went to a gay sex club by the "_____ _____."

Another boy sees me commit the "blender cover up." I'm afraid he'll snitch on me to get an eventual plea deal. I run away screaming because I don't want to take responsibility for my actions. THE WEAVER shows up and does a shift move to get those apprehended to calm down and accept their fates. Everyone continues going berserk. OPRAH is unexpectedly among the arrested and en route to jail as well, which astonishes the public who watch the story unfold live.

Once in prison, the "potential snitch" cruises for sex. He inspects other inmates' anuses by holding a mirror affixed to a straightened length of hanger wire a few inches off the floor. If he sees something he likes, he whistles provocatively.

I interact with prisoners from the opposite side of bulletproof windows. I've avoided capture. I'm a free man. I've chosen to be a monk. I wear all white. I'm not wearing shoes.

Ethereal diamond and gold light radiate from my chest outward as a continuing prayer for those incarcerated. *I'm dedicated to their liberation.* My head has been shaved completely. The act of shearing renders me permanently bald.] //

⁜

Maj. = 0- THE WEAVER: #0474
OPRAH: #0828
OUTWARD: #0929, #1201
SHAVED: #1082

⁜

#0468 - January 10, 2019 @ 04:34 (San Francisco, California)
*Odd nonsensical interactions. Some abstract. Some with a potential linkage between the first and final scenes. *

[0468.1 / 1130] [I predominantly focus my attention on a teenage software engineer who has massive responsibilities, but doesn't fully grasp the scope of his impact. He's overwhelmed and distracted by handheld technology.]

[0468.2 / 1131] [I urinate over the shoulder of a woman who sits reading a periodical at a cafe table. Her back faces me.]

[0468.3 / 1132] [A group of young children are chaperoned through a mall. They want to go to a store that sells various colors of glitter spray paint. The store is engineered to be *"experiential and highly intoxicating to the senses."* The teacher takes issue with a particular shade of gold spray paint promotionally offered at the store.]

[0468.4 / 1133] [I pass a large stack of odd shaped floppy disks, which appear similar to old Nintendo cartridges. A note on top of a stack is labeled with a SLAYER logo. Seems it's an input to an odd karaoke machine. This is an old program that was rigorously used, had a successful and full useful life, and has now been placed aside.]

[0468.5 / 1134] [I wear pajamas as I make my way to an appointment with THE DRUMMER *(balanced, sane, and rational)* who tells me, *"I'm the only one who ever stays in the band."*]

[0468.6 / 1135] [I pass by a male mannequin with a giant phallus that has a brass padlock for a Prince Albert.]

[0468.7 / 1136] [A yacht-rock old money husband and wife stand next to a cream-colored kiosk selling university memorabilia. They're both White, blonde, shiny toothed and wear matching sweaters tied around their necks.]

· · ·

[0468.8 / 1137] [A classic model Chevy backs out of an indoor stall. It moves very slowly. The driver sits so low the top of his head can barely be seen.]

[0468.9 / 1138] [Back with the young distracted engineer, I internally lament THE CHILD may take a similar career path and will resultantly become despondent and withdrawn. A friend snaps me out of my thoughts when he surgically inserts a small microchip in the fold of my right wrist. I pat the young engineer on the back. He decides to *"finally take a break."* He exits as my friends and I start playing a board game.] //

⁎⁎

Maj. = 3- THE CHILD: #0488
PADLOCK: #1052
DISTRACTED: #0943, #0953, #1132, #1149, #1176
CREAM: #0947, #0964, #0987, #0989
THE DRUMMER: #1033

⁎⁎

#0469 - January 11, 2019 @ 02:37 (San Francisco, California)

[0469.1 / 1139] [**"53 Foot Tall Grandmother Arrested!"** A headline scrolls across the bottom banner of a news program. An odd scene unfolds where I'm holed up in a McDonalds with a bunch of fratty middle aged guys who are all friends and have participated in some sort of white-collar crime. *"No fewer than three of the alleged suspects inside own Ferrari's."* Nonsense inflammatory turns of phrase are used to increase station viewership and roil public outcry to spur a group arrest. I'm annoyed. I appear guilty by association. I haven't done anything wrong. A plot to smuggle me out of the McDonalds in a very conspicuous way emerges: *I'll sit on the shoulders of others, while wearing a giant cloak. We'll use steel hospital crutches for balance. I'll wear a rubber grandmother mask. We won't fool anyone. We're not even trying.*] //

⁎⁎

McDONALD'S: #0915
MASK: #1076, #1083, #1196
NEWS: #0906, #0962, #1141

⁎⁎

#0470 - January 11, 2019 @ 04:00 (San Francisco, California)

[0470.1 / 1140] [THE ORPHAN has a very specific feedback tracking process that requires the use of a database interface and lengthy alpha strings as a primary key (*"BBXXQQRRSST-TYYKKDD..."*). She intensely groups and reviews customer responses to her most recent series of classes.]

[0470.2 / 1141] [I'm cooking. I want to bake a pizza. The microwave doesn't work. I look in an oven and discover already baked pepperoni and cheese pizzas left warmed at high temperatures. I don't remember putting them in the oven.]

· · ·

340

[0470.3 / 1142] [*"You see...I'm asking you these inquiry questions so I'll get off your back! Who asked you to chastise me?"* I ask a young woman who has really been up my ass today to get a handle on my travel details for an upcoming trip.] //

⁎⁎
ASS: #0879
TRAVEL: #0961, #0965, #0976, #1023
THE ORPHAN: #0629
⁎⁎

#0471 - January 12, 2019 @ 07:31 (San Francisco, California)

[0471.1 / 1143] [THE CONFIDANT and I wait in an airport terminal for a transfer. He's calm. I'm impatient and would rather be outside.]

[0471.2 / 1144] [I'm in a house where a series of elevators move between floors. The elevators all have furniture in them that don't necessarily fit (*oversized formal couches, etc.*) making them inefficient and challenging to use.]

[0471.3 / 1145] [A family gathers to exchange gifts on the stairwell at a public transit station. One festive gift is a long flat rectangular box wrapped in colorful, shiny paper with the word **"OPERATIONS"** vertically spelled in large glitter foam block letters across one side. The gift is handed to an older woman.] //

⁎⁎
Maj. = 16- THE CONFIDANT: #0756
ELEVATOR: #0816, #0860
CALM: #0932, #1063, #1121, #1135
⁎⁎

#0472 - January 13, 2019 @ 03:25 (San Francisco, California)
Confusing. Three layers of simultaneous activity. In aggregate it would be utter nonsense and nonlinear. Decoupling the scenes to their components yields the following: *

[0472.1 / 1146] [1) I'm on my way to an orgy at THE ARCHITECT and THE DESIGNER's newly renovated home.]

[0472.2 / 1147] [2) I'm made acutely aware of the severe impact the US Government shut down has on broad segments of the population. The shared pain and anxiety are tremendous. Everything appears brown and smoky.]

[0472.3 / 1148] [3) I'm engaged in a terse conversation with THE NURSE from across a busy intersection at a crosswalk.]

. . .

[0472.4 / 1149] [1] I wear a backpack with a speaker blaring, "**THIS IS AMERICA.**"]

[0472.5 / 1150] [2] A young woman walks down a grassy hill descending toward a beach at night. It's warm and windy.]

[0472.6 / 1151] [3] THE NURSE gives me continuous (*and unsolicited*) feedback. It feels cartoonish and has a "Lord of the Rings" quality.]

[0472.7 / 1152] [1] I walk towards the sex party house, then turn and walk back up a hill two blocks, passing two guys I want to fuck. I saw them on the social media invite, but they're still en route to the party. I pull my ball cap down past my eyeline and avoid them. No hellos. No eye contact. Total ignorance.]

[0472.8 / 1153] [2] Large gold-colored coins, the diameter of a coffee mug are embossed and painted with black accents. The contrasting colors make The Great Seal of the United States of America pop. An objective is to find objects to throw at the coins, which seem to behave like miniature black holes. Whatever's tossed toward them is sucked into the void, never to be seen again.]

[0472.9 / 1154] [3] THE NURSE's feedback grows in intensity from across the street. She waves her hands at me and laughs while excitedly telling me, *"YOU'RE ALWAYS LATE!"*]

[0472.10 / 1155] [1] From inside the house I cross through an open lanai that has cheesy repurposed 1960's patio furniture. The walls are pistachio green. Narrow and tall white diamonds offset the peculiar color choice for the wall. At a glance it appears similar to a giant backgammon board. I just know the patio is being watched by energies that aren't aligned for me, so I quickly duck inside and observe the party in progress.]

[0472.11 / 1156] [2] I see an advertisement for a television special hosted by THE MAGI-CIAN, in which the game is to unlock the physics mystery as to why the Golden Gate Bridge is the, *"only truly seismically solid manmade structure."* The ad backgrounds are all black. Simple red line histograms emerge as THE MAGICIAN amiably invites the public to join in the conversation asking: "**WHY DOES IT WORK?**"]

[0472.12 / 1157] [3] I get fed up with THE NURSE's unsolicited feedback and begin blowing it back at her.
"HEY...you're in FANTASY! F-A-N-T-A-S-Y! DO YOU GET THAT!? NOTHING YOU'RE SAYING MAKES ANY SENSE TO ME!!" It's possible I'm being an asshole. I don't want to listen to her anymore.] //

⁂

Maj. = 13- THE NURSE: #0481, 14- THE MAGICIAN: #0510
Min. = ♥- THE ARCHITECT: #0637, ♠- THE DESIGNER: #0637
AMERICA: #0887, #0891, #0902
TALL: #0818, #0819, #0878

⁂

#0473 - January 14, 2019 @ 01:00 (San Francisco, California)

[0473.1 / 1158] [I lay on my back on a hill in what feels like an urban combat zone. Helicopters circle overhead. Nearby a camera crew films a reality TV show, which might be a cable news program. I feel like I'm going to be captured. I could be in Turkey, perhaps Syria. No matter where, it's an oppressive state. My goal is to sprint from the hill back to a large concrete building without being apprehended. I make it to the building.

Once inside I realize I'm surrounded by a group of people who work for Apple. THE MEEK is among them. She wants to invite a colleague to class, scribbling a name on a scrap of paper and handing it to me. She realizes the person she wants to invite sits next to someone else we know from work. Asking for an additional free enrollment makes her feel awkward.] //

⁂

HELICOPTER: #1033
COMBAT: #1030, #1152
TURKEY: #1073
THE MEEK: #0889

⁂

#0474 - January 4, 2019 @ 02:34 (San Francisco, California)

[0474.1 / 1159] [THE PAINTER (*fiery, opinionated, and fancy*) walks with me down a concrete path in a condo development. We pause and lay down with a group of men who are being social and playful on a short green hill.]

[0474.2 / 1160] [I exchange newly published books with a friend.]

[0474.3 / 1161] [I meet a small framed man with dark hair. His name is "Angel." He invites me to visit his high-rise residence. We enjoy conversation as we ride a gondola up to the condo, encountering some friends who are skeptical of my new friendship. Once inside "Angel" asks me to consider taking over his lease. The rent on the unit is $16,000 per month. At the end of the quarter, it'll increase to $20,000 per month. THE WEAVER and THE CARPENTER would be on the hook for the bill. *It doesn't seem like a very good deal.*

Small pairs of glowing red-gold eyes peek at me from inside a dark bathroom. I coax them out. They reveal themselves as small burgundy robed beings. In an adjacent room, a group of skeletons have sex. It looks awkward because they don't have skin, and there's a space between the bodies where genitals would ordinarily be. They appear to float.]

· · ·

343

[0474.4 / 1162] [A house band breaks down their equipment after a performance. One of the band members pauses and comes over to speak with me. For the next show he's curious if I'd be willing to make a scale model of the planet Pluto, with three of its moons included. *"The white one needs to be the furthest away to indicate it's appropriately spinning in the direction of the sun."* He tells me more as we discuss the specific requirements for the project.] //

***

Maj. = 0- THE WEAVER: #0476, 1- THE CARPENTER: #0479
HOOK: #0968, #1060
BURGUNDY: #0931

***

#0475 - January 16, 2019 @ 04:00 (San Francisco, California)

[0475.1 / 1163] [I park a bicycle in front of a Chinese market. I don't have a lock so I contemplate bringing the bike inside with me while I shop. Once inside I interact with a smartphone app *(all in Mandarin characters and voice activated)*. I easily understand where to go to get what I want. On the top floor stands a stylish children's playset with colorful tubes and zig-zagging slides. The kids playing want me to join them on a trip down the "**BIG GREEN SLIDE.**" I take a look over the edge. The slide spirals around all the way to the ground floor where I began climbing, so I decline their invitation. Instead, I play with a father and son at a small table. The boy is under five years old. The father hands me a sheet of braille. Rubbing the tip of a finger across the vertical row of dots reveals small dabs of orange, green, and blue. I playfully fill in the white space on the card and create a tri-color bar chart. I'm fully engaged and satisfied.]

[0475.2 / 1164] [I'm on stage in Las Vegas performing with LADY GAGA's band. Sportscasters give play-by-play commentary for the performance. LADY GAGA emerges in a peach toned latex body suit that outlines all the curves of her body, including her labial folds. Part of the performance intended to shock the audience involves her peeling the latex off her right breast. The missing rectangular portion reveals a circular nipple. Her mascara is running. The commentators have plenty of sensationalist fodder to choose from as they shape the advancement of her career narrative.] //

***

LADY GAGA: #0481
TIP: #0862, #1035, #1194
PEACH: #0848, #0867, #0988
SLIDE: #0878, #0909, #0919

***

#0476 - January 17, 2019 @ 03:00 (San Francisco, California)

[0476.1 / 1165] [I'm THE TOP OF THE WORLD *(fun loving, gregarious, and free)*. I experience a split reality, where in one I'm isolated at home and in the other I'm about to undergo chemotherapy for stomach cancer. I move between disjointed realms...*possibly parallel universes?* Abundant supplies and food are made available for me to sustain myself during the extended *"at home"* period of solitude.

"ASHA." "METTA." "BODHICHITTA."

These words seem to be all around. THE WEAVER stops by and attempts to read them from a laminated menu. She can't pronounce them. I help her. The menu is plain white and the words are written in a font that looks kind of like *"sad clown-ish"* mascara running down a cheek.

Things begin calmly when I'm alone, then become chaotic. In one moment, I jump to the main level of the solitary healing space. Massive quantities of food are delivered on dollies and wheeled down from a semi-truck. The delivery crew is composed of samurais. Boxes of pho, udon, soba noodles, bean sprouts, gallons and gallons and gallons of soy sauce that I don't remember having made an order for roll through the room and down into the basement. It doesn't make any sense. I can't eat any of it. It's frustrating, it's sad, and it hurts.

In the hospital, I stand on a balcony railing looking out on black nothingness. My preference is for solitude and quiet, but I feel obligated to let more people stop by my hospital room. Each has their own opinion(s) about which course of therapy would suit me best. I find few of them are helpful. After feigning receptivity, I want to hear none of them. Many more people stop by and strongly suggest what to do, based on their experiences. One guy wearing a cowboy hat describes his journey with cancer in detail. A quick series of 1:1 interactions blip by, after which I'm directed to navigate my own healing journey.

"You are to suffer this quietly and by yourself, then go forth and tell no one," an invisible guide declares.

I've decided to share my journey, and everyone else's stories get lobbed on to my already exhausted spirit. I'm confused. People's "caring" becomes the thing that holds me apart from my healing. I feel loved by those around me, yet forced into a plan of action. Different conversational tones call in different beings. Different types of healing are offered by a range of hosts including a benevolent Frenchman. A half step shift from the pure aligned healing tone is disruptive and negatively impacts the macro-overarching process.

Back at home, I'm hungry. In the moment I feel the urge to eat, the massive stores of food delivered downstairs disappear. When the hunger pangs subside, all of the food reappears. A chemo drug is pumped into my veins and I can feel it burning me from the inside out. I hobble to a refrigerator filled with peanut butter and chocolate flavored nutritional shakes. I'm able to open and sip a peanut butter shake as a medical crew swarms in and takes my vital signs next to a large X-Ray machine.

People's unsolicited opinions continue to flood in. A gospel choir sings in a nearby room. ARETHA FRANKLIN adds an occasional vocal flourish. DUKE ELLINGTON and other jazz greats play a piece that features a giant marimba and a futuristic set of oversized vibes that whir like a chorus. Music is abundant in the space.] //

***

Maj. = 0- THE WEAVER: #0477
ARETHA FRANKLIN: #0872
PARALLEL: #0819, #0831, #0909, #0932
PEANUT BUTTER: #1056

***

345

#0477 - January 17, 2019 @ 05:21 (San Francisco, California)

[0477.1 / 1166] [I'm at a laundromat washing a load of clothes. I'm engaged in conversa-tion with a petite Vietnamese woman who repeatedly invites me to help her practice her *"3 or 4,"* meaning three of four foreign languages. English is among them. She's insistent we prac-tice together, but I don't know how to help her. The lids of the washing machines look like giant device controls for a CD player. She keeps insisting I help her. I maintain my position that I don't know how.]

[0477.2 / 1167] [I'm at an ironic pep rally where KORN plays a farewell concert just before a season ending high school football game. I look for THE WEAVER to deliver her a hand-written thank you note, as I drive around a gravel parking lot at the back of a semi-truck fleet yard. I easily identify the band's truck. Their roadies have left a stack of small used guitar amplifiers behind the tail. A father and teenage son sit by a flaming oil drum near the guitars. The father roasts hot dogs over the oil drum with his back to the boy, who sits quietly licking half a lemon. The son doesn't respond when I ask him, *"Does that taste good?"* I knock my hand on the back of the truck thinking I'll find the band, but they're not there.] //

✲✲

Maj. = 0- THE WEAVER: #0482
KORN: #0666
FAREWELL: #1165
LAUNDROMAT: #0943
CD: #0857
✲✲

#0478 - January 17, 2019 @ 06:37 (San Francisco, California)

[0478.1 / 1168] [I fully record a dream from a deeper dream level, and wake in the current dream realm without my work. I'm in a yoga studio. I begin to lead a class with my eyes closed. I can hear people talking and I guide them to become quiet. I leave the room momen-tarily. When I return, I discover there is no class and I'm hours early for the next one.

I'm very confused for a moment. I dictate my experience into a phone recorder, while standing in front of a large plate glass window. I'm startled when I see a golf cart hit the building at full speed. I run towards the wreckage and find a middle-aged Black man passed out behind the wheel. He awakens when I tap him and reverses direction to park the cart. Someone jumps off the back of the cart and another jumps on to ride as it pulls back from the wall.

I realize I'm recording a dream. This frustrates me. I fumble with my phone, not able to activate the recorder as desired. My capture method fails. I keep talking anyway as extra dream detail unfolds, without recording it.] //

✲✲

CART: #0967, #1016, #1024, #1078
EXTRA: #0817, #0855, #0977, #1035, #1073
FULL SPEED: #0886
✲✲

#0479 - January 18, 2019 @ 03:03 (San Francisco, California)

[0479.1 / 1169] [THE DANCER and THE ATHEIST have an argument at home. The lights are low. They don't try to hide their conflict. Frustrated, THE ATHEIST walks into another room soothed by the soft touch of flannel pajamas on his legs. He's placed his oversized jeans neatly over the top of a couch. In another room, I stack a series of three green Lutheran Books of Worship on a wooden shelf THE CARPENTER built. THE CARPENTER sings, "Blessed Assurance" with a deep vibrato from his workshop in the garage.]

[0479.2 / 1170] [I stand and balance on the top edge of a wooden fence. THE DANCER wears different masks and tries to *"get me."* One is the face of a sinister clown, which she wears amiably and ironically, since she's embodying the thing that most terrifies her. Part of the fence is covered by a navy-blue quilt.]

[0479.3 / 1171] [We ride roller coasters as a family at night. One is the *"The Vortex"* at Kings Island.] //

⁂

Maj. = 1- THE CARPENTER: #0487, 2- THE DANCER: #0488, 8- THE ATHEIST: #0488
GARAGE #0810, #0847, #0876
ISLAND: #0815, #0821, #0950, #0984, #1025

⁂

#0480 - January 18, 2019 @ 08:35 (The Presidio of San Francisco)

[0480.1 / 1172] [I'm shown an image of people weaving a complex red basket with fabric generated by their minds. A voice behind me says, *"When we meditate, we do our part to map the Genome of God."*]

[0480.2 / 1173] [I observe a yoga class where a woman wearing green stretchy leggings receives an ungrounded assist to her pelvis. Her left hip dislocates and causes her instant and extreme pain. She yelps and cries out, writhing on the floor. The class halts. Neither the teacher nor the assistant has insurance. This generates a lot of fear with the studio owners about the, *"extent of their legal liability."*] //

⁂

RED: #1028, #1057, #1061
MAP: #0868, #1023, #1094, #1171
INSURANCE: #1026

⁂

#0481 - January 20, 2019 @ 05:03 (San Francisco, California)

[0481.1 / 1174] [MADONNA dances shoulder to shoulder between two men on stage, at the top of a pyramid. One tier down on the pyramid, I'm one of two men who similarly support LADY GAGA in a kick line. MADONNA becomes annoyed. The crowd seems to be there for GAGA, though it's MADONNA's headlining production. *Her name is on the venue marquee.*]

[0481.2 / 1175] [I wake up in a large gothic hall. I sit up and meditate.]

[0481.3 / 1176] [I teach a 45-minute yoga class. Students distribute themselves oddly through a narrow and deep practice hall. I call just a handful of poses and suddenly realize time has expired. I quickly head toward the door. Prior to exiting, THE NURSE hands me a purple towel, invites me to take a child's pose, and says, *"Stay if you want."* I move closer to the door and encounter THE KITKAT (*present, consistent, and dedicated*), who smiles and wraps her arms around me in a warm hug. Small green hummingbirds fly out of the center of my chest and up into a sky light where soft gold light flows down into an already amber lit space. *"My, the little birdies are really flying out of you this morning!"* THE KITKAT remarks as we giggle.]

[0481.4 / 1177] [I meet THE CONDUCTOR (*skillful, honest, and desirous*) and his husband THE ORIGAMIST (*sharing, permissive, and artful*) en route to a public concert on Hawaii. Both are huge pot smokers. After the show they invite people up to their condo to autograph their refrigerator (*as one would a high school yearbook*) to ceremonially mark their move out of the unit. A small dirt pathway leads up a rocky hillside to their home. THE CONDUCTOR is apprehensive about the number of people who are making the trek up the hill because it may tip off the cops, kill the party, and *"harsh the chill vibes."* On the route up to the house stands a single 6"x6"x8' tall wooden post, on top of which is a gallon sized black plastic vessel full of synthetic protein powder. People climb the post, repeatedly pick up the protein, inspect it, set it down, and then descend the post. No one wants to claim the protein, nor carry it away.] //

✲✲

Maj. = 13- THE NURSE: #0494
LADY GAGA: #0612
MADONNA: #1006
PYRAMID: #0899, #0965
ROCKY: #0945, #1010, #1046
THE CONDUCTOR: #1070
THE KITKAT: #1422

✲✲

#0482 - January 21, 2019 @ 03:02 (San Francisco, California)

[0482.1 / 1178] [THE WEAVER meets two men at a prestigious bank branch. One of them is Swiss, the other is Italian. While engaged in group conversation I'm skeptical of a claim the Italian man makes, and I challenge him to a $100 bet. I lose the bet because THE WEAVER is onsite for a reason different from what I understood.

"Hey, do you know my new friend 'Chris?'" I say wryly to THE WEAVER, referencing the man I've lost the bet to.

She nods. I quietly present my wallet and extend "Chris" a crisp, new $100 bill to clear my debt. It's playful. As I thumb through my wallet, I realize I have another $100 bill.]

[0482.2 / 1179] [THE NUN and I sit across from one another in the breakfast room of "Grandma's Estate," sharing conversation over a cup of tea. We use *the fine china."*]

[0482.3 / 1180] [SHARI BAPTISTE sits on a panel discussing the practice of being a *"Trance Medium."* The light is low and earth toned. A fairly large group has gathered for the talk. She shares an anecdote describing when she saw her brother BARON *(at age 17)*, step out of his body for three minutes and bring through *"higher knowledge."* When he emerged from the experience, he had no recollection of what he said. SHARI's speaking style is evocative and emotionally charges up the group.]

[0482.4 / 1181] [THE WEAVER doesn't know I made the $100 bet with "Chris." I keep this minor fact withheld.] //

✼
✼✼

Maj. = 0- THE WEAVER: #0487
Min. = ◆- THE NUN: #0542
BARON BAPTISTE: #0499
KNOWLEDGE: #0802, #0950
$100: #1131

✼
✼✼

#0483 - January 21, 2019 @ 04:27 (San Francisco, California)

[0483.1 / 1182] [*"I understand, more and more, that simple things bring me pleasure,"* I say to myself as I ride a fat-tired bicycle with oversized wheels down a highway. I'm en route to the University to teach a class scheduled to begin at 6:00pm. I keep riding the bike, but I leave my body. With a blink I'm surrounded by a sea of loving faces. All crave *"more insights and detail"* from the stories I shared with them while I was *(apparently)* channeling from the spirit realm to the prime material plane. It's a bit awkward because I have zero recollection of any of these conversations.]

[0483.2 / 1183] [I find myself hugging the torso of a tall sinewy man. I want to linger there with my arms wrapped around him. A young lesbian couple enters, one of whom has a cute pink butch hairstyle. I ask them,
"Hey what's your opinion on..." They cut me off saying,
"It's just what happens when you leave your body."
"You're right," I affirm and continue, *"I tend to do that a lot."*
They take increasingly less notice of me and fall gazing into each other's eyes. They know they only have eight more hours together before they'll never see one another again. Their noses nuzzle. They simply savor the moment without words.]

. . .

[0483.3 / 1184] [I land in my body, en route to the 6:00pm class. I'd rather just go home. A tablet computer nearby live streams from a cafe in Israel. Dozens of people drift in and out of the frame. It's peaceful. People are civil.] //

⁂

PLEASURE: #0881
BODY: #1004, #1011, #1019, #1022, #1043
PEACEFUL: #0930

⁂

#0484 - January 21, 2019 @ 06:04 (San Francisco, California)

[0484.1 / 1185] ["*You've been TRICKED! Your phone dictation did not work!*" a raspy voice whispers behind me.]

[0484.2 / 1186] [I'm in a social scene near a large bridge. A group of young doctors share a condo and decide to throw an impromptu party. THE PSYCHIATRIST invites me to join them. We walk from the bridge to their building, then up a few flights of stairs to their unit. Strong sexual energy ping pongs around the group. The decor feels like a bachelor pad, though the space is occupied by beings of multiple genders. I'm transfixed by the inefficient placement of a grandfather clock in the dining room.

Next, I find myself drunk and being fondled by someone. The entire room upends like a dump truck and topples me down a garbage chute. I emerge from a stinking pile of wet trash and stumble on to a public green space. Small groups of people quietly sit knee to knee in telepathic communication circles as I traverse a pathway composed of small circular concrete steps. Among the meditators is THE ANGRY SPRITE (*informed, discerning, and vast*), whose hair has grown long and grey. I'm confused by seemingly random patches of long catfish whiskers on his unshaven face. I attempt to tap in with him multiple times. He politely declines and is insistent that he's not who I think he is.

My drunkenness amplifies as I stumble back up the stairway. I think I'm heading back to the party, but find myself in a large library study hall, where a long wooden rectangular table is populated by a series of students who listen to THE WORLDBRIDGER deliver a lecture on "*the practice of being a trance medium.*" Handouts are distributed, but they're in a pictograph script I don't understand.

I exit and head to the condo. I sit in front of a TV and contemplate masturbating to porn. The TV feed is interrupted with ciphers from the pictograph code in the lecture. I know I'm supposed to understand.

'I'm consciously incompetent.'] //

⁂

Maj. = 7- THE WORLDBRIDGER: #0528
Min. = ♠- THE PSYCHIATRIST: #0489
CLOCK: #0877, #0932, #0994
INCOMPETENT: #1193
THE ANGRY SPRITE: #1393

⁂

#0485 - January 22, 2019 @ 07:49 (San Francisco, California)

[0485.1 / 1187] [I shadow THE SHARED HEART at a *"Level 2"* training program. A quadriplegic participant is wheeled on a stretcher into a hallway adjoining the assembly hall. THE SHARED HEART and I review his participant statement and application. THE HILLBILLY takes an expanded content delivery role and organizes participants for an immersive *"Magic Carpet"* experience. A team member responsible for event technology misfires a celebration music cue that disrupts group flow, creating a moment of confusion that mildly annoys THE SHARED HEART.

She and I go for a brisk walk up a concrete hill, offering one another acknowledgements. We discuss the disproportionately high number of deaf teachers in Kenya, and adaptive pedagogical methods used to assist their continuing education. We think hand clapping may be useful to cue transitions and develop different patterns of six *"mini rhythms"* that can be used like Morse code to wordlessly lead classes.

Our walk concludes. She says, *"You're ready to lead the program, but change your haircut so you'll be more easily accessible and approachable to participants."* I feel inspired.] //

✲✲

Min. = ♣- THE HILLBILLY: #0642
LEVEL: #0803, #0815, #0820
INSPIRED: #1021, #1092, #1146
CODE: #0804, #0845, #0856, #0976
THE SHARED HEART: #0499

✲✲

#0486 - January 22, 2019 @ 14:30 (San Francisco, California)

[0486.1 / 1188] [I enter my art studio to find THE PILOT looking at various works in progress. He takes a 36" square blank canvas off the wall and sets it in the middle of the room. He squirts orange fluid acrylic paint on to the center of the canvas, then uses a paint knife to spread it. His choice of tool confuses me. A quarter sized circle in the middle of the canvas remains white and unsullied. I become incensed.

"My privacy has been violated!" I yell at him with increasing agitation. He keeps doing what he's doing, and pays me no attention. Another man enters and asks me very specific questions to which I don't have answers. I become so frustrated with the situation I throw both of them out of the art space. I immediately feel paranoid. *"I'm being watched."*] //

✲✲

Maj. = 6- THE PILOT: #0492
BLANK: #0811, #0876, #0891, #0936
CANVAS: #0979, #1072, #1087, #1128

✲✲

#0487 - January 23, 2019 @ 01:23 (San Francisco, California)

[0487.1 / 1189] [I visit with THE POSTMASTER and THE FARMHAND, both out of body. Both in their 80's, they live in a *"spiritual assisted living"* community. They discuss how long they think they'll *"make it."*

"Perhaps the 90's? Maybe to 100?"
"Mercy, that's a long time to be alive," THE FARMHAND says.
Within the complex are a series of futuristic therapy pools, with spa-jets that create marvelous amounts of bubbles and fizz. I want to play and splash in the pools, but it appears there isn't time for that. This is likely our last visit. I'm told to finish eating. An overt flavor of cilantro seems out of place as I finish a half slice of cinnamon toast topped with sliced strawberries.

I have to go to the bathroom just as we're about to depart. THE FARMHAND takes me back to her room where a portable commode is placed at the foot of the bed. I kneel down to pee while still talking to her. She remains in front of me, watching, rendering me mildly embarrassed. I finish and zip up my pants. On the way out with THE WEAVER and THE CARPENTER I notice a piece of art on the kitchen wall made of shiny copper. As I get closer, I notice it's made of melted pennies. I stare at it while THE POSTMASTER tells the tale of how he came to own it.] //

⁂

Maj. = 0- *THE WEAVER: #0513,* 1- *THE CARPENTER: #0488*
Min. = ♣- *THE POSTMASTER: #0556,* ♥- *THE FARMHAND: #0556*
STRAWBERRIES: #0801, #0807
ZIP: #0865, #1016, #1086
EMBARRASS: #0957, #1137

⁂

#0488 - January 23, 2019 @ 04:00 (San Francisco, California)

[0488.1 / 1190] [I'm in a two-story house. I walk up a dark stairwell towards a lit area at the top where I find THE CARPENTER and THE CHILD playing on a trampoline. They both laugh and enjoy each other's company. THE DANCER and THE ATHEIST shine a flashlight at me when I ask them where to find the bathroom. Once there, I notice the toilet is just a small a hole in the shower floor. I shower while simultaneously peeing and pooping. Though odd, it seems cleansing and efficient.] //

⁂

Maj. = 1- *THE CARPENTER: #0489,* 2- *THE DANCER: #0494,*
3- *THE CHILD: #0544,* 8- *THE ATHEIST: #0561*
ODD: #0801, #0815, #0840
HOLE: #0841, #1026, #1139

⁂

#0489 - January 23, 2019 @ 04:40 (San Francisco, California)

[0489.1 / 1191] [I watch an advertisement for a children's game. Kids in an oversized dollhouse don *"cookie and donut"* costumes sewn in felt. The music is dissonant and increasingly cacophonous. A giant hand reaches in, grabs one of the "cookie-kids" and splits the child in half. The half of a cookie with legs and an ooey gooey center remains. Though gruesome and terrifying, the mood remains playful. I flip to another channel and watch ads for Levi's jeans.]

. . .

[0489.2 / 1192] [I walk through an alley passing service entrances to various restaurants and clubs. I walk by a young woman who's on the verge of passing out. I stop to check on her, slapping her on the cheek to rouse her. I offer her some water and a crust of bread.

"Why would you do that?" THE CARPENTER asks.

*"**Because right now I'm serving her,**"* I respond without thinking.]

[0489.3 / 1193] [I turn to face a gravel parking lot and find myself teaching a yoga class to a large group. We don't use mats. THE PSYCHIATRIST is my playful counterpart. We tag team teach. Mid-class the crowd divides in half. One group lines up against a wall like the receiving line at a wedding. A cage opens. Released doves fly up toward the sky. The birds ascend and swirl about and around THE PASSIONATE BRAZILIAN (*inviting, curious, and quiet*) who rhythmically spins and twirls on a set of gymnastic rings without a shirt.

*"**That's my hot friend,**"* I say to the group as he twirls aerially above us. The room becomes brighter and brighter until I wake up. //

⁂

Maj. = *1- THE CARPENTER: #0495*
Min. = ♠- *THE PSYCHIATRIST: #0532*
HALF: #1115, #1157, #1158
COUNTERPART: #0871, #0926, #1109
RECEPTION: #0855, #0905, #0959, #1183, #1197
THE PASSIONATE BRAZILIAN: #0725
⁂

#0490 - January 24, 2019 @ 06:26 (San Francisco, California)

[0490.1 / 1194] [This feels like a nuanced and detailed STEPHEN KING miniseries that would likely fill this entire book if I could recall everything. One segment involves me (*as a man*) running from a large monster that chases me through a castle. The second (*as a woman*) finds me running away from a toxic relationship with another man and woman. The third, a train scene. The fourth, life in and out of a stressful household so real I wake up believing I'm still in it. Very unsettling and exhausting.] //

⁂

KING: #0874, #0925
MONSTER: #1041, #1072
TOXIC: #0989

⁂

#0491 - January 25, 2019 @ 04:56 (San Francisco, California)

[0491.1 / 1195] [I have sex with THE RAINMAN (*musical, appreciative, and intelligent*). I press down on his shoulders with my forearms as I orgasm strongly.]
[0491.2 / 1196] [I zoom in on an S _____ C_____.]
[0491.3 / 1197] [I teach a class in Silicon Valley.] //

⁂

ZOOM: #0970, #0985, #1099, #1193
DOWN: #0805, #0810, #0814, #0815
PRESS: #0823, #0850, #0970, #1076

⁂

#0492 - January 25, 2019 @ 07:10 (San Francisco, California)

[0492.1 / 1198] [I'm at a party. Handbags and accessories are distributed as gifts. THE KIND HEART and THE PILOT are both drunk and attempt to have a conversation seated on the floor with their backs against the wall. They laugh at each other. Their speech is slurred. Neither can understand the other. I write a thank you card and hand it to the host as I leave.] //

⁂

Maj. = 6- THE PILOT: #0571, 21- THE KIND HEART: #0655
HOST: #0813, #0831, #1035
FLOOR: #0803, #0807, #0809, #0819

⁂

#0493 - January 26, 2019 @ 05:56 (San Francisco, California)

[0493.1 / 1199] [I'm a prison steward. I calmly move from cell block to cell block tending to my tasks as assigned. I need to buy a belt. My pants are loose at the waist. I take an escalator down to the basement then sift and sort through a variety of luxury branded retail (*YSL*, *LV*, *etc.*). I look for the *"right one"* and don't find it. I ascend the escalator. When I get to the top, I encounter a woman who gives a tarot reading to a client named "Amber," myself and another man. At the conclusion of the reading, she declares: *"On the 16th, our lights will shine, but the light of the world will dim."*

I look at a painting on the prison wall. I see an image of a human being with a spinning galaxy spilling light from each of the major energy centers. I notice *"subordinate chakras," "mini-chakras,"* and bigger *"macro-chakras."* Dark space behind the middle of them *"shines"* through.

"Amber" is a steward of the prison as well. She changes her clothes repeatedly, while I sit in conversation through a wall with a different person. She chooses a white polo shirt and jeans. I comment her selected look is *"so plain in comparison to the other styles,"* she modeled. She walks towards "Ward E" of the prison and speaks without pause: *"It's really challenging when they interact with you on one side, and you're on your own side... (because Andre keeps sending me those notes telling me he feels like he's looking directly into my soul and I had to tell him 'I hate to break it to you honey you weren't') ...but we have to give 'em a little bit of hope, right?"*] //

⁂

TAROT: #0813
CONVERSATION: #0819, #0820, #0824, #0826
CELL: #0862, #1139

⁂

#0494 - January 27, 2019 @ 05:13 (San Francisco, California)

[0494.1 / 1200] [THE NURSE leads a team who prepares for the grand opening of a new community gathering area. She spends time contemplating the best way to set up a new office at the back. Each item of furniture is selected and placed with intention.]

[0494.2 / 1201] [THE GAMER (*slutty, humorous, and crass*) stands next to a cobblestone wall, wearing a jockstrap. The stone wall is cold. It's cloudy overhead. We flirt. We giggle. I want to fuck him. His hair is longer than I remember. I grab him from behind and press my dick against his bare ass.]

[0494.3 / 1202] [THE DANCER and I look for keys behind a bed. We find a mouse. We discover a trail of thick strangely weighted and unusually heavy plastic pennies that lead us out onto the front lawn. Plastic hamburgers rain down from the sky onto the roof of the house. They slide to the edge and cascade down to a series of bushes below. I gather the plastic burgers in piles and throw them at THE DANCER.]

[0494.4 / 1203] [I get a haircut. The person giving me the haircut works for a large multinational firm. They pepper me with odd comments. *"It's $2.75 to take off your sweatshirt."* I refuse to pay and simply say, *"No, we're just not gonna do that."* I'm handed a menu of odd assessments and charges printed on a vertical half sheet of letterhead.]

· · ·

355

[0494.5 / 1204] [A giant aged hand paints a sign for "LUNDELL FARMS" on the exterior wall of a barn that faces the road.]

[0494.6 / 1205] [I descend a large stone staircase into a subway station. I'm the only one there. The track is lined by opaque glass plates.] //

⁎⁎

Maj. = *2- THE DANCER: #0538, 13- THE NURSE: #0561*
COLD: #0876, #0898, #0909, #0929, #0943
OPAQUE: #1087, #1143

⁎⁎

#0495 - January 28, 2019 @ 03:43 (San Francisco, California)

[0495.1 / 1206] [I encounter a voluptuous embodiment of THE ROLLERGIRL (*methodical, scrappy, and robust*). She has curvy buttocks and large breasts. Her fully exposed left breast hangs out of a corset as she casually talks to me. A large muscular man named "Brent" enters and quickly sweeps her up onto his shoulder. He carries her up an escalator and out of sight. I hear them have joyful sex. I'm mildly confused because I thought THE ROLLERGIRL was lesbian.]

[0495.2 / 1207] [I consider buying an Armani bow tie. The clear box packaging has a masking tape X across the front.]

[0495.3 / 1208] [THE BADASS (*sure footed, raspy voiced, and powerful*) enters with authority. She joins a group that gathers at the base of an escalator. Someone runs down the escalator to express concern about a certain type of smoke they smell. THE BADASS chimes in,
"Don't worry about it. If THE CARPENTER finds them it's just a big punishment. He probably found them doing something they shouldn't. He'll just force them to do a lot more of it."
Apparently, THE CARPENTER was a heavy smoker and has a lot of addictions. He refuses to transfer said addictions to his children.]

[0495.4 / 1209] [I'm part of a crew. We help bands move on and off stage. I'm a career road-ie. I never know who I'm supporting until just hours before performances occur at large festivals. My current assignment is to support a second stage headliner. The lineup is presented in reverse order on a small tablet with a three-column interface. I've been selected to roadie for STS9 for their next tour.] //

⁎⁎

Maj. = *1- THE CARPENTER: #0513*
ESCALATOR: #0809, #0844, #0865, #0897, #1000
BREAST: #0900
SMOKE: #0868, #0885, #0897, #0998
LESBIAN: #1060, #1166

356

THE BADASS: #0933
⁎⁎

#0496 - January 29, 2019 @ 07:45 (San Francisco, California)

[0496.1 / 1210] [I pass a young male/female couple on a city sidewalk at night. Their connection is intense and brooding. The female is blonde. She's dressed like a flapper. Her face is covered in black and white grease paint. She looks like an evil clown. When they pass in the opposite direction, she attempts to provoke me by nudging me hard in the front left shoulder. They both turn around, follow, and taunt me. They bark threats and harmful intentions.

"I'm going to stab you, Motherfucker."

"Yeah, and I'm going to cut your heart out and carve it up!"

I just keep walking, knowing they're still behind me. I enter a building and attend a socialite's dinner on the top floor. I catch a glimpse of myself in a gallery mirror. I now have the same greasepaint mask as worn by the threatening young woman.

I descend a back staircase, spinning quickly down past a series of floors. On the ground floor, I pass a round white linen table in a corner of the room near the staircase. The young man and woman sit down to enjoy a meal, dressed impeccably and sans makeup. I lean in to apologize to them for running away. They publicly humiliate me by rising from the table, derisively laughing, and pointing. The woman shares she's a psychiatrist/psychotherapist. In a moment of pity, she flings her business card at me saying,

"Oh honey, I'll work with tragic little you."

I book an appointment with her.]

[0496.2 / 1211] [I sit in my apartment holding a cell phone, debating whether or not to call GRANDMA. I get the sense she's going to pass away soon. This makes me feel incredibly sad. I want to call her to say goodbye, but I freeze and keep staring at the phone. The family surrounds me in debate. Some believe her pending death will model the way for the rest of us. Others believe that she is doing it to hurt "HRR."

Another opinion is, *"She's doing this for the best of us."*

I sit with my phone in hand while debate continues between family members.] //

⁎⁎
Maj. = 11 - GRANDMA: #0557
EVIL: #0909
TRAGIC: #1133
MAKE UP: #0807, #1025
⁎⁎

#0497 - January 29, 2019 @ 14:15 (San Francisco, California)

[0497.1 / 1212] [I flirt with a tall slender Asian man in his 20's. He sits in a high back upholstered chair in the lobby of a hotel. I'm inordinately tall and reach over the top of the chair to unbutton his polo shirt. We start making out. My body arcs over the top of the chair, while my feet remain on the floor. His ethnicity and gender change. The kissing continues. When we pause, he's taken the form of a White woman with curly shoulder length hair. We

never fully disrobe, yet I still find it to be a deeply gratifying and satisfying sexual experience. The interaction concludes. Before she pedals away on a bicycle I ask with a simple, honest grin,
   "That was really great! I appreciate it. How was it for you?"
She scrunches her face and winces.
   "Oh. I see. You didn't like it."
She nods her head in agreement.
   "Your expression is strong and pure. Thank you for letting me take what I needed to tune up to your frequency."] //

✽✽
POLO: #0889, #1062
CURLY: #0909, #0959, #1163
DISROBE: #0878, #0910, #0968
✽✽

#0498 - January 30, 2019 @ 05:50 (San Francisco, California)

[0498.1 / 1213] [I sit on a kitchen countertop flirting with a guy. I'm distracted by a television that screens old episodes of a comedy review. A young, buxom, and toothy BETTE MIDLER makes her debut. She wears a red blouse with white polka dots and a pair of clam digger jeans. The crowd roars with laughter. Tonight's her springboard to stardom.]

[0498.2 / 1214] [I'm struck by a wildly fast-moving series of images and impressions. I fly through different cities, houses, and public spaces across different timelines and realms. I cross multiple other dimensions with attributes I'm not fully able to grasp, nor understand. The collective mind works with a mantra in thousands of dialects: *"Make an impact in the moment in right action. Intend Act Integrate."*
Static. Popping noises. Droning tones. All carry and communicate the same mantra.]

[0498.3 / 1215] [I sit on the floor of a room in front of a row of four women. One of them is THE CONVERT, another is THE ASH (*healing, expressive, and calm*). The other two women are not recognizable. The walls of the room are large and made of gold. A senior teacher stewards a humility practice between me and the women. We complete the exercise. I exit the room.]

[0498.4 / 1216] [I stare at a charity's information kiosk which promotes a fundraising opportunity to: **"Sell and distribute sacred 'perks!'"** *"Perks"* are circular pewter medallions strung on lengths of thick gauge steel. *"Perks"* are shrink wrapped in plastic, in groups of eight. Suggested retail for an individual *"perk"* is $40. A box of eight retails for $320. I buy two boxes, assuming I'll pay for them as I make individual sales. I'm instantly billed $640 and now carry a debt. One of the medallions in the first box is bent and disfigured. I debate whether or not to put it back on the table and take another.
   Meanwhile, a young Native American woman with a plume of purple hair enters identi-

358

fying herself as the "Daughter of the Chief." She draws attention and reverence from others who encircle her.] //

✲✲

BETTE MIDLER: #1028
DEBT: #0842, #0968, #1122
INDIVIDUAL: #0850, #0878, #0951, #0963
THE CONVERT: #0815

✲✲

#0499 - January 30, 2019 @ 08:16 (San Francisco, California)

[0499.1 / 1217] [I stand outside a large community forum at night. A group of people gather for a conference keynote. I stand in a backstage hallway with BARON BAPTISTE and two others who fit him and me with head mics. The session commences and BARON begins addressing the group from backstage. I listen to him comment on a particular portion of the prior session breakout discussion content (*in which I'm also enrolled*).
"*The point is* ambiguity. *How do you behave when things are unclear?*"
I place both of my hands on the center of my chest. "*Do you still show up?*" He asks. I allow a couple of moments for the words to land in my body before responding, "*Always.*" My word rattles around in my heart and settles. I lean in to hug him. He whispers in my right ear, "*I wouldn't do that in front of the big group. I need you to know this is about people who are deeply committed to their communities. In some cases, they are so indebted they actually miss "the yoga" and aren't participating in their own recovery.*"
As we move apart BARON becomes THE SHARED HEART. She winks at me and then walks into the room to start the next session.] //

✲✲

BARON BAPTISTE: #0551
WHISPERS: #0812, #0844, #0852, #0859, #0886, #0889, #0907, #0922
RECOVERY: #1055, #1135
THE SHARED HEART: #0611

✲✲

#0500 - January 31, 2019 @ 04:00 (San Francisco, California)

[0500.1 / 1218] [I'm downtown in a park, walking towards a party. Something intense has occurred inside the house (*my intended destination*). I'm not sure what, and enter, noting suspicion hangs heavy in the air. A guy who has profound acne all over his body wants to "*commiserate*" with me. He persuades me to disrobe and enter a bathtub with him as negotiations continue. He looks me intensely in the eyes as I lather up my hands. I offer to wash his back. He finds this sexually arousing. I'm disgusted when he turns around and reveals a back of hairy, pus laden pimples. The gourd-like bumps feel like oversized braille, as I draw small circles from the top to the bottom of his back with soap.]

[0500.2 / 1219] [People are fitted for rings and other jewelry at a trade show.]

· · ·

359

[0500.3 / 1220] [I know to take a particular route home from a party, but go off route by one block and find myself in a dark and brooding alley with dilapidated buildings.

Shattered glass everywhere.

I turn around and return to my point of origin.

I choose a different street and encounter a homeless woman who says, *"I'll see you later."* I pass a couple of others who ask for help, but I quickly bypass them. A friend wants to join me for a walk. I decide he's not trustworthy and ask him to continue on his way. A man in a penthouse looks down at me on the street. He holds important information related to an espionage case I would find useful, but it's best if I avoid him.]

[0500.4 / 1221] [A group of us gather around a collapsible six-foot table. Aluminum foil trays hold large portions of shredded roast beef in au jus. Sandwiches on sourdough bread are made for us by pairs of floating hands. Perhaps I'm at an outdoor Red Cross relief station. The meat on my bread is still covered with protective plastic film, yet I accept the sandwich I'm served. I feel my teeth cut through the plastic as I eat. I don't mention the plastic to anyone. A woman stands nearby. We discuss flying Tomahawk Helicopters. We're both pilots. I'm there to sharpen my combat flying skills. Other participants wear beautiful *"techno jewelry"* that tracks their every move.] //

✲✲

JEWELRY: #0903, #0923, #1066
ACCEPT: #0805, #0883, #0917, #0948, #0950
RED CROSS: #1133

✲✲

#0501   February 1, 2019 @ 03:57 (San Francisco, California)

[0501.1 / 1222] [A young family shops at an antique store. Among a pile of stacked furniture, the mother finds a hand knitted oven mitt with the word "IOWA" cross stitched along one side. The mitt is shaped like the state of Iowa. She contemplates stealing it. It reminds her of home.]

[0501.2 / 1223] [UNCLE FRED WAHPEHPAH appears in front of me in a log cabin and smiles.]

[0501.3 / 1224] [In a dystopian, post-apocalyptic reality a series of helicopters lift giant semi-trucks off the ground and tow them up into the sky until they disappear.] //

✲✲

IOWA: #1043, #1066, #1155
CABIN: #0826, #0889, #1116, #1121, #1138, #1172
DYSTOPIA: #0845

✲✲

#0502 - February 2, 2019 @ 02:40 (San Francisco, California)

[0502.1 / 1225] [It's night time. A team gathers for a final meeting before their company grand opening. Oddly, THE FIDUCIARY attends. He's not on the staff. I bypass him looking for THE OWNER *(creative, connected, and abundant)*. Some spaces inside the building still need deep cleaning. The bathrooms are out of sorts. Toilets are covered in shit. A dress rehearsal of the showroom *"big reveal"* involves opening two large wooden vault doors. The doors fall off their hinges and collapse inward, revealing a long, empty, and pristine hall. The paint is crisp and freshly dry. Fans circulate air to minimize fumes.] //

✵
Maj. = 9- THE FIDUCIARY: #0550
PRISTINE: #0919, #0998, #0999, #1099
CRISP: #0811, #1001, #1028
THE OWNER: #0534
✵

#0503 - February 2, 2019 @ 04:51 (San Francisco, California)

[0503.1 / 1226] [I walk through the aisles of a hardware store looking for a broad range of household items. I'm repeatedly acknowledged by the staff.
"Thanks for being in 'the work.'"
"Thank you for remaining available."
"We appreciate your engagement."
I ponder whether or not I'm a celebrity. If I was, it would be a gross distraction from what I'm here to do. I stay with this question as I purposefully move down each aisle, one breath per step.] //

✵
HARDWARE: #0935, #1183
QUESTION: #0868, #0962, #0972, #0987, #1077
AISLE: #0961, #1019, #1187
✵

#0504 - February 3, 2019 @ 04:18 (San Francisco, California)

[0504.1 / 1227] [I get dressed in reverse order. I pull my flannel pajamas over my gym shoes. It seems normal and mundane, so much so I almost forget it's a dream. I wear my underwear, t-shirt and socks all on the outside of my suit.] //

✵
REVERSE: #0855, #0905, #0925, #0931, #1044
NORMAL: #0836, #0889, #0934, #1120, #1194
✵

#0505 - February 3, 2019 @ 05:28 (San Francisco, California)

[0505.1 / 1228] [A film trailer narrator reads behind me during an active scene in a corporate office tower: *"As a new global executive with expansive reach and power, he was advised by his leadership team to find a partner who had a decidedly non-strategic role. Perhaps a day laborer. Something basic, necessary, productive and contrary to his principal modality. He must do this...for the purpose of play."*] //

⁑

NARRATOR: #0983
CONTRARY: #0840, #1163
PLAY: #0817, #0824, #0825, #0830, #0847

⁑

#0506 - February 5, 2019 @ 03:50 (The Presidio of San Francisco, California)

[0506.1 / 1229] [I'm in an area that reconfigures from an airport, to a train station, to a private residence. A group of powerful women work behind the scenes in operations roles to troubleshoot challenges with an application interface. Typed characters seem to systematically drop from strings of text and leave blank spaces on screen.

I perform a user acceptance test and squint through one eye as I bite my tongue. The screen looks like a digital version of the game *"Hangman"* (or a puzzle on *Wheel of Fortune*). I'm moderately frustrated. I'm not able to read, nor understand the output. Amidst my working, the women want to establish a new name for their team. They decide to discuss it further after their weekly post-work meditation gathering.

[0506.2 / 1230] [Back in the airport I encounter THE ROMANTIC who quickly darts in and out of the scene. At the train station he passes me and smiles as he departs on a train, intending to stop at the next station to meet someone for a date. We share an unspoken, but acknowledged attraction.]

[0506.3 / 1231] [In a private residence it appears THE ROMANTIC and I are roommates. THE ROMANTIC removes his shirt exposing his overbuilt torso. He uses an asthma inhaler. His attention quickly turns to a young man who waits for him on a dock that extends out into a vast moonlit lake. He sprints out of the house and towards the dock. I find myself removing a t-shirt, and another, *then another*. *"I must be wearing at least 15 layers."* I feel like a magician pulling a strand of handkerchiefs from my sleeve. My bare skin is never revealed.

I see THE ROMANTIC magnetically connect face-to-face with the guy on the dock. They tackle each other and enjoy a rowdy and sweaty sexual encounter under the moon. They quickly part ways, disinterested in each other once they both get off.] //

⁑

Maj. = 15- THE ROMANTIC: #0628
WHEEL: #0871, #0876, #0880, #0907, #0945
TACKLE: #0880

⁑

#0507 - February 6, 2019 @ 02:04 (San Francisco, California)

[0507.1 / 1232] [I sit leg over leg with a man, performing a healing rite. *This is normal. I've*

had to give up hundreds of thousands of sankalpas on my path to wholeness. Just keep doing it."]
//

⁎⁎

UP: #1081, #1082, #1083, #1087
PERFORMING: #0917, #0986, #1066, #1080
THOUSANDS: #0944, #0982, #1002, #1004, #1062

⁎⁎

#0508 - February 6, 2019 @ 06:17 (San Francisco, California)

[0508.1 / 1233] [*"I'm late! I don't belong here!"* I'm on my way to training and not certain I've packed everything I need. I'm greeted by a number of people including someone who offers to give me a ride. A frenetic group has gathered inside a large log cabin. Things move so quickly at times it becomes blurry. I pass two women who laser-etch figurines into mirrors. The shapes are crude. The glass cracks. Little shards scatter across the table top. The group agrees to *"not be late."* I become distracted. I blink and find myself in an empty garage, holding my bags and wondering where everyone went. LESLIE KNOPE from Parks and Recreation makes a cameo and tries to give me some advice. I walk out onto a rolling green hillside and see three large groups gathered. A man gives his opening remarks as motocross riders with abnormally thick tires on their bikes flip and somersault overhead. *"I'm late. No one wants me on their team. I've failed."*] //

⁎⁎

RECREATION: #0937, #1114
ROLLING: #0848, #0865, #0872
OPENING: #0857, #0866, #0867, #0879

⁎⁎

#0509 - February 7, 2019 @ 03:22 (Scotts Valley, California)

[0509.1 / 1234] [*"I use my body to author my own story."* - Mantra repeated by a group in a large lecture hall.] //

⁎⁎

AUTHOR: #0969
STORY: #0801, #0875, #0888, #0890
LECTURE: #1038, #1050, #1097, #1130, #1194

⁎⁎

#0510 - February 7, 2019 @ 05:26 (Scotts Valley, California)

[0510.1 / 1235] [THE MAGICIAN and I sit across from each other sharing conversation when I notice I've lost a ring I've worn on my left hand for lifetimes. I lean toward him and whisper, *"This is inspired."* THE MAGICIAN pushes his chair back and leaps repeatedly into the air, joyfully performing toe touch straddle jumps. A woman wearing green exits a cabana. I see her bald husband through a large picture window. *"She married our daughter,"* she says with affirmation as she points to someone behind me. I look down, find my ring on the side-walk, and put it back on my hand.] //

⁎⁎

Maj. = 14 THE MAGICIAN: #0532
RING: #0878, #0916, #0923, #1086
GREEN: #0842, #0850, #0856, #0899

⁎⁎

#0511 - February 8, 2019 @ 02:25 (Scotts Valley, California)

[0511.1 / 1236] [I'm stuck in a repeated hologram where I access and escape from a grand estate with a wrought iron fence.

THE FIRST TRIP: I'm a servant for a family. Their coat of arms is checkered with black and white. I escape and run down a back alley.

THE SECOND TRIP: The stakes become mortal. I could die if I'm caught. I take a similar exit path and find myself cornered by flash bulbs and a large press corp.

THE THIRD TRIP: I experience relief. Only some of the people in the manor want me dead. The servantry asks me to stay with them.

THE FOURTH TRIP: I find myself distributing gifts beautifully wrapped in pistachio green paper. I hand a gift to a teenage girl wearing a pink ball gown. She smiles at me, and I realize all have gathered there for a *"D_____RK."* The threat level subsides.

THE FIFTH TRIP: I understand I'm in a simulation. I easily bound up and over what was previously an incarcerating iron fence. I repeatedly jump over, land on the ground, and run through slushy snow in a dark alley.
"...I'm in training."] //

⁎⁎

WROUGHT IRON: #0922, #1154, #1173
FLASH: #0825, #0874
COAT OF: #0813

⁎⁎

#0512 - February 12, 2019 @ 06:50 (San Francisco, California)

[0512.1 / 1237] [I take a rideshare at night. THE KOKORO (*scholarly, uplifting, and exploratory*) drives. She doesn't trust my directions and alters the route. This frustrates me. I urge her to pull the car over and let me out. I exit the car, as does she. She runs around the

364

front of the vehicle intending to strike me. We become adversaries. I grab her firmly by the hair and move her out of my way, though I instantly feel bad when I do this. I've applied *"unnecessary and abusive force."*]

[0512.2 / 1238] [I find myself in a large inn-like residence in Napa, California set within a beautiful fruited vineyard bathed in soft gold light where an executive offsite meeting is underway. Those in attendance are expected to stay onsite multiple weeks to accomplish a lengthy list of strategic objectives, while *"leveraging the surrounding natural environment to their energetic advantage."*]

[0512.3 / 1239] [A cop car sits on the right-hand side of a banked downhill curve on a mountain highway. I point the vehicle out to the driver of my car who has ample time to respond by slowing and drifting to the left.]

[0512.4 / 1240] [Everyone is supplied rolls of ticker tape on which the Grand Staff is printed. Musical notation manifests on the ticker tape in patterns of blue, yellow, and red dots. When tossed upward, the air plays the piece as the tape drops to the street.] //

⁎⁎

TICKER TAPE: #0945
WEEKS: #0874, #0912, #0952, #1058, #1133, #1147
CURVE: #0900, #1099

⁎⁎

#0513 - February 12, 2019 @ 08:49 (San Francisco, California)

[0513.1 / 1241] [I buy thick chocolate pretzels from a shop at the top of the hill. Post purchase, I take a long walk back to the car to meet THE WEAVER and THE CARPENTER. They forgot I made the trip to buy the pretzels, and hand me their empty shopping bag to make a return trip. I walk back up the hill to the shop. This time I purchase dark chocolate and sea salt toffee squares and a box of *"brownie muffins."*]

[0513.2 / 1242] [I'm in my home kitchen. I'm quickly alerted to a police presence who will soon break through the butler door. In the midst of this, I scatter brownies across a butcher block countertop and dice them into *"fours"* or *"quarters."* Among the different varieties are, Chocolate Chocolate Chip, Chocolate Chip, and another peculiar one I can't pronounce. I expeditiously toss used cupcake papers in a nearby garbage can.

Two pieces of art composed of gift-wrapping paper and fabric are prominently displayed on a nearby wall. Both are my creations. I take them off the wall, remove their frames, and then hurriedly roll the canvases up together *(which distorts and crumples the crisp gift wrap)* before loading them into a brown cardboard shipping tube. Their partial destruction becomes the prevailing *(and unintended)* quality of this period's artistic output where thematically all pieces are: **"Mangled." "Rolled." "Restored."**] //

JOSHUA D. LUNDELL

⁕

Maj. = 0- THE WEAVER: #0523, 1-THE CARPENTER: #0520
SALT: #0845, #0879
GIFT: #0885, #1001, #1075
DISPLAY: #0803, #0875, #0891, #0898

⁕

#0514 - February 13, 2019 @ 03:53 (San Francisco, California)

[0514.1 / 1243] [I'm on the set of a television show. I've said something that will be used to characterize me as the "**black sheep**" of the program. I spend the rest of the time attempting to repair/remove that single sound bite.]

[0514.2 / 1244] [I deliver a giant paper tree to THE JESTER's front yard. We stand up a giant ruler on end that extends beyond the top of the tree to take a measurement. Some pieces of paper detach and float airily to the ground. Something's unclear. Can I leave? I'm asked to *"perform toe touch straddle jumps as a distraction."* THE SOCCER COACH (*observant, tactile, and quiet*) demonstrates and continues when we're asked to repeat the motion 1,000,000 times.]

[0514.3 / 1245] [Someone paints and needs *"thicker varnish."* I'm asked to go to a supply shop to buy some pitch. I feel suspiciously surveilled as I complete the task. Much more occurs here and quickly fades.]

[0514.4 / 1246] [*"But that's just sort of 'the jam.'"* I need to exchange something at a dinner table, for something less valuable than I would happily trade *"them"* for.]

[0514.5 / 1247] [I've filled out the answers to a test. A voice from an overhead speaker provides the answers, and what proportion of *"us"* get the answers right. It feels like *"Big Brother's House."*]

[0514.6 / 1248] [A husband and wife live in an opulent modern palace where multiple realities converge. I'm left feeling overwhelmed and exasperated as the walls cave in and wake me up.]
//

⁕

Min. = ◆- THE JESTER: #0560
HUSBAND AND WIFE: #0878, #1190
BROTHER: #0895, #0914, #0949, #0964, #1018

⁕

#0515 - February 13, 2019 @ 09:48 (San Francisco, California)

[0515.1 / 1249] [MICHAEL JACKSON performs duets on stage in a woodland amphitheater with his wife, at the conclusion of a morning television program broadcast. A conductor plays a series of unique alien keyboards and synthesizers that float and glow. A house musician in the ensemble actually leads the group from the left-hand side of the stage. I feel sad. Though I watch the performance from a seat in the audience, I know that MICHAEL has died. He's not really there. A doctored version of the film with him superimposed on stage with the band will be later presented on television.] //

⁎⁎

MICHAEL JACKSON: #1085
GLOW: #0831, #0937, #1080, #1087
AUDIENCE: #0824, #0853

⁎⁎

#0516 - February 13, 2019 @ 10:51 (San Francisco, California)

[0516.1 / 1250] [I'm in a haunted house in a repeating scene. The house is dirty on the inside and keeps getting dirtier. Numerous "plastic cats" and other inanimate objects randomly show up in ways that distract those who occupy the home. Small children wear soiled clothes and play on a squalid floor. A fruit bowl milled from a tree stump holds bundles of dried white sage crammed up and under its entire exterior rim. A blond woman squats in front of a laptop in the kitchen. *"This house is, 'possessed.'"*] //

⁎⁎

DIRTY: #0904, #1052, #1131
REPEATED: #0849, #0923, #1152
LAPTOP: #0962, #0980, #0990, #1035

⁎⁎

#0517 - February 15, 2019 @ 06:00 (San Francisco, California)

[0517.1 / 1251] [I'm in highly specialized training. I'm infused with informatic detail that passes through me like water vapor. I immediately let it go.] //

⁎⁎

WATER: #0822, #0841, #0862
VAPOR: #0900, #1064
DETAIL: #0814, #0833, #0851, #0930

⁎⁎

#0518 - February 16, 2019 @ 04:07 (San Francisco, California)

[0518.1 / 1252] [*NIGHTMARE! * - I'm at THE OB/GYN's (*conservative, particular, and opinionated*) house at night. Huge stockpiles of food have been prepared for a party. "Open Gym" is hosted in an adjacent salon. While I perform an L-Sit on the parallel bars a woman aggressively grabs my broken left foot. I fall from the apparatus when she touches me and land hard on the ground below. I decide she's a good coach and a marvelous teacher, though her methods are unorthodox. "Open Gym" concludes when a group of 10 women advise me that, *"'Brad' wanted it this way."*]

. . .

[0518.2 / 1253] [A game begins. People disappear one at a time, children first. People attempt to manipulate the game by running unit tests on code they've written. A giant Black man appears and exposes his anus. I inspect hologram tables covered with food. Ham has been minced and formed into the shape of a vertically split pineapple. THE CONNECTOR and I take turns chewing large bites from the odd SPAM-like form of meat. A woman breaks free of the game, declares herself a *"twin,"* and proceeds to knock over multiple 50-gallon drums of human blood to convince other people she's *"murdered someone."*]

[0518.3 / 1254] [I cross a street in front of a cop car while carrying bags of groceries. I hurry to get out of the street as quickly as possible.]

[0518.4 / 1255] [A woman at a buffet smiles and delightedly exclaims, *"YOU GIVE ME GOOD ENERGY!"*] //

✲✲
Maj. = 4- THE CONNECTOR: #0526
NIGHTMARE: #0929, #1047
50: #1069, #1198
FORM: # 0819, #0887, #0919, #0934, #1000, #1011, #1076
✲✲

#0519 - February 16, 2019 @ 08:30 (San Francisco, California)

[0519.1 / 1256] [I mourn the death of a friendship. The grief period ends. A stereo plays morose music at low volume in the dark, even after I've turned it off.]

[0519.2 / 1257] [I'm an operations job at Bank of America. *"This is a nightmare,"* I mutter under my breath on a loop while sitting at a desk.] //

✲✲
MOURN: #1033
LOW VOLUME: #1066, #1130
DARK: #0970, #0972, #0976, #0995, #1017, #1020, #1024
✲✲

#0520 - February 17, 2019 @ 03:09 (San Francisco, California)

[0520.1 / 1258] [Waves crest overhead and will imminently crash onto a beach. They freeze in frighteningly gorgeous patterns when hit with a burst of super chilled air. They'll later thaw and be reabsorbed by the ocean. The waters roll in, freeze instantly, and dangle precariously overhead like lethal icy stalactite daggers.]

. . .

[0520.2 / 1259] [I work to pass cooperative legislation between the states of Hawaii and Pennsylvania. The occasion becomes festive when large celebratory banners are hung in front of a municipal building. No one comes to vote at the session. I pass out multiple copies of my document to the press junket, printed on delicate tissue paper.]

[0520.3 / 1260] ["*BOLD FELICIDADES!*" A crowd shouts at THE RAPTOR to celebrate his technical achievement on the set of a feature film. A special effect was successfully rigged to the high heel of an actor's shoe. The small magnesium mortar explodes during a one-time take where the actor kicks her leg overhead like a can-can dancer. The frame is captured perfectly and will save the producers thousands of dollars in post-production expense.]

[0520.4 / 1261] [I play in a band with THE SPECK (*artful, longing, and committed*). We loosely jam on the track, "OPIATE" by TOOL through small amplifiers attached to our belts while seeking out a rehearsal space. We encounter THE CARPENTER wearing a luchador mask. He claims, "*it will help conceal his identity.*" The only rehearsal spaces we find are industrial refrigerators full of butchered meat hanging from large "S" hooks. Sausages, hamburgers, steaks, float in neatly vacuum sealed pouches in coffin shaped coolers full of blood. Futons placed around the perimeter aim to make the horrid space inviting. We don't rent the room because it lacks sufficient electrical outlets for our band equipment.] //

⁎⁎

Maj. = 1- *THE CARPENTER: #0544*
Min. = ◆- *THE RAPTOR: #0916*
TOOL: #0560
DELICATE: #0964
RENT: #0881

⁎⁎

#0521 - February 17, 2019 @ 05:58 (San Francisco, California)

[0521.1 / 1262] [I have a compound fracture in the top of my left foot which becomes increasingly severe. The more attention I bring to it, the more protruded the bones become. The top of my foot gushes blood. I walk to two different locations. One is down a slight hill through a gated courtyard where a yoga class is about to commence. A second is a meeting area deep in a basement where students previously gathered. I'm accused of taking shortcuts. *"I may have, but wasn't aware."*]

[0521.2 / 1263] ["*CALL ME ISHMAEL,*" loops in my mind as I walk towards a lodge where a "sacred peanut ceremony" takes place. A man hands out compotes of soy sauce with scallions, which I politely decline. I enter and walk toward the front of a classroom, knowing I want to leave the class before it begins. I remember my foot is broken and needs tending to.]

· · ·

369

[0521.3 / 1264] [The confidence of a neighborhood community has been shaken by a brutal crime. I leave a small red wagon over the entrance to a secret tunnel *(through which criminals regularly escape a prison)* as a clue for the police.
"I've escaped using this route many times and want to seal it off for good."]

[0521.4 / 1265] [I'm at a baseball game. I stand in front of a young boy about to hit a ball. He says, *"I'm going to hit it!"* I shout, *"If you do, I'll catch it with my teeth!"*]

[0521.5 / 1266] [People take photographs with their faces obscured by silly masks fastened at various heights in a chain link fence that extends for miles.] //

⁂

SHORT: #0816
SAUCE: #0868, #1176
SECRET: #0996, #1001, #1037, #1066
GAME: #0858, #0862, #0868, #0878, #0893

⁂

#0522 - February 18, 2019 @ 06:44 (San Francisco, California)

[0522.1 / 1267] [I stand over a body of water atop a small outcropping of rocks. I use a spear to stab a fish in the head and draw it up from the water. I've caught a 5lb salmon. I pick it up by the gills and walk towards a temple where I'm hoping the head injury I've given the fish can be healed. When I look down, the salmon has transformed from flesh and bone into a bronze statue. I recognize the temple entrance as the front door to a wizard's house. I set the bronze statue in a carved-out area next to the door.]

[0522.2 / 1268] [I search for chocolate in a Chinese grocery. I search high and low as innumerable Asian women swarm around me at waist level. I see a small tray that has the variety of chocolate I seek, cut in half, with a hardened nougat center so old it's not chewable. I complete my shopping trip. I leave the store and have a misunderstanding with the valet as I attempt to retrieve my vehicle.] //

⁂

SALMON: #1047
WIZARD: #0805
HALF: #0810, #0825, #0851, #0863, #0877, #0888

⁂

#0523 - February 20, 2019 @ 06:55 (San Francisco, California)
*Jolted out of deep sleep. *

[0523.1 / 1269] [I call THE RADICAL HIPPIE *(honest, essential, and fun loving)* to see if she'll sell me MDMA.]

. . .

370

[0523.2 / 1270] [I unpack a shoe box, revealing a pair of bright orange leather wingtips.]

[0523.3 / 1271] [JAMES FRANCO acts like a total creep to multiple women at a house party.]

[0523.4 / 1272] [*"Focus on the number 17."*]

[0523.5 / 1273] [I drive through a grocery store parking lot and note a series of glass houses built between large buildings. Some are embedded in the hillsides, their large spiral multi-level staircases viewable from the front. THE WEAVER sits next to me in the car saying, *"Why would you want to go up and down all those stairs?"* I float up and out of the car and into a house where I float through an endless art gallery that extends through the vacuum of space.] //

⁎

Maj. = 0- THE WEAVER: #0524
CREEP: #0833
WINGTIP: #0816
THE RADICAL HIPPIE: #0687

⁎

#0524 - February 20, 2019 @ 08:25 (San Francisco, California)
*Out of deep sleep. *

[0524.1 / 1274] [I've taken up residence with a new family. I'm in a bedroom arranging a sex date with a new partner. When I duck my head under the covers of a bed, I find a guy blowing me. It feels nourishing and playful. We press our bodies against each other and *"Invite in Eros."* When I come up for air, I roll over and am back-to-back with THE WEAVER. *'Do you know where I put my ring?'* I ask. She doesn't respond. She's asleep.]

[0524.2 / 1275] [THE CHEMICAL BROTHERS have a heated debate with record label executives on the final track listing for their forthcoming album.]

[0524.3 / 1276] [A grandfather clock chimes. My attention is drawn to a portrait of "mom," whose face is contorted and disfigured.]

[0524.4 / 1277] [I'm at a carnival midway deciding which game to play. I'm drawn to one where the prize is a box of oversized Reese's Peanut Butter Cups filled with *"crunchy puffs."* I look down and discover I'm wearing my previously missing ring.]

[0524.5 / 1278] [I'm back in bed with THE SEX FRIEND (*primal, aggressive, and generous*). We're about to fuck as I wake up.] //

⁂

Maj. = 0- THE WEAVER: #0533
GRANDFATHER CLOCK: #0905, #0942
ALBUM: #0857, #0935, #1012, #1072, #1077

⁂

#0525 - February 21, 2019 @ 06:20 (San Francisco, California)

[0525.1 / 1279] [*"amer-AR-CANA! amer-ARCANE!"* is rousingly sung in refrain by a Gospel choir.]

[0525.2 / 1280] [I watch a performance of "Dear Evan Hansen" from the balcony of the Music Box Theater. Green holograms enhance the final tree planting scene.]

[0525.3 / 1281] [I steal a car from a parking garage.]

[0525.4 / 1282] [A woman runs through a secret tunnel beneath her house.]

[0525.5 / 1283] [Confrontational sexuality. My bones are bruised. I've been brutalized.] //

⁂

STEAL: #1194
BRUISED: #0889
GOSPEL: #0872, #0914

⁂

#0526 - February 22, 2019 @ 05:00 (San Francisco, California)

[0526.1 / 1284] [I wrap up my daily desert work on the Burning Man Temple. I discuss going to a KMFDM show with some teammates. Everyone's really drunk. The project is sloppily executed. My phone is crushed under a crane hook, leaving the device mangled and barely functional. Cartoon thought bubbles sprout from my head. A cartoon version of me plays out various fantasized scenarios where I purchase a new device.

The crew selects music tracks from a catalog stored on large white crystalline discs. I'm fascinated by the discs as they glow. I blink and discover I'm the only crew member onsite.

THE CONNECTOR yells at me through a megaphone to *"Hurry up!"* so I can make it to the *"Snow Plow Day Party"* hosted by *"Comfort and Joy."*

"Wait...am I back in the desert? I don't remember traveling here."

In a tent, I catch a glimpse of myself in a full-length mirror and notice I'm wearing a onesie half zipped up in the front. My exposed chest is oddly muscular. I vainly admire my overbuilt pectoral man-beef for a moment.

I exit the tent, greeted by two young twin girls. I discover a small black helium balloon which I push towards one of them. In unison we say to each other, *"You'd be fun to play with!"* A heavy, mysterious serpentine energy surrounds the girls.

372

Attention returns to my barely functional phone. When I stare at it, it magnetically reconstitutes itself. The glass casing remains totally shattered, rendering the device useless.] //

⁂

Maj. = 4- THE CONNECTOR: #0568
HELIUM: #0848
TWIN: #1053, #1131, #1153
COMFORT: #0957

⁂

#0527 - February 23, 2019 @ 06:18 (San Francisco, California)
*I wake up with strong pressure in my upper back. Vast amounts of sensation. *

[0527.1 / 1285] [The scene begins in a hotel lobby. I execute a well-timed comedic moment and leave a group gathered in uproarious laughter. I proceed to a private room and receive a series of chiropractic adjustments from THE ALIEN NATUROPATH. He makes multiple attempts to straighten my spine, then pauses to say, *"This one is very very deep,"* before performing a series of acrobatic contortions to deliver the needed therapy to my lumbar column.]

[0527.2 / 1286] [I pull a muscle in my back as I sleep on the floor in a row of people. I rise and walk through a series of rooms not moved by nor engaged in what I observe. I arrive in a room that has long, narrow, clear plastic tubing running from a bar into a solid wood wall. I fill the tubes with water and coffee as people approach and make requests. I'm happy and remain in service, though my back hurts. A group gathers to *"spark a revolution."*]

[0527.3 / 1287] [I pass a series of glass houses that have thick black steel girders supporting their oversized picture window panes. On the street I encounter someone familiar, who lives in one of the modern looking, highly stylish abodes. I'm able to see the interiors of all the units, and their respective goings on. The homes are close in proximity and divided by simple cobblestone breezeways. The energy is odd in this community. I quickly realize it's a homeless encampment in a futuristic city. The tenant I recognize is the mentally unstable *"first partner"* or *"first boyfriend"* of a close friend who's decided to overtake their living space. His presence generates confusion in an otherwise orderly and robust community.] //

⁂
PRIVATE ROOM: #0905
IN SERVICE: #0845, #0896
COBBLESTONE: #0820, #0929, #0944, #1176
THE ALIEN NATUROPATH: #0847
⁂

373

#0528 - February 24, 2019 @ 03:00 (San Francisco, California)

[0528.1 / 1288] [I'm awakened in the middle of the night, while laying on a couch in my office. A small group session is in progress. THE WORLDBRIDGER has his hands placed on THE CROWN PRINCE's (*studious, revealed, and benevolent*) head and offers healing touch. THE WORLDBRIDGER says, *"Go pink in the brain."* I perk up at his utterance and thank him for the insight. *"It's useful guidance."*

THE CROWN PRINCE is a newly outed homosexual. Knowing this makes me want to kiss him. I'm a bit dizzy as I stumble towards a large coffee bar to fix myself a mug. The black liquid goes cloudy brown when I hit it with cream. A group of advanced students have started to gather for their 4:00am class.

I open an accordion tri-fold binder that holds an assortment of business card sized "thank you" notes decorated with cute cartoon animals who express sweet heart felt musings, similar to what my mother would regularly leave in my elementary school lunch box.

I need to drive home. I look down at my wrist. I notice the small postage stamp sized screen on an electric ring I wear has been totally smashed, leaving my finger with a deep bone exposing cut. I'm not bothered by the bodily injury and focus on fixing the screen ring without my tools.] //

♣
Maj. = 7- THE WORLDBRIDGER: #0616
DIZZY: #0817
CUT: #0957, #0979, #0995, #1014
♣

#0529 - February 25, 2019 @ 00:54 (San Francisco, California)

[0529.1 / 1289] [I run around a large track with athletes at a celebration. Round tables are stacked high with piles of large chocolate bars. When I open one, I discover the chocolate is old and has been exposed to heat. I open a few hoping for a different outcome, *but they're all spoiled.*]

[0529.2 / 1290] [I'm part of a project team where I'm responsible for building out a spiraling roller coaster mine train through a giant glacier. Once completed, a male passenger takes the first ride. He forgets to fasten his seatbelt. His full attention remains oriented on resolving a grievance over the phone. The train ascends, drops, then loops. The man is hurled from the train and plummets to his death. It's later learned the matter he disputed while on the phone before the accident was, *"an incorrect charge of $188 assessed to the device he was using at the time of his demise."*]

[0529.3 / 1291] [I sit at a conference table discussing _____ with other people who have very strong opinions about "the landlord." *"The community did this to itself!"* I say as I sit back from the table and request we *"solve any other interpersonal problems telepathically."*]

· · ·

[0529.4 / 1292] [I'm on an icy planet. Star Wars characters chase me during a strong storm. Loud symphonic music booms like a film soundtrack.] //

⁂

GLACIER: #0926
CONFERENCE: #0986, #0989, #1028, #1044
FILM: #0995, #1019, #1028, #1082, #1083

⁂

#0530 - February 25, 2019 @ 03:15 (San Francisco, California)

[0530.1 / 1293] ["**ADVENTURES IN ALIGNMENT!**" scrolls across a marquee. "**Meditation! Group Yoga!**" Follow.]

[0530.2 / 1294] [GAVIN NEWSOM asks me to quickly come with him down a staircase past the press pit. We pass AMY POEHLER, who cracks a few jokes and attempts to delay our departure from the conference center. GAVIN provides me with myriad leadership insights as we briskly walk.] //

⁂

AMY POEHLER: #0691
GAVIN NEWSOM: #1354
PRESS: #0850, #0869, #0874, #0970
ALIGNMENT: #0878, #0998, #1053
LEADERSHIP: #1042, #1044, #1057
MARQUEE: #1100

⁂

#0531 - February 26, 2019 @ 00:41 (San Francisco, California)

[0531.1 / 1295] [It's *"eternal night"* in a crystalline ice world. Snow lightly falls all around, softly lit by a midnight sun peeking up from the horizon. On a large screen, a camera feed casts a young DJ actively remixing tracks on-the-fly during a global EDM conference. Tremendous collaboration between artists occurs across multiple remote physical locations. The camera toggles to a snowy outpost in Sweden where a young man offers a vocal sample:

"I left my job to WORK my REAL job...
...I left my job to get AT my REAL job."

I lay prone in the snow. I scratch my fingers into the fresh powder like I would on an LP or Serato record, leaving trails in the pristine snow. I control the global experience through my touch.

"**Hey DJ SPIN THAT SHIT!**" I say on blast to myself as I *"scratch the snow."* I bring my hand up. The beat drops. The party pops.]

. . .

[0531.2 / 1296] [We're at home. I've put something on the stove to warm. I get preoccupied with other tasks and don't notice the food burn. This happens three times. THE LAWYER reprimands me for wasting food, then slips out for a moment to run an errand. When he returns, he tries to shame me into different behavior. When he's done yelling, I tell him, *'I'll clean up and buy more food. My feelings are hurt. I'll get over it.'*]

[0531.3 / 1297] [LED kiosks covered in snow blink soothingly.]

[0531.4 / 1298] [The more I speak, *the more impaired my hearing becomes.* My left ear seals over. I rattle my head violently in an attempt to loosen the earwax buildup that mutes my sense of hearing.]

[0531.5. / 1299] [I spend a moment in a European ski village. I may be back in Sweden, but I'm there and gone too fast to discern. During the blink, I see a drunken shaggy haired version of THE POLITICIAN *(boorish, competent, and confrontational)* stumble out of a pub and face first into the snow in front of a huge mountain range. When I help him to his feet he wants to fight. I point him in the direction of his hotel and he lumbers away like a zombie.]

[0531.6 / 1300] [I share a conversation with a shadowy figure across a table. We wax poetic about, *"the burdens one must bear if they want to become a world class DJ."*] //

⁎⁎

Maj. = 5- THE LAWYER: #0561
FIGURE: #0817, #0933, #0945, #1018, #1060
BLINK: #1052, #1133, #1167, #1196, #1199

⁎⁎

#0532 - February 26, 2019 @ 03:25 (San Francisco, California)

[0532.1 / 1301] [I'm in a futuristic "Ender's Game" type of scene. I'm challenged with a group of committed cadets to *"up level."* The tone is suspenseful. The lighting is sharp and precise. A series of small packets are placed on stainless steel surgical trays in front of us. I empty the contents of the packets on my tray. A pile of pills rests before me. *"All but one pill is aligned for me to take."* Something seems wrong about a grey silicone gel cap I've left on the tray. My commanding officer suggests I have to take it to complete the exercise. *I believe it will kill me if I do.*]

[0532.2 / 1302] [THE SMILE *(gregarious, flirtatious, and vulnerable)* sits a few tables down from me in a cafe. He sports salt & pepper hair and has gained a lot of weight. I walk towards him and tap him on the shoulder. It takes a few minutes before he recalls who I am. He eventually recognizes me and invites me to sit at the table.]

. . .

[0532.3 / 1303] [THE MAGICIAN and THE TRAINER (*embodied, humorous, and challenging*) take a yoga class led by THE PSYCHIATRIST.]

[0532.4 / 1304] [*"I always bring you out of hiding,"* I tell "JOHN," playfully from across a table. *"Yeah, it happens when I'm horny,"* he flirtingly shoots back.]

[0532.5 / 1305] [I'm laying down. *"Did I take the grey silicone pill? Did someone spike my drink? Reality feels super charged."* I breathe and sense with my entire being. A soft warm hand is placed on my forehead as a voice says, *"Things are going really well for you."* I sit up and look at a handheld device. An app with a yellow and grey grid for a background delivers specialized tasks and training to me in real time. Another screen fills with detailed stats and visually conveys my personal metrics. The multi-dimensional sine wave-like pattern uniquely ties to my spirit's *"energetic signature."*] //

⁑

Maj. = 14- THE MAGICIAN: #0544
Min. = ♠- THE PSYCHIATRIST: #0652
MULTI-DIMENSIONAL: #0870, #0895, #0999
PILL: #0973, #1149
THE TRAINER: #0538

⁑

#0533 - February 26, 2019 @ 06:31 (San Francisco, California)

[0533.1 / 1306] [I visit a military rehabilitation center. THE WEAVER travels with me. THE ALLY (*informed, resilient, and patriotic*) is our onsite chaperone. Many of the wounded have energetic lassos wrapped around their weapons. They feel the phantom pain of limbs that aren't physically there. On a wall of "Before and After" photos, one *"before"* shows a soldier after his face was blown off in combat by an IED. The *"after"* photo is THE ALLY as he now stands before us. We pass by a firing range where people use THE ALLY's *"after"* photo for target practice, but THE ALLY isn't bothered by this. THE WEAVER and I depart the facility and help each other climb down an oversized flight of stairs.]

[0533.2 / 1307] [I wander a complex concrete maze within a house. I find a door to the outside. It's nighttime. The air is still. I pass a pile of long rectangular objects (*clocks, artwork, mirrors, etc.*). I pick up what I can and take it back inside. The house is full of young men in their 20's.]

[0533.3 / 1308] [*"Our thing is on the 15th,"* CHLOE SEVIGNY shouts at me from the ground level of a construction site. *"Yes, but this matters more right now,"* I say as I point at a series of holes that have been drilled incorrectly into a load bearing stud. I need a structural engineer's input to proceed. The carpenters used an incorrect countersink, and drilled the holes (*which now look like the outline of the Olympic Rings centered in a trapezoid*) too deep.] //

377

Maj. = 0- THE WEAVER: #0544
MILITARY: #0976, #0999
DRILL: #0865, #0904
⁎⁎

#0534 - February 27, 2019 @ 05:26 (San Francisco, California)

[0534.1 / 1309] [I'm in a brightly colored tattoo parlor with a lobby full of smooth cast resin furniture. A gorgeous smooth skinned Russian man (*blonde hair, striking features, functionally lean and muscular*) approaches me. His torso and chest are wrapped in plastic cling. He's excited to model a new piece of body art. He proudly shows off a block letter tattoo that reads, "**HELL YEAH**" across his toned pecs. The tattoo glows like neon. Light emanates from his chest. We gaze at each other without speaking. Our shared intimacy is deep.
A thought bubble portal appears next to us on a nearby wall. We observe a half man/half pig hybrid being prepped for a tattoo under the aid of anesthesia. It's overweight. Artists and doctors vigorously push excess belly skin and fat around as they shave and sterilize the front of its body. All will eventually be covered with ink.]

[0534.2 / 1310] [*"How long are you here?"* "A while. I should go to the kitchen."]

[0534.3 / 1311] [THE HILL (*delightful, sensitive, and loving*) and THE SMOKE SCREEN (*cool, conversational, and team oriented*) facilitate a group discussion in a room where boxes are piled high. The colors are vibrant. The air is thick like cotton candy. They look at me mid-session and say,
"We want to leave."
"That's not my problem," I say, taking a seat and proceeding to have most of my hair cut off by THE OWNER (*reserved, focused, and broadly aware*). After she's done, I feel awful.
"No! I wanted to grow my hair for 1001 dreams!"
In a distracted moment, I lost sight of that goal.]

[0534.4 / 1312] [I'm DAVID BOWIE. I wear a bespoke suit and shoot an impromptu documentary inside the Kennedy Compound (*which feels like a ritzy amusement park for the elite*). A carriage with six white horses pulls a newlywed couple on a public procession.
I sneak inside a building and snake up a staircase to the 13th floor where my camera crew is promptly abducted. I proceed down a hallway, then up another flight of stairs. The 14th floor is a public school for underprivileged kids who wait after hours for their parents to retrieve them. I'm surprised by this and proceed up another staircase. When I get to the 15th floor, I'm startled to discover a hospital dedicated to serving children with special needs and disabilities.
A crude intake process removes kids from their wheelchairs and walkers and positions them head to toe on a long serpentine conveyor belt that resembles a luggage carousel at an airport terminal. Some of the children don't know what's happening and cry out for their parents. The snaking conveyor belt extends as far as my eyes can see.] //

⁎⁎

DAVID BOWIE: #1203
HORSES: #0833
CARRIAGE: #0856, #1198
NEON: #0961, #0995, #1201

⁎⁎

#0535 - February 27, 2019 @ 06:29 (San Francisco, California)

[0535.1 / 1313] [*"You'll hear thunder near the basement of S_____thoughts,"* a voice says to me from the dark.]

[0535.2 / 1314] [A small snail shell device is used to catch stray hockey pucks on the street. This seems like a normal day-to-day occurrence.]

[0535.3 / 1315] [I watch a VHS cassette on a small TV set with the **Grim Reaper** at sundown. I casually peek under the hood and see its skull enshrouded in sheer black fabric. I'm wearing jeans and have a hoodie pulled up over my head. The **Grim Reaper** pulls my hood back to my shoulders with both its boney hands.
"You are a S_____," we utter to each other at the same time.]

[0535.4 / 1316] [I'm a white vaporous apparition floating like mist in the nave of a large gothic cathedral. Light flows in through ornamented stained-glass windows. I'm multi/cross-dimensionally manifested. I keep losing a large white pointy hat that designates my esoteric station. I observe myself floating in front of a bejeweled man with a long white beard. He may be a saint, but I don't remember his name.]

[0535.5 / 1317] [*"You're now officially on the backside of the mountain,"* a voice omnisciently croons. It continues, *"It's safe. Trust me. Take it easy. It's me."*] //

⁎

THUNDER: #0867, #0994
GRIM: #1069
MIST: #0850, #1132
FLOATING: #0817, #0836, #0841, #0884, #0909, #0979, #1111

⁎

#0536 - February 27, 2019 @ 08:28 (San Francisco, California)

[0536.1 / 1318] [*Geometric abstraction* A black background is periodically disrupted by brilliant flashes of white light. Percussive. Sharp. Fast. High volume. Vibrant contrast. I receive a direct transmission on, *"how to best proceed with the 'mirrored art piece.'"*]

. . .

[0536.2 / 1319] [A voice reminds me, *"All models lack correctness, though some may be useful...for a time."*]

[0536.3 / 1320] [It becomes clear all I wish to achieve will manifest by serving others through, *"the science of flow"* and *"peak-to- 'peek' service."*]

[0536.4 / 1321] [I'm shown an image of myself giving reiki sessions while using biofeedback tools.] //

⁂

BRILLIANT: #0852
SERVING: #0997, #1064
WHITE LIGHT: #0940, #0952, #0987, #1021, #1163

⁂

#0537- February 28, 2019 @ 02:41 (San Francisco, California)

[0537.1 / 1322] [I enter a long room which feels like a gymnasium. A chain oval is strung around the center. THE NEUTRAL GUIDE holds a clipboard and asks me to check in for class. I ask her where to sit. The mood of the room is resistant. People seem to be on edge as they gather. A young woman approaches me and tenderly touches my arm. After a silent moment she quietly says, *"You seem disrupted."* She quite clearly sees a valence I wear that as yet I'm not aware. I thank her for her insight. I look for my friend THE PUBLIC MEDIUM, but don't see him in class. Perhaps he's advanced to a different level. Cutting through a moment of confusion, I choose to stay where I am.] //

⁂

Maj. = 18- THE PUBLIC MEDIUM: #0556
Min. = ♥- THE NEUTRAL GUIDE: #0771
INSIGHT: #0887, #0900, #0928, #0929
TENDERLY: #0999, #1005

⁂

#0538 - February 28, 2018 @ 04:20 (San Francisco, California)

[0538.1 / 1323] [I'm inside a small-town general store. Large, deep, and tall wooden shelves make the place feel like a library. I notice a few people dart in and out quickly using a portal to get to a secret gathering site. The staff doesn't seem to mind us coming and going without buying anything.
"We have an easement."
"They know what we're up to here," a young woman says to me as she passes through a bookcase and disappears in a carnival glass colored flash of light.
I get a nod from a cashier to proceed, and discover myself in a classroom seated in rows. I sit on a desk with my legs dangling over top. We prepare to *"run energy."* An assistant teacher makes a passing comment about suicide that disrupts my process.
I pause class with an ask,

"I need a teacher's help today. Please slow down."

We complete the exercise, and at its conclusion I discover I'm sitting next to the same young woman that I met in dream [0537.1 / 1322].

"I saw you last night. You seem different now," she says.

"I'm glad I know you, because you can see what I can't."]

[0538.2 / 1324] [I wander the halls of a dormitory looking for a men's room. I'm in a stately women's building and have to duck into a ladies' powder room to urinate. The toilet has a wide mouth bowl that sits low to the floor set near the center of the room. The wall behind the toilet is transparent. A woman in a corset and bustle daintily sits reading a book and eating petit fours while I pee a few feet away from her. She doesn't seem to notice me.]

[0538.3 / 1325] [Drunk drivers. Boxes of _____.]

[0538.4 / 1326] [THE TRAINER *(rhythmic, somatic, and supple)* leads a group of fancily dressed women in a primal movement course.]

[0538.5 / 1327] [I'm in a hotel lobby at a publicity event, standing in front of a large multi-tiered waterfall. HEIDI KLUM, wearing a red one-piece swimsuit, swan dives head first from the top of the highest waterfall to the lowest pool. She miscalculates the descent and grazes her entire right-side ribs on the sharp granite edge of the bottom pool. I instantly feel her pain in my body. I immediately break out in a cold sweat and my breathing quickens. The pain intensifies as HEIDI exits the pool uninjured and participates in an interview with a BOB BARKER looking host. Mid-interview a large screen pops up beside them. HEIDI is challenged to digitally *"clap back"* on a social media platform after a woman in the audience challenges her. Unintentionally, the exchange becomes a rap battle between the two women. HEIDI's unexpected lyrical slams and flows *"break the internet."* In the midst of the media blitz, I'm still buckled in half with pain.

"Take a breath. Check in. Where are you now?" a voice I don't recognize gently coos in the center of my head.

"When I get hurt like that, I just have to keep dancing," THE DANCER turns to me, saying *(in seeming response to the voice)* while I'm overwhelmed and breathless.]

[0538.6 / 1328] [TOM BRADY swims naked in an infinity pool at golden hour. His muscular buttocks occasionally break the surface of the water like a dolphin's dorsal fin. At dusk the pool becomes a foamy hot tub. HEIDI KLUM approaches, enters the pool, and then spanks TOM on the ass. They giggle and embrace. TOM buries his face in HEIDI's chest. She pauses to wink at me before facing him and sharing a deep kiss. They fawn over each other's beauty while repeatedly sexually pleasuring one another. *They enjoy each other. They appreciate each other. They're connected.*] //

⁎

Maj. = 2- THE DANCER: #0542

HEIDI KLUM: #0761
DRUNK: #0848, #0860, #0957, #1031
HOT TUB: #1137, #1146

⁎⁎

#0539 - February 28, 2019 @ 07:00 (San Francisco, California)

[0539.1 / 1329] [The vibe is overtly mysterious and dark. A hotel hosts an overnight seminar. THE BODHI PUNK (*skeptical, raw, and hard charging*) has the same conversation multiple times with the doorman about how he needs to leave to get his, *"guy stuff."* The doorman insists there are no, *"ins and outs."* I've been onsite for a while and I'm on my way out.
"I intend to get home ASAP."] //

⁎⁎

OVERNIGHT: #0876, #1074, #1126
DOORMAN: #1143
VIBE: #0948
THE BODHI PUNK: #0577

⁎⁎

#0540 - March 1, 2019 @ 03:48 (San Francisco, California)

[0540.1 / 1330] [I'm in a film, scheduled for summer release. My character is charged with teaching a group of grade school children how to fly a plane.
"I only have three months to get this rag tag dysfunctional group of kids to come together and take flight."
My co-instructor is a middle-aged Black man who wears a headset at a desk and eats multiple submarine sandwiches. It feels similar to a *"Little Rascals," "Sandlot," "The Mighty Ducks"* trope. The tricky bit is I don't know how to fly airplanes and have to teach myself as I concurrently train the children.
I practice taking off and landing a commercial jet. The angles of ascent and descent initially startle me. I don't like the strong downward pressure I feel in my belly. Over time this naturally subsides and I gain confidence. The flight deck is an opaque grey wall with a simple desk. Oddly, it has no windows. My counterpart continues to eat his sub sandwiches, engaging only in key moments of the takeoff and landing processes where the flat, grey wall at the nose of the plane goes transparent. The grey dissolves like mist and reveals the sky above on takeoff, and the runway as we approach for landing.
"He's an expert. In three months, I have to be able to do this by myself."]

[0540.2 / 1331] [I'm in a gallery. In the center of the room stands a small figurine on a pedestal covered by a glass dome. It's unclear what it's made from. It's simply illuminated overhead by a single soft gold light. The object is a Mobius strip, two toned black and white with the words **"BE HERE"** printed in contrast (*white letters on black and vice versa*). It's simple, elegant, and easy to gaze at (*which I do for some time*).]

. . .

[0540.3 / 1332] [I'm a member of a documentary crew. We meet to discuss how we can generate content that's engaging and interesting without engineering interactions with our subjects, which proves difficult. The set up we've been given requires us to disrupt a group of high school students. To maintain our integrity, we don't. The output we generate is considered bland and declared *"boring"* when we review dailies with producers. One such instance of a *"fall flat"* occurs when I'm asked to go undercover in a classroom.

"Man, it's been a long time since I've been inside a classroom. If there are individual submissions, be sure you print out all your stuff for us so we have it. Boy will those dot matrix printers be noisy," I nonsensically say among subjects with a chuckle as I break character mid-scene.

An awkward pause follows with no response from students. My ill-fated attempt at humor doesn't land. My technology references date me.] //

⁎⁎

CLASSROOM: #0832, #0859, #0877, #0891, #0938
JET: #0982, #1164
CHUCKLE: #0887, #1177

⁎⁎

#0541 - March 1, 2019 @ 05:58 (San Francisco, California)

[0541.1 / 1333] [I'm at a kink party. Multiple rooms have large televisions mounted on the wall which screen action from various other geographic locations. I'm particularly taken with a handsome young man who presents in solo from Israel. He has a black Mohawk and olive skin. He steps through the television and into my room. He and I talk for a few minutes. He gives me an awkward *"chest only"* hug. His hips and abdomen sway back and away from me. He stands on his toes in a pair of black leather boots. I don't find the expression sexy and I pull away.]

[0541.2 / 1334] [I'm an eight-year-old boy at a friend's house for a slumber party. We decide to creep down to the kitchen to hunt for snacks in the dark. In the pantry, we find a container of adult gummy vitamins and gleefully open them. We eat handfuls at a time while rambunctiously commenting,

"These will make us grow up faster!" "We'll be sooooo strong!"

We flex our little prepubescent arms which at present, lack bicep definition. We giggle and notice other bags of Haribo gummy candies in the pantry. When I've eaten until my belly is swollen with gelatin I lumber back.

"I should really cut sugars out of my diet," I say while reclining and patting my tummy with one hand. I use the other to slam more gummy candy in my mouth.]

[0541.3 / 1335] [I'm a young girl. I put on sock puppet shows from behind my bed. My hand animates my favorite creation, a sock decorated with green sparkles and lace. This character doesn't have a name, but has many imaginary friends.]

. . .

[0541.4 / 1336] [I'm on set taking a smoke break with my crew. We light up cigarettes and reminisce on, *"what a shitshow it was filming SARAH SILVERMAN's first comedy special, 'JESUS IS MAGIC.'"*] //

⁂
JESUS: #0609
SOCK PUPPET: #0874, #0982
PANTRY: #0815
⁂

#0542 - March 2, 2019 @ 07:16 (San Francisco, California)

[0542.1 / 1337] [I'm in a glass walled chapel in a forest, possibly at altitude. I sit in a small glass room that surrounds my church pew. I can reach a breadbox sized Lucite box overhead if I extend my arm straight up. The box is locked.

"It's a receptacle for monetary and energetic gifts to the church."

I slip a manila envelope full of prayers into the overhead box as a service is about to start. THE NUN makes some announcements to the group as THE SOOTHSAYER *(mysterious, thoughtful, and humble)* quickly reviews his speaker's notes at the back of the chapel.

The group readies itself for meditation, with the exception of a young man with a shaved head. He turns to look back at the rows behind him with a fist placed under his chin. He attempts to talk to the woman in the next pew. THE NUN questions him, to which he responds,

"I don't have to meditate because I have a doctor's note."]

[0542.2 / 1338] [I'm with THE DANCER at a retreat center. As we walk down a dimly lit hallway she points to her right and says, *"Topher and Dan's dads created the idea for mobile phones over there in 'Suite W' of 'Tower J' when they stayed here years ago. They conceived and designed the first 'cellular transmitter,' the first widely adopted version of the microchip."*] //

⁂
Maj. = 2- THE DANCER: #0545
Min. = ♦- THE NUN: #0664
CHIN: #0938, #0950, #1139
MEDITATE: #0935, #1096, #1126, #1193
THE SOOTHSAYER: #0613
⁂

#0543 - March 3, 2019 @ 02:16 (San Francisco, California)

[0543.1 / 1339] [***"As a designer of systems (technical, organic, and cultural) it was my job to know people's current processes better than they did,"*** I say sitting across the table from an interviewer. We share a meal at a hamburger stand inside a large train station. We have an elaborate, nuanced discussion about how the hamburger stand could partner with the train station in increasingly beneficial scenarios.

"Consider a burger is $.50, then suppose ticket prices drop for a specified period of time. Then during that window burger prices go up to $.52, also suppose ________, and also suppose ________."

The list of variables and suppositions grows long.

"The timing of a sale makes it reasonable to schedule large price fluctuations. It's not a conspiracy, price fixing, nor collusion...it's just business."

We look out a rain speckled window as gray turns to twilight, then dark night. A single nickel seems to magnetically hold itself to the window as rain pelts it outside. The coin slides down the glass in a slow arc that decreases at an increasing rate.

"It's the late 1940's somewhere in the USA."] //

⁎⁎

HAMBURGER: #0915, #0937
RAIN: #1022
TWILIGHT: #0887, #0970

⁎⁎

#0544 - March 3, 2019 @ 04:14 (San Francisco, California)

[0544.1 / 1340] [I'm in the basement of a large house looking for a missing vial of LSD. I open a bedroom door and am startled to find THE CHILD asleep. I realize I'm at THE WEAVER and THE CARPENTER's house. I quickly and forcefully pull the door closed, easing it softly shut at the last moment so as to not wake the young girl. I hastily grab stacks of blue Post It notes and handfuls of blue highlighters. I realize I look like I've gone mad as I rush upstairs with an arm load of random office supplies and fling them out a window and across the lawn at night. The mood is suspicious.]

[0544.2 / 1341] [A middle aged White man is bristly deposed by a female lawyer who is as meticulously manicured as she is precise and surgical with her cross examination and questioning. The deposition occurs in a public courtroom full of spectators. She ridicules and humiliates the man to wild satisfaction of the public crowd gathered to observe.]

[0544.3 / 1342] [I'm at the back of a movie theater with a friend. We're about to see a documentary. We walk down the aisle and sit in the front right corner seats and quickly become engrossed in the film. In the climactic scene our chairs transform into a tilt-a-whirl cart and make a strong multi-G pivot to the left. We take a victory lap around the theater. The car parks itself in its starting position and we de-board the ride. We're asked to join THE MAGICIAN onstage to facilitate a post screening Q&A.]

[0544.4 / 1343] [I'm moonwalking in roller skates, I slide up and down in the splits from side to side while standing in place, showing off my renegotiated contract with gravity.] //

⁎⁎

*Maj. = 0- THE WEAVER: #0548, 1- THE CARPENTER: #0545,
2- THE CHILD: #0556, 14- THE MAGICIAN: #0547*
ROLLER SKATES: #1061
VICTORY: #0817

⁎⁎

#0545 - March 3, 2019 @ 06:10 (San Francisco, California)

[0545.1 / 1344] [*Polyrhythmic hand clapping. * Various percussion instruments in a dark space create sounds and flashes of light.]

[0545.2 / 1345] [Rising flashes of activity blip and fade. The scene stabilizes. I watch myself add illuminative gold accents to a power blue canvas which radiates and glows from the center out in a fiery spiral.]

[0545.3 / 1346] [I walk across a gravel parking lot with THE CARPENTER and THE DANCER on a grey afternoon. We start picking on each other.
"I make $8,000 a year," THE DANCER proudly declares.
"When are you gonna get a REAL job," I shoot back, *though I've been unemployed for over a decade.*]

[0545.4 / 1347] [I attend a film screening with THE PERVERT (*horny, explicit, and artful*). The presentation is highly anticipated. Content passes over, through, and between a series of holographic screens. Ghosts do a serpentine dance in an intricate braided pattern. The background is shiny emerald green obscured with occasional puffs of black smoke. Scenes featuring hyperventilating humans flash on the screen. THE PERVERT absolutely hates the film and states a dozen reasons why, as we exit the theater. Our departure is nearly made permanent by the reversing back fender of a pistachio green and white two tone 1957 Chevy. The tailfin of the car narrowly avoids gouging my left side.]

[0545.5 / 1348] [I exit a port-a-potty at a music festival and squat down to talk to a young boy (*under five years old*). His dad stands 20 feet away and encourages him to punch me in the face. "Why don't you hit him?" the dad casually commands. The boy winds up to strike. I put my hand up and say, **"How about a high five instead?"**] //

✲✲

Maj. = 1- THE CARPENTER: #0552, 2- THE DANCER: #0548
HIGH FIVE: #0908, #0954, #0996, #1077, #1121, #1167
PERCUSSION: #0822, #1147
THE PERVERT: #0635

✲✲

#0546 - March 3, 2019 @ 23:30 (San Francisco, California)

[0546.1 / 1349] ["*EMBODY it. Where in your body do you FEEL it?*" a council of voices ask me under a spotlight. I'm seated at a circular table. I can't see anyone else sitting around it. More occurs here, and quickly fades.] //

✲✲

EMBODY: #0858, 0933, 0941, #0963

FEEL: #0929, #0933, #0936, #0939, #0943
SPOTLIGHT: #0857, #0905
⁎⁎

#0547 - March 4, 2019 @ 22:38 (San Francisco, California)

[0547.1 / 1350] [A group of us gather at my large house. THE MAGICIAN asks me where the bathroom is. I point him in the direction of a half bath with a pocket door from where some light shines. Abundant humor flows through the group. Lots of jokes are cracked. THE GOLDEN SHADOW (*wise, quiet and observant*) and I are assigned as roommates for the weekend. From her knapsack, she brings out a palm sized object that looks like a hunk of glass Swiss cheese. Upon inspecting it, I realize it's a delicate and ancient glass paged book of poems. Circles in the cheese are magnifying glasses intentionally placed over keywords in each of the poems. This object excites me. *"I have so many questions I want to ask!"*
A startled married couple by the names of "Josh" and "Brent" enter the room and inquire as to why we're there. They claim we're in their house. I walk out to the dock off the back porch where I see a cameraman get pulled into the lake and drowned. I didn't see him, but I'm sure THE MAGICIAN holds the bearded obese man underwater. I'm scared when I see bubbles of struggle rise to the surface. I walk away to avoid witnessing anything else. I send the traumatic scenario a healing of gold light and ruby hearts.] //

⁎⁎
Maj. = 14- THE MAGICIAN: #0587
MAGNIFYING GLASS: #0876, #1003, #1053
DROWNED: #1024, #1069
THE GOLDEN SHADOW: #1210
⁎⁎

#0548 - March 5, 2019 @ 03:36 (San Francisco, California)

[0548.1 / 1351] [Abstract graphics in shades of pink, green and purple. Looks like an "M" with a colon to its right on a rectangular background. **"M:"**]

[0548.2 / 1352] [I mountain bike with a group down narrow paths at a large pitch. We stop at a steep staircase and walk our bikes down and through an intricate maze. We realize we're in a giant Aztec temple. We become stuck in a basin. After searching for an exit, we spill out onto an epic view of a deserted ancient city in ruins.]

[0548.3 / 1353] [I'm part of a crew working an AMON TOBIN concert. We acknowledge a couple on the crew (*a bearded man and dreadlocked woman*) and give them a gift of four front row tickets to a show of their choice. We pass out hand sized cardboard cutouts of the state of California and flip them over the tops of our fingers like quarters.]

[0548.4 / 1354] [Most of the dream takes place on a wedding day. THE DANCER is beautifully dressed and working with some strong emotions leading up to the ceremony. She decides she wants to talk to THE WEAVER, but the group has decided this defies convention and prevents her from making contact. She sneaks around a back corridor and enters a suite where THE WEAVER readies herself. Just as she goes to the tap THE WEAVER on the shoulder a group of us grab THE DANCER and pull her away quickly in the nick of time.

"Phew, that was a close call," we collectively think, as we gently close the door without disturbing THE WEAVER in her regal quarters.

THE DANCER is frustrated we foiled her plan and stands in an outdoor cobblestone corridor under a gothic archway. Rain begins to pour down, melting her perfectly appointed hairstyle. Similarly, her white satin dress begins to spot and then is soaked, five minutes before the wedding. Her face collapses into her hands and she weeps. The mood becomes sad and defeated.

"Let's get you covered up and inside," I soothingly whisper while ushering her up the stairs and into the chapel.] //

⁂

Maj. = 0- THE WEAVER: #0552, 2- THE DANCER: #0557
WEDDING: #0840, #0905, #0959, #0988, #1078
SUITE: #0856, #0957, #0995, #1057, #1108, #1194

⁂

#0549 - March 6, 2019 @ 03:22 (San Francisco, California)

[0549.1 / 1355] [During a morning session, I place a red leather handbag on a chair to save a seat for a friend at a convention hall. We're there to observe the application of a new travel safety protocol that will globally cascade to all major airports and train stations. The goal is to "hack" the security person at the point of entry. The system fails if a weapon of any sort makes it through security. *"This is gun control, amplified,"* the demo begins as the security guard engages and disrupts the model perpetrator by using a series of simple and direct vocal cues: *"I see something. I'm saying something."*

A lot of doubt is cast on the robustness of this process, but I'm moved by what I observe. I believe it's simple, effective, trainable and repeatable. The class is open to the public and SOPHIA PATRILLO (*Golden Girls*) enters and takes a seat next to me. At break, I grab a plate at the lunch buffet with a coconut cake donut, but promptly place it in a bus tub when I notice someone has licked the pastry.

"All the donuts have been licked!" I whine as I put an entire tray of them in the black plastic tub.

The afternoon session centers on how to curtail firearm violence. Two students take the stage to demonstrate a protocol to minimize the prospective impact of a violent event. A use case is actively modeled to show their procedure in practice. A rogue customer (*in the demo*) takes a ticket stub to a counter and trades their voucher for a *"non-ticket."* This leads customers to say something specific, which in turn triggers the ticketing agent to say something, which then leads to a large-scale security response. The demo proves *"the protocol is valid, but the response level is arguably excessive."* Though impractical, the collective agrees the student submitted proposal is inspiring.

At the next break SOPHIA sits in a high back maroon leather chair, bumping an annoying verbose student from her preferred seat. SOPHIA and I giggle quietly. SOPHIA places her handbag on a chair to save a seat for another student.]

. . .

[0549.2 / 1356] [SAME DREAM, double exposed two degrees to the right and a fraction of a second behind [0549.1 / 1355].] //

⁎
⁎⁎

COCONUT: #1200
MAROON: #0900, #0919, #1133
DOUBLE: #0863, #0872, #0875, #0908, #0910, #0936
COUNTER: #0891, #0937, #1001, #1026, #1088, #1194

⁎
⁎⁎

#0550 - March 6, 2019 @ 04:56 (San Francisco, California)

[0550.1 / 1357] [I move fast through a series of remote locations, supported by a gold and white guide. The guide consolidates into a female form. We pause and walk on an island beach. The woman escorts me and describes various energies of the islands. Her tone is casual with occasional pedagogic flourish. I'm drawn to an island called *"Pono Pono"* which has a warm rich fecund energy, ripe with marvelously large, lush, succulent trees. The plants are enormous, soft, supple, and nourishing. Their colors are vibrant activated shades of green. I choose a living space across from "Pono Pono" where I can view the island from my window and enjoy it. The island softly speaks its truth and gains my perpetual endearment when it whispers, *"This is a place where gods come to experience vulnerability."*]

[0550.2 / 1358] [I'm on the second floor of a house. I move in and set up a brand-new life. When I look out my bay window, I discover the view is stunningly beautiful and from a much higher vantage. I'm a bit unsettled because I'm not sure what my life will be like in this new place. **Optimism prevails.** I unpack a few boxes, dust off my kitchen appliances, and begin putting them away. The shelf where I place my toaster oven has to be cleaned. Multiple dead crickets and roaches lay upturned on their backs. An event down the hall hosts small groups of people who work to design new public park spaces. THE FIDUCIARY is part of a small group. He doesn't speak but actively contributes through sign language and touch. His preferred currency is *"hugging."* I lay down on the floor next to him and give him a giant bear hug, in front of the team as they continue to work.] //

⁎
⁎⁎

Maj. = 9- THE FIDUCIARY: #0615
SUCCULENT: #0836, #1111, #1158
BRAND NEW: #0881

⁎
⁎⁎

#0551 - March 6, 2019 @ 05:45 (San Francisco, California)

[0551.1 / 1359] [I teach yoga to a large group from the back of a gathering space. BARON BAPTISTE coaches me from the side.]

. . .

[0551.2 / 1360] [I sit next to a woman at a workshop. She takes an interest in my notebook, grabs it, and flips through it. She's curious if I've taken session notes, but seems disappointed when she discovers nothing in the notebook but multidimensional scribbles and doodles.] //

⁎⁎

BARON BAPTISTE: #0576
WORKSHOP: #0847, #0896, #0957, #0980
NOTEBOOK: #0971, #0988, #0995, #0997

⁎⁎

#0552 - March 6, 2019 @ 07:45 (San Francisco California)

[0552.1 / 1361] [I'm in a dark bedroom. Curtains are drawn. A few rays of light poke through. I tie myself up. My ass is in the air. The door is slightly ajar. I wait for someone to enter. The anticipation grows exquisite. Microscopic hairs on the small of my back stand on end when I hear the door creak open. I find the anonymity incredibly sexy.]

[0552.2 / 1362] [ENYA ascends a staircase backstage just moments before she makes her debut concert performance. She stands alert in a black and red lace gown listening to an overture she's written for the occasion. She's delighted by her supporting musicians and rests in a moment of deep satisfaction in their shared, conscious co-creation. In a few moments the curtain will raise and she'll find herself feeling both exposed and confident.]

[0552.3 / 1363] [THE WEAVER and THE CARPENTER dress for a formal event. They've hired a worker at the last minute to help fix something in the bedroom (*perhaps attaching a firebox to a wall*). My lofted bunk bed needs a screw replaced in one corner, but I make no mention. The worker enters carrying a toolbox. A sticker on its side reads, *"Shit doesn't happen to US. We make shit happen to IT."*]

[0552.4 / 1364] [I'm in a BDSM dungeon surrounded by red light and a thick pall of sweat and body odor.]//

⁎⁎

Maj. = 0- THE WEAVER: #0555, 1- THE CARPENTER: #0556
ENYA: #0753
SEXY: #0895, #0910, #0957
BDSM: #0872

⁎⁎

#0553 - March 6, 2019 @ 08:57 (San Francisco, California)

[0553.1 / 1365] [*"Make it relatable."*
"Make it relatable."
"Make it relatable." A voice says repeatedly.] //

⁂

VOICE: #0812, #0823, #0839, #0852, #0886
REPEATEDLY: #1173, #1186

⁂

#0554 - March 7, 2019 @ 04:04 (San Francisco, California)

[0554.1 / 1366] [Various industries and municipalities make power grabs for a new alternative energy source. Their shared desire is to fractionalize ownership of a single physical hub, but the major players have an incorrect understanding. A Swedish firm secretly integrated a self-sustaining system in public transportation infrastructure that extends across borders and through large land masses. Rectangular diodes in the rails transfer energy to transport vehicles that run along the tracks. Excess energy is placed in complementary cells onboard vehicles in real time. The (ORBITAL ENERGY EXCHANGE LITE COMET) provides renewable energy and transportation to a vast and geographically dispersed population.]

[0554.2 / 1367] [My coffee date with ALEXANDRIA OCASIO-CORTEZ quickly lights up, then fades.]

[0554.3 / 1368] [I sit in the library of a large manor home with rich wood walls, elegant rugs, mirrors and hanging tapestries. JOHN PAUL JONES and JIMMY PAGE enter and drop equipment cases, then go warm their hands by a large stoked hearth. JOHN PAUL JONES opens a case revealing a bass guitar made of Lucite. He grabs it aggressively by the strings and yanks it from the case, muttering small complaints under his breath. The body of the instrument cracks and two of the four strings snap. *"Seems you'd rather play a broken bass?"* I inquire.] //

⁂

ALEXANDRIA OCASIO-CORTEZ: #1406
ENERGY: #1141, #1150
INSTRUMENT: #0966, #1093
LARGE MANOR: #0849, #0856, #0859, #0944

⁂

#0555 - March 7, 2019 @ 22:05 (San Francisco, California)

[0555.1 / 1369] [THE WEAVER and I walk towards a car on a cloudy day. I recall a memory of my dog CHARLEE as a puppy. I feel sad.
"I miss her," I tell THE WEAVER.
"I should've fed her less."]

[0555.2 / 1370] [*Much men*] //

⁂

Maj. = 0- THE WEAVER: #0557

PUPPY: #0871, #0997, #1060
CLOUDY: #0945, #0988
✢

#0556 - March 8, 2019 @ 02:45 (San Francisco, California)

[0556.1 / 1371] [THE AYURVEDIC walk outside on a wintery night. Snow blows all around her as she walks towards a house with soft yellow light pouring from a window.]

[0556.2 / 1372] [MARK ZUCKERBERG chauffeurs me around a college campus in a car. He keeps trying to convince me he was *"ready for the college tune up."* I describe my university experience to him as, *"overwhelming."*]

[0556.3 / 1373] [I go to a dark house. I enter "Ashley's" bedroom. No one's there but the bed is unmade. I lay down and notice the sheets stink of stale sweat and body odor. The sheets have not been changed in many years, perhaps an indeterminable amount of time. The bed is a portal, a launch pad to deep esoteric levels of dream state. I fall through and pass a number of people I don't know. I briefly see THE PUBLIC MEDIUM before he flies away and I'm left alone.
'I'm in limbo. The 'in between.' Perhaps a Bardo realm."]

[0556.4 / 1374] [THE FARMHAND and THE POSTMASTER offer to take THE NEWLY-WEDS *(optimistic, connected, and cosmopolitan)* on a weekend tour of Eureka Springs, Arkansas for their honeymoon. The four of them pile into a car and begin their road trip.]

[0556.5 / 1375] [I'm back in "Ashley's" bedroom. A black unlit Christmas tree ominously looms in the corner.]

[0556.6 / 1376] [THE FAIRY GODMOTHER teaches a college level course on United States Foreign Policy. The pace of the course quickens beyond my aptitude. I disconnect from the content and start thinking through the most effective ways to cheat on the upcoming exam. The class is taught in the study of a quiet bed and breakfast. I enter a sunroom. I notice a small square end table made of mahogany with a crystal candy dish on top along with stacks of yellow legal pads and partially unwrapped artisan chocolate bars. I find a bar of lavender chocolate alluring. As I lift it to my nose to smell it THE FAIRY GODMOTHER pops her head through the butler door and tells me to, *"just eat it or it'll get stale."*]

[0556.7 / 1377] [The family enjoys an outing in a public park with lots of light heartedness and laughter. A series of airplanes zoom overhead leaving the sky streaked with rainbow trails of smoke. The planes loop as I attempt to take a few photos of the dispersing rainbow ribbons in the sky, but my camera doesn't have a quick enough frame rate to capture the twinkling colors. THE CARPENTER and THE CHILD play in the short grass. It's hot outside.

THE CHILD falls down. She sweats profusely. THE CARPENTER runs over and sprays her with a water mister. They laugh. I feel alarmed because I think THE CHILD shows symptoms of Type 1 Diabetes, yet I don't say anything. I don't want to disrupt their fun. I observe them from a few steps away until I wake up.] //

⁎⁎

Maj. = *1- THE CARPENTER: #0558, 3- THE CHILD: #0561, 18- THE PUBLIC MEDIUM: #0621*
Min. = ♦- *THE AYURVEDIC: #0793,* ♣- *THE POSTMASTER: #0671,*
♥- *THE FARMHAND: #0659*
PORTAL: #0998, #1053, #1153
THE FAIRY GODMOTHER: #1111

⁎⁎

***

PART 8 - BRIGHT DARKNESS

#0557 - #0642

"Ev'ry sight these eyes behold
Does a different charm unfold;
Flashing gems and sculptur'd gold,
Still attract my ravish'd sight.
But to hear fair truth distilling,
In expressions choice and thrilling,
From that tongue so soft and killing,
That my soul does most delight."

-Queen of Sheba: Solomon

* * *

March 8, 2019 - May 5, 2019

⚜

⚜ 8.1 - THE BOOK OF PISCIS AUSTRINUS: 0557-0573 ⚜

#0557 - March 8, 2019 @ 05:18 (San Francisco, California)

[0557.1 / 1378] [I've decided to become a monk. I enter a monastery and surrender all my possessions. I'm given a set of chimes on a leather string. I take a vow of chastity (*which I instantly confuse with a vow of silence*). I climb up numerous ladders made of wooden dowels. Each ascends through a small square cut in the corner of a floor. On one level I ascend past a memorial chapel where a service is in progress. The next level houses a simple card table full of laminated prayers. The next level, a school for young children. I tire from climbing and hop off the ladder, stopping at my assigned living space. I encounter a woman who introduces herself as my roommate. She's not a monk. Her stuff is scattered everywhere as she unpacks. I say nothing as she hurries around. I leave my quarters and go to a dining hall where a beautiful blonde-haired man approaches me and invites me to join him for sushi. I don't remember him. Is he my partner? I wonder. I overhear an aggressive conversation occur nearby.

"What do we do if the technology fails?"

"Just. Keep. Going."]

[0557.2 / 1379] [I'm at a theme park with the family. We wait in line for our turn on a wooden roller coaster which boasts a series of steep cascading drops. We take the ride. GRANDMA takes the ride with us. When it completes, THE WEAVER has a very specific request for me to play a RASCAL FLATTS song she loves for GRANDMA. I'm not familiar with the song. THE WEAVER is rabidly insistent on creating a shared musical moment to remember our group ride. She's made the circumstances extremely significant. THE DANCER becomes visibly frustrated with me as I fumble with the phone to find the music. She screams and snags the phone from my hand. I say nothing.

We adjourn to a hot tub where a red mohawked version of THE FLIRT joins us and expresses his overt excitement about seeing a CIRQUE DU SOLEIL performance. THE DANCER pushes THE FLIRT's head under the hot tub water destroying his red mohawk. The scene devolves into hysterics. THE DANCER is ultimately embarrassed by her reaction. She ruined THE FLIRT's expensive color work.]

[0557.3 / 1380] [THE KOAN (*youthful, exuberant, and songful*) taps me on the shoulder and tells me to come with him. He and I get in the back of a pickup truck which speeds across a white desert plain at speeds of over 100mph.

"I'm taking you to sushi at 'SAMANCO'S PIG.'"

The truck moves faster. My neck will snap with any quick turn or shift in direction. The vehicle slows and we creep down the main street of a sleepy rural Midwestern town. We roll by a house with a large orange mail box. Large white block letters written across the mailbox read: RAYS CHEX. Only "Ray's" paychecks go in the repository. The homophonic spelling makes me giggle while thinking, *"Sun Cereal."* The truck rolls to a stop in a garage parking lot near a farmhouse with a white split rail fence. Within the fence is a square patch of short well-manicured emerald green grass, unmarred by the building's foot traffic. A large sign

hangs over the front door: SAMANCO's PIG. The location, name, and the pig icon confuse me. THE KOAN waves at me to follow him inside insisting,
"*This is THE place for sushi.*"]

[0557.4 / 1381] [I look at a journal where I've started an entry and have either lost interest or fallen asleep. A series of words fades into a scribble that crosses over multiple pages. It begins looking like a sine wave-like script and rapidly devolves into a flat line.] //

✲✲

Maj. = 0- THE WEAVER: #0560, 2- THE DANCER: #0561, 11- GRANDMA: #0597
BLOCK LETTERS: #0803, #0846, #0906, #0919, #0979, #1056
SLEEPY: #0846, #0922, #1073
THE FLIRT: #0563
THE KOAN: #1125

✲✲

#0558 - March 9, 2019 @ 04:00 (San Francisco, California)

[0558.1 / 1382] [I'm on an airplane that rolls quickly up and down a hilly runway. As the plane takes off, I tumble heels over my head and have a vision of the plane exploding in under sixty seconds. I don't want that to happen. I change my thoughts. The flight stabilizes. I'm more fully aware my thoughts are powerful. They create reality.]

[0558.2 / 1383] [I encounter a male Latin lover named "Eros" in a large bathroom on the upper deck of a jumbo jet. We canoodle and flirt on a large round white satin mattress. Our sexual encounter trends from gentle to aggressive. I tear his underwear and penetrate him. He tells me he loves me as I thrust harder. He puts his hand to my mouth and tells me he's changed his name to "Agape." I'm still tuned in to the frequency of "Eros." At the moment, I don't have an equally vulnerable response to meet him where he is.]

[0558.2 / 1384] [World War II: THE CARPENTER holds an important military role, account-able for the "nuclear codes," a series of computer punch cards in a shoebox. The word "NUKES" is crudely printed in black letters across the top of the box.
"*Why do we do what we do?*" THE CARPENTER asks his soldiers.
"*TO PRESERVE THE FATE OF THE FREE WORLD, SIR!*"
The group cheers as THE CARPENTER ducks into an office with an opaque glass door. The word "GENERAL" is printed on the door in similar crude black block letters. I use a restroom adjacent to the office. As I urinate, I overhear someone in the desk pit get wildly and publicly reprimanded for placing a hyperbolic margin trade that's rendered the firm insolvent.]

[0558.3 / 1385] [An olive-skinned child shoots a Tootsie Roll gun on a public bus, creating nuisance and alarm.] //

⁎⁎

Maj. = 1- THE CARPENTER: #0568
AGAPE: #0885, #0927
WHITE SATIN: #0844, #1173

⁎⁎

#0559 - March 10, 2019 @ 03:00 (San Francisco, California)

[0559.1 / 1386] [I'm a woman. BARBRA STREISAND is my best friend. She and I text Spotify song links to each other as we chat over lunch. We enjoy our monthly "lady day out." She's so lovely to be around. She knows how to make me laugh.]

[0559.2 / 1387] [It's the distant future. I'm a member of a spy team. My team attempts to infiltrate and apprehend an enemy group. We proceed in a line along a narrow path between two concrete walls. I break from the group and slink sideways through a slit in the wall. I'm instantly captured under an interstate overpass. My surrender is uneventful. Unexpectedly, my captors show me the technology I intended to steal when I ask. They aren't threatened by my curiosity and give me all the information I request. A large hologram composed of colorful triangles hovers in front of me as a download is sent to the center of my head. One of my partners is captured and stands across from me. Our captors fit him with a mask and feed him pure oxygen as he's given the same holographic cerebral "brain bath" transmission.

Once complete, we're both taken to a social event at a large concert hall. A dance party is underway, and a DJ performs. I wear headphones and stream my own music. I gain access to a special area where people wear zippered onesies. Interpersonal conflicts are settled with "dance offs." The mood is playful and fun.] //

⁎⁎

BARBRA STREISAND: #0788
DANCE: #1155, #1191
OXYGEN: #1101, #1146
EAR PLUGS: #1088

⁎⁎

#0560 - March 11, 2019 @ 03:58 (San Francisco, California)

[0560.1 / 1388] [I'm at a gas station at night during a rainstorm with THE WEAVER.]

[0560.2 / 1389] [I've moved back into THE JESTER's home on "Buckingham Dr."]

[0560.3 / 1390] [I play with a toddler. The young boy grips a flat square toy. Round black and white buttons line the edge of both sides. It lights up and plays simple music.]

[0560.4 / 1391] [I sit back and admire a large orange mural.]

. . .

[0560.5 / 1392] [I listen to someone's advance copy of the new TOOL album. I'm not impressed by it.]

[0560.6 / 1393] [I run around the main level of a corporate plaza between skyscrapers.]

[0560.7 / 1394] [I compete at a gymnastic event. THE KIWI (*deliberate, adventurous, and lonely*) supports me as I psyche myself up to perform a routine. One guy completes a high bar routine in reverse, beginning with a "stuck" dismount. Another does a one arm handstand on the parallel bars.]

[0560.8 / 1395] [I get ready for bed and notice I have a severe sunburn on half of my face. I look in the mirror at the splotchy red marks and ask THE WEAVER,
"Why didn't you tell me to reapply sunscreen sooner?"] //

⁂

Maj. = 0- THE WEAVER: #0580
Min. = ◆- THE JESTER: #0747
TOOL: #0792
PARALLEL BARS: #0831, #0909, #0932, #0933, #0953, #0967
SIMPLE: #0969, #0983, #1000, #1023, #1044, #0163
SUNSCREEN: #0838, #0857
THE KIWI: #0603

⁂

#0561 - March 12, 2019 @ 03:04 (San Francisco, California)

[0561.1 / 1396] [I take a cab ride. I'm astonished by the beautiful psychedelic sunset occurring out the left side window; soft pastel tones, scattered across the sky in jagged geometric patterns. It's captivating and soothing to behold.]

[0561.2 / 1397] [THE KANGAROO hosts a party at a new home. He offers me a black can of beer, then quickly turns away to have sex with a large Black man. THE KANGAROO quickly grows bored and becomes fascinated with an obese Latinx man on the other side of the room who he proceeds to have another impromptu sexual encounter, simply to gather more data for his self-described, "fuck model."]

[0561.3 / 1398] [I work in a large warehouse event space with a team of five. We're tasked to create a solution to lift a soundboard supported by a PVC pipe frame. We make various lift attempts with ropes made from red Licorice and thick, sturdy hemp. Neither option achieves the intended result. THE LALA looks on supportively as our coach, though we repeatedly fail.]

. . .

[0561.4 / 1399] [I'm in THE LAWYER's home. I discover a fully furnished basement level, pristinely clean and rarely used. One of the rooms has taupe shag carpet. Abundant natural light flows in from a series of rectangular windows. A kitchen/bar area filled with campy decor items is organized for storage, but all items remain unboxed and have likely been there for years. I'm particularly captivated by a series of high back wrought iron bar stools with black diamond shaped seats.

Am I in a video game? Small green jewels hang in the air above various items. They pulse and seemingly suggest I take a closer look. The green gemlets can be plucked from their stationary hover posts and collected. I check my phone and notice THE CAMERAMAN (*rugged, productive, and inquisitive*) tagged me as the host for this weekend's impromptu, "misfit dinner party." I don't have a space of my own that fits "no fewer than 9 guests" as the invite conveys. THE LAWYER's basement would be a perfect location, but I'm concerned "the misfits" will ruin the space. I hesitate accepting the request to host.

I walk out the brightly lit basement back door and spill out onto a cobblestone pathway that traverses an impeccably manicured lawn. I walk to the edge of an unfilled pool where THE NURSE gives directions to a construction crew. They dump and spread multiple tons of beach sand along the perimeter of the pool. These small sand dunes are essential. They'll create a particular action shot the director of a documentary desires.

"The pool gets filled next. Then the whales get flown in later tonight," THE NURSE says as work continues all around us.]

[0561.5 / 1400] [THE ATHEIST and I laugh as we set pairs of photos side by side. One set of photos are of a large dog making different human facial expressions. The other set are of THE CHILD mimicking what the dog does in the paired image. We laugh until our sides ache.]

[0561.6 / 1401] [I'm back poolside after work has concluded. An animatronic hippo rests motionless in the center of the pool, as a "budget conscious" alternative. Flying in a pod of live whales for one shot was deemed too extravagant by the producers.]

[0561.7 / 1402] [I wear white crew socks and put on a pair of antique roller skates. They don't fit my feet. They come alive and begin to pull me on an adventure out and onto a busy city street against the flow of rush hour traffic. I scream a few times as I dart between cars fast approaching from the opposite direction. The skates laugh and spark as they increase their speed.]

[0561.8 / 1403] [THE DANCER and I rent a car on a blustery winter night. A paper-thin layer of snow and ice coat the vehicles and parking lot. We don't seem to notice this as we continue chattering. We're surprised when the vehicle's wheels spin wildly after I firmly hit the throttle.]

[0561.9 / 1404] [I'm head server at a black-tie caterer. A disagreement during an event erupts between female members of my team. A younger woman accuses the eldest woman on the

team of stealing gratuities. A collection of bills falls from the old woman's apron on to a silver platter. I'd previously defended her, though I now know that I too have been duped. I angrily scream at the old woman in front of the group,
"*STOP IT! STOP IT! STOP IT! STOP IT!*"]

[0561.10 / 1405] [I convince a group of students to attend a lecture given by THE LALA.] //

⁂

Maj. = 1- THE DANCER: #0580, 3- THE CHILD: #0566, 5- THE LAWYER: #0582,
8- THE ATHEIST: #0610, 13- THE NURSE: #0592
Min. = ♦- THE LALA: #0570, ♠- THE KANGAROO: #0786
BLACK: #0858, #0867, #0872, #0878, #0883
SILVER PLATTER: #0820, #0920
THE CAMERAMAN: #1272

⁂

#0562 - March 12, 2019 @ 06:20 (San Francisco, California)

[0562.1 / 1406] [I'm in the hospital. I've sustained a significant injury to my neck and hip, which leaves me in substantial pain. The entire right side of my body is incapacitated.]

[0562.2 / 1407] [I take a city bus one stop past where I normally get off. The next stop is multiple miles away with no returning public footpath. I can't simply double back and walk home. I'm not sure what to do. I keep riding. The bus drops me off at the end of the line.]

[0562.3 / 1408] [THE FBI AGENT (*gregarious, direct, and powerful*) and I share a casual conversation over tea.]

[0562.4 / 1409] [I'm behind a sound mixing board in a dark room blaring the song "PARADISE CITY." A side door opens. Light flows in. It's the middle of the day.]

[0562.5 / 1410] [Someone hands me a small candy in a red wrapper. Without thinking I open it and pop it in my mouth. I taste chocolate, peanuts and peanut butter. I realize I've broken my "no sweets" contract and spit it out before swallowing it. I know I owe the NRA $5000 for failing, but try to rationalize my lack of presence as an "honest mistake."] //

⁂

MIXING: #0830
CASUAL CONVERSATION: #1196
SIDE DOOR: #1152
HONEST: #0891, #0907, #1168

⁂

#0563 - March 13, 2019 @ 02:56 (San Francisco, California)

[0563.1 / 1411] [I'm at a suburban home with a large flat, grassy backyard. It's dusky. THE MODERN CAVEMEN *(curious, entrepreneurial, and muscular)* have invited me to their home for dinner. They share a multilevel property. They chop and sauté vegetables over flame in a modern kitchen with large windows. The action in the space speeds up making some details ambiguous.

I find myself thumbing through a stack of mail, noting an invitation printed on thin 8.5" x 11" Styrofoam. An image of THE FLIRT and THE C-SUITE *(masterful, linguistically cunning, and precise)* embracing is set above text that identifies them as sponsors for a popular annual community fundraiser.

I pass THE BOSS in a hallway who says, *"Be sure to call me in six months about those five cyber jobs."*

A couple takes selfies with a handheld device that produces a spiral of images similar to what one would receive from a photo booth. The image orientation is backwards from what I would expect.

I stop to watch a guy give a live demonstration of a new masturbation device constructed of a vertical rod and two flat elements that squish his penis like dough.

A woman approaches me to flirt. Across the room, I see a man get angry as she touches my arm. I quickly respond,

"Dude, I'm not a threat...I'm gay."

THE MODERN CAVEMEN take me out a back door and on to a cat walk. DANNY ELFMAN-like Simpson's theme music accompanies us at low volume. We approach a cabinet where one of THE MODERN CAVEMEN plucks a small hypersonic aircraft from a storage rack and holds it in front of his chest. He tosses the plane towards a coworker who stands and shouts up at us from a lower level.]

[0563.2 / 1412] [I'm in a basement bedroom next to a bunk bed. I see a disembodied head slink its way across the parquet floor, using its spine as a bloody tail to inch along. The severed head attaches itself to random objects, attempting to find a body. It may be mentally retarded. Its eyes have been severely injured. The head uses a simple single word vocabulary that it constantly repeats as it follows me. Perhaps the head used to belong to the decapitated body of an obese man that lays bloodily nearby?] //

⁎⁎

BUNK: #0858, #1153
VEGETABLE: #1071
THE BOSS: #0618
THE MODERN CAVEMEN: #0662
THE FLIRT: #0887
THE C-SUITE: #1419

⁎⁎

#0564 - March 13, 2019 @ 06:30 (San Francisco, California)

[0564.1 / 1413] [Part of this dream involves being at a yoga studio, attending a class where the incorrect teacher has been scheduled. I fall asleep on my mat. I'm clapped awake and open a side door to let fresh air flow in as a woman next to me is given some water in a paper cone.]

[0564.2 / 1414] [I'm at a county general store where among myriad activities I take note of a whiskey barrel full of sawdust and partially eaten oversized donuts. They're unappetizing.]

[0564.3 / 1415] [A stapler-like device dispenses different types of silhouette pellets: 1) Birds in flight and 2) Shark teeth. It repeatedly breaks as I try to repair it.] //

⁂

SILHOUETTE: #0855, #0867, #0929, #0933, #0941, #0944
FRESH: #0813, #0878, #0995, #1024, #1144
OVERSIZED: #1059, #1085, #1089

⁂

#0565 - March 14, 2019 @ 07:30 (San Francisco, California)

[0565.1 / 1416] [Mostly abstraction, but some of it involves working with three young men from down the street. We discuss starting a band.]

[0565.2 / 1417] [I enter a house occupied by THE COUTURIER and her roommates, who all lounge around in a loose cuddle puddle after a party. They may be watching television as they drift in and out of consciousness. I'm protective of an oversized JBL cylindrical speaker which I hold on my lap. I climb up into a crawl space bedroom with the speaker and fall asleep with it on my chest. The space overhead is draped with a single white bed sheet held up in the middle by a thick white dowel. More happens after I wake from my nap, but the detail quickly dissolves.] //

⁂

Min. = ♣- *THE COUTURIER: #0835*
DOWEL: #0897, #0927
CRAWL: #0829, #1169, #1181, #1200

⁂

#0566 - March 15, 2019 @ 05:16 (San Francisco, California)

[0566.1 / 1418] [I'm in a tropical climate in an urban environment. I might be in a large city in south Florida. A large storm seems to be moving through. I experience myself on both sides of it. I'm out of body on the side of the storm after it's passed. A gorgeous sunset across a dark cloudy sky illuminates the city. In my body, I can see the storm approaching from behind the wheel of the rental car I'm driving. Some friends are with me. We're driving across a bridge on our way to a large sporting event. We plan on tailgating.]

. . .

[0566.2 / 1419] [Some ambiguity occurs. I get an omniscient glimpse of myself and THE CHILD sharing blue ice cream with chocolate chips served on sugar cones. We lick our treats and giggle, sharing a sweet moment between uncle and niece. She's perhaps 7 or 8 years old.]

[0566.3 / 1420] [I blink again and I'm back along the coast line, near a levee wall that feels alien and futuristic. After some frenetic travel I have multiple short interactions with two teenage boys. They stand across from me shaking a small tincture bottle of a substance they call "LSD." They're on bikes on the first fly by. They return another time on skateboards, and I follow them. Once home and inside, I peek in on them. One boy puts an uncovered plastic beaker on top of a refrigerator to hide it from his parents. The substance in the beaker is a red liquid, which they test to confirm is actually "LSD." A few droplets splash out of the beaker and on top of the fridge. A few drops land on the boy's hand. He doesn't realize he's dosed himself as he and his friends get back on their bikes and ride toward the storm.] //

⁎⁎

Maj. = 3- THE CHILD: #0597
TEENAGE BOYS: #0999
FLORIDA: #0841, #1029, #1103

⁎⁎

#0567 - March 16, 2019 @ 04:48 (San Francisco, California)

[0567.1 / 1421] [This hologram is dark and terrifying. The bulk of the scene takes place at an art gallery and centers around interactions between myself and three other people. I might be a woman, but that's not clear. A large hall presents an installation in a square on the floor marked by burgundy velvet ropes. People are invited to peer over the ropes and walk around the piece. A female performance artist enters the square and begins skillet frying raw chicken. She's attacked from behind and bludgeoned to death. Onlookers believe the dead body is part of the installation. Another woman outside the roped off square becomes suspicious and is similarly killed. The gallery curator discovers the grisly scene and promptly calls the police. I'm not sure of my role. Am I a witness? An accomplice? The gallery calmly clears as police sirens approach.] //

⁎⁎

VELVET: #0931, #0956
INSTALLATION: #0837, #0916, #0943, #0987, #0999, #1050, #1080
WITNESS: #0880, #0908, #0937, #0944, #0961, #0999, #1005

⁎⁎

#0568 - March 17, 2019 @ 03:31 (San Francisco, California)

[0568.1 / 1422] [I drive a dune buggy across the sand.]

[0568.2 / 1423] [I'm at a concert hall with THE CARPENTER. We purchase tickets to see NINE INCH NAILS. We enter the venue, then discover ourselves back outside in line. When we return to the ticket counter the agent (*a large fat man with a booming voice*) points to me and says, *"THIS GUY!"* He prints me two tickets, both front row VIP seats that each cost $1139. THE CARPENTER is reluctant to accept but I grab his hand and we head inside. It's extremely hot within the venue. The air is humid and thick. TRENT REZNOR has unexpectedly thick and long hair. His face is lit by bright white LED's. He embraces a young woman onstage, recognizing her as the key performer in the live band. He seems prepared but tired and sad.]

[0568.3 / 1424] [I'm in a forest near a log cabin. LUKE PERRY passes me dressed in pantomime drag. A red curly wig hides under a large brimmed hat. He carries a pink parasol.]

[0568.4 / 1425] [I'm back at the NINE INCH NAILS show and am momentarily confused by orchestral music created by the band.]

[0568.5 / 1426] [I'm at the Burning Man temple. A table inside seemingly offers different varieties of screen-printed napkins. I pick up a stack of "HBS Graduation" napkins and give them to THE FLASH. THE CONNECTOR finds out what I've done and becomes sad. I've taken something off an altar. It wasn't just a table. THE FLASH returns the napkins and other items to THE CONNECTOR, acting as a steward and the interaction resolves.]

[0568.6 / 1427] [I stand in front of three TV screens in a dusty tent. A game is underway. The objective is to stack white dots in increasingly complex patterns as said dots jump between screens from left to right. The challenge is to keep the dots on all three screens in play. Players balance different levels of complexity at the same time to advance to higher levels. I create patterns with up to six dots, while maintaining the "5's, 4's, 3's, 2's and 1's."] //

**

Maj. = 1- THE CARPENTER: #0580, 4- THE CONNECTOR: #0570
TRENT REZNOR: #0762
LUKE PERRY: #1081
NINE INCH NAILS: #0755
DOTS: #0956, #1003, #1028
COMPLEX PATTERN: #1172, #1177
THE FLASH: #0946

**

#0569 - March 17, 2019 @ 05:26 (San Francisco, California)

[0569.1 / 1428] [Parts of this feel like a horror movie. I watch a disc with three hollow daggers attached to it hover above the ground and quickly fly towards a body, plunging itself into the person. Observing the act feels dark and brooding.]

[0569.2 / 1429] [THE FEELER shows up, but I'm not sure why she's come. She says nothing.]

. . .

[0569.3 / 1430] A blurry scene momentarily sharpens and fades as a voice speaks, *"This is an experiment. ____ _ ____."*]

[0569.4 / 1431] [I stand on a busy street corner. Seems I'm a tour guide leading a group. I ask them to participate in a vocal exercise. I take cues as to which words to use from a green awning on a nearby building. An image of an all-white traffic signal seems useful. It's animated. Is it nonsense? It's printed on durable waxed cloth. THE BONSAI (*shy, quiet, and sweet natured*) doesn't initially buy into the tour, nor my presentation style. After some coaxing he leads the exercise for me. Much more occurs but fades as I wake up.] //

✼✼

Min. = ♣- THE FEELER: #0666

EXPERIMENT: #0853, #0976, #0998, #1006, #1171, #200

TOUR GUIDE: #0929

HOLLOW: #0902, #1157, #1177

✼✼

#0570 - March 19, 2019 @ 03:43 (San Francisco, California)

[0570.1 / 1432] [*So much happens so quickly I instantly forget. *]

[0570.2 / 1433] [I'm in a parking lot. I'm next to two other guys named "Josh." We stay inside our "lines" as we talk. THE LALA's up an incline and smiles as we shout back and forth about funding strategies for a startup. We're keen to select the aligned venture capitalists in forthcoming funding rounds. One of the "Josh's" looks like THE CONNECTOR's roommate. The pace is quick. It's night time. There may not be an atmosphere on this planet. Black space.] //

✼✼

Maj. = 4- THE CONNECTOR: #0583

Min. = ♦- THE LALA: #0571

INSTANTLY: #0801, #0814, #0844, #0852, #0858, #0871

✼✼

#0571 - March 19, 2019 @ 05:48 (San Francisco, California)

[0571.1 / 1434] [I travel with a group, predominantly by air. A lot of what I experience is classroom oriented. We're given multiple assignments to complete using computers. I am less familiar with computers than my counterparts. My eyes become overstimulated by screen light, which makes me feel anxious. Additionally, requested computer work puts me into overwhelm. I can't move quickly enough to meet due dates.

We move as a group, working as we cross through a Korean airport. We leave the airport and travel by car. I'm assigned to drive, since I'm the slowest and fail to complete my computer tasks. I drive down a dirt road crying and nonsensically babbling because I've failed.

"The Earth has a pulse!" "The Earth is _____." "The Earth is _____."
I make a variety of advocating statements in defense of the planet. THE LALA coaches and provides some reassurance as I navigate my struggle. I don't want to forget. It's very challenging.]

[0571.2 / 1435] [I go upstairs to ask THE PILOT a question. The lights are low. I notice a piece of art I gave him has been tossed out into the hallway and destroyed. The hooks and shoelaces have been pulled off from the edges of the 36" x 36" square canvas frame. A single shoe lace remains, but all of the mirrors have been pried off. A black canvas with a shoe glued to it remains. It's been used and discarded. I barely recognize it.] //

⁎⁎

Maj. = 6- THE PILOT: #0656
Min. = ♦- THE LALA: #0573
PULSE: #0844, #0874, #0996, #1078, #1168
SHOE: #1024, #1132

⁎⁎

#0572 - March 20, 2019 @ 08:30 (San Francisco, California)

[0572.1 / 1436] [I'm at a large outdoor gathering at an amphitheater temple space fashioned from large stones. A group of us face a rectangular opening where a large brilliant gold sun shines, perfectly centered. The mood is positive and social. A small white sun passes in front of the gold sun creating a much anticipated "super solar eclipse." I consider taking a picture, then turn away and photograph a dark forest quickly illuminated by a rush of brilliant diamond gold light.]

[0572.2 / 1437] [I hover in space in front of a giant moon eclipsing the sun. The vast center of the eclipse is black, cold, still and neutral. The rim of the eclipse is a precise, pristine ring of pure diamond light.] //

⁎⁎

BRILLIANT: #0830, #0852, #0854, #0856, #0874, #087
FOREST: #0972, #1140
DIAMOND LIGHT: #0893, #0976, #1083, 1193

⁎⁎

#0573 - March 21, 2019 @ 02:49 (San Francisco, California)

[0573.1 / 1438] [I'm FREDDY MERCURY, out of body and hovering near a stage where hundreds of thousands of fans clamor before a giant red velvet curtain that reads, "QUEEN." The crowd is underwhelmed when the curtain rises to reveal THE QUEEN OF ENGLAND behind a podium who gives "State of the State" remarks. This humors me.]

[0573.2 / 1439] [I beta test a new fitness app on a phone while walking under a freeway overpass. Only half the content is reviewable and I don't find the experience engaging. I wouldn't use it.]

[0573.3 / 1440] [A group moves their business operations hub to "Mason City, Ohio." As they establish a call center, I'm asked if I have connections to the "Bush Family." I make incongruent and incoherent comparisons to the Kennedy Family saying,
"What happened in Kennebunkport was SO DAMN GOOD."
I wink at the boss believing I'm aware of what REALLY happened at Chappaquiddick. I make a bunch of cold calls and instantly convert them to large recurring donations. The female lead exclaims,
"Give this guy a job!"]

[0573.4 / 1441] [JOE BIDEN and I sit under a tarp in a homeless encampment. As we talk, we take small brown packages from large cardboard boxes and split their backs open. Small almond sized candies are inside; chocolate covered cacao nibs, dusted in darker chocolate. As I eat them, I realize each one costs me $5000. I just ate $25,000 worth of candy with a casual lift of a palm to my mouth. I'm more preoccupied with the exorbitant expenditure then telling JOE,
'I know he's not going to win the election.']

[0573.5 / 1442] [I'm invited to join a card game. Among those playing; THE LALA, THE NEUROSCIENTIST (*gritty, forward moving, and grieving*) and THE LACHRYMOLOGIST (*willing, purging, and unapologetic*). All players have brought their own coins for wagering. I'm most fascinated by THE NEUROSCIENTIST's, who has a series of tiny silver stars scattered near his side of the table which look like rank pins found on the shoulders of a military general's uniform. My coins are three different sizes and have been asymmetrically stacked and welded together. I toss my cards to the center mid-hand because I don't understand how to play the game. The table plays on without me.] //

⁎⁎

Min. = ◆-*THE LALA: #0633*
ELECTION: #0952, #0988
GENERAL: #0829, #0878, #0943, #0979, #1155, #1179
MASON: #1082
THE LACHRYMOLOGIST: #0631

⁎⁎

♣ 8.2 - THE BOOK OF URSA MINOR: 0574-0581 ♣

#0574 - March 21, 2019 @ 04:43 (San Francisco, California)

[0574.1 / 1443] [TENAYA THE CAT whistles on top of a garbage can in an alley.]

[0574.2 / 1444] [It's night. Pitch black. I'm struck from behind by a fast moving, black car. My upper leg breaks and my body is tossed into the air. This happens a few times. I wake up on the floor next to THE PIXIE saying,
"I need to take the cues. I need to write this down."
The scene starts again. Each time more team members are present when I wake up mangled on the floor. I've shown up for them in the past, so they show up for me.
"If I don't take the cues, I'm not taking care of myself," I say as I write a thorough account of everything I've remembered.
I find myself at the beginning of the scene. The car hits me again and startles me out of sleep.] //

✲

Min. ♠- THE PIXIE: #0654
TENAYA THE CAT: #865, #1112
WHISTLE: #0865, #0873, #0874, #1171
PITCH: #0967, #0982

✲

#0575 - March 21, 2019 @ 05:53 (San Francisco, California)

[0575.1 / 1445] [I'm a teenage female gymnast, training for elite competition. The gymnasium and equipment are pristine. The coaches are focused, precise, exacting and flow from an intention of compassion.]

[0575.2 / 1446] [I wear a hoodie to cover up sunburn on my back and face. I've surfed all morning. I walk towards a cabana hearing others debate an event schedule.
"It's 5 to 9."
"No, it's 9 to 5."
"11am to 1pm is the hottest part of the day," I break in.
The conversation shifts to discussion about the optimal time to be out of the sun, yet on the beach. Heat radiates off the back of my body into my hoodie.]

[0575.3 / 1447] [A young girl sits at a round white-cloth table in a pristine dining room.
"We have an identity crisis here," I say jokingly.
"Wasn't I already here?"
The young girl appears confused and remains silent as I continue.
"Did you see me sit down?"
"Who was here first?"
My last question prompts an adult female teacher to intercede.]

[0575.4 / 1448] [I'm in the clubhouse. I pass by a table with snacks for sale, but no clerk is present. A thick reed woven basket holds triangular segments of blueberry waffles dusted with powdered sugar. I justify chowing down on a couple because they're supposedly "Whole Grain & Organic." My eyes catch a glimpse of thin, ovular, palm sized treats composed of three layers: Rice Crispy, Toffee, and Chocolate. I take four of them. As I eat the first, I realize I've just spent $5000. An adjacent case displays tiny Japanese petit fours. I look through the Lucite display case and am amazed by their detail and how they hover in space, defying gravity.] //

⁂

CLERK: #1110, #1161
WHOLE: #0917, #0983
$5000: #0815
RICE: #1091

⁂

#0576 - March 22, 2019 @ 05:41 (San Francisco, California)

[0576.1 / 1449] [I'm at a gathering where hundreds of people wear white. It's prayerful and light. A group of women stand shoulder to shoulder in a long straight line. I turn around and discover a larger man and petite woman staring angrily at me. Both brandish bloody knives. They intend to kill me. I turn away from them to view the line of women. The couple stands in front of the line and moves methodically from one woman to the next, slicing the left eye of each with a straight razor. The petite woman commits all the corporal violence. The man stands behind her. They're after *"LEANDRA."* BARON BAPTISTE leads the bigger group in a meditation as more women are maimed and bleed.]

[0576.2 / 1450] [Scene in a restaurant.]
[0576.3 / 1451] [Image of a small child.]
[0576.4 / 1452] [A man wraps his head in plastic cling, attempting to suffocate himself.] //

⁂

BARON BAPTISTE: #0603
KILL ME: #0834, #0977
LEFT EYE: #0892, #1085
SUFFOCATE: #1034

⁂

#0577 - March 22, 2019 @ 06:34 (San Francisco, California)

[0577.1 / 1453] [I surprise myself! I've just given my second reading with my eyes open. I attend a lecture on the "self-transforming mind." I intuitively read the group as it gathers and receive an insight: *"The aligned path for this lifetime initiated after an experience at age 12."*

The lecturer, a small Asian man, laughs as he pulls the classroom door closed.

"You all are so funny to witness the first time you arrive here. Once embodied you will be the best humans ever!"

He references seeing the world from one's direct connection to the divine and the peculiar phenomenon that renders us dumb while in the experience. The group is neutral and present, yet most can't speak. Some need help blinking their eyes. They're supported.]

[0577.2 / 1454] [THE BODHI PUNK *(skeptical, experienced, and candid)* asks me to lead a drum circle in a spacious hexagonal teak wood cabin with vaulted ceilings.]

[0577.3 / 1455] [I want to sing. I stop a crowd in the street and invite everyone to participate.] //

⁂

SING: #0821, #0830, #0868, #0914, #0929, #0933, #1074, #1145
DRUM: #0860, #0868, #0933, #0953, #0987, #1033, #1102
READING: #0813, #0886, #0970, #1063, #1101, #1152, #1178

⁂

#0578 - March 23, 2019 @ 05:18 (San Francisco, California)

[0578.1 / 1456] [A group of pre-teen kids gather in an alley at the intersection of "Van Ness & Seitan," in an industrial area of a city. Two boys challenge each other to a foot race. I watch from behind a chain link fence. The course is one lap, and a straight line out and back. At the far end stand large rectangular wooden boards that must be climbed up and over upon the return. The course is divided directly down the middle by a high fence. One of the boys injures his left foot on the way back to the finish line. He loses. The other wins.]

[0578.2 / 1457] [I'm in a snowy town, perhaps an English village. Another similar aged boy and I share an adventure. We're thinking up ways to get inside "Willy Wonka's" chocolate factory. It's playful, musical and exciting to be characters in the sequel to a beloved childhood story.] //

⁂

CHAIN LINK FENCE: #0864, #1088
LEFT FOOT: #0960, #1022, #1105, #1183
ADVENTURE: #0865, #1168

⁂

#0579 - March 23, 2019 @ 08:07 (San Francisco, California)

[0579.1 / 1458] [THE THERAPIST *(feminine, guided, and receptive)* drives a car. I sit in the back seat as we talk. It's sunny. The windows are down. The air rushing through the cabin makes it difficult to hear her speak.]

[0579.2 / 1459] [I'm very satisfied with the video presentation I've created. When I share my joy with coworkers, I realize I deleted the final content and didn't save it. There's no back up. THE CONCIERGE *(aware, soothing, and supportive)* is nearby assisting a group of women. My backpack and fedora have been moved behind a customer service desk so they're out of the way.]

[0579.3 / 1460] [A team of people sells products at a convention, with client servicing and fulfillment supported by an offsite call center. "RAJ" calls me and wants to renegotiate a deal. He sold me a curio cabinet "As Is" and left a bunch of family heirlooms and items of signifi-cance *(to him)* in it when I made the purchase. I ponder whether to renegotiate the agreement, given this new information. I was aware of the items when he made the offer, "As Is." When he arrives joined by a woman, I don't recognize him.] //

⁑

DELETED: #1080

CUSTOMER SERVICE: #0867, #0977, #0979, #1159

BACK UP: #0897, #0974

THE THERAPIST: #1220

⁑

#0580 - March 24, 2019 @ 02:38 (San Francisco, California)
*I recall ~20% of the details of this dream. *

[0580.1 / 1461] [THE WEAVER, THE CARPENTER, THE DANCER and I have a discussion about a bizarre object in the center of a round table. The whole scene rapidly goes abstract and other details dissolve.]

[0580.2 / 1462] [I gather with my bandmates for the first time in years. We decide we want to tour again, but will only do it *"without the masks."* We're in a loft at night. Some scratch tracks play to set the mood. I grab my bass guitar and realize my chops are hella rusty. There's a lot of work to do before we tour.]

[0580.3 / 1463] [I'm in Firefighter Training with many others. Today's exercise takes place in an old brick warehouse surrounded by steel scaffolding and thick white canvas tarps. Training concludes and I go home.
My luxury condo building is ablaze. I pass by some neighbors I don't know but recognize as reality TV personalities *(PARIS HILTON, etc.)*. They're drunk on champagne, talking, and don't notice me as I walk by carrying my firefighter's suit *(which is neatly folded and very heavy)*.
I share the condo with a young heterosexual couple. When I go inside, I hear them enjoying a sexual encounter. An older female neighbor puts her foot in the doorway to block its closure and asks to see them. I ask her to come back later. I change out of my sparkly black sweater and put on my firefighter gear. I think it'll help people know it's time to evacuate. When they leave, I'll have more space.
I'm surprised when I go to the backyard and notice time has stopped. People are frozen mid-conversation, seated in various configurations around square propane fire pits at night. I see time as a wave. It moves closer from the right side of the space, to left, reanimating people as it washes over them.
"Time" is fluid and non-uniform.
I'm no longer concerned about the fire or smoke in the building.] //

⁑

Maj. = 0- THE WEAVER: #0591, 1- THE CARPENTER: #0582, 2-THE DANCER: #0610
BASS: #0853, #0860, #0868 #0953, #0961, #0971, #1039, #1102, #1110, #1189
HETEROSEXUAL: #0924, #1106, #1185

⁑

412

#0581 - March 25, 2019 @ 03:57 (San Francisco, California)

[0581.1 / 1464] [Production on a classic movie is underway. Dancing sequences similar to those in "Singin' in the Rain" are created in large chunks and will be cut in around the plot as it's filmed. Dancing is considered "filler."]

[0581.2 / 1465] [I have to return a rental car to the parking lot at a gas station. A large breasted woman drives the vehicle. We turn down a very steep hill. I'm seated behind her and grab her breasts so they don't fly up and obstruct her vision as we descend.]

[0581.3 / 1466] [I'm in a garage. Multiple cats run around.]

[0581.4 / 1467] [I'm in an office where THE FOUNDER (*silly, youthful, and good humored*) reprimands and dismisses a junior member of a cycling team. I ask THE FOUNDER to reconsider. THE DIPLOMAT (*balanced, open, and dedicated*) endorses THE FOUNDER's decision. The dismissal is tough for THE FOUNDER to make because the offending young man is from his home state of Kansas. THE FOUNDER introduces me to his newborn son. I pour myself a cup of coffee fashioned from a cardboard paper towel tube. How it holds liquid, I don't understand. Coffee isn't even an office perk. How did I get it?] //

⁂

COFFEE: #0817, #0870, #0899, #0933, #0939, #0975, #0989, #1004
RENTAL CAR: #0890, #0895, #0909, #0913, #0969, #1187
NEWBORN: #0916, #0952, #1108
THE FOUNDER: #1378

⁂

413

#0582 - March 26, 2019 @ 00:09 (San Francisco, California)

[0582.1 / 1468] [I'm in a mountain town. It's likely 1870. A new invention *(the cable car)* scales the side of a mountain, transporting people to new, never before seen heights.]

[0582.2 / 1469] [In a crevice between mountains a giant elk antler swivels to show the direction of the wind. The antler's suspended by a couple of large clear elastic bands which permit it to slowly descend from the top of the mountain to the bottom each day.]

[0582.3 / 1470] [*"Come for the final minutes of THE CARPENTER's last day,"* a voice beckons.]

[0582.4 / 1471] [*"Use Vagus nerve breathing to reduce recall time."* This seems very important.]

[0582.5 / 1472] [*"Bring others along for the ride (.... the next time around)." "Full engagement."*]

[0582.6 / 1473] [*"I didn't see how flawed and incomplete the previous model was before now."*]

[0582.7 / 1474] [THE LAWYER and I share a small condo. He's a giant. I'm small.]

[0582.8 / 1475] [Mountains.]

[0582.9 / 1476] [*"I may get right back to that..."*]

[0582.10 / 1477] [Sipping a delicious microbrew.] //

⚜

Maj. = 1- THE CARPENTER: #0584, 5- THE LAWYER: #0583

CABLE CAR: #0803, #0990, #1115

WIND: #0865, #0892, #0899, #0924, #0925

⚜

#0583 - March 26, 2019 @ 01:46 (San Francisco, California)

[0583.1 / 1478] [Creating video testimonials for Burning Man.]

[0583.2 / 1479] [Feeling pretty lighthearted and somewhat drunk I let THE CONNECTOR give me a haircut. I think I ask her to only trim the back and sides. When I come to, I realize she's cut most of the length from the top of my head, including "the swoop" in front of my eye line. I'm confused and sad for a moment, and then my attention quickly shifts.]

[0583.3 / 1480] [A group sets up a square barrier *(100 feet on a side)* to create the perimeter for a temple. THE LAWYER delivers orange plastic fencing on spools with his white SUV. He searches for a delivery confirmation signature. Night falls across the desert. Major art projects are illuminated by flood lights and surrounded by clear inflatable structures. These initially seemed like a good idea, but in practice actually suck dust inside from the surrounding ground.]

[0583.4 / 1481] [*"Sometimes relevant information comes through when we get dirty."*] //

⚜

Maj. = 4- THE CONNECTOR: #0660, 5- THE LAWYER: #0665

GOOD: #1073, #1095, #1146, #1155, #1183

DIRTY: #0870, #0904, #1052, #1131
HAIRCUT: #0819, #1000
⁂

#0584 - March 26, 2019 @ 03:07 (San Francisco, California)

[0584.1 / 1482] [THE CARPENTER jumps through a door with the intention of startling me. *"You're always letting the _____ in,"* he says. He hands me a piece of firm white cardstock with a series of horizontal lines drawn on it. I write alphabet characters in yellow marker across the grid of black, blue and red lines.] //

⁂

Maj. = 1- THE CARPENTER: #0598
HORIZONTAL: #1085, #1095, #1158
BLUE: #1085, #1109, #1129, #1133, #1141
⁂

#0585 - March 26, 2019 @ 03:56 (San Francisco, California)

[0585.1 / 1483] [I sit on the floor in an upstairs bathroom at night with THE SEASON *(fluid, expansive, and grounded)* and THE DEVOTEE. We've stayed up really late talking and giving each other tarot card readings. It's nearly 4:00am. I stand up and gather our drinking cups. We've used Riedel white wine glasses for our water. I pick up four of them with one hand. They first clink together in a clover formation, then settle into a diamond pattern as I lift them from the coffee table. Unintentionally, the door to our room slams really hard. For a moment we're afraid we've awakened everyone else in the house. When I open the door, I'm relieved because I hear a TV on downstairs. Someone else in the house is awake. There hasn't been any disruption.] //

⁂

Min. = ♠- THE DEVOTEE: #0759
DOWNSTAIRS: #0803, #0813, #0841, #0857, #0904, #0913, #0916
DRINKING: #0965, #0999, #1193
THE SEASON: #0618
⁂

#0586 - March 27, 2019 @ 06:47 (San Francisco, California)

[0586.1 / 1484] [I learn to drive while sitting in my 8th chakra. The car is new and somewhat challenging to control. The vehicle pulls out of a two-car garage and descends down a grassy hill to a parking lot where THE TRANSLATOR leads a class. It starts to rain. The class moves inside. I look for a bathroom. The one I enter may have a large man inside, who's asleep in a stall. An overflowed toilet spills a thick green gooey ooze all over the floor and swirls towards a drain in the center of the room. I try another bathroom door. I'm unable to enter. The room behind the door is stacked floor to ceiling with chairs.] //

⁂

Maj. = 19- THE TRANSLATOR: #0703

415

GRASSY: #0944, #0980, #1080, #1184, #1191
DRAIN: #1186
8TH: #0890
.*.*

#0587 - March 28, 2019 @ 03:44 (San Francisco, California)

[0587.1 / 1485] [STEPHEN COLBERT is my student. He leaves me a voicemail.]
[0587.2 / 1486] [People gather for a ceremony.]
[0587.3 / 1487] [WARREN BUFFETT approaches as I stand in line. He's very old and has difficulty walking. I invite him to cut the line.]

[0587.4 / 1488] [I'm in Sedona, Arizona. I stand outside a geodesic "Bio dome." A black oily fluid leaks up from cracks in the ground. I see a rainbow inside through the dome's thick clear glass. Some people complain they'd wish the town wouldn't just be known for, *"this expensive and stupid project."*]

[0587.5 / 1489] [A woman makes a difficult decision. I high five her for being a _____.]

[0587.6 / 1490] [I eat a plate full of chicken and onion tacos at an upstairs pub table. THE MAGICIAN climbs a small spiral staircase and catches me with my mouthful.]

[0587.7 / 1491] [I pass by an older Black man. I'm intrigued by his "snap on" toupee.]

[0587.8 / 1492] [THE KETTLE (*dramatic, reactive, and mean*) is assigned as my dancing partner. We're supposed to rehearse a duet as an homage to CHARLIE CHAPLIN, wearing bowler hats and using canes. THE KETTLE stays on the far side of the rehearsal space and remains passive.]

[0587.9 / 1493] [A group of young men sit in a dark room lit by television. They train small black birds with large yellow and black eyes how to speak.]

[0587.10 / 1494] [*"The 'LAST' day of the world is when 'THEY' show up."*]

[0587.11 / 1495] [A woman finds a used sheepskin condom on the floor of her steampunk, Victorian era boudoir. She furiously interrogates her husband. I'm crouched naked in a wardrobe listening to them fight. What she doesn't know is I was the condom wearer and her husband was the bottom in our male:male sexual encounter.]

. . .

[0587.12 / 1496] [My left foot is broken and clicks with crepitus as I walk.] //

⁂

Maj. = 14- THE MAGICIAN: #0593
OILY: #0876, #1048, #1175
REHEARSAL: #0853, 0953, #1110, #1183
LAST: #1080, #1081, #1094, #1095, #1128, #1131, #1144
NAKED: #0841, #0881, #0908, #0949, #0995, #1043, #1074
THE KETTLE: #0603

⁂

#0588 - March 29, 2019 @ 02:20 (San Francisco, California)

[0588.1 / 1497] [Mostly an abstraction about shopping. Woke up quickly and recall faded instantly.] //

⁂

SHOPPING: #1170, #1195, #1201
ABSTRACTION: #0862, #0927, #1061, #1160
INSTANTLY: #0801, #0814, #0844, #0852, #0858, #0871

⁂

#0589 - March 30, 2019 @ 05:45 (San Francisco, California)

[0589.1 / 1498] [Everyone I see is playing a game on their phones called, "My Emperor" ...or some title with the word "Emperor" in it. Simple instructions ask users to scroll to another screen and click a square shaped tile, but no one chooses to do this. Clicking the tile stops the game.

Once free from the electronic trance I delete the game from my phone and mention to others they can do the same. Most prefer looking at their phones. It helps them cope with the banality of life.]

[0589.2 / 1499] [I'm invited to observe a large group of people gathered to interview for less than a handful of jobs.

A colleague of mine and I shift attention to THE TRINITY *(resourced, complimentary, and engaging)* who stands up and begins demonstrating her ability to "channel." We both consider THE TRINITY a *"wide open space."* She's in contention for one of the jobs.]

[0589.3 / 1500] [I skip rapidly down a marble staircase to a basement, while practicing a 17 second per side box breath. I fail on the third side of the box, taking a few heaving inhales to restore and calm my breath.] //

⁂

17: #0825, #1036
THIRD: #1037, #1125, #1145, #1152, 1153
SCROLL: #1193

417

TILE: #0891, #0892, #0931, #1048, #1084, #1139, #1154
THE TRINITY: #0628
⁎⁎

#0590 - March 31, 2019 @ 02:47 (San Francisco, California)

[0590.1 / 1501] [THE OCCUPATIONAL THERAPIST (*overworked, and anxious*). Unclear.]
[0590.2 / 1502] [*"FIX IT!"* is chanted and sung in exultation.]
[0590.3 / 1503] [Interaction with THE WHITE RABBIT. Unclear.] //

⁎⁎
Min. = ♦*- THE WHITE RABBIT: #0793*
UNCLEAR: #0820, #0824, #0835, #0854, #0868
FIX: #0890, #0997, #1158
THE OCCUPATIONAL THERAPIST: #0658
⁎⁎

#0591 - March 31, 2019 @ 04:20 (San Francisco, California)

[0591.1 / 1504] [I attend a gymnastics class with THE WEAVER. I do giants on the high bar. It's tremendous fun to swing around and around! I take a spiral staircase to a vault runway at the bottom. A giant green DOS prompt reads: *"SPIRAL DOWN FROM THE INSIDE OUT."*]

[0591.2 / 1505] [I show THE LITTLE BROTHER (*athletic, adventurous, and loving*) a photograph of me standing next to a giant tree, the top of which looks like a burger in a seeded brioche bun.]

[0591.3 / 1506] [A dinner conversation sounds gossipy until a person sarcastically exclaims, *"YEAH THAT DOES SOUND FUN! DO THAT! KEEP DOING EXACTLY THAT...FOR THE GOOD OF HUMANITY!"*] //

⁎⁎
Maj. = 0- THE WEAVER: #0598
HIGH: #0900, #0908, #0913, #0917, #0922
PROMPT: #1176
⁎⁎

#0592 - March 31, 2019 @ 05:06 (San Francisco, California)

[0592.1 / 1507] [I'm at a yoga studio and unable to open my _____. Students begin to gather for class. Small odd shaped bottles of bright fluid marked for sale cool in the fridge behind the front desk. A woman disrobes and takes a shower in the middle of the space in full view of the public. She's comfortable and confident.
I wake up and realize I overslept and missed my class. When I arrive at the yoga studio the lights won't come on. I share an unclear interaction with a male student. A family asks if I

carry the *"Power of R_____"* as I shove a backpack under a table. THE NURSE shows up and leads the class.]

[0592.2 / 1508] [I encounter myself on the street. We pause for selfies. I place a green Post It note on the chest of "other me." We both wear the same pair of jeans.] //

⁑

Maj. = 13- THE NURSE: #0642
PUBLIC: #1176, 1179
POST IT: #0971, #0972, #1150
LIQUID: #0853, #0874, #0891, #0895, #0920, #0926, #0955, #1001

⁑

#0593 - April 1, 2019 @ 03:46 (San Francisco, California)

[0593.1 / 1509] [I'm on a ship at night. A ritual is under way. A group of people gather wearing robes with awkward face obscuring hoods. They look like anthropomorphic squid. THE MAGICIAN leads a procession. I notice one of the robed beings carrying an infant with red glowing eyes. I'm not supposed to see this. The baby is quickly taken away. I know it's killed.

"That's not our concern," THE MAGICIAN says when I later inquire.

"I'm not supposed to do any of it. I'm not supposed to be here. I need to leave," I say when I notice the ship sinking.

As I scramble away, I pass THE BODYBUILDER (*gregarious, showy, and peak performing*) who offers me a glass of orange "TAMPON-ico" juice.] //

⁑

Maj. = 14- THE MAGICIAN: #0610
RITUAL: #0809, #0841
GLOWING EYES: #0943, #0962, #0976, #1172

⁑

#0594 - April 1, 2019 @ 05:46 (San Francisco, California)

[0594.1 / 1510] [A gopa gives dikshas to a group of pilgrims in a California hotel ballroom. 61% of attendees have strong opinions about where they live.

While on a walk, I take a business card from THE VISIONARY (*resolved, motherly, and optimistic*) as we pass. I use the number on the card to call her as I enter a restaurant for lunch. I'm surprised to find her working behind the bar and fielding my call. She upholds the valence of a corporate executive, though has organized her life to do work that gives her the most satisfaction. She's masterful at talking with people and counseling them through family crises.]

[0594.2 / 1511] [I celebrate the start of a new era in Japan but do not understand the spoken nor written languages.] //

⋆⋆
OPINION: #0813, #0952, #0983, #1063
BUSINESS CARD: #1066
MASTERFUL: #0933, #0963
⋆⋆

#0595 - April 1, 2019 @ 07:30 (San Francisco, California)

[**0595.1 / 1512**] [I'm at a party with THE BAKER (*manic, chaotic, and struggling*) and THE TRAINEE (*modest, caring, and studious*). Our conversation stalls when we're unable to recall a fact without using our phones to confirm. I say,
"The answer's on the tip of my tongue!"
I encounter THE INSPIRATION (*observant, articulate, and in service*) in a hallway. We trade notes on the *"current health of the program."* THE PSYCHEDELIC STEWARD (*ethereal, not relatable, and beyond the pale*) works with a client nearby.
I pass a table covered with large purple crystals, on which people dump small baggies of ketamine and cocaine. I toss what I have on the pile and walk away. I encounter an Indian classmate who runs briskly to sign in for class. He asked for my help, but I forgot which section he attends.]

[**0595.2 / 1513**] [I've incorrectly logged multiple items in a journal. Everything is out of order. Multiple pages between various entries are blank.] //

⋆⋆
KETAMINE: #0887
OUT OF ORDER: #0901, #0902, #0915, #0920, #0945, #0978, #1001
HEALTH: #0845, #0878, #0915, #1073, #1176
PARTY: #1111, #1117, #1141, #1145
THE INSPIRATION: #0597
THE TRAINEE: #0645
⋆⋆

#0596 - April 3, 2019 @ 08:43 (San Francisco, California)

[**0596.1 / 1514**] [I'm beginning to understand how to better navigate dream space. I find myself in a variety of situations (*at home, in public, and in interpersonal agreements*) and navigate them concurrently:

- I create experiments in a laboratory to enhance my neuroplasticity.
- I have a sexual encounter with a man.
- I create a household.
- I hug my inner child twice (once as a boy, another as a girl).
- ...Concurrent experiences converge into a bright stream of refracting light.]

[0596.2 / 1515] [I reprimand a group of adults gathered at a restaurant for a dinner meeting. They want to build a factory next to a low-income school. It would be cost effective, but the fumes would place hundreds of Hispanic children at risk of chronic pulmonary disease.]

[0596.3 / 1516] [Images of cats. Images of dogs. Fast motion and flight.] //

⁎⁎

CONCURRENTLY: #0943, #0952, #0954, #1067
CONVERGE: #0929, #1086
INNER: #0812, #0819, #0836, #0874, #0877, #1011, #1019
CATS: #0913, #0972, #0975, #1000
DOGS: #0972, #1048, #1058, #1141, #1147, #1157

⁎⁎

#0597 - April 4, 2019 @ 02:34 (San Francisco, California)

[0597.1 / 1517] [I'm in a hotel ballroom, set for a group discussion and exercise. As I enter the building, I notice a large sign with thin capital letters reading "LANDMARK" affixed to the exterior of the structure, just above the main door.

I've been selected as a temporary leader of the group by program facilitators. The intensity of the exercise increases quickly until the coherence of the group breaks. I'm swiftly ushered into a conference room with no exterior windows, where a male facilitator begins screaming at me at high volume. I simply sit and smile at him saying things like,

"Oh this is the part where I'm supposed to say _____, and then you say _____, right?"

His agitation (*or act*) swiftly neutralizes. He shakes my hand, congratulates me and says,

"Thank you for the resistance."

His fingernails are on the pads of his fingers, where a fingerprint normally would be. The facilitators leave to incite another layer of anxiety among participants. I remain in the room pondering what would happen if they picked a temporary leader who happens to be mentally unstable.]

[0597.2 / 1518] I'm at a cafeteria and handed a sloppy plate of food. One half is filled with spaghetti and runny tomato sauce; the other half chicken soup which comingles with the spaghetti noodles. I eat it and observe a group of men who step into round steel garbage cans filled with trash. They're instructed by stern women to search for specific items. Some of the women aggressively push the men down into the garbage cans.

A fierce "Chola" with gorgeous face tattoos takes a drag off a cigarette, looks at me and says,

"People's understanding of heart rate variability is incorrect. When you fall asleep on your face it stimulates hundreds of nerves and distorts the intended biomechanical process. If you sleep on your back, you'll get a more accurate reading with less interference."

Her fingers are normal.

THE INSPIRATION (*focused, available, and quick*) sits nearby on the floor working diligently. Her right leg is broken and in a cast. Her husband enters. THE INSPIRATION introduces him to her coworkers, who until the moment they meet, had no idea THE INSPIRATION was married.]

. . .

[0597.3 / 1519] [I live at GRANDMA's house. I occupy a main room at the front. I've decorated shelves with large crystals and sacred stones collected throughout my travels. It rained all night. The temperature rapidly drops, quickly coating the house, lawn, and streets in a thick layer of ice illuminated by moonlight.

I bilocate to the driveway to see if we'll be able to take the car out. No. The ice is too thick. From inside the house, I look at the large stones I placed amongst the front bushes. Of the 7-8, I'm mostly intrigued by how a large rectangular cube of blue stone encased in ice has been moved two feet to the right, leaving a deep square imprint in the ice. I can see the men in garbage cans from **[0597.2 / 1518]** off in the distance. Their heads pop up like a "Whack-A-Mole" game just prior to being pushed down over and over.]

[0597.4 / 1520] [I enter an odd living room with a car parked along one side, a couch on the other. THE CHILD climbs up on my lap, after I take a seat on the couch. We watch a show where people demonstrate how to soothe an infant by taking the back of its hand and gently tapping it to an adults' mouth (*who awkwardly says, "Knock, Knock, Knock!"*). The baby onscreen giggles and the adults follow suit. THE CHILD changes the channel. We watch a video by the band "Meat Puppets" where nude Sesame Street-like puppets dance around. Breasts and genitals are blurred out. It's not very interesting. I play with THE CHILD. As I tickle her feet, I notice the nails of her pinkies are on the underside of her toes, which I find deeply disturbing.]

[0597.5 / 1521] [This sequence involves being in a movie and concurrently observing it from a seat in a theatre. Beside me are cinephiles who have deep knowledge of the supporting cast member's acting resumes and can recite the lengthy and detailed CV of every film and award received by the crew won, in chronological order. Big stars from classic Hollywood stroll leisurely into frame. YUL BRYNNER. RICARDO MONTALBAN. Mostly men with strong onscreen machismo and swagger.] //

⁂

Maj. = 3- THE CHILD: # 0610, 11- GRANDMA: #0748
BALLROOM: #0904, #0909, #0910, #0957, #0959
PUPPET: #0874, #0982
NORMAL: #0836, #0889, #0934, #1120, #1194

⁂

#0598 - April 5, 2019 @ 06:00 (San Francisco, California)

[0598.1 / 1522] [A Latinx family is in the process of moving. THE FUNKY MONKEY (*sarcastic, informed, and contrary*) helps them pack boxes. He also folds his clothes, including a series of yellow shirts hanging in a closet. A little girl and boy are in the house. The house used to be FRANK ROBINSON's home. The big sister picks on the little boy. The father requests an Uber to transport the family downtown to a park. He becomes frustrated when he learns of a 35-minute wait for the car. The family could actually get there faster on foot, but choose to remain in the comfort of complaint. I discover myself in the backyard observing the kids. THE WEAVER and THE CARPENTER think the kids are old enough to take care of themselves. My intuition suggests otherwise as I hover cautiously nearby. The kids don't know I'm there.] //

⁎⁎

Maj. = 0- THE WEAVER: #0605, 1- THE CARPENTER: #0603
FRANK ROBINSON: #0809
CLOSET: #0930, #0973, #0995, #1018, #1041
HOVER: #0878, #0994, #0998, #1129, #1193

⁎⁎

#0599 - April 6, 2019 @ 01:59 (San Francisco, California)

[0599.1 / 1523] [Visits from Gold Beings and Angels! Geometric abstractions! Crystal vases pull gold waves into their centers. Each vase has a jewel at its core. Each jewel, a different color. The vases press waves out and forward from their centers, speaking a vibrational language I don't understand. Waves of soft pastel light hang in trails in the air overhead. It's revealing. The tone is warm, inviting, and mysterious.] //

⁎⁎

ANGELS: #0862, #0867, #0998
VASE: #1047
MYSTERIOUS: #0914, #0950, #0957, #1168

⁎⁎

#0600 - April 10, 2019 @ 04:13 (Ojai, California)

[0600.1 / 1524] [A vast social scene takes place concurrently in Africa and Europe. Giant alpine mountain horns are blown to the delight and fanfare of revelers scattered across a mountain range. I'm with my "best friends" "Jared and Jaret" in an amphitheater. They're both convinced I need to loosen up and have a good time. I make a comment about how "Jared" doesn't have good decision-making skills,
"Because he hangs out in 'Stalker Houses' like Buffalo Bill's from 'Silence of the Lambs' with people he dates." "
Jared" remains confused as to why none of his relationships last. We point humorously at his obvious blind spots, which remain unknown to him.
I take my turn to blow the horn, pausing when I realize I've jumped ahead of someone in line.
"Is this cool?" I ask, before being waved on.
When I put my mouth to the horn, I find it odd that all I have to do is pass air through it without pursing and buzzing my lips. Each time a horn sounds it's met with cheers and increasing joy. This crowd is excited! The mood is light. It's fun to be around this group of people.] //

⚜

OBVIOUS: #0906, #0926, #1149
MOUNTAIN RANGE: #0808, #0982
BUZZING: #0887, #1143
BLIND SPOTS: #1196

⚜

#0601 - April 11, 2019 @ 03:15 (Ojai, California)

[0601.1 / 1525] [I attend a "Fans Only" concert on an insanely large jumbo jet. The metal band PANTERA reunites. The event is generally disorganized. People don't know where to go, nor when the show will start. Many get lost once their tickets are taken. It's well intended yet radically fuel inefficient *(once we take off)*. I feel giant cat claws aggressively rip at the interior of my chest, demanding my heart open ever wider.] //

⚜

TICKET: #0820, #0837, #0855, #0888
FUEL: #0962, #1072
HEART: #0887, #0976, #0983, #0999, #1053, #1084, #1143, #1171

⚜

#0602 - April 11, 2019 @ 04:46 (Ojai, California)

[0602.1 / 1526] [I've returned to my dormitory for the last weekend of school. I arrive around 4:00am. As I enter, people gather to discuss a significant incident that occurred while I was away. I don't have much information, but I gather THE TIGER MOM *(emotional, sensual, and tactile)* had a pet bunny rabbit, and that bunny gave birth to many, many other bunnies.

People generally dismiss me. One guy cleans out a refrigerator and stacks white cylinders on top of (*and next to*) one another. He continues, as I pick up a can of beer with a 6-ring plastic topper still affixed. I'm timid and don't ask him to put the remaining beer in the fridge for me. I also find a small aluminum bat in the entryway. My room is at the end of the hall on the left.] //

⁜

BEER: #0848, #0940, #1194
ALUMINUM: #1071, #1078
BAT: #0815
THE TIGER MOM: #0810

⁜

#0603 - April 11, 2019 @ 06:15 (Ojai, California)

[0603.1 / 1527] [I practice teaching. THE KIWI (*chill, flat, and neutral*) provides feedback on my technique. I complete three rounds of training exercises. THE KETTLE (*distant, afraid, and dismissive*) walks on the opposite side of the street, down a large hill and out of sight. My path leads me to a grocery store. Here I receive detailed feedback on my teaching from the register clerk. THE COYOTE (*earthy, tricky, and wicked smart*) mans another till at the store while spinning an impromptu DJ set. I'm drawn towards a large black and white mosaic on the wall, which I sit beneath and meditate. BARON BAPTISTE tells THE COYOTE to, "*Put on that song I like.*" The movement in the sequence speeds up. Most other details pass me by.]

[0603.2 / 1528] [I sit at the supper table with an Irish family. They lovingly gaze at their new baby. THE CARPENTER sings a greeting song to the infant. The family takes its turn creating a song. We create a family song in shared celebration of this new, precious life. The song celebrates, "Innocence." A young boy sits on our side of the family's supper table. He feels let down and dismissed by his father. THE FLORIDIAN (*community oriented, syncopated, and externalized*) chides the family as the scene speeds up and dissolves.] //

⁜

Maj. = 1- THE CARPENTER: #0607
BARON BAPTISTE: #0641
TECHNIQUE: #0896, #1058, #1105
MOSAIC: #1181
INFANT: #0887, #895, #0947, #0974, #1000
THE KETTLE: #0642
THE KIWI: #0815
THE COYOTE: #0692

⁜

#0604 - April 12, 2019 @ 05:02 (San Francisco, California)

[0604.1 / 1529] [I boil large cauldrons of eggs assisted by two older eyeless women who both wear black cloaks. The eggs are intended as gifts. One of the women gives me a white egg speckled with small brown spots. The egg is unusually oblong. I crack and empty its

425

contents into a bowl. Tiny mushrooms grow out from the yolk. I accept the gift. I eat as much of it as I can to be polite.] //

⁂

CAULDRON: #1062
MUSHROOM: #0922, #1132
POLITE: #0883, #0937
OBLONG: #0914, #0940

⁂

#0605 - April 13, 2019 @ 05:29 (San Francisco, California)

[0605.1 / 1530] [I participate in a household where numerous adults interact with a comparable count of kids. One little boy seems out of place as he scatters his toys around the room. THE WEAVER and I stand next to each other and simply observe.
"He hasn't experienced putting one toy away before taking another out."
She silently agrees by offering a nod.
The child's godfather makes negative comments intended to shame the boy, as the boy continues taking more toys out. I immediately call the godfather out.
"I see what you're doing there. Every time you do that going forward, I'm going to make you WRONG in front of that little boy, just so he knows with certainty what NOT to do to other people. You're an adult. You know better, and what you're doing DOES. NOT. HELP."] //

⁂

Maj. = 0- THE WEAVER: #0619
WRONG: #0982, #0985, #1023, #1114, #1187
HELP: #0906, #0914, #0915

⁂

#0606 - April 15, 2019 @ 06:21 (San Francisco, California)

[0606.1 / 1531] [Most of the dream takes place in an office where a number of German and Russian speaking people collaborate. On the file cabinets dividing workspaces are stacks on stacks of packaged foods in boxes (*various types of meal replacement "bars"*). I climb up on the median, sifting and sorting through the stacks until I find a black wrapped "RXBar." The text and nutritional information on the package are printed in German. I unwrap it and take a bite. It sticks to my teeth like caramel tar, effectively sealing my mouth shut. Even in this predicament I think, *"There's such a bounty here I could take enough home for a lifetime and no one would ever notice."*
Walls of food extend as far as my eyes can see. Beyond the office, a "precision coach" teaches a group of people how to flip and somersault by jumping from a rooftop, to a miniature trampoline, and bounding into a foam pit. A young woman gets coached rigorously on her form.
My attention shifts when I notice a television show being filmed in the office. Signs with the words "MIRROR" and "WINDOW" denote the name of the program. The two words are layered on top of one another rendering a rune-like result. The show logo is a black background with white block letters. A team works feverishly to complete prep tasks for production on the next episode.]

426

. . .

[0606.2 / 1532] [I'm asked to write a piece of computer code on a green screen terminal. I'm astonished by how quickly the dormant skill set returns to my fingers. It's so elegant and fun to navigate the nuances, subtleties, nested statements and the like to contribute to a clean executable program. The data set I've been asked to work on has 11.6 billion rows. The experience seems ordinary, realistic and wakefully lifelike. It doesn't feel like work.] //

✲
✲✲
GERMAN: #0905
RUSSIAN: #0806, #0837, #0878, #0933, #0976, #0990, #1046, #1164
PREP: #0821, #0829, #0929, #1085
ORDINARY: #0994, #0998
✲
✲✲

#0607 - April 16, 2019 @ 03:49 (San Francisco, California)

[0607.1 / 1533] [I'm in the garage of a neighbor's house, where I drop a classic car into neutral and roll it towards a flimsy set of balsa wood cabinets. The fender barely taps the cabinet doors and they snap. A door to the back yard is open. A strong wind gusts through, sending broken shards from the cabinet down the driveway and into the street. I gather the scattered fragments and put them in a pile on the garage floor.
The home was recently scorched by a large wildfire. The owners don't have the funds to repair it. THE CARPENTER and I stand on the driveway discussing how we might best help. A small stream of gasoline flows down from the back of the garage, which pools in a gutter and flows down the street to a drain. The fumes are intense.
I discover myself at the back of the garage wading through chest deep water. The car tapped and turned a spigot at the back of the destroyed cabinet and as a result, water filled the space. I move in quickly and dive towards the spigot in an attempt to shut it off. The water pressure is high and presses me away the closer I swim. THE CARPENTER urges me to get out of there. My attention shifts to recovering my phone from the flooded garage floor. I believe the phone is down there...but I'm not certain.]

[0607.2 / 1534] [I'm a woman in a 1930's social scene. I flirt with men coyly, *"Oh darlings, I have MANY lovers."* The men I'm attracted to are all significantly older.]

[0607.3 / 1535] [I observe a young family. Mom, Dad, Boy, and Girl attend a birthday party and intend to be there just briefly. They say, *"Oh, so we're doing an out of body thing tonight? Is that what this game is about? Is that the game?"*] //

✲
✲✲
Maj. = 1- THE CARPENTER: #0610
SHUT: #1087, #1095, #1113, #1150
BIRTHDAY PARTY: #0972
✲
✲✲

427

#0608 - April 16, 2019 @ 04:21 (San Francisco, California)

[0608.1 / 1536] [A group of people sit and share conversation at a large gathering. An older man with long grey hair offers remarks to the group. He says something that resonates with a younger person seated outside under a starlit gazebo. A young man responds by interjecting, *"So to simplify, what I think I hear you saying is that we're all a 'We.'"* The young man turns toward me and winks. I affirm with a nod. A young blue haired woman named "Sherri" rises to give her talk. She stands behind me to the right just past a pergola draped with green vines and ivy. I encourage her to step forward to the front of the group. She stays in place, responding, *"I would, but I practiced from back here."*]

[0608.2 / 1537] [I open the doors to a bedroom. I notice a bunch of large cockroaches on a wall over a bed that quickly scatter and descend behind the headboard. I know I don't want those in the space, and I've encouraged *(and demanded with success)* those beings go away.]

[0608.3 / 1538] [The grey-haired man from [0608.1 / 1536] continues with his remarks, proceeding to comment how, *"You know how ya...ya cord...hmph ya just 'plug in' to something and walk away thinking you've got it...you've just GOT it? Well, ya need to keep aware of the need to keep tuning that up."* THE GAME DESIGNER *(sharing, guided, and platinum skinned)* says, *"Oh, like that time we went to Brazil!"*] //

✳

BEHIND ME: #0801, #0857, #0858, #0868, #0929, #0943
VINES: #0850
PLUG: #0962

✳

#0609 - April 16, 2019 @ 04:35 (San Francisco, California)

[0609.1 / 1539] [JESUS CHRIST stands before a group of Pharisees. I observe them critique his physical stance, suggesting small pivots and adjustments to the alignment of his joints. This is intended to generate a statuesque public posture. They are supportive. They also offer candid edits to the text of a forthcoming sermon. JESUS lovingly looks at the group, pauses to connect eye to eye with few of the men gathered and says,

"I'm simply going to say what needs to be said, concern free."

Not another word of critique is voiced. The brilliant group of men falls silent in loving, mutual appreciation.] //

✳

JESUS: #0752
POSTURE: #0934, #1123
CANDID: #0828, #0979
CONCERN: #0804, #0842, #0857, #0858, #0968, #1015, #1120
EYE TO EYE: #0980, #1001, #1084

✳

#0610 - April 16, 2019 @ 06:14 (San Francisco, California)

[0610.1 / 1540] [A family experiences a large catharsis. I request that everyone says what they need to say. THE DANCER and THE ATHEIST are across the street, pushing THE CHILD in a stroller. THE DANCER's eyes are red and puffy from crying. I rush across the street to prevent them from getting hit by a car, just moments before SPLAT! Maybe I've been struck? Everything is white. I'm not sure what happened to me, but I know that they did not get hit.]

[0610.2 / 1541] [My phone completely shatters in half vertically. I show it to THE CARPENTER and say,
"This doesn't make any sense."
This has happened frequently enough that I know it indicates that I'm dreaming and I'll wake up.]

[0610.3 / 1542] [THE MAGICIAN angrily yells at us for *"JUST NOT GETTING IT!"* His tone doesn't resonate with me. I'm flat to the conflict and go to the bathroom because I'd rather masturbate. I blink and find myself in bed having a sexual encounter with an invisible being. I repeatedly check in to confirm that it's my guide "L." It feels good, nourishing, and healing to be loved and penetrated by my guide. Before the sensations grow too intense, I check in to see if it's still "L."]

[0610.4 / 1543] [I'm at a yoga studio. THE LOVE STORY AUTHOR *(dutiful, prayerful, and honest)* passes by as I thumb through a book left on a table. She taps me on the shoulder and says, *"Hey!"* She's recently experienced significant family trauma and leaves. I contemplate sending her an email because I want to join her team. I don't mention it. Another time will be more appropriate.]

[0610.5 / 1544] [I look at a series of old Polaroid photos of a tiny paraplegic man sitting with legs outstretched like a Ventriloquist's doll on the lap of an extraordinarily large man. Like Darth Vader, they both raise their arms with a closed fist and telepathically crush a beer can. The caption on the photo says, "Crushin' it!"
A series of tiny man memes emerge, the most notable being: "When you can't go snow-boarding cuz there's too many freshies, so you have a little car instead!" written on a photo of the man seated in a tiny convertible filled with snow.]

[0610.6 / 1545] [I bask in gold light, touching my face with the back of my hand. I definitely had a sexual encounter with the Holy Spirit in [0610.3 / 1542]. I am blissed out.]

[0610.7 / 1546] [I acknowledge a woman for being baptized. She says, *"Oh, you don't know what that was really about. Next time I see you I'll tell you more so you have context."* We each head into different bathrooms.] //

⁂

Maj. = 1- THE CARPENTER: #0618, 2- THE DANCER: #0611, 3- THE CHILD: #0648,
8- THE ATHEIST: #0774, 14- THE MAGICIAN: #0633
MY GUIDE: #0821, #0953, #0992, #1076, #1165
CONTEXT: #0998
HOLY: #1078, #1133
CONVERTIBLE: #0967, #1104, #1180

⁂

#0611 - April 16, 2019 @ 08:57 (San Francisco, California)

[0611.1 / 1547] [I attend training. THE SHARED HEART asks me to join her on stage and have an encounter with her guide, "Dr. Habib Rajnesh." She places her forehead on mine to create a spirit-to-spirit connection. As images quickly flicker in, THE SHARED HEART says,
"No, not you right now 'Susan.'"
The persnickety guide departs.
THE SHARED HEART has multiple guides. After a couple seconds of dark lag, a slideshow emerges on a screen in the center of my head. The first slide is playful and animated: *"Warning: Extreme Content. BEWARE!"* Another flashes an image of a blue Buddha. Another requests a day of prayer for "Krishna." Other images flow in as we demonstrate co-creation to the group.
I have an out of body guide named "L." I call on "L" to show up. A presence touches me in the middle of the back.
"If it's 'L,' please touch me on the cheek."
The cheek touch doesn't happen. I know the presence behind me is not my guide. I ask again to establish a new connection. "Dr. Habib Rajnesh" pops in and out of my experience.]

[0611.2 / 1548] [A young woman doubts herself. A group of us stands to reassure her. Another young woman is seated directly behind me. She doesn't stand. I open a cabinet and find an assortment of fruit juices.]

[0611.3 / 1549] [I'm at a wedding venue, similar to the Palace of Fine Arts in San Francisco. Two weddings are scheduled at the same time. I attend both concurrently. One takes place in a courtyard, where all chairs are lined up in the sunlight. A second larger ceremony occurs where the chairs are set in a semicircle. Half are located in the shade. I'm the only person in bespoke suiting. A member of the larger wedding party is upset and dismissive to the staff and guests. THE DANCER sits next to me and doesn't recall attending the smaller ceremony with me.] //

⁂

Maj. = 2- THE DANCER: #0634
BESPOKE: #0945
WARNING: #0846, #1062, #1201
THE SHARED HEART: #1251

⁂

#0612 - April 17, 2019 @ 03:14 (San Francisco, California)

[0612.1 / 1550] [I'm in BRADLEY COOPER's body. I walk up to a piano and sit down next to LADY GAGA. We're performing at the Oscars. We sing our song. The final time we hit a C Maj. Chord, the onlooking crowd roars with applause. We give each other a warm embrace as camera bulbs flash. Staring into each other's eyes we both say, *"You're a gift."* We break out in laughter when we say the phrase at the exact same time.] //

⁎⁎

LADY GAGA: #0622
LAUGHTER: #0929
EMBRACE: #0892, #0953, #0983, #1198
APPLAUSE: #0815, #0878, #0904, #0910, #1096, #1103, #1157

⁎⁎

#0613 - April 17, 2019 @ 06:20 (San Francisco, California)

[0613.1 / 1551] [THE ADVANCED STUDENTS (*individuated*) "practice resurrection."]
[0613.2 / 1552] [I playfully tackle THE SOOTHSAYER (*open, honest, and available*) at the waist while giving him a healing. His pants fall down as he tumbles backward, exposing his genitals. THE ASSISTANT and I cover him with a purple bathing towel as he rests. One other person witnesses this.]

[0613.3 / 1553] [I contemplate taking a third dose of nitric oxide supplement.]

[0613.4 / 1554] [I walk through a housing development that has a theme park-like mall in the center called, "Le Boudon." I think it's a weird concept. Slate roofed Lilliputian structures scatter across the residential land grid where my parents have chosen to retire. I consider purchasing an unfinished home two parcels away from my parent's lot. The windows are not yet installed, yet high tech fixtures and features exist in the kitchen and bathrooms including bidets and toilet seats with pulse monitors. A great room has five tall, narrow rectangular spaces for windows. I stand and look at the light pouring in as I contemplate other places I might live. I become less inclined to buy, the more I sit still.
A family inhabits the unfinished house, and decides to go out for dinner. They invite me to join them. I notice a bag of uneaten food by the door which I would prefer. Within the bag I find half of a burrito filled with glass noodles and hash brown potatoes. I consider eating all of this food and going out with the family for another meal. I feel gluttonous.] //

⁎⁎

POTATOES: #1073
GRID: #0804, #0925, #0963, #0989, #1003, #1083, #1172
SLATE: #0857, #1104
THE ASSISTANT: #0715
THE SOOTHSAYER: #1078
THE ADVANCED STUDENTS: #1108

⁎⁎

#0614 - April 17, 2019 @ 08:04 (San Francisco, California)

[0614.1 / 1555] [I've broken out of prison. I drive a car from a woodland hideout toward an urban cityscape roughly 100 miles from where I grew up. I'm supposed to meet with a friend, but I've forgotten their address. I continue driving around, confused because I have no means of reintegrating with society. I know I'm an hour by car from where I need to be. I wind up at THE PROFESSOR's (*generous, intellectual, and mobile*) house, where I feel a few moments of sweet relief. He has a reputation for serving refugees.]

[0614.2 / 1556] [I've been truant to the same math course many times. I already know the content. Going to class would be a waste of teacher's time (*and mine*). The tradeoff is, I don't graduate...and it's graduation day! I see students in cap and gown filter across a crosswalk under an overpass to catch buses to commencement exercises. I hear a young woman behind a chain link fence deliver a class using a new age sounding teaching script, talking about, "*seeing things through the lens of the mind.*" Her syntax makes me giggle.]

[0614.3 / 1557] [I drive back toward the city, not knowing what's to become of my life. I'm unsure I'll have a place. With this newfound freedom, I find myself wishing I hadn't broken out of prison and hoping on some level I can find my way back in.
   "Sorry ego...that ain't happening."] //

⁎⁎

REFUGEE: #1122, #1135
GOWN: #0815, #0897, #0999, #1001
CROSSWALK: #0806
THE PROFESSOR: #1083

⁎⁎

#0615 - April 18, 2019 @ 05:18 (San Francisco, California)

[0615.1 / 1558] [Role Playing Game: People wear thick rubber masks of the Teenage Mutant Ninja Turtles (*Michelangelo, Donatello, Leonardo and Raphael*) in a dark space seated on gymnasium bleachers.]

[0615.2 / 1559] [Choice making in an office scene. THE FIDUCIARY wants to kill me, and I'm aware of the multiple ways he's wanted to previously attempt it. I'm not surprised by any of the methods he contemplates.]

[0615.3 / 1560] [People wear rubber face masks to celebrate discernment and decision making on a game show.]

[0615.4 / 1561] [I hold a stone drinking mug. Someone fills it with liquid epoxy. I take time to carefully paint the inside of the vessel with the clear coat and wait patiently for it to cure.

The strong odor makes me a little dizzy.]

[0615.5 / 1562] [I'm outside in the jungle. I bushwhack through some thick leaves and brush with a machete and discover a parking lot.]

[0615.6 / 1563] [THE FIDUCIARY and I rent a shared desk space at a lawyer's office. He now outwardly debates verbally with himself about all the ways he could possibly kill me. He decides to push my face into a paper shredder. My bottom lip and tongue get pinched between the bladed rollers.]

[0615.7 / 1564] [I observe a game where people spontaneously mutate into fast moving columns of light and complex trans-dimensional shapes. Beings begin by juggling neon balls and increase speed until the movement becomes so fast, they appear as "atomic" spheres of light made of colorful blips funneling around a nucleus. A being creates a cube of light by leveraging new "quantum" capabilities to the astonishment of onlookers. The colors are rich and permeated by a soft white bright light.]

[0615.8 / 1565] [I wake from one dream into another with crippling pain between my right-side ribs. I've been pierced in the side with a spear. My hands and feet throb and bleed. My legs have been crushed. Bones protrude from both shins. A Roman centurion walks through the otherwise black vacuum-like space. *"Is this what it feels like to get crucified?"* I ask just before waking in a momentary daze.] //

⁎⁎

Maj. = 9- THE FIDUCIARY· #0681
RIBS: #1039
SOFT WHITE: #0987, #1087
BONES: #0976, #0996, #1039, #1167
RAPHAEL: #1025

⁎⁎

#0616 - April 18, 2019 @ 06:57 (San Francisco, California)

[0616.1 / 1566] [I observe a healing encounter. I watch THE WORLDBRIDGER walk to a wall and have a conversation with a blinking light bulb. From the lightbulb he pulls a clear pearl shaped crystal. He places the crystal pearl in a ring and points it at an oil painting of a boy I don't recognize.

"He's coming. He's coming. He's coming," THE WORLDBRIDGER says repeatedly (*and calmly*).

I'm not supposed to have seen this...but I did. I consider the experience profound and sacred. It's been a strong contributor to my growth.] //

⁎⁎

Maj. = 7- THE WORLDBRIDGER: #0628

433

PEARL: #0876
GROWTH: #0886, #0891
⁎⁎

#0617 - April 18, 2019 @ 08:38 (San Francisco, California)

[0617.1 / 1567] [A group of us practice bilocating down a series of video game tunnels. Giant 8-bit crabs attempt to capture us. Our in-game skill level and team coherence quickly increase. My skin is blue and pixelated.]

[0617.2 / 1568] [A young African American woman rides in a car with my family. She chaperones us to a dessert bar just off the freeway. An attractive short-haired deaf man signs, *"I love you"* at me as we peruse rows of sweet treats. Melted sundaes with stale cinnamon toast are the favored item, but they're not appetizing to me. I think they're gross and don't eat anything.] //

⁎⁎
GROSS: #0801, #0879, #0890
SIGNS: #0837, #0865, #0909, #1158, #1201
FREEWAY: #0852, #0919, #0936
⁎⁎

#0618 - April 19, 2019 @ 05:01 (San Francisco, California)

[0618.1 / 1569] [I'm at a summer camp at night, accompanied by THE CARPENTER. He and I sit in a large cathedral. A congregation sings joyful hymns. THE BOSS plays an ornamental pipe organ. I glance up and see a vast mosaic image of a glowing being within a shattering heart that's reconstituted by Divine Love.

We attend a funeral while at the cathedral. A man offers a eulogy from an elevated stone pulpit. Light piano music plays in the background. Final prayers are offered. I sit behind the piano as the benediction is offered. I match bass notes from the pipe organ with my left hand. I strike major tones when the organ resolves on a minor. This sounds good to me, but the dissonance is off putting to many. Those with perfect pitch aren't neutral to the intonation.

THE CARPENTER and I exit the cathedral and descend a staircase where I encounter THE MINISTER (*modest, aligned, and sweet*) and THE SEASON (*feminine, friendly, and supportive*). They suggest I participate more fully next time in the offertory music program.

We discover ourselves at Camp Ramah in Ojai, California, surrounded by children and "Journey of Hope" participants who share a friendship visit with special needs campers.

THE CARPENTER inflates a number of yellow balloons inside a larger yellow helium balloon. Once he's inflated 100 small balloons within the large balloon, he releases the zygotic/star-like creation next to a tree that has no leaves.

The group begins singing camp songs accompanied by an acoustic guitar while seated around a small campfire.

"I bet we'll hear 'Hava Nagila' again," I say with hands in pocket and nudging THE CARPENTER with an elbow.

"Well, I didn't get dressed up to hear that," he responds.

"What do you expect, we're at a Hebrew summer camp.") //

⁂

Maj. = 1- THE CARPENTER: #0648
100: #0999, #1048, #1086
DIVINE LOVE: #0856
ORGAN: #0812
THE BOSS: #0640
THE SEASON: #1273

⁂

#0619 - April 20, 2019 @ 04:58 (San Francisco, California)

[0619.1 / 1570] [An older African American man sings a soulful song about sexuality while I visit with some neighbors on a driveway. Another older man passes us on the sidewalk. Now in his 90's, we're surprised to learn he walks 10 miles a day, and has done so since his 50's. There's mutual concern for a cat that's been walking around "The Basement," and may have been impacted by "The Ghosts Down There."]

[0619.2 / 1571] [I witness the launch sequence for a rocket. A large man with braces comedically does partial push-ups while leaning on the back of a dining room chair. He's a villain with a single question. We don't know the answer, even though he asks repeatedly. We question him. He doesn't know what he's done, nor why the device he built has a large digital clock that counts down from 10...9...8...]

[0619.3 / 1572] [THE WEAVER calls a family meeting. Everyone who attends gets to select the role they want to embody. *"Daddeeeee." "Mummmyyyyyy." "Sissssyyyy." "Baybeeeee."* It all feels a tad silly and hammed up like a reality show put on, similar to an episode of THE OSBOURNES.] //

⁂

Maj. = 0- THE WEAVER: #0626
DRIVEWAY: #1049, #1061, #1120, #1157, #1201
ROCKET: #1019

⁂

#0620 - April 21, 2019 @ 04:37 (San Francisco, California)

[0620.1 / 1573] [I'm in a training facility where people declare their life purpose. One person passionately steps forward into a more fully embodied version of their particular "thing." THE STUDENT (*accountable, loving, and committed*) hangs a banner that reads: *"Helping alcoholics find their sobriety."*]

[0620.2 / 1574] [THE MBA CANDIDATE (*cynical, unsure, and hurting*) participates in a game between rival MBA programs. He runs down a racing lane lined by massive rows of rustling bright yellow feathers towards a finish area. He's interrupted mid-stride by a monstrous entity that pops up from the ground and swallows him whole. THE MBA CANDIDATE sinks

instantly into the floor and disappears into a quicksand like mass of yellow feathers. I witness this from a catwalk above. Among a group of friends I say,
"There's only one school we all want to go to, right?"
The group says, *"BERKELEY!"*
I yell, *"STANFORD!"* even though I want to go to Berkeley and have already been accepted.]

[0620.3 / 1575] [Large quantities of food are distributed after the filming of a game show in a major urban center. It moves me to see how much of this bounty is given to the homeless and disadvantaged. More and more unloads from the truck. No one who is in need is turned away from nourishment. The effort is directed by members of "The Clash." JOE STRUMMER pushes a cart stacked with cereal boxes down a ramp and into the hands of an eager public. Other people stop what they're doing and contribute to an ever-growing outpouring of generosity and goodwill towards shared humanity. Plated meals from fine dining establishments find their ways to hungry mouths, who appreciate and enjoy each bite. For some, it's their first taste of crab meat. Chefs become involved in the direct exchange and are moved to tears *(as am I)* by the beauty of the moment. Everyone participates.] //

⁑

CATWALK: #0915
GAME SHOW: #0868, #0943
GENEROSITY: #0879, #0905
THE STUDENT: #1009

⁑

#0621 - April 23, 2019 @ 06:09 (San Francisco, California)

[0621.1 / 1576] [I'm on my way out to socialize with some friends when I'm quickly pulled aside and asked to participate in a voting process. Instead of punching a hole and drawing lines from the privacy of an individual booth, it's requested I step through a detailed scene-to-scene process *(almost conveyor belt-like)* where I have to view all the potential downstream impacts of a decision before I'm allowed to make a ballot selection. The experience occurs as arcane and inefficient as the path winds in a serpentine pattern in/outdoors and up/down staircases to different above/below ground levels of a building.
A group of suit donning auditors each pitch me one by one on why they would be "The Best." When I determine this is a superlative designation, rather than an elected post with influence I quickly lose interest. I experience all of them as "close talkers" and generally annoying. I quickly tick a box just to get them out of my space. I use a mechanical pencil to fill in the ballot.]

[0621.2 / 1577] [I sit on a stone staircase. A woman ascends from below me with a tray of snack foods.
"Take as many as you'd like," she says, extending a tray of treats towards me as a small token for having completed a challenging process.
Rows of tables at each level of the stairs beneath me stage other scenes for me to observe. I'll eventually be required to make another decision.]

[0621.3 / 1578] [I eat two small green "Matcha Mochi" truffles. I'm pretty sure they're THE PUBLIC MEDIUM's recipe. I spend a significant amount of time reviewing a series of nine hand drawn renderings of a park and its impact on an ancient tree: Proposed waterways, scenic bridges, a moat around the tree, a couple of simple benches beneath its shady branches.

I'm urged to consider the option that has the most favorable impact on the emotional life of the tree and select one that optimally enhances its quality of life.

Overall, I'm annoyed that this dream sequence resulted in my forgetting the one immediately before, even though it's apparent I'm truing up my human-to-nature ethics.] //

⁂

Maj. = 18- THE PUBLIC MEDIUM: #0637
NINE: #0857, #0982, #1088, #1117
TOKEN: #1069
OPTION: #0906, #0987

⁂

#0622 - April 24, 2019 @ 06:35 (San Francisco, California)

[0622.1 / 1579] [I'm at a camp. A family vacations in the woods. Women distribute blue velvet suits to camp attendees. I leave before picking mine up. I'm invited to a group event but I choose to duck down in an empty swimming pool on a front lawn. I try to distract myself with porn on my phone, but I'm unable to operate it. I see people on the front porch of the house look in my direction. A group of lean and muscular male neighbors are next door on their lawn, but aren't very talkative. None of them wear shirts, but wear similar board shorts and flip flops.

"Hey Stephanie, you can't hide from YOURSELF!" I yell, and wave at LADY GAGA as she ducks into a car and drives away.

An awards ceremony follows her departure.

I feel sad, alone, and away from my family.]

[0622.2 / 1580] [I inspect tiny houses with cut out windows designed to hold sacred objects and statues. People in this town don't require a lot of personal space. Images of the Virgin Mary. Miniature Buddhas. Feels like I'm taking a tour of oversized doll houses.] //

⁂

LADY GAGA: #0888
VACATION: #0803, #0817, #0818, #0841, #1183
AWARDS: #0815, #0850, #0872, #0910
VIRGIN MARY: #1185

⁂

#0623 - April 24, 2019 @ 08:12 (San Francisco, California)

[0623.1 / 1581] [I walk from one location to another at training. Severe weather prevents me from traversing the grounds on my intended path. I arrive at a clubhouse which sells soft serve ice cream, and a single text book that describes a method for skipping steps in a hierarchy. I'm more intrigued by a bizarre sign that suggests we eat a scoop of ice cream on half a bagel. It seems weird to me and I don't buy anything. A session is about to begin and people start to move as a group towards a gathering space. I enter a woodland environment. A woman asks me to pick her up a snack from her cabin. I look as I pass by but am unable to find the item she asked for. I may be a woman. I'm surrounded by women at this training. It's overcast and cool. The environment is supportive and friendly. The session topic centers on STI reduction and prevention.] //

⁂

CABIN: #0826, #0889, #1116, #1121, #1138, #1172
ICE CREAM: #1095, #1133, #1158
WOODLAND: #0850, #0888, #0898, #0996, #1165, #1187

⁂

#0624 - April 25, 2019 @ 06:00 (San Francisco, California)

[0624.1 / 1582] [A concert occurs in the basement of a house. It's dark. The music is rowdy and low fidelity. The YEAH YEAH YEAHs emerge onstage and the energy level rises instantly. THE DEAR HEART (*queer, embodied, and eager*) creates mandala and Metatron patterns on the poured concrete basement floor with black chalk and paint.

The energy of the scene turns dark when I observe a group of young Caucasian men brutalizing another. The group forces the subdued man to drink molten lava while he's tied to a St. Andrew's Cross. He screams and writhes as it burns him up from the inside out. The men take the remains of his body and hack it up into segments that fit in a series of small cardboard boxes, which are promptly taped closed and neatly stacked by a wall of freezers.

Elderly women have a party upstairs. They send a bellboy down with boxes of sausages and bacon to be stored in the basement deep freezers. The old women want ice cream, which they believe will be found in the basement. In fact, the ice cream is out in the street melting in the sun under a hot pink sky. The owners of the house return, reminding me I've been in charge of everything while they've been away. I'm responsible for the butchered body in the basement, but initially I don't accept that as my reality.] //

⁂

HOT PINK: #0850, #0941
PAINT: #0813, #0823, #0847, #0853, #0941, #0955, #0987
BUTCHER: #0868, #1095, #1107
THE DEAR HEART: #0677

⁂

#0625 - April 26, 2019 @ 02:34 (San Francisco, California)

[0625.1 / 1583] [Temple movie. Something about DAVID FRANCO. Something joyful occurs in a parking lot of a large festival. Unclear. Fast and confusing.] //

⁂

MOVIE: #1001, #1067, #1092, #1145, #1146, #1149
JOYFUL: #0920, #0980

438

TEMPLE: #0805, #0834, #0907, #0937, #1000, #1031
⁎⁎⁎

#0626 - April 26, 2019 @ 04:12 (San Francisco, California)

[0626.1 / 1584] [Temple movie continues. I live with THE WEAVER. We follow a guy down an alley to an "X-Games" event. WAH! gives sound healings for $2. Makeshift tables are set everywhere. The scene feels suspicious. THE WEAVER and I get separated and I don't make an effort to call her.] //

⁎⁎⁎
Maj. = 0- THE WEAVER: #0629
SOUND: #0857, #0889, #0953, #0957, #0994
EFFORT: #0900, #0922, #1073
⁎⁎⁎

#0627 - April 26, 2019 @ 06:45 (San Francisco, California)

[0627.1 / 1585] [I'm abducted while on a trip to France. I leave my body and float around new, tall, high rise condo buildings with efficient plumbing. JOSH GROBAN and CHUCK NORRIS promise to pay my ransom. My vision is fuzzy as I take a bike ride. The ride ends at a camp where people practice yoga and eat pasta. I take up residence in a small cottage in a green space. From afar I see a tiny man nearly crushed under the fist of a giant man sitting at a round table while campers showcase their summer projects.] //

⁎⁎⁎
ABDUCTED: #1052
SUMMER: #0841, #0850, #0876, #1023, #1032
FRANCE: #1128
⁎⁎⁎

#0628 - April 28, 2019 @ 03:50 (San Francisco, California)

[0628.1 / 1586] [I travel to receive healing from THE WORLDBRIDGER. I sit in an outdoor amphitheater where I watch him do his work. THE ROMANTIC sits in the row behind me. His eyes glow green and he has a golden braid dangling from the back of his head.
"I tried to call you a couple of months ago. Sorry, that didn't work out."
Our exchange is friendly. We stand up and walk from the woodland outdoors to a sanctuary.
As I walk downstairs, I'm stopped by a man who says,
"Wait, I've got it...it's your toes."
I'm still a student and in training so I don't fully grasp what he's sharing with me and I continue onward.
A woman with short blonde hair, perhaps a twin to THE TRINITY (*sweet, reverent, and surrendered*) goes just before me to receive a healing. When she completes, she looks at me and says, *"Wow you look really weird."*
I don't have a full interaction with THE WORLDBRIDGER but he does come near,

439

tapping me on the elbow as he passes. A band of musicians walks directly behind him. What I find most attractive about him is my perception of his ethics and integrity. He's able to move a lot of energy, and he does work from a good, aligned space.

I see entities leaving through the floor in patches and patterns of "dark light." Some are pixelated, others are cloudy and mist-like. Occasionally one passes through that looks like a dot matrix ASCII art image. It's easy to differentiate between ones that are useful and those which need to be cast out. I sit next to an older woman. We discuss having similar propensities for discernment, as the healing service continues.]

[0628.2 / 1587] [I stand next to a body of water, Caribbean in feel. I step on to a docked yacht and realize the tide from a cresting wave may drag me out to sea. I step on and off the gangway just quickly enough to avoid being swept away by the surf.] //

✲✲

Maj. = 7- THE WORLDBRIDGER: #0693, 15- THE ROMANTIC: #0688
MATRIX: #1102, #1113, #1165
ETHICS: #0998
OCCASIONALLY: #1155, #1159
THE TRINITY: #1004

✲✲

#0629 - April 28, 2019 @ 05:52 (San Francisco, California)

[0629.1 / 1588] [I'm seated at the far side of a swimming pool as I talk with THE ORPHAN about how to decode a message. We want to gain access to a new level of a high frequency healing realm. We review a lengthy user agreement before we're allowed to play at that level of the game. One codicil involves agreeing to attend an ARIANA GRANDE concert. As THE ORPHAN and I read through the agreement we realize we may have bitten off more than we can chew. A lone African American child cries in the wading area of the pool. We note that if we become agitated by her cries it reduces the amount of time we're allotted to play in the desired up-level realm.

We attempt to hack the code, but new segments we're provided are lengthy and time consuming. Portions we've previously decoded and submitted don't carry forward in aggregate. THE ORPHAN and I each have our own unique puzzles to solve. The numbers run across our laptop screens like a perpetual string of embossed credit card digits. We accept the scenario is much more complicated than either of us expected it to be.]

[0629.2 / 1589] [I'm on a train where a male passenger becomes frustrated and exits before his intended stop. Anticipatorily I ask THE WEAVER, *"It's only 2 hours until the ARIANA GRANDE concert. Are you excited?!"* The train is full. We'll arrive at the concert venue soon!] //

✲✲

Maj. = 0- THE WEAVER: #0642
ARIANA GRANDE: #0662
THE ORPHAN: #0646

⁎⁎

#0630 - April 29, 2019 @ 01:42 (San Francisco, California)

[0630.1 / 1590] [I'm at the concluding session of a conference. People stand to offer remarks on what they've learned, and what they will take from the experience back out into the world. A woman stands and delivers a talk about her dad who recently passed away, and describes two periods of trauma that were released through use of a particular breathwork technique.] //

⁎⁎

TRAUMA: #0864, #0983
TECHNIQUE: #0896, #1058, #1105
REMARKS: #0811, #0880, #0910, #0926, #0949

⁎⁎

#0631 - April 29, 2019 @ 02:54 (San Francisco, California)

[0631.1 / 1591] [I enter a gathering space with THE LACHRYMOLOGIST *(subtle, prolific, and discerning)* for a morning ritual. We're with three other guys in a basement. We've agreed to meet at 1:50am to have a conversation on leadership next steps for an incubating start up. He's occupied with another activity. When he pauses, I ask him if he's enjoyed the event. After another lengthy pause he responds.
"It's been really good to connect to all the things between my heart and head that make me human."
I enter a bathroom with narrow walls. Thin plastic sheets separate the showers and toilets. A woman bathes on the men's side. Her presence informs my decision to not defecate in the toilet on that side of the room. The space feels very nourishing, warm and while inside I'm invited to pick up where we left off working at 1:50am.] //

⁎⁎

OCCUPIED: #0820, #0860, #0961, #1114, #1128
MORNING: #1031, #1058, #1073, #1105
THE LACHRYMOLOGIST: #0633

⁎⁎

#0632 - April 29, 2019 @ 03:09 (San Francisco, California)

[0632.1 / 1592] [An abstract vibrational language plays through an overhead PA like Morse code. It repeatedly says, *"ALL IS GOOD. ALL IS WELL,"* in low frequency tones that hang in the air like cloudy puffs of Braille.] //

⁎⁎

FREQUENCY: #0887, #0992, #0998, #1193
CODE: #0804, #0845, #0856, #0976
LOW: #0826, #0840, #0844, #0870, #0874, #0894

⁎⁎

⁎⁎

#0633 - April 29, 2019 @ 04:22 (San Francisco, California)

[0633.1 / 1593] [I'm at a hotel pool at night. THE IRONMAN (*exhausted, sad, and seeking*), THE LACHRYMOLOGIST (*balanced, open, and free*) and I do a breathing exercise while submerged in water, moving very deliberately and repeatedly uttering specific sounds. The effects of underwater grief processing and catharsis are thought to be tremendously therapeutic. We are encouraged to scream as loudly as possible while underwater to precipitate catharsis. There seems to be even more therapeutic value being submerged in street clothing and walking under water while screaming. I surface and exit the pool.

I walk by a hot tub I sat in earlier, and discover I mistakenly left my little pink credit card holder behind. I remember I left my pink wallet next to the hot tub earlier in the night during an ecstatic breathing practice. I notice I've left a crumpled up $20 bill where I left my wallet. I'm surprised no one took it.

THE MAGICIAN enters and intends to complete a personal session in the pool. I enter the hotel lobby basically naked, noting the environment seems socially conservative. THE LALA has a heated exchange with a person in the group as we fill out hold harmless forms to participate in another exercise. Older people enter the space in large numbers. We discuss the best place to find breakfast food within the compound as I walk down a long hallway flanked by rows of slot machines until I find a bathroom.] //

Maj. = 14- THE MAGICIAN: #0640
Min. = ◆- THE LALA: #0970
BREAKFAST: #0870, #0985, #1036, #1073, #1145
CREDIT CARD: #0915, #0975, #0977, #1026
THERAPEUTIC: #0896, #1085
THE IRONMAN: #0683

#0634 - April 30, 2019 @ 04:54 (San Francisco, California)

[0634.1 / 1594] [I win a foot race and am awarded a medal. The next race starts as THE DANCER and I ascend an escalator. She wears a pearl necklace. She lacks a racing credential but the necklace distracts security. She advances to the next segment with me. We make our way to the stage and stand together until we notice two people coming towards us, we identify as "VILLAINS." The assembled crowd "boos" them as THE DANCER and I run to cross the finish line. She and I have a decision to make: Do we confront them? Do we flee?]

[0634.2 / 1595] [A buffet line splits into two large levels, one up an escalator, the other down. In the mirror I notice I have three small braille-like dots on my cheek that appear to be unconnected endpoints of an equilateral triangle. A young tattooed man behind the register grabs my attention. I want to connect and flirt with him, but I feel shy. The vibe of the scene is sweet and vulnerable.] //

Maj. = 2- THE DANCER: #0648
SWEET: #0850, #0851, #0892, #0914, #0951

SHY: #0948
VILLAIN: #0864, #0924, #0944

⁂

#0635 - April 30, 2019 @ 06:31 (San Francisco, California)

[0635.1 / 1596] [We're on what seems to be a four-day trip. Overall, the scene is docile, tame, and familiar. I'm on a retreat with a brother and sister. We do things mom and dad would not approve of, but they're fun for us. We're being deceptive on mom and dad's sweetly planned trip. We've found a sandwich baggie full of drugs. We do all of them.

We descend a large tree and admire fractal-like pods extending out from its trunk. The tree wants us to harvest its fruit. Most of this occurs at night. A crowd of people gathers to hear us discuss what we've learned. We hand out laminated cue cards to people so they can reenact scenes from our exploits.

We await the arrival of THE PERVERT (*direct, taboo, and dark*) to help with stage direction for the panel discussion. We're momentarily excited to see a similar looking man enter the rear of the venue with a woman. We mix some powder in water in an oversized plastic syringe. Clear flexible tubing replaces the needle. We try to intubate ourselves onstage for shock value but are unsuccessful before THE PERVERT takes control of the scene.]

[0635.2 / 1597] [A group scouts locations for a film shoot. They're keen on an Italian market in an LA suburb that has its original 1970's retro awning.] //

⁂

PODS: #0952, #1084
LAMINATED: #0932, #0933, #1133
FRACTAL: #0924, #0949
THE PERVERT: #0837

⁂

#0636 - May 1, 2019 @ 02:39 (San Francisco, California)

[0636.1 / 1598] [I traverse an airport terminal, intending to board a flight to Bulgaria. I quickly rifle through a packed bag and pull out a small grey steel fire box. The fire box contains only a few items, one is a bag of white coffee beans which have been ground into fine powder. I stand next to a couple who've lost their luggage. I see an ad on the television in the terminal featuring reindeer and moose. I pour some of the white powder into a plastic cup (*damp on the inside*). When the powder comes into contact with the water droplets it sticks to the side of the cup and turns brown. The trip will be fairly short, so I have no concerns that I don't have enough clean clothes for the flight, or the fact that I left most of my money (*read: all of my cash*) at another airport in a locker. I keenly review the contents of the fire box and feel satisfied I've left a reasonable amount of room in my bag to bring home souvenirs from the trip.] //

⁂

BEANS: #0897, #1158
TERMINAL: #0878, #1148

LOCKER: #0868, #1196

⁂

#0637 - May 1, 2019 @ 04:05 (San Francisco, California)

[0637.1 / 1599] [I've joined a team at a real estate start up. I don't care which team member gets what client. I declare, *'I'LL SPEAK MY MIND AS FREELY AS I WANT!'* because it'll give them a better sense of who I really am. I invite them to cut me off when I annoy them. The workday ends. I explore our office park and take an elevator ride to the opposite side. I'm disoriented for a moment when the doors open and I have to climb out from eight feet below. THE PUBLIC MEDIUM and THE BAPTIZED ONE *(casual, slow, and attentive)* both remain in the office, talking to a third office mate.

I say goodbye and travel to THE ARCHITECT and THE DESIGNER's new home which boasts a beautiful, geometrically complex pool with a retractable greenhouse roof. On top of an infinity edge constructed from unique angles and slants across multiple tiers floats a nice soapy layer of white foam. I enter the pool fully nude and wade through it without getting wet. I tell myself, *'I'd love to be a houseboy here.'*

A birthday party was recently hosted at the home. Eating in the pool is a household habit. THE DESIGNER and I eat dinner on floating trays as he describes the great design and innovation that "Jacob" brought to the project *(referencing the party decor)*. Unexpectedly he discloses an emerging desire to adopt a child.

I clip the ribbon of a small cluster of mirror ball balloons. They float toward the glass ceiling, pulled upward into a swirling exhaust fan. When struck by the fan blades they erupt in scatters of tiny squares that glisten and sparkle on the pool deck.

I exit the pool. I urinate in a stylish bathroom and notice my penis is thick, long, and fully functional. I feel confident it's time to start dating again.] //

⁂

Maj. = 18 THE PUBLIC MEDIUM: #0682
Min. = ♥- *THE ARCHITECT: #0700,* ♠- *THE DESIGNER: #0700*
THICK: #1141, #1142, #1154, #1181, #1188, #1196
DATE: #1076, #1079, #1084, #1091, #1108

⁂

#0638 - May 2, 2019 @ 04:03 (San Francisco, California)

[0638.1 / 1600] [I'm building a temple. On the second day of work, the entire thing burns down. The project hosts three active construction sites in different physical locations, so no one is too concerned with the loss. I step through a portal and get transported back to 2012, where I see BEYONCÉ tear up and remark on how much she's moved by another structure built by the team and the community's participation in other's healing. She thanks me for my contribution as we watch the sunset. The structure burns in front of us, which feels deeply satisfying and aligned. We're old friends who love and respect each other deeply.] //

⁂

BEYONCÉ: #0645
ONSITE: #0830, #0855, #0974, #1028, #1133
OLD FRIENDS: #0889, #0898, #0915

⁎⁎

#0639 - May 3, 2019 @ 00:05 (San Francisco, California)

[0639.1 / 1601] [I'm in a sci-fi reality and become aware of an energetic "Lurker" program; a thin black mesh-like entity worn close to my skin like a wetsuit. It meanders and shape shifts when I bring my visual attention to it.] //

⁎⁎
SHAPE: #0811, #0965, #1100, #1198
ENTITY: #0834, #0926, #0934, #0973, #0976
MESH: #0804, #1101
⁎⁎

#0640 - May 4, 2019 @ 06:15 (San Francisco, California)

[0640.1 / 1602] [A young boy plays with a clear lacquer toy. *"CHECK OUT THIS TRICK!"* he shouts at me, flipping it around and scattering small colorful balls within the cube-like object. Two women sit nearby eating toast for breakfast and gossip about a female neighbor with bipolar disorder, who hurls large pieces of furniture down from her balcony as they hurl insults up at her. I fly up and out of my body to observe the woman from up close, and realize she's my new neighbor. I don't want her to know where my rented room is.]

[0640.2 / 1603] [I attend a board meeting at Davies Symphony Hall. DENISE MENELLY says to THE BOSS, *"Any protesters that show up are yours to handle."* I nod in agreement.]

[0640.3 / 1604] [I stand at the corner of Tree St,, Tree Ave and Tree Blvd. THE PARTNERS (*supportive, playful, and persistent*) (THE ATTRACTOR & THE ARBORIST) and I skip away from the intersection saying, *"We love to stick together!"* It feels familiar and friendly as we trespass across finely manicured lawns.]

[0640.4 / 1605] [THE MAGICIAN runs an offsite. PRINCE is in my small group. He begins to make up a song about the violets and other flora around us. I'm eager to share uninterrupted eye contact with him.]

[0640.5 / 1606] [THE PIANIST (*soulful, recovering, and gentile*) and I return to Davies Symphony Hall post board meeting for a performance. Seats are stacked close together and our legs are 4x as long as they normally would be (*as are everyone else's*). This makes the hall seem steep, and the descent to the stage...sharp.]

[0640.6 / 1607] [I return to my room and deadbolt the door (*multiple locks top to bottom*) to prevent my bipolar neighbor from breaking in.] //

⁜

Maj. = 14 = THE MAGICIAN: #0654
TREE: #0924, #0926, #1002, #1055
TOAST: #0841, #0897
THE BOSS: #0685
THE ARBORIST: #1060
THE ATTRACTOR: #0929

⁜

#0641 - May 5, 2019 @ 02:50 (San Francisco, California)

[0641.1 / 1608] ["Tales of the City" motif. ANNA MADRIGAL and other characters are present.]
[0641.2 / 1609] [A mean and aggressive woman gives a talk at a leadership gathering. I call her out, then exit the building. With my back turned she leaps from the stage and chases me, drawing audible gasps from the crowd. Later, when I share tea with BARON BAPTISTE, he doesn't have any recollection of the event, even though he was onstage with the woman while she ranted.]
[0641.3 / 1610] [THE SOUND ENGINEER *(in service, disciplined, and responsive)* and a woman talk about surrendering to invisible forces. Their healer quarters are combined with a lover's suite in a hotel. Two men nearby work on laptops while naked in bed together.] //

⁜

BARON BAPTISTE: #0797
NAKED: #0841, #1161, #1166, #1184
SHARE: #0970, #0979, #0998, #1047, #1073

⁜

#0642 - May 5, 2019 @ 05:35 (San Francisco, California)

[0642.1 / 1611] [THE NURSE and THE HILLBILLY attempt to take an online test in a parking lot. THE KETTLE *(angry, manipulative, and ungrounded)* and I have an epic public throw down. THE NURSE and THE WEAVER watch and do not intervene. When we're done fighting, we're told *"Lick your own wounds, Band Aids are in the fridge."*]
[0642.2 / 1612] [I demonstrate an ability to read minds.]
[0642.3 / 1613] [THE ROADRUNNER *(timid, and strong)* and I cuddle on the couch.]
[0642.4 / 1614] [Popcorn burns on a stovetop.]
[0642.5 / 1615] [*"This trauma must be healed,"* a voice says as a knife spins in mid-air. *"This goes in your eye now,"* the voice plainly continues.]
[0642.6 / 1616] [I yell at a woman.] //

⁜

Maj. = 0- THE WEAVER: #0648, 13-THE NURSE: #0649
Min. = ♣- THE HILLBILLY: #0646
POPCORN: #0841, #0863, #0865, #0889, #0969
EYE: #1088, #1151, #1158, #1175
THE KETTLE: #1071

⁜

PART 9 - PLATEAU

#0643 - #0720

"When you're finished with the mop then you can stop
And look at what you've done
The plateau's clean (no dirt to be seen)
And the work it took was fun.
There's nothing on the top but a bucket and a mop
And an illustrated book about birds
You'll see a lot of there, but don't be scared
Who needs actions when you got words?"

-Curt Kirkwood

* * *

May 6, 2019 - June 21, 2019

#0643 - May 6, 2019 @ 06:06 (San Francisco, California)

[0643.1 / 1617] [I run exercises with teacher trainees and invite them to, *"Get bodied, then go from there. Intend. Get bodied. Choose."* The eleven of them have fun and explore.] //

⁂
INVITE: #0920, #0927, #0928
CHOOSE: #0852, #0856, #0882, #0895
EXPLORE: #0939
INTEND: #0850, #0865, #0869, #0872
⁂

#0644 - May 6, 2019 @ 07:04 (San Francisco, California)

[0644.1 / 1618] [We stop in various places in a city to collect snacks en route to a training. I find a large wad of cash as I descend a staircase and head out to a promenade. Time runs short. I need to be at training in 20 minutes to be adequately grounded, but I'm pulled into an exercise where members of a focus group are encouraged to make a scatterplot of large polka dots on a whiteboard. I jump up mid-exercise and ask them to identify which dots they contributed *(intuitively, without guidance)*. My interjection disrupts the facilitator. He and I move to the back of the room to discuss what the shared intention was.]

[0644.2 / 1619] [I observe a scene in a house where multiple guys look at their phones and debate whether or not to drive a Porsche to a party. Masses of dead leaves pile up within the tri-level home. I descend to the basement where I encounter a woman who is angered by a trans-identified person's misuse of another's pronouns and unconsciously running her mouth.
   "Boys should have boy names. Girls should have girl names. It's annoying to have to call a girl a boy and a boy a gir-"
   "Shut your face." I interrupt her droning whining and shame her in front of the group gathered.
   One of the guys scrolls through images on a 3D hookup app on his phone, pausing to covet the profile pic of a unicorn-like dude photographed in front of a white background. Unicorn dude's pinned an image of 3D calf tattoos to the profile, which rise from the phone screen and pulsate. A lightning bolt jumps up from the back of his legs seemingly taunting us to, *"Look here."*
   THE REFLECTION is among those in the house, seeking future interviewee prospects for his podcast. He's on the hunt for new perspectives currently underrepresented in the zeitgeist.] //

⁂
BASEMENT: #0811, #0815, #0820, #0821, #0833
SHAME: #0829, #0929

PROMENADE: #879
3D: #0931, #1086, #1200
THE REFLECTION: #1063
⁂

#0645- May 7, 2019 @ 05:48 (San Francisco, California)

[0645.1 / 1620] [I follow GAY HENDRICKS in to a grocery store. We walk to the back, disrobe, and then enter a hot tub. I trust him as he guides my erect penis in to a woman named "KATIE."]

[0645.2 / 1621] [I attend a production meeting where we discuss how to pull off a large headlining event at Coachella. Paper thin "brass nickels" the size of paper plates have been minted by festival promoters, as a means to facilitate onsite transactions. They're absurdly large for their relative value. Comparable to modern yap stones, they make no sense.
HBCU students prepare for a giant parade as I walk by. THE AUSSIE *(expressive, bubbly, and large spirited)* and THE TRAINEE *(meek, doe eyed, and quiet)* are among dancers who rehearse and perform with BEYONCÉ.

[0645.3 / 1622] [Later, BEYONCÉ and her family spend time casually socializing at home. They throw shade during a gossipy discussion about "Carla," her dad's girlfriend. "Carla's" obnoxious. Her sole priority is to get pregnant at any cost.] //

⁂
BEYONCÉ: #0689
WALK BY: #0806, #0812, #0858, #0908
LARGE: #0801, #0806, #0815, #0816
PARADE: #1166, #1171
THE AUSSIE: #0712
⁂

#0646 - May 7, 2019 @ 07:02 (San Francisco, California)

[0646.1 / 1623] [THE HILLBILLY attempts to fix urinals. Two small black buttons on the tops of the urinals, if pressed together, will cause an overflow. They take quite a while to drain.]

[0646.2 / 1624] [I'm on a street corner by a sewer grate. I fart. It stinks. Someone walks up next to me and reacts to the smell, which I blame on *"sewer gas."*]

[0646.3 / 1625] [I encourage a group of people to, *"ride the magic carpet."* I speak of it as a rite of passage, not realizing someone in the group is on deck and ready to take a ride. I stop myself before I give away any more detail. The woman could be THE ORPHAN. It could also be THE BARKEEP *(teacher, longing, and striving).*] //

449

☆
Min. = ♣- *THE HILLBILLY: #0649*
SEWER: #1133
PASSAGE: #1282, #1295, #1385
MAGIC: #0820, #1181
THE ORPHAN: #0949
☆

#0647 - May 8, 2019 @ 08:40 (San Francisco, California)

[0647.1 / 1626] [Kids create computer programs using small cubes with two thin ribbons on top in what feels like a playful and curious classroom. Grey/Black, Grey/Grey. The position of the ribbons determines the machine's output. Bands of scotch tape on the edge of a round wooden table cover over stickers (*pairs of googly eyes, cartoon characters, etc.*).]

[0647.2 / 1627] [I attend a neighbor's birthday party. Her person of interest doesn't show up to celebrate. It's awkward and sad for her and the attendees.]

[0647.3 / 1628] [I'm in a seaside cove with THE SEX THERAPIST (*bright, deep, and feminine*). We watch kids play on an army tank submerged in water. They dangle and leap from the cannon. A nude Black man suns himself nearby. He's embarrassed. His penis smells like feces. The odor causes him to stay a comfortable distance away.] //

☆
COMPUTER: #0962, #1009, #1054, #1056
RIBBONS: #0854, #1021, #1092
CANNON: #0807, #0899
☆

#0648 - May 9, 2019 @ 06:52 (San Francisco, California)

[0648.1 / 1629] [The family is at school with THE CHILD. *"I don't want to play with you!"* she says to us and other members of the class. At the end of the day, the teacher distributes certificates.]

[0648.2 / 1630] [I'm on a ship with a crew of Navy men. The ship takes on water and slowly sinks. We do our best to get the engines turning and run ashore at the last possible moment. THE DANCER, THE WEAVER, THE CARPENTER and THE CHILD park a car at a dock next to the ship and ask me, *"What happened?"* They enjoy a picnic as the sailors walk around and disappear up into the jungle just beyond the parking lot.]

[0648.3 / 1631] [A group of female models with brightly toned hair are notified by a photographer that they've been selected as members of a new rock band. They're promptly made up to be shot for their new album cover. The five women stand in a line jamming and riffing.

Each break into a series of five holograms. 25 women stand in a square grid, brightly ornamented and "rock out in unison."]

[0648.4 / 1632] [An older man passes away. His family gathers to mourn and prepare his favorite meal one last time. An older woman sobs and laughs as she serves steamed broccoli atop piles of potted meat covered in gravy. A couch is available to sit on, though the upturned cushions reveal some large fresh stains. They could be chocolate, shit, or blood. It's not certain. The shaggy couch has rectangular cushions of various sizes that don't really fit the form of the furniture.] //

⁎⁎

Maj. = 0- THE WEAVER: #0654, 1- THE CARPENTER: #0657,
2- THE DANCER: #0667, 3- THE CHILD: #0667
NAVY: #0945, #1190
SHAGGY: #0919, #1001

⁎⁎

#0649 - May 10, 2019 @ 08:37 (San Francisco, California)

[0649.1 / 1633] [**MANTRA:** *"Practice and teach tools while asleep."*]

[0649.2 / 1634] [I'm in the basement of a house that may be haunted. Tenants share fear of a poltergeist. The being has a large yellow ball over its head surrounded by a series of four blue tubes. The being was last spotted in an old bathroom. I teach THE NURSE, THE HILLBILLY and a young boy how to *"use the tools of grounding and protection"* in the instance they encounter the ghostly presence. The young boy may have created a bomb. He holds a crudely soldered box with a grid of sliding switches and knobs. The adults move quickly to diffuse the device.]

[0649.3 / 1635] [I follow a three-legged dog down a hill. I start again. Each time the pursuit increases in intensity though I meet the challenge squarely. I feel competent, awake and well-practiced.] //

⁎⁎

Maj. = 13- THE NURSE: #0653
Min. = ♣- THE HILLBILLY: #0664
THREE: #0805, #0807, #0808, #0817
MANTRA: #0879
BALL: #0962, #1075, #1104

⁎⁎

#0650 - May 11, 2019 @ 08:18 (San Francisco, California)

[0650.1 / 1636] [Sex dream in a frat house. The environment feels juvenile. THE FIT BOY (*square chested, tattooed, and confident*) and I watch porn. Seems like similar scenes are

451

happening in the surrounding dorm rooms. THE FIT BOY and I have a lurking suspicion the laptop will explode if the pornography stops, so we keep watching.] //

⁂

SEX: #0835, #0856, #0863, #0876, #0878
LAPTOP: #0962, #0980, #0990, #1035
DORM ROOM: #1128

⁂

#0651 - May 12, 2019 @ 05:01 (San Francisco, California)

[0651.1 / 1637] [*"Cause it. Cause it in your body. Decide. Some of you don't want to take responsibility,"* I say to a class while leading practice.] //

⁂

CLASS: #0903, #0918, #0927
TAKE RESPONSIBILITY: #1157
DECIDE: #0922, #0923, #0926, #0929

⁂

#0652 - May 13, 2019 @ 02:22 (San Francisco, California)

[0652.1 / 1638] [THE PSYCHIATRIST and I take a trip together. We enjoy free drinks on the plane. When we arrive at our hotel, a circuit party thumps within. Go-go dancers gyrate all around us on top of large steel boxes. *"That was more meaningful than just masturbating,"* THE PSYCHIATRIST laughs and continues, *"I think we get free drinks here too, but we have to wait in line."* We walk into the golden lit hotel atrium and pass under a thick sheet of warm water, smooth as glass in appearance. It seems we're staying at a "flow-tel."] //

⁂

Min. = ♠- *THE PSYCHIATRIST: #0663*
GOGO: #0913
FREE: #0859, #0909, #0917, #0976

⁂

#0653 - May 14, 2019 @ 05:13 (San Francisco, California)
*Multi-layer, nuanced dream. *

[0653.1 / 1639] [A woman on horseback rides up a hill. She's apprehended by a Shaolin monk who guffaws, *"HAH HAH HAH!"* as he plucks her up and off the horse and flies away with her under his arm.]

[0653.2 / 1640] [I fumble with a set of keys as I approach a house on a hilltop. A tall man emerges from behind. The energy of fear palpates between us. Things don't seem to end well for me.]

. . .

[0653.3 / 1641] [THE COCK (*convincing, witty, and syncopated*) and I run between houses, playfully hiding from something. We might be roommates. We seem young and giggle when we momentarily consider hooking up again after 17 years before light heartedly crowing, *"NAAAAHHHH! NOPE!"*]

[0653.4 / 1642] [I look down and notice my voice recorder has been running for 5 full minutes. I realize, *"Oh, I'm still asleep."*]

[0653.5 / 1643] [I'm at a harvest party at a workplace. THE NURSE wears a large grey costume wig. *"Wow that really works for you!"* I compliment. A half set table sits adjacent to us with plushie spider toys and pairs of shoes piled on top, yet to be arranged. Remaining inventory rests in a box by an office door.]

[0653.6 / 1644] [I'm a sex party. A hot guy catches my eye then passes by. THE POCKET GAY (*good natured, accepting, and funny*) flirts with me and gives me a blowjob. THE POCKET GAY offers me a *"full sexual healing."* After I cum, I pull my dick out of his throat and incredulously declare, *"You guys...look. It's straight! Like it used to be. Do you see that? It's perfect! Even a little purple at the end."*] //

✶✶

Maj. = 13- THE NURSE: #0814
17: #1036, #1070, #1081, #1151
HALF: #0916, #0925, #0950, #0960
CUM: #0873, #0952, #1090

✶✶

#0654 - May 14, 2019 @ 06:39 (San Francisco, California)

[0654.1 / 1645] [I'm in a Midwest town for a yoga retreat. 11 people are packed into my hotel room. I'm surprised to see so many bodies when I open the door fully aroused and intending to masturbate. THE PIXIE is in the room. Another among the 11 is a married woman who seems to know me. She's the only heterosexual.
"It's fine. Don't worry. No one in there wants to sleep with you," I say to her, allaying her fear of committing adultery.]

[0654.2 / 1646] [I'm in another Midwest town. I walk up the driveway to a house. A woman stands in the center of a cul-de-sac and shouts to me,
"I GET THE SENSE THAT THERE'S A SPIRIT IN THERE."
"Yes. Surrender. Holy Spirit. All of that's here and available," I casually respond.
Abundant dark energy hangs between me and the house. A sign just above the doorbell displays my name and a message: *"Your status has been upgraded from bronze to silver."*]

. . .

[0654.3 / 1647] [I walk through the door of my hotel room where a group sexual encounter unfolds.
"Who are you?" a guy in the fuckpile asks as I toss my keys on the credenza.
"I'm ME and this is MY room."
Everyone laughs.]

[0654.4 / 1648] [I'm in the back of a pickup truck. A guy appreciatively hands me a small burlap satchel full of chocolate covered blueberry snacks as compensation for letting him stay in the room.]

[0654.5 / 1649] [I'm back by the crowded room. I drink a Mexican Coca Cola from a bottle. A small stone, shaped like a sunflower kernel clicks against the front of my right incisor as I drink the soda. I hear THE WEAVER in the other room greeting others as they arrive.]

[0654.6 / 1650] [THE MAGICIAN sits on a picnic bench two tables over from me. I consider asking him for a job, but don't. He looks exhausted. Perhaps another time.]

[0654.7 / 1651] [In a hotel lobby, I recognize a woman. I'm confused for a moment. She appears taller than I remember. She's married to a man named "Chris McGill."
"You were in the sex party room, concerned you'd cheat on her husband. You didn't!"]

[0654.8 / 1652] [Slowly I realize I'm recording a dream within a dream. I record over a precious recording that had, *"all the information."* I laugh when I realize what's happening because my memory will be muddled and distorted] //

⁎⁎

Maj. = 0- THE WEAVER: #0662, 14- THE MAGICIAN: #0755
Min. = ♠- THE PIXIE: #0865
DARK ENERGY: #1047
CHEAT: #0850
BENCH: #0967, #0972, #1081, #1177
DREAM WITHIN A DREAM: #0856, #0911
INFORMATION: #0942, #0983, #0996

⁎⁎

#0655 - May 14, 2019 @ 08:04 (San Francisco, California)

[0655.1 / 1653] [THE KIND HEART joins us at a bistro table. His hair is really long, half pink, half black, and twisted into micro-dreads. *"We grow our hair out to hide the shape of our hearts,"* he laments. He's gaunt. A webbing of light blue veins topographically protrudes through the skin of his left cheek.]

. . .

[0655.2 / 1654] [I'm in a giant mansion owned by THE BELKS. The home is two streets over from a giant institute, "The GATES Foundation." Both giant buildings are in the center of a small hilltop town.

THE PHILANTHROPIST's mother recently passed away, after turning 102. The family, in their grief, has started the search for a new executive director of their charitable trust. I meander through large regal hallways as I stay tapped into the family conversation. I float in, and out, and between buildings on occasion flying up and back to take in majestic views of town. I crawl in valleys and creeks behind the large manor homes as I watch storm clouds bank up.]

[0655.3 / 1655] [I float above a grassy hillside and watch a pack of golden dogs aligned head to tail undulate rhythmically in various wave-like patterns. When the 14 dogs achieve coherence, they move to the edge of a cliff, jump, and cascade like lemmings into the sea below.]

[0655.4 / 1656] [I'm encouraged to, "go watch the manta rays play." I crouch down on my knees and forearms and crawl along a small gravel path. I peek off the edge of the trail into a moat and see the large creatures dance and court. I float on the surface of the water, hypnotized by the manta rays swooping below. Once they depart, I crawl from the water back to the gravel path on the side of the home. I peek in on the family eating in a formal dining room. I make my way to a wooden gateway, rise to my feet, and walk up the driveway towards the street realizing I'm equidistant from "The BELK Institute" and "The GATES Foundation."]

[0655.5 / 1657] [A woman who leads my team passes my desk. She demands that I download Instagram so I'm aware of team, "shout outs."
"Is the same information on Facebook?"
"Yes."
I promptly delete Instagram.] //

⁎⁎

Maj. = 21- THE KIND HEART: #0656
PLAY: #0929, #0939, #0942
MAJESTIC: #0803, #0919, #0957
DELETE: #0844, #0962
THE PHILANTHROPIST: #0959

⁎⁎

#0656 - May 14, 2019 @ 09:43 (San Francisco, California)

[0656.1 / 1658] [Sex dream. Not sure who I'm sleeping with. It feels like we're drunk. My vision is blurry. I see a tattoo on his right hip and side that extends up to his armpit. Our skin glistens with sweat. I'm on top. My mind drifts...

-- {THE SKEPTIC (lonely, longing, and objective) hits on THE KIND HEART, who walks away without speaking. THE PILOT observes the interaction. Immediately afterward a giant surge of *energy passes through the room. An entity floats through the space unhooking "Gender Stereotyping" cords.}--*

...I'M GUIDED BACK to my partner every time my attention drifts. He reaches back and brings me inside him firmly as our eyes lock. It feels masculine and primal. High degrees of shared presence and respect exist between the two of us.]

[0656.2 / 1659] [It's stormy. I'm on an island under a cabana on an outcropping of rocks where I encounter THE BRAIN *(playful, scientific, and analytical)*. We share conversations about neuroscience and *"the nature of the mind."* The conversation speeds and fades just as I wake up.] //

✱✱

Maj. = 6- THE PILOT: #0679, 21- THE KIND HEART: #0715
OUTCROPPING: #1004, #1062
DEGREE: #0874, #0894, #0905, #0919, #0963
THE SKEPTIC: #0852
THE BRAIN: #1114

✱✱

#0657 - May 15, 2019 @ 07:13 (San Francisco, California)

[0657.1 / 1660] [I feel sad. I've abandoned my dream work practice.]
[0657.2 / 1661] [I enter a mansion through the rear door and descend a staircase to the basement. Once inside I see a poltergeist hover and traverse just inches above the floor. I hide from THE CARPENTER behind his workbench, who enters wearing bright orange everything from head to toe: *jumpsuit, ball cap, and a pair of plastic dayglo glasses.*
I run away. THE BARBIE *(gorgeous, alive, and happy)* shouts and points until I agree to let her come with me. We run to a tiny used car with a manual transmission, hop in, and then take a meandering seaside drive without a planned destination.] //

✱✱

Maj. = 1- THE CARPENTER: #0660
DAYGLO: #1136
AGREE: #0938, #0940, #0948
SEASIDE: #0841, #1001, #1010, #1104

✱✱

#0658 - May 15, 2019 @ 09:09 (San Francisco, California)

[0658.1 / 1662] [THE HEALER shows off his new "high and tight" haircut. His hip length ponytail is gone.]

[0658.2 / 1663] [I've regained consciousness after a dental surgery. THE GREEN TARA *(intense, direct, and messy)* helps me up from the chair. I feel really stoned. We walk to a parking lot.

456

"Remember you're teaching my class at 5pm." She says as she gets in a car and drives away.

I stumble in the direction of my home and notice it's 4:28pm. I try to order a car, but my phone interface repeatedly freezes. I have no way to call THE OCCUPATIONAL THERA-PIST *(new, eager, and helpful)* to let her know I'll be late. I also have no way of getting across town in time to teach. I have to accept that I'm going to be absent. I stand in my pink light and shout out, "*L!*" "*L!*" "*L!*" hoping I'll get some sort of miraculous help from my guide. Some people nearby watch me talking to thin air and decide I'd be, *"interesting to hang out with."*] //

⁂

Maj. = 20- THE HEALER: #1224
INTERESTING: #0895, #0959, #1080
"L.": #0821, #0826
HAIRCUT: #0819, #1000, #1113, #1146

⁂

#0659 - May 16, 2019 @ 07:22 (San Francisco California)

[0659.1 / 1664] [Frenetic scene where I'm on a ship pushing back from port. The ship becomes holographic, then transparent, and finally begins to sink. This indicates the crew and passengers are purging collective trauma from their nervous systems as a *"cohesive community."*]

[0659.2 / 1665] [THE FARMHAND offers me $1000.]

[0659.3 / 1666] [I'm on land and observe a crew painting a building. They have issues pres-surizing their paint guns. Gold paint splatters out of the air sprayer nozzles. Thick blobs drop and create pudding-like puddles on the pavement]

[0659.2 / 1667] [Apples.] //

⁂

Min. = ♥- THE FARMHAND: #0671
NERVOUS: #0852, #0864, #0878
PUDDLE: #1142

⁂

#0660 - May 16, 2019 @ 08:25 (San Francisco, California)

[0660.1 / 1668] [At a woodland training, participants throw blue popsicles at a white parchment paper wall. One woman doubts her ability. Her Popsicle bounces off the paper and back towards her. *"This is 'Level 2,'"* a bodiless voice comments.]

[0660.2 / 1669] [I'm at a street fair on the extreme south end of San Francisco. The roads are paved, but barely inhabited. I'm supposed to pick up THE CONNECTOR from the hospital following her knee surgery, but it's unclear from which hospital I'm to retrieve her. A phantom image of THE CARPENTER stands in the driveway as I turn my car around.] //

✵

Maj. = 1- THE CARPENTER: #0678, 4- THE CONNECTOR: #0707
FAIR: #0828,
SURGERY: #1107, #1139

✵

#0661 - May 17, 2019 @ 02:16 (San Francisco, California)

[0661.1 / 1670] [I'm in a ceremony with my fellow samurai. We've been blessed. We have the opportunity to confront, thank, and *(possibly)* release five of our oldest habits who stand before each of us like statues on small circular platforms.

THE KIDDO *(exact, rational, and sober)* ups the ante by suggesting we draw forth our katana and place blades at the throats of our embodied patterns of thought. We look them in the eye and quickly decide if they live or die. A row of lifted blades, crossed over our heads sets the tone for the exercise. Practice begins. Each samurai has unique selection criteria to determine, *"what's best to kill off."*

Stakes grow mortal when the embodied habits are invited to lift their blades to our throats. With swords held to one another's necks, we continue. The background is pitch black. Our swords burn blue like ice. When I see a single water spot on the otherwise impeccable blade of one of my habits, I quickly lop off its head. The ritual remains precise and reverent.] //

✵

BLADE: #0862, #0935, #1078
BLUE: #0924, #0932
MORTAL: #0917, #0939, #1068
HABITS: #0951, #1115
THE KIDDO: #0969

✵

#0662 - May 17, 2019 @ 03:30 (San Francisco, California)

[0662.1 / 1671] [A group of bro-ish young men sit atop an overpass and become startled when a semi-truck drives beneath, nearly striking their dangling feet. The guys set up a bouldering wall style obstacle in the middle of the freeway, then climb up it briskly when the cops arrive to confront them.]

[0662.2 / 1672] [I'm at a concert arena. I observe a group of clean-cut White guys take the stage wearing red t-shirts which read, "**THE REPUBLIC**" in white block letters. I watch the video of their performance from my seat, projected on a large screen. They're wildly popular, but I don't know their music. I consider them,

"Generic and forgettable. They're just normal guys I've seen on an average day in a cafeteria lunch line."]

. . .

458

[0662.3 / 1673] [I'm backstage sitting on the floor as I get a haircut.

"Pop music could be so good if artists would take some time to live and connect with what they're creating," I complain to THE WEAVER.

She and THE MODERN CAVEMEN laugh at me as a song from the *"fourth"* ARIANA GRANDE album blares through speakers overhead.

The bassline and synths are boring, uninspired, and predictable.

"If only they'd take the time to let the real music come through!" I lament.]

[0662.4 / 1674] [I write detailed dreams down in a poetry journal. I scribble dream fragments around *"poetry entry #102,"* which features short text organized in the shape of a diamond.

As soon as I finish jotting down my dream fragments, I realize I'm sleeping then wake up.]
//

⁎⁎

Maj. = 0- THE WEAVER: #0669
ARIANA GRANDE: #0988
POETRY: #0857
FRAGMENTS: #824, #0874
ENTRY: #0805, #0855, #0878

⁎⁎

#0663 - May 18, 2019 @ 06:06 (San Francisco, California)

[0663.1 / 1675] [I'm house sitting and looking after two young boys. I'm frustrated because I'm unable to keep after them. The experience suggests my parenting skills would be poor. I don't like it.

We spend a significant amount of time outside migrating from one place to another.]

[0063.2 / 1676] [**Two neighbors:** one drives a basic functional white car; the other a smaller red performance vehicle.]

[0663.3 / 1677] [I've been tasked with selecting a bottle of wine for a gift for a friend who's achieved a significant career milestone. I shuffle through a variety of opened and half consumed bottles on a small rolling stainless steel cart. I pick up a bottle with a black label at the suggestion of THE PSYCHIATRIST, who sits nearby carving up the *"Aristotle 8"* steak he's ordered to celebrate completion of his first year of residency.

"The price of the steak will make your toes curl (*under breath* $250), but hey...I figured I've earned the right to go big," THE PSYCHIATRIST says lifting fork to mouth, smiling as he eats.] //

⁎⁎

Min. = ♠- THE PSYCHIATRIST: #0814
YOUNG BOYS: #1163
CURL: #0841, #1039

⁎⁎

#0664 - May 18, 2019 @ 08:34 (San Francisco, California)

[0664.1 / 1678] [I attend a party in a woodland gathering hall. Attendees from across various eras of my life wander through the space. Members of my spiritual family have recently adjourned a session and depart through a side door down a dimly lit stone staircase. I pass THE NUN and turn invisible. I'm embarrassed to admit I've eaten one of two small round chocolate disks, dosed with a drug. I'm anxious. I've left the other disc in the side door of an SUV parked in the lot, concerned it will be found by the drug dogs that wander the grounds.

THE HILLBILLY leads a leadership forum in an adjacent room. He laughs as he scribbles content on a whiteboard. The entire group convenes in a long hallway with a glass ceiling. A central table is covered by a thin yellow plastic coating. I'm seated to the left of the host. I welcome a mother accompanied by her two teenage sons, one of whom may just have undergone significant surgery. The energy in the room is unsettled, which in turn makes not knowing what drug was in the chocolate disc I consumed that much more upsetting. I breathe and reassure myself I'll be able to ride out the experience. The teenagers are older versions of the boys I babysat for in dream [0663.1 / 1675].] //

✲✲

Min = ♣- *THE HILLBILLY* = *#0957,* ♦-*THE NUN: #0685*
STONE STAIRCASE: #0821, #0851, #0861
TEENAGE: #0820, #0832, #0963
WOODLAND: #0996, #1165, #1187

✲✲

#0665 - May 19, 2019 @ 06:00 (San Francisco, California)

[0665.1 / 1679] [I stare at a bulletin board papered with a variety of print advertisements for local businesses. The board is adjacent to a large window that looks out on a woodland area with a gravel parking lot. Two advertisements catch my eye, the first for a one-bedroom unit listed for $1000 a month, and the other a one-bedroom apartment offered at $10,000 a month. Both are located in different neighborhoods in San Francisco. I note an initial price of $100,000 per month has been "whited out" on both ads and revised down. I want to tour the listings and call the real estate agent, who represents both properties. $1000 a month is oddly low and too good to be true. Pondering a move feels like I'm deceiving THE LAWYER, even though he's not dependent on me for rent.] //

✲✲

Maj. = 5- *THE LAWYER: #0677*
LOCAL: #0888, #0902, #1155, #1176
ONE: #1149, #1152

✲✲

#0666 - May 20, 2019 @ 05:22 (San Francisco, California)

[0666.1 / 1680] [I play bass for different hard rock and metal bands at a benefit concert. I gather backstage with members of KORN and THE EVIL TWIN (*tricky, sharp, and wild hearted*). As we chat, I quickly learn he doesn't know I'm a live session performer for big name acts, but he's familiar with my work as a studio producer. The crowd gathered is enormous. The event will produce significant social good.

I sit in a large hot tub with my back pressed against the jets looking at the giant crowd gathered for the performance. Rows of eyes extend further than I can see. The attention feels electric. Stagehands request we move backstage and gather next to a huge steel cage. "DISTURBED" takes the stage. Members of the band SLIPKNOT casually mill about as their singer COREY TAYLOR is fitted for a new mask. Sewn strands of micro-LEDs around the eye holes will aid his ability to navigate a dark stage at the bookends of each performance.

The energy builds. The venue bursts with fun and fury. My toes are behind a 2" taped white line that indicates the dividing line between preparation and performance areas. *"I'm ready to leap past the line and launch into flow."* THE THINKER and THE FEELER are backstage, along with every other couple I've ever stood up for in a wedding party. They've gathered to support me. It feels like I'm home.

I realize I don't know any of the music, and have no idea how the performance will unfold, yet I decide the most important things are:

"1) ONLY play the notes of which I'm certain."
"2) DON'T overdo it."

I don't have phone numbers for any of the guys in the band, though I want to stay in touch after we conclude. I'm especially drawn to JONATHAN DAVIS.] //

⁎⁎

Min. = ♠- *THE THINKER: #0678,* ♣- *THE FEELER: #0678*
KORN: #0857
JONATHAN DAVIS: #0669
SLIPKNOT: #1069
HOT TUB: #1076, #1087, #1137, #1146
GOOD: #1015, #1023, #1046, #1056
PHONE NUMBER: #1014
THE EVIL TWIN: #0770

⁎⁎

#0667 - May 20, 2019 @ 06:54 (San Francisco, California)

[0667.1 / 1681] [A Russian man asks me to be the publicity chief for his political campaign. My key task is to organize a baptism for his daughter using Google to generate event itineraries and directions. Problem is, *"I don't know how to use Google."* I sit on the ground in a parking lot next to a car, unable to get my phone to link up to a Wi-Fi network. I have to call myself from a landline to get my cell phone to connect to the Russian man. I text him, *"I'll get in touch later,"* though the message fails to send.]

[0667.2 / 1682] [I descend a staircase and see my family sweetly gathered and lightly interacting. THE CHILD wears a miniature blue "Temple Crew" hoodie. She's very young and at the moment, very sleepy. She peeks at me out of one eye. I smile, *"Sleep young lady. You are soooo tired!"* She briefly rejuvenates before burying her face in THE DANCER's chest with a yawning giggle. I'm proud of how much she's grown.]

. . .

[0667.3 / 1683] [We're on the deck of a yacht, backlit by a rusty sunset. I stand near a billion-aire and comment that I like his tennis shoes.] //

⁂

Maj. = 2- THE DANCER: #0685, 3- THE CHILD: #0710
RUSTY: #0949, #1014, #1144
PEEK: #0910, #0944, #0947, #0951

⁂

#0668 - May 21, 2019 @ 02:04 (San Francisco, California)

[0668.1 / 1684] [I gather crew members selected by the Senate for a major interstellar mission. They eagerly finish up personal art projects, paperwork, and errands prior to depar-ture. My phone has shattered. The glass casing has separated and fallen off the device. I need to replace it prior to lift off.]

[0668.2 / 1685] [I'm at a concert hall where a conductor gives a pre-performance lecture. He plays motifs and small segments of a piano concerto to complement and underscore his talking points. He describes a composition technique of BEETHOVEN's as a, *"Mercurial 'Fuckwith's' Trick."* He substitutes the term *"fuckwith,"* with a German equivalent to sound intel-lectual and socially acceptable, which makes me giggle.
    The conductor feels *"found out"* for a moment. I nod to assure him his quirky secret is safe. After all,
    "I don't speak German. *wink*"]

[0668.3 / 1686] [I prepare for the space mission, part of which now involves the transport of small dogs (Chihuahua's, etc.) to the surface of the moon. THE FIREFIGHTER helps organize the group's migration.
    We're confused for a moment. Crew members wear space suits, but the dogs don't. In a blink we seem to have arrived on the surface of the moon. Some spectators take photos of the space-suit-less dogs, though this seems like it'll be bad publicity for NASA.
    We feel quite stupid when we realize that we're still on earth, in an immersive training exercise. The dogs have been locked in a clean room with the crew to test a specific hygiene protocol. The dogs will eventually travel with us, but as crew we have a lot more readiness training to complete.
    We're summarily demotivated when we realize we've traveled a total of 100 feet inside a building.] //

⁂

Min. = ♥- THE FIREFIGHTER: #0669
LUDWIG VAN BEETHOVEN: #0095
SHATTERED: #0841
HYGIENE: #1133
CHIHUAHUA: #0922

⁂

#0669 - May 21, 2019 @ 03:27 (San Francisco, California)

[0669.1 / 1687] [I'm in Bakersfield, California at the home of JONATHAN DAVIS. He and his family interact in a very calm and normal way. No rock star valances. Just normal people living their lives.]

[0669.2 / 1688] [I gather some friends for a road trip to San Francisco. The drive is leisurely and fun. Our group of friends grows in number as we proceed. We pick up a hitchhiking gay couple. I know one of them and meet his partner for the first time. We pause to stretch at a rest stop and make friends with a mother and teenage son.

The rest stop has a series of small cabins encircling a koi pond. THE WEAVER stands on the opposite side of the pond from me. I run and leap into the water. My expected splash underwater is interrupted when I absorb a stone strike to the chest. I surface (*gasping in pain*) and rest my forearms poolside. My armpits to toes dangle below in lukewarm water. While in the pool I attempt to use the bathroom. I'm constipated.

While at the rest stop galleria the group becomes transfixed by unique framed art pieces composed of black symbols on white parchment, supplemented with diffused watercolor-like pink and purple gram stains; each illuminated from behind by an amber lamp. When we consider how we might purchase the installation as an investment THE FIREFIGHTER admits,

"It's not what you think. All of the sculptures are made from compressed cocaine."

We pile back in a car and careen at high velocity down a one lane road towards a stop sign. It appears we're heading for a collision with a vehicle fast approaching from the opposite direction. For a couple of tense moments I think,

"We're all going to die."

As the road opens up to two lanes, my fears are quelled.

We eventually arrive at San Francisco International Airport where THE FIREFIGHTER lovingly greets and embraces a group of friends he hasn't seen in years. THE FIREFIGHTER remains endearing and affectionate with everyone he meets, then invites his friends on a ride around the perimeter of a parking lot on a large flatbed truck. Their legs dangle off the back and sides. Just off the edge of the lot is a steep cliff. THE FIREFIGHTER notices the risk and avoids driving off it as his friends remain distracted by their own laughter.] //

⁎⁎

Maj. = 0- THE WEAVER: #0672
Min. = ♥-THE FIREFIGHTER: #0815
JONATHAN DAVIS: #0984
VELOCITY: #0929
HITCHHIKING: #1144

⁎⁎

#0670 - May 21, 2019 @ 06:33 (San Francisco, California)

[0670.1 / 1689] [I'm 12 years old. I pack up a vintage SEGA Genesis gaming console in a clear plastic garment bag before deciding whether or not to take it back to THE BRIT's (*sarcastic, brotherly, and athletic*) house for tonight's slumber party. The instruction manual needs to be printed. We'll wait to do it at their house because it's more efficient. We pile into a car.

The car backs in and out of a driveway multiple times because I'm just not sure I have everything I need. A young woman I don't know drives the vehicle. She curiously questions, *"What else we might need to get complete and proceed to the next step?"*] //

⁎⁎

SLUMBER PARTY: #0924, #0934, #0950
MANUAL: #0819
GARMENT BAG: #1078
NEXT STEP: #1031

⁎⁎

#0671 - May 21, 2019 @ 07:35 (San Francisco, California)

[0671.1 / 1690] [THE FARMHAND uses an extremely complex process for cleaning and disinfecting the kitchen table. She uses multiple coarse white powders, sand, gasoline, and a giant turkey baster-like device to move coagulated goopy gel-oil from the table to a yellow mop bucket.
"Wow, you're really strong!" I remark as she pumps her bicep like ROSIE THE RIVETER.
THE POSTMASTER sits down and wants to take a pain pill for his shoulder.
"You don't need that!" THE FARMHAND scolds, taking the pill from his hand and popping it in her mouth before continuing, *"We'll take care of what we need to when we arrive,"* as we finalize preparations for a trip.]

[0671.2 / 1691] [I'm a research scientist working on a PhD in a *"dream efficacy lab."* I intend to contact CG JUNG while in dream state. I've completed a vast body of research and gathered many profound insights, but he holds a couple of key pieces of information that will inform my pending dissertation defense.]

[0671.3 / 1692] [Space travel. Astronauts are stacked in square LEGO-like containers with windows at front. The launch sequence doesn't go as planned and a couple of the blocks tumble forward as the rest of the pile lifts off.]

[0671.4 / 1693] [A comedic sequence ensues where a female executive occupies the entire back row of a passenger jet. She pranks people from behind a wooden desk where there would ordinarily be a row of seats. She presses a red button. Another passenger gets a pie in the face. *"I control the mischief,"* she states with a grin into a camera.]

[0671.5 / 1694] [The female executive kicks to a handstand and leaps up a full flight of stairs while upside down. At each new level she engages a cartoon character in hand-to-hand combat, delivered comedically with onomatopoeic sounds (*SPLAT! BOP! HONK! ZING!*). The shot pulls back to reveal her endless climb up the exterior of a building.]

. . .

[0671.6 / 1695] [**Sex Dream:** I encourage a partner to use my kink tools to sound himself. *"I'm excited to watch him do it. It's an honor to have a porn star I really want to fuck, use my gear,"* I say as I invite a group of five or six other guys to watch him perform.] //

✼✼

Min. = ♣*- THE POSTMASTER: #0687,* ♥*- THE FARMHAND: #0763*
PASSENGER: #0837, #0890, #0933, #0936
STRONG: #1031, #1053, #1063, #1078
FUCK: #0804, #0834, #0926, #0932, #0985

✼✼

#0672 - May 22, 2019 @ 04:04 (San Francisco, California)

[0672.1 / 1696] [THE WEAVER wants help tidying up under the furniture.]

[0672.2 / 1697] [THE WEAVER meets SKRILLEX after he plays a set at EDC Las Vegas. He welcomes us on a tour of his stage set up. A game is underway where people are allowed onstage five at a time. We look for SKRILLEX's journals. We know six of them are hidden throughout the set like items to be found on a scavenger hunt. As I rifle through shelves filled with junk, I notice some of them belong to me: *old books, greeting cards and gifts given to me by THE CLUB KID (chaotic, unhinged, yet caring).* The objects hold no emotional charge, nor attachment. I leave them where they rest.]

[0672.3 / 1698] [THE WEAVER points our group's attention towards a water feature across the street in THE NEIGHBOR's *(successful, retired, and easy going)* front yard accented with two large plush toy walruses. THE WEAVER grows nostalgic, reminded of when we were small children and THE DRONE PILOT *(young father, patriotic, and committed)* was just a baby.

We walk back up the driveway of our home and meet a woman who points to Bellagio-esque fountains lining both sides of the driveway. Per her remarks, *"Such a project was a difficult feat to pull off in a suburban front yard. I'm entitled to premium billing for the work."*

THE WEAVER entertains none of the claim. *"That's ridiculous. You're a professional. It's your job. It's something you're supposed to be able to do. You're not getting paid extra simply for doing your job."*]

[0672.4 / 1699] [I'm behind the DJ console at the EDC Las Vegas main stage *(a nondescript particle board table finished with a thin layer of red vinyl).* Onlookers are a bit confused and underwhelmed when they compare what they see to last night's "Beat Match/Spin Off" throw down between the headliners, who all put up $100,000 to compete.] //

✼✼

Maj. = 0- THE WEAVER: #0698
SKRILLEX: #1391
WALRUS: #0932
PROFESSIONAL: #1052, #1056, #1075

✼✼

#0673 - May 22, 2019 @ 06:02 (San Francisco, California)

[0673.1 / 1700] [In a Spanish cafe, I order a coffee and take a seat in a barber chair as a group of people form a line towards the street. Those queued chew coca leaves and share conversation. One woman is underwhelmed by the sensation of the plant moving around in her body. My hair is long and I request the barber, *"give me an undercut to the skin"* as I sip my medium roast and watch the world pass by.]

[0673.2 / 1701] [I wait outside a studio to teach a class. A married couple stands nearby. It seems all the students in this class are married. Everyone is a bit agitated in what's termed, *"Wednesday Night Normal."*]

[0673.3 / 1702] [I'm at the back of a concert hall. THE DULCE DE LECHE (*dramatic, studious, and unsure*) is my guest. He wants to stand closer to the stage. He steps down and over rows of chairs, clobbering numerous people's shoulders and laps along his path. I can't stop him. Intervening wouldn't really matter. He enjoys himself as he "live tweets" his entire experience to a group of followers as he progresses towards the performer.] //

⁎⁎

Min. = ♣- *THE DULCE DE LECHE: #0682*
SKIN: #0844, #874, #891, #0900, #1193
MARRIED: #0875, #1026, #1164, #1166
CONCERT: #0841, #0855, #0857, #0879, #887

⁎⁎

#0674 - May 23, 2019 @ 04:32 (San Francisco, California)

[0674.1 / 1703] [I'm in an office collaborating with a team on a spreadsheet. Our primary aim is to, *"appropriately highlight a series of squares and rectangles to offset and highlight key data for executive review."* We're a strong group and quickly gain coherence.

We have a dual shared agreement to both *"embody and live the same core values,"* while, *"sourcing and sharing inspirational materials."* We read from a book titled, *"Journey to the Heart"* before every meeting.

I make my way to the back door. Outside I notice a discarded stack of old mail, boxes, bank records, and sundry items left behind by the prior residents of the office. Their copy of *"Journey to the Heart"* sits soggy and rotten in a black trash bag.

Snacks in the mini-fridge need to be replenished. A clear plastic can of soda is partially frozen from the bottom up towards the center, creating an icy cone within.]

[0674.2 / 1704] [I lay down on the couch to take a nap. I realize we may be experiencing an earthquake. The couch begins to rumble and convulse.

"Who's giving me a massage?" When the rattles intensify, I playfully call out,

"WOAH! It's a Riiiiiiiide!" to an empty room.

"L" wakes me up and I notice I've left the TV on.] //

⁂

JOURNEY: #0885, #0943, #1109
HIGHLIGHT: #0989, #1055, #1086
CONE: #0801, #0803, #1095
NAP: #0833, #0969, #1111

⁂

#0675 - May 23, 2019 @ 06:48 (San Francisco, California)

[0675.1 / 1705] [*Wild sex dream with a guy named "Chris."* We've never met before. I fall asleep on a couch. When I wake up, I find him underneath me as I vigorously fuck him. The connection is stellar. We pause and head to the bathroom. We stand in front of a giant window where the curtains have been taken down. A group of people on the street see us, causing some controversy among them. They attempt to slut shame us, though "Chris" and I are further turned on by *"being revolting"* to them. Once we finish, "Chris" puts his clothes on and leaves. As the door clicks shut, I realize I don't have his number. I'm left mildly confused and wanting more with him.] //

⁂

WILD: #0850, #0871, #0926
SLUT: #0894, #0895, #0937, #1080
UNDERNEATH: #1024, #1157, #1163
TURNED ON: #0996, #1158

⁂

#0676 - May 23, 2019 @ 07:19 (San Francisco, California)

[0676.1 / 1706] [A large business transforms its central focus from restaurant administration to building interactive play spaces for children. The leadership team actively seeks new investment to support the strategic shift. They need $85MM to fully fund, renovate, and reopen to the public. They occupy an unfurnished giant warehouse, floors covered with industrial office carpet. Hotel banquet room dividers run on tracks suspended from the ceiling.]

[0676.2 / 1707] [I leave a lecture hall to use the bathroom. When I return, I'm called to participate in a debate. I take a seat across the table from JORDAN PETERSON and we engage in an intense, yet civil disagreement. Each of us earns points by flagging the other's logical fallacies when we lick a fingertip and make a checkmark in the air. My phone rests on the center of the table and records our entire conversation.] //

⁂

OFFICE: #1102, #1103, #1108, #1139
DATE: #1076, #1084, #1087
RECORDS: #0823, #0966, #0971
CIVIL: #1122

⁂

#0677 - May 24, 2019 @ 04:51 (San Francisco, California)

[0677.1 / 1708] [I'm on a flight that makes an abrupt landing. THE LAWYER sits in the front row. I'm in the back row. People think we're going to crash, but we don't. Upon exiting the plane, I meet a young man from New York who plays music on an acoustic guitar. His sister sings. I acknowledge them,
"Being creative partners with a sibling must come with a unique set of challenges and circumstances."]

[0677.2 / 1709] [I walk by THE DEAR HEART (*sensuous, provocative, and playful*) as he works at his desk. He comments at my back body as I pass.
"You're repressed."
"You experience me as repressed?" I pause and smirk over my right shoulder.
"Yes," he states confidently while looking down at his paperwork before continuing, *"Want to role play?"*
"You mean role model...as you tend to?" I say with a wink as I crouch to meet his eyeline.
"Well yeah," he says sweetly grinning.
We share a friendly kiss across the desk as our heads fall in towards each other and become one.] //

⁂

Maj. = 5- THE LAWYER: #0682
NEW YORK: #1141
BACK ROW: #1003, #1175
THE DEAR HEART: #1143

⁂

#0678 - May 24, 2019 @ 05:20 (San Francisco, California)

[0678.1 / 1710] [THE FEELER is mentally unwell. She's in the basement of a house. It's snowing outside. THE THINKER wants to finish a remodel to the house and hops in his truck to pick up more supplies. People walk from the street up a driveway as he backs slowly towards them. He pauses at the street when I ask if he needs help. He speeds away without answering.
Silence falls when I see THE FEELER stand on her second story bedroom window sill, intending to jump to the edge of a babbling brook below.
I tell her to, *"Throw a purple flower before you do it!"* just after she leaps.
She lands hard on the stony creek bed and bruises her tailbone. Another friend follows her out the window.
When I meet them at the edge of the creek we're sling-shotted into outer space. We look back and see the pale blue dot of Earth hanging in a void. We return to the Earth's surface and enter an old house in the center of a wheat field. Once inside we observe a woman remove a children's shirt from a shopping bag with the phrase **"It's a Wonderful Life"** crocheted across the front.
The woman exclaims, *"My son will love this!"*
Her comment doesn't make sense to us.
We descend to the basement where we find two large refrigerators. One contains a

dismembered, mutilated body; the other has vertical slits in the door and is understood to be the, *"Home of The Demon."* THE THINKER appears at my right.

"Do you have a match?" I ask as he pulls two from his pocket and hands them to me.

Damp and difficult to light, I repeatedly strike them against soggy flint paper. I drop a lit match through a window of, *"The Home of The Demon."* which lands on a stack of dry tissue that quickly erupts in flame and engulfs the tiny basement abode. I drop the second match at the base of the refrigerator and blow at it so it will cast sparks and ultimately smoke the demon out. When conjured, the demon manifests as a large snake with a mask-wearing human head. The fridge becomes a furnace. As the flames rise, we watch both aspects of the demon dwelling fire char, then fizzle and dissolve.

THE FEELER begins to feel better. She's eager to try on the child's top the other woman left behind. When she puts it on and buttons it, the middle button becomes a beady, blinking human eyeball.

"Do you see that?" I ask her, pointing to the now red irised reptilian eye suspended before her solar plexus.

THE FEELER doesn't, and instead says, *"Ever notice THE CARPENTER, THE CATHOLIC, and THE CHOCOHOLIC all have the same face?"*] //

⁂

Maj. = 1- THE CARPENTER: #0687
Min. = ♠- *THE THINKER: #0728,* ♣- *THE FEELER: #0728,* ♣- *THE CATHOLIC: #0695*
IT'S A WONDERFUL LIFE: #0905
DEMON: #0998, #1191
THE CHOCOHOLIC: #0871

⁂

#0679 - May 25, 2019 @ 08:39 (San Francisco, California)

[0679.1 / 1711] [Four guys want a 6:30pm reservation at Green's Restaurant in Fort Mason. Today's THE PILOT's birthday who arrives at dinner late, as expected declaring, *"I've been tricking with a group of Russians after taking a lecture-based course led by DONALD TRUMP. Happy Bee Day to Me!"* After dinner concludes we ride together in an SUV. I drive. It's icy. The brakes don't function. The vehicle fishtails. The frame bleeds and blurs as I wake up.] //

⁂

Maj. = 6- THE PILOT: #0694
DONALD TRUMP: #0748
VEHICLE: #0807, #0842, #0847, #0861
LECTURE: #1038, #1050, #1097, #1130, #1194

⁂

#0680 - May 26, 2019 @ 09:45 (San Francisco, California)

[0680.1 / 1712] [I hover beneath a plane as it approaches a runway. The landing gear won't function. I sense a wide range of emotions from the passengers and crew. Some are calm. Some experience elevated caution. *"No fewer than three people onboard are **terrified**."*] //

⁂

LANDING: #0835, #0939, #1115, #1147
CALM: #0824, #0825, #0837, #0858, #0886

⁂

#0681 - May 27, 2019 @ 07:48 (San Francisco, California)

[0681.1 / 1713] [I fall asleep. I wake up believing it's 1:34pm, which puts me into a momentary panic that wakes me into another dream.]

[0681.2 / 1714] [A young transgender man attempts to get his first new job, in a new city, embodying his new identity. He lands an interview working at a financial services firm. His mentor is THE FIDUCIARY.]

[0681.3 / 1715] [I interact with a young woman who's a bit of a trickster. She playfully taunts me with questionable intent pouring from her eyes. She convinces me to take a drag off a cigarette. As I hold it to my mouth, she quickly pulls out a Polaroid camera and snaps an image of me in the act. I grab the photo from her hand as it develops. In her other hand she holds a stack of candid photographs of me doing things that are, *"out of alignment."* She retreats, taking the photos with her. I want to destroy the candid photos. I don't want to be held to account at my present level of ethics for choices that were made in the past at different levels of awareness. I'm frustrated, though I appreciate her role in *"the game."* I'll make a different choice next time.] //

⁂

Maj. = 9- THE FIDUCIARY: #0682
IDENTITY: #0905, #1158, #1183
MENTOR: #1058

⁂

#0682 - May 28, 2019 @ 4:36am (San Francisco, California)

[0682.1 / 1716] [THE DULCE DE LECHE *(reactive, cruel, and selfish)* and THE LAWYER arrive home late at night. They both wear bulldog harnesses, promptly drop their bags, and adjourn to their bedroom to have sex after spending their time away on vacation in separate bedrooms. I sit at a table with our other roommate sipping tea and talking while we overhear the others moan through the wall.]

. . .

[0682.2 / 1717] [THE PUBLIC MEDIUM owns and operates an adorable urban shop, full of enchanted stones and books. He doesn't recognize me at first when I walk in. I come into focus when he puts on a pair of studious spectacles. Books seem to neatly hover in the hallway, without shelves.

He and I sit for an intuitive session at a heavy, small square wooden table. We review a "pop up" book where seemingly light and joyful images split apart at the center to reveal darkness, beasts, and *"monsters within."* A giant black balloon protrudes up and out of a book from a small meek image of a forlorn person. We move from the table to a bed. THE PUBLIC MEDIUM lays the book down on the duvet. It slides towards the foot of the bed. Feeling exhausted, he lays down unable to continue our conversation. My invisible guide hints to repeatedly chant: "**NAM MYOHO RENGE KYO**" to clear oppressive energy from the space.

While chanting, I exit through a side door and see a public pool with a series of volleyball nets in the water that stand but aren't under sufficient tension for game play. THE FIDU-CIARY walks in naked, swollen in the upper body from an arms and chest workout. *"Looking pretty buff there, bro"* I say stupidly with a wink. He winks back. We practice yoga asana together and create "Bird of Paradise" poses on the pool deck. Some quirky energy flutters through the space which we accommodate.]

[0682.3 / 1718] [I sit in a room with JOE ROGAN and JACK DORSEY while they record a podcast. I repeatedly try to make a point that, *'any time an online service suspends or prohibits speech by 'killing off avatars,' it results in the death of debate and discourse."* No one wants to hear me. Current state's a slick process that as is, effectively nullifies and murders *"free speech."* I remain frustrated, which renders me unable to effectively make a salient argument. DORSEY's responses are short, quiet and infrequent and visibly frustrate JOE ROGAN over the course of the long form conversation. I contemplate submitting a question to their head of public policy by clicking on a green rectangular button on my phone screen. The woman in the role has an impressive CV. Her prior assignments are prominently displayed on her profile.] //

⁂

Maj. = 5- THE LAWYER: #0720, 9- THE FIDUCIARY: #0693, 18- THE PUBLIC MEDIUM: #1011
Min. = ♣- THE DULCE DE LECHE: #0763
BIRD: #957, #1055, #1143
BALLOON: #0848, #0961, #1178

⁂

#0683 - May 28, 2019 @ 07:50 (San Francisco, California)

[0683.1 / 1719] [THE IRONMAN *(recalibrating, optimistic, and gentle)* and I have a lover's quarrel. SELENA GOMEZ is our heterosexual third. We travel to a resort town in Colorado. The name of the town begins with a "C," which none of us can recall. We drive to the park entrance and learn the per car entry fee is $3000. We must pay before we can proceed. We park near a series of ATMs where we encounter THE ICEMAN and THE MOTIVATIONAL SPEAKER *(aware, sweetly surrendered, and loving)*. They ask me if I have any cash. I give them the last $60 from my pocket so they don't have to pay a foreign transaction fee. They say they'll do me a solid, *"the next time you need to withdraw cash from a French bank."*

Park rangers tell me I can put the $3000 entry fee on a credit card if I recall the name of the resort town. Not a possibility. I can't remember, nor can THE IRONMAN. Somehow, we're persuasive enough to get in and make the subsequent drive to "C_____."

Our mountain chalet has an outdoor bedroom. The bed is surrounded by a ring of large leafy trees. Logs of Palo Santo smolder in hubcap sized holes in their trunks. The space feels friendly, flowy, and pure. SELENA adjourns to the powder room and is gone for a while. Later, we see her working out in our personal gym next to a huge kidney bean shaped outdoor pool. CLAY AIKEN supposedly shares the property with us, but we never see him.

THE IRONMAN and I call for SELENA as we lay on the bed. We're frustrated she doesn't answer and start hooking up without her.

"No! Wait! This is the part where we all get laid," she says as she gallops in with her hair down, wearing just a flannel shirt.

Later, the unremembered name of the resort town continues to befuddle us. Our neighbors know the names of all the mountains and the names of the ski runs, but no one can recall the name of the town!]

[0683.2 / 1720] [We move through a set of amusement park turnstiles and find ourselves on set preparing to film an episode of a reality show. Before filming commences, the staff psychologist gives each of us an individual wellness check. We each are issued a personalized "punch list" chart with accompanying notes. Myriad blurred out items on my list have small green check marks in their boxes at left. I can only read one item on the list: "Moderate compulsive desire...as related to professional success."] //

⁎⁎

CLAY AIKEN: #1230
POCKET: #0830, #0850, #0897, #0944, #0989, #1012
POSSIBILITY: #0828, #0917, #0974, #1183
TREES: #0924, #0939, #0963, #0970, #1011
TURNSTILE #1069
THE ICEMAN: #0735
THE IRONMAN: #1133

⁎⁎

#0684 - May 28, 2019 @ 09:35 (San Francisco, California)

[0684.1 / 1721] [MANTRA: *It's my work to simply let these old energies come up and go out without needing to analyze or understand what they're about.*" I repeat this as I cover myself with a soft grey blanket. The blanket is speckled with miniature animated white-hot galaxies composed of *"ultra-super-mega-giant"* swirling stars.] //

⁎⁎

MANTRA: #0879
WHITE HOT: #0924, #0925
ULTRA: #0815, #0976
OLD: #0976, #0977, #0982

⁎⁎

⁎⁎

472

#0685 - May 29, 2019 @ 08:07 (San Francisco, California)

[0685.1 / 1722] [Large commencement event. Keynote speaker. Absolutely massive crowd. I interact with the speaker before he gives his remarks. THE BOSS is present, wearing an obscene amount of eyeliner. I introduce THE BOSS to THE DANCER. We're gathered to celebrate the completion of a large project. THE NUN has a role reviewing my submission. I'm the last graduate to have my final project reviewed by the management team.] //

✽✽

Maj. = 2- THE DANCER: #0703
Min = ◆- THE NUN: #0870
CELEBRATE: #0813, #0820, #0849, #0850, #0916
FINAL: #0926, #0943, #0952, #0969, #0990
THE BOSS: #1076

✽✽

#0686 - May 30, 2019 @ 04:01 (San Francisco, California)

[0686.1 / 1723] [Alien abduction in the woods. Grey white slender humanoid beings. A white flash of light descends from the sky overhead. I experience intense heat then feel and smell my skin burning. Quick action startles me out of sleep as I hear a voice calmly say, *"They'll put four more symbols in you after they 'buzz.'"*] //

✽✽

SYMBOLS: #0831, #0942, #1149
FLASH: #0805, #0825, #0874, #0893, #0909
SMELL: #0848, #0874, #0900, #0956

✽✽

#0687 - May 30, 2019 @ 05:27 (San Francisco, California)

[0687.1 / 1724] [In a summer cottage, I move between a boat dock and a basement. While in the basement I eat half a sandwich THE CARPENTER left in a refrigerator earlier that day.]

[0687.2 / 1725] [I ascend from the basement and discover I'm in a 1970's tri-level house. THE ACTOR is there with THE RADICAL HIPPIE *(loving, quiet, and direct)*. He doesn't want to talk to me so I leave him alone. He doesn't know that I see him after I leave the room. He lays down on a couch to rest. Two young girls with colorful foam "pool noodles" play nearby. THE CARPENTER dares one of the girls to wake THE ACTOR up by thumping him on the head with the pool noodles.
"Dude, just stop it. That's not necessary," I say with slight annoyance.]

[0687.2 / 1726] [Outside eating more of the sandwich down on a boat dock.]

· · ·

[0687.3 / 1727] [Woodland scene. Non-intrusive ghosts and spirit energies curiously hover around. THE POSTMASTER arrives. He's younger, slim, and *"hipster fit."*
"I see you really helped yourself at the 'Jeesh Perk' party," he says.
"What are you talking about?" I say, utterly confused.
THE POSTMASTER laughs and wraps me in a powerful hug. His small obsidian earring is funny and out of character.
He whispers, *"I got that because I wanted it. Only took lifetimes to decide"*]

[0687.4 / 1728] [Produce in the fridge needs to be eaten. It might spoil. I'm full from the sandwich, but I don't want the potatoes to rot. The sandwich is gone.] //

⁂

Maj. = 1- THE CARPENTER: #0692, 10- THE ACTOR: #0719
Min. = ♣-THE POSTMASTER: #0763
HIPSTER: #0920, #1084
SPOIL: #0947
THE RADICAL HIPPIE: #0837

⁂

#0688 - May 30, 2019 @ 07:37 (San Francisco, California)

[0688.1 / 1729] [THE ROMANTIC and his roommates occupy a house. Inside they sit together dutifully working on laptops. I'm more interested in being outside by the mushroom shaped swimming pool out back. I debate jumping in the pool until one of the roommates approaches and asks, *"Are you new here?"* He harasses me a bit as I take my contact lenses out. I can't find my phone, but know I've lost a bit of time. I have no idea how to get home. I likely spent last night at the property, yet I didn't interact with anyone. The tenants are young and ambitious, tunnel visioned on acquiring money and professional accolades. They huddle around a glowing box on a card table, blithely unaware of the filthy floors and carpets. They don't have many amenities besides the pool, but they're proud they now officially own their first home.] //

⁂

Maj. = 15- THE ROMANTIC: #0803
CONTACT LENSE: #0835
HOME: #0924, #0927, #0939

⁂

#0689 - May 31, 2019 @ 03:08 (San Francisco, California)

[0689.1 / 1730] [I ascend a staircase to a bedroom where I startle a woman, but charm her with a song. She harmonizes with me as I sing. The rest of the dream involves ascending to the top of trains, boats, and other conveyance where each time I sing and harmonize with BEYONCÉ. We're connected and supportive creative partners. It's tremendously fun to sing at the tops of our lungs with our faces and hair blown by the wind. Singing feels like a natural, obvious, and casual Saturday afternoon habit. *"There's nowhere else I'd rather be."*] //

474

⁂

BEYONCÉ: #0728
HARMONIZE: #0917, #1130
LUNGS: #1028, #1133
NATURAL: #0821, #0907, #0920, #0934, #1062

⁂

#0690 - June 2, 2019 @ 2:00 (San Francisco, California)

[0690.1 / 1731] [An odd, contorted demon follows me into a house. I climb up on a perch and see it attempt to hide in a dark corner. I begin singing and whistling as I contemplate how I'm going to eliminate it. The skin of the being's face is pulled tightly back at the corner of its eyes and mouth resulting in a horrible, wincing grimace. Its limbs are bent backwards at the joints resulting in its lumbering, awkward, crab-like gait. I take a number of heavy breaths to calm myself down and return to a deeper state of sleep without interacting with the demon.] //

⁎⁎

CLIMB: #0808, #0811, #0841, #0844, #897
CONTEMPLATE: #0805, #0857, #0898, #0899, #0998
SKIN: #1068, #1076, #1060, #1174

⁎⁎

#0691 - June 2, 3019 @ 03:30 (San Francisco, California)

[0691.1 / 1732] [AMY POEHLER goes blank while standing at a mic during a standup comedy performance. I and other friends in the crowd support her by coming up to the mic stand and tapping it with a wood block. Our wood block taps loop to create a community rhythm. AMY finds this helpful and steps closer to her *"creative flow channel."* We teach her how to sing a magic spell. The demon from dream [0690.1 / 1731] enters from the side door. The group quickly leaps up and bludgeons it to death with golf clubs. While horrific and brutal, the action is aligned. The demon wanted it to end this way. It was ready to surrender its karma. It appreciates being, *"snuffed out to be reborn."*] //

⁎⁎

AMY POEHLER: #0948
FLOW: #1046, #1062, #1064
GOLF: #0887, #0922, #0957, #0982, #1011
BLANK: #0935, #1184
LOOPS: #0921, #0976, #1086, #1163, #1194

⁎⁎

#0692 - June 3, 2019 @ 03:57 (Santa Cruz, California)

[0692.1 / 1733] [I play bass. THE CARPENTER plays guitar. We jam on the song "Take Your Whiskey" by Van Halen.]
[0692.2 / 1734] ["**Ice Cream Koozies**" are the hot new product!]
[0692.3 / 1735] [THE COYOTE (*tricky, mythic, and solitary*) and THE LAUGHING MONKEY (*artistic, broad, and calculating*) design acoustically perfect rooms.]

[0692.4 / 1736] [*"Who's a Pi Kapp?"* I say behind the right ear of an unidentified celebrity seated at a round white cloth draped dinner table. I walk away before the person turns around.]

[0692.5 / 1737] [I DJ with CDs in the dark in a large empty music hall. Music equipment gathered in the round is stacked neatly on a series of tables. I spin a, *"one track set."*] //

⁑

Maj. 1- THE CARPENTER: #0698
ICE CREAM: #0830, #1016, #1095, #1133, #1158
TAKE: #0922, #0928, #0931

⁑

#0693 - June 4, 2019 @ 04:00 (King City, California)

[0693.1 / 1738] [THE WORLDBRIDGER stands behind a counter and closes up a small-town general store at the end of a working day. He tells me, *"Burners care to a point."* The day's business is done. I'll have to buy my tea and olive oil the next time I stop through this part of town.]

[0693.2 / 1739] [A man my age burns his entire right leg when he falls on smoldering coals in an acre wide fire pit dug in the Presidio of San Francisco. He doesn't notice the burns. I smell his singed flesh. He and I walk to a parking lot. People notice the man's injury but refuse to help him. I'm upset by the lack of care and compassion he's shown by the community. THE FIDUCIARY rides through the parking lot on a bike. Once out of sight, I contemplate calling him, or writing a letter to tell him, *'I feel hurt. I miss our friendship.'*]

[0693.3 / 1740] [Small bubbles in a plastic cup filled with tea, rise up and rest on the surface of the liquid like a cluster of soapy white corpuscles.]

[0693.4 / 1741] [*"We've unwrapped RxBars and won't be able to serve them." "THE WARD OF GAIA wants a blueberry one." "We only have chocolate." "I know she doesn't want that flavor."*] //

⁑

Maj. = 7- THE WORLDBRIDGER: #0763, 9- THE FIDUCIARY: #0697
Min = ◆-THE WARD OF GAIA: #1224
FLESH: #0976

⁑

#0694 - June 5, 2019 @ 03:18 (Paso Robles, California)

[0694.1 / 1742] [THE PILOT learns to swing back and forth with me on long wind chime poles controlled by gas powered foot pedals.]
[0694.2 / 1743] [Green smoothie pours fluidly and at vast quantities through the back of a brown wicker chair.]
[0694.3 / 1744] [I've hired a private pilot that offers passengers sedatives in pill form.]

477

[0694.4 / 1745] [A Russian Man wields his fists and yells when I inquire about renting his box truck for a road trip. *"WHERE YOU WANT DRIVE MY TRUCK??"*] //

⁑

Maj. = 6- THE PILOT: #0696
SMOOTHIE: #1071
FIST: #0887, #0903
PRIVATE: #0926, #0974, #1023, #1055

⁑

#0695 - June 5, 2019 @ 05:34 (Paso Robles, California)

[0695.1 / 1746] [I head down an alley where I encounter a woman walking her black French bulldog. The dog can talk and switches places effortlessly with a similarly sized gray mutt that sits attentively perched on a vertical wood fence. *"THE CATHOLIC, is that you?"* I say, quizzically to the woman, who doesn't respond]

[0695.2 / 1747] [I drive a semi-truck around a parking lot and out into traffic on a busy city street.]

[0695.3 / 1748] [A wire centipede made of projector slides runs beneath an intense light which produces animations as it skitters about. Its long and looping body creates complex patterns on a stark black background.] //

⁑

Min. = ♣- THE CATHOLIC: #0763
DRIVE: #0936, #0972
WOOD: #0925, #0959
ALLEY: #0874, #1167

⁑

#0696 - June 6, 2019 @ 03:06 (Santa Maria, California)

[0696.1 / 1749] [I text JARED LETO to rekindle our friendship *(and perhaps, romance)*. I campily woo him, *"You holding your own head at the MET gala was EVERYTHING."*]

[0696.2 / 1750] [I take a car ride down a dirt road to a theme park. THE PILOT navigates. The rain prevents us from riding roller coasters. We shift our attention to re-imagining the Italian national anthem, intending to submit a score to an international songwriting contest.]

[0696.3 / 1751] [THE COOK *(candid, contrary, and snarky)* offers me pepperoni pizza bread made from croissants. THE COOK disapproves of how it pulls apart. He hands me a piece so large I laugh as I hold it to my torso and say, *"Where is this gonna go?"* We belly laugh. It's absurd.] //

478

⁂

Maj. = 6- THE PILOT: #0715
LAUGH: #0922, #0947, #0948
THEME PARK: #0850, #0915, #0985

⁂

#0697 - June 7, 2019 @ 04:03 (Lompoc, California)

[0697.1 / 1752] [THE FIDUCIARY stops by a party and attempts to mend our broken friendship. My intentions are clear. I simply miss my friend. THE SEX WORKER pops up between us as we talk and says, *"Oh Honey. His blushy facial colors show he actually wants none of that. We're all just a bunch of mean girls at our core."*]

[0697.2 / 1753] [I ride a bus that loops repeatedly to the left. At the point of origin, each time, I'm kicked off the bus and have to beg to get back on.
"You don't have to blame yourself," I sob to the mob onboard, while I stand outside, denied a ride.
As the bus drives its circuit without me, I'm given clear instructions on how to, *"get back onboard."*
THE QUEER appears as an eager, and playful helper who shows me, *"which snack foods would be persuasive enough for me to gain back a seat."*
"We're all just a bunch of mean girls. Just mean, mean girls." THE SEX WORKER says on a loop from inside the bus.] //

⁂

Maj. = 9- THE FIDUCIARY: #0714
MEAN: #1103, #1104, #1171
BLAME: #0834
THE QUEER: #0699
THE SEX WORKER: #0717

⁂

#0698 - June 8, 2019 @ 04:05 (Ventura, California)

[0698.1 / 1754] [I'm friends with NEIL PATRICK HARRIS. He quickly texts me a new phone number to use just before the line we're speaking on drops and goes static. I redial. We talk. He requests I return an odd "U" shaped device made of bent 6' lengths of square pipe with a single thick tire in the center. When in motion, riders look like the Vitruvian Man standing on a set of rolling football end zone uprights. NEIL loaned the device to the San Francisco AIDS Foundation to promote their AIDS LifeCycle event. It was too large to be shipped home after he used it to complete the ride years ago and he left it in their charge. I end our conversation saying, *"Call ya later, bro."* The word "bro" sounds really weird and out of place. After we hang up, I remember he and his family live in LA. We could have arranged a dinner meet up this week. *Opportunity missed!*]

.　.　.

479

[0698.2 / 1755] [THE SOUTHERN GENTLEMAN *(gentle, aware, and handsome)* drives a convertible full of girlfriends up the PCH. He lives in San Francisco now. I really want to date him.]

[0698.3 / 1756] [A woman at city hall indignantly shouts, *"Carbon reduction efficiencies from going vegan are a farce and I have the data to prove it!"* Another declares, *"San Francisco has become tedious and unlivable because of all the odd incremental laws and use taxes recently passed by the city government to fund their undeserved pay increases."*]

[0698.4 / 1757] [A conveyor belt runs just below water level under a Roman bridge. This area has quickly garnered a reputation as a preferred gathering place for young mothers and their newborns. Women pushing strollers wave at one another and socialize as little ones coo.]

[0698.5 / 1758] [THE WEAVER and THE CARPENTER shop for appliances. A space in their kitchen that used to house a dishwasher profusely leaks water on a tile floor while they're away.] //

✶✶

Maj. = 0- THE WEAVER: #0700, 1- THE CARPENTER: #0700
CONVEYOR BELT: #1105, #1115, #1176
ROMAN: #0910
BRO: #1109
THE SOUTHERN GENTLEMAN: #1427

✶✶

#0699 - June 9, 2019 @ 06:05 (Los Angeles, California)

[0699.1 / 1759] [A group of super villains gather in a houseboat. I battle them. I'm angry at myself for being attracted to them. The houseboat swirls and spins down a raging river. I'm deeply attracted to a bald man because I'm unable to place his accent. I observe him, observing THE QUEER and others who've gathered at a wooden rectangular table to eat. If he kills them, I'll kill him. With this understanding, I go hand-to-hand with a variety of villains of varying skill. Most of them have a super power. I'm frustrated that I've been chosen as sole representative from my cadre of superheroes to fight. I don't want any of the conflict.]

[0699.2 / 1760] [I peel multiple sets of contact lenses from my eyes. At first my irises sting. The whites of my eyes stain pink, then red with blood.]

[0699.3 / 1761] [*"JOURNEY OF HOPE"* cyclists move through a residential area. Some miss a route turn. Everyone's on the same team. Those directing traffic don't stop in a visible location so I assume their responsibilities. We agree we've been tricked by our leader, THE SWEET D *(energetic, erratic, and playful)*. The bald assassin from **[0699.1 / 1759]** appears on a

hilltop overlooking us with arms crossed, laughing as we decide how to get back on track.]
//

⁂

SUPERHEROES: #0965, #1069
BLOOD: #1008, #1133, #1139, #1144, #1184
MULTIPLE: #0937, #0943, #0945

⁂

#0700 - June 10, 2019 @ 05:47 (Los Angeles, California)

[0700.1 / 1762] [THE CARPENTER creates a plan to smuggle our family out of North Korea. He works covertly with the Pentagon to wrap the landing gear of our outbound flight with plastic explosives, which will detonate while our family is in transit later today. The plane will crash over international waters where the US Government intends to rescue us.]

[0700.2 / 1763] [I observe a scene in a Wild West town. A woman aggressively unloads a car, unpacking vast quantities of cleaning supplies onto a driveway. I'm upset because I have to restock everything she's previously removed from the cupboards inside the home (*THE ARCHITECT and THE DESIGNER's third residence, which they now inhabit exclusively*). They've purchased an entire desert town on a mountain called "King Man," Arizona.]

[0700.3 / 1764] [We pass THE WEAVER in line to board the doomed North Korean plane. We take our seats in front of a large square window that will allow us to witness the crash as it happens. I want to be fearless, but as the plane takes off, I close my eyes and fold my face to my lap.] //

⁂

Maj. = 0- THE WEAVER: #0701, 1-THE CARPENTER: #0703
Min. = ♥- THE ARCHITECT: #0857, ♠-THE DESIGNER: #0927
ARIZONA: #1013
LAP: #1163, #1198

⁂

#0701 - June 11, 2019 @ 06:50 (San Francisco, California)

[0701.1 / 1765] [I give a guitar lesson and demonstration.]
[0701.2 / 1766] [I give a gymnastics demonstration.]

BOTH *demonstrations are given to the same gathered crowd*

[0701.3 / 1767] [THE M&A ATTORNEY's (*multi-faceted, intelligent, and open*) idea of vacation is to bill $700 per hour at her law office. Breaking from convention, she and "Todd" agree to take a vacation from running their Michelin starred waterfront restaurant: "ODD TODD."

481

The kitchen along the back wall displays the word "TODD" spelled in steel circus font, marquis bulb lit letters over the stove visible through the glass wall on the street facing side of the restaurant. The letter "T" buzzes like a Jacob's ladder and blinks the name of the restaurant in Morse code:

O D D T O D D.

--- / -.. / -.. / - / --- / -.. / -..

I tell THE WEAVER she'd, *"enjoy them as a couple"* as we take a leisurely stroll in and sit at a table. THE RODIN *(flexible, active, and hardworking)* busses tables. I admire the definition and vascularity in his arms. His muscles flex in little percolating blips as he makes small quick circles with a bleached rag to sterilize tables for tonight's service. As he passes, I notice his nametag confusingly reads: "ZIZAK."]

[0701.4 / 1768] [THE BOUNCER *(large, raw, and gritty)* becomes violent and throws classroom chairs in my direction. He pitches an apple at my face. It strikes me in the mouth, bloodies my lips, and displaces most of my teeth.
"I WOULD NEVER ALLOW YOU TO TEACH AT MY SCHOOL. DEMONS OUT!" I yell, spitting blood as I'm barely able to articulate the words.] //

✲

Maj. = 0- THE WEAVER: #0703
MOUTH: #1098, #1144, #1157
BLIPS: #0934
THE BOUNCER: #0718
THE RODIN: #0785
THE M&A ATTORNEY: #1084
✲

#0702 - June 12, 2019 @ 02:51 (San Francisco, California)

[0702.1 / 1769] [I think I have strep throat. I drink gallons of water to soothe the scratchiness. I'm a roadie supporting the AIDS LifeCycle California coast bike ride. Everyone is tired, frustrated, and ready to give up.] //

✲

TIRED: #1001, #1060
GIVE: #0976, #0986, #0989
SOOTHE: #0897, #0964
✲

#0703 - June 12, 2019 @ 06:46 (San Francisco, California)

[0703.1 / 1770] [I run an indoor marathon. I look for my bib number while I'm on the course. My number is 711. THE YOUNG AUDITOR *(curious, supportive, and service oriented)* shouts to me, *"That whole thing starts way later!"*]

. . .

[0703.2 / 1771] [THE TRANSLATOR gives THE WEAVER and THE CARPENTER a tour of a prep school.]

[0703.3 / 1772] [I adopt a litter of gold and black puppies and walk them around off leash. When I return home the fence around the puppies is just inches tall, but they remain orderly and contained.]

[0703.4 / 1773] [THE WEAVER and THE DANCER lead a group of children.]

[0703.5 / 1774] [I'm asked to fly to LA for the night. My job is to chop onions. THE CATCHER (*centered, humble, and respectful*) is the co-pilot. THE CHAMPION OF LOVE (*expressive, accommodating, and vulnerable*) would have met me in LA but his prescriptions changed to better manage a pre-existing condition: ***Deep Chronic Heartbreak.*** He's out of work and lost his insurance, making his medicine so cost prohibitive he can't travel.] //

✳
✳✳

Maj. = 0- THE WEAVER: #0708, 1- THE CARPENTER: #0717,
2- THE DANCER: #0719, 19- THE TRANSLATOR: #0753
ADOPT: #0902
FENCE: #1000, #1074, #1086, #1088

✳
✳✳

#0704 - June 12, 2019 @ 14:05 (San Francisco, California)

[0704.1 / 1775] [A large mass gathers for a rally. ROSE NYLON lifts a round protest sign that looks like a giant aspirin (*white circle split vertically down the middle*). Block letters around the edge spell out: *"I BARELY STARTED YOU!"* ROSE taunts those marching in the parade by thrusting the sign towards them.] //

✳
✳✳
RALLY: #1201
PROTEST: #0907, #1124, #1188
ASPIRIN: #0811

✳
✳✳

#0705 - June 13, 2019 @ 01:29 (San Francisco, California)

[0705.1 / 1776] [A group of guys run a race, attempting to escape from a school. One has a 9V battery sized device attached in front of his right eye that could detonate and blow off his head at any moment.]

[0705.2 / 1777] [A group of men guard the back door of a house. Inside, other men haze younger men by dunking their heads in liquid filled garbage cans. They empty solid-colored cans of beer on the heads of the neophytes. The ceremony is rowdy. It's unclear whether or

483

not the young men will be killed. Action moves from third person to first person perspective. *I observe the action, then I'm in it.* The drift between experiences continues for some time. Bored with the circumstances, THE TATER *(playful, anxious, and illusive)* suggests that another young man and I go to the hot springs to chill. We ask him to join us. He contemplates and debates for some time until ultimately deciding not to come along.] //

✸

HOT: #1188, #1137
MIRROR: #0883, #0919, #0954, #0995
DRIFT: #0917, #0951, #1144
THE TATER: #0865

✸

#0706 - June 14, 2019 @ 02:40am (San Francisco, California)

[0706.1 / 1778] [Abstraction of a group event. I drive a car with paint on the windshield. The paint begins as a clear coat. It changes color as it dries, the process sped up by the wiper blades spreading it across the glass. It mostly turns shades of red. The red gets brighter and brighter until I wake up.] //

✸

WINDSHIELD: #0889, #1021
GLASS: #0942, #0943, #0943
CLEAR: #0922, #0924, #0931, #0933

✸

#0707 - June 14, 2019 @ 04:48 (San Francisco, California)

[0707.1 / 1779] [Freeze frame image of THE CONNECTOR.]

[0707.2 / 1780] [A wine chiller bag full of ice submerged in a river empties its contents and infiltrates the clear, pristine water source.]

[0707.3 / 1781] [A challenging, conflicted scene occurs behind a makeshift riot barrier beyond my line of sight.] //

✸

Maj. = 4- THE CONNECTOR: #0712
BARRIER: #1115
BEYOND: #1193, #1195

✸

#0708 - June 15, 2019 @ 07:38 (San Francisco, California)

[0708.1 / 1782] [Fuzz balls on a sweater.]

· · ·

484

[0708.2 / 1783] [THE WEAVER gives me $20 multiple times as I repeatedly change clothes, pausing while naked to admire my body.]

[0708.3 / 1784] [I'm a grade school teacher. My class takes a field trip to an aquarium.]

[0708.4 / 1785] [CHER stands at the back of an auditorium. She wears a black Chanel dress, black sunglasses, and a black wig. I sit down on steps as she passes, then exit the venue.] //

⁂

Maj. = 0- THE WEAVER: #0717
CHER: #1023
FUZZ: #1063, #1175
$20: #1055, #1165

⁂

#0709 - June 15, 2019 @ 04:57 (Big Sur, California)

[0709.1 / 1786] [I run energy standing up in a shower. Soft gold light surrounds me.] //

⁂

ENERGY: #0935, #0936, #0940
SHOWER: #0808, #0854, #0857
SOFT: #0803, #1087, #1162

⁂

#0710 - June 16, 2019 @ 05:05 (Big Sur, California)

[0710.1 / 1787] [I work for a caterer arranging flowers in a hotel restaurant. I learn the meat a kitchen crew pulled from the freezer for daily prep expired yesterday. THE FIFTY POUND BRAIN (*savvy, sought, and learned*) is responsible for building the basement addition to the property. I provide him intermittent construction support when he asks.]

[0710.2 / 1788] [I talk with various celebrities outside a formal event. We observe children playing a game where they build a scale model of New York City from building blocks.]

[0710.3 / 1789] [I give THE POLYMATH (*unattached, tactile, and adventurous*) head immediately after he's fucked someone else. My technique is so rough that he stops me mid-act.]

[0710.4 / 1790] [THE CHILD collects coins and tells me detailed stories about where she found each of them.]

. . .

[0710.5 / 1791] [I visit THE FIFTY POUND BRAIN in his basement bunker. I'm aware I have to redo some of the work he completed. A series of six fist sized holes drilled in a vertical line to support a staircase will need to be cut out and reinstalled. The holes are full of a hardened amber colored resin.]

[0710.6 / 1792] [I'm given a small golden egg with a phone number scribbled on it.]

[0710.7 / 1793] [THE POLYMATH invites me to lay down next to him on the ground after dispensing fuel at a gas station. I decline because I notice a security camera observing us. Rolls Royce and Maybach roll through and park on a grassy lot near a mansion beyond the gas station.] //

✲✲

Maj. = 3- *THE CHILD: #0712*
AMBER: #0850, #0892, #0943, #1060
DECLINE: #0819, #0865, #1088, #1107
THE POLYMATH: #0741

✲✲

#0711 - June 16, 2019 @ 07:02 (Big Sur, California)

[0711.1 / 1794] [A street festival begins to close down. A person at the base of a large, colorful tube slide distributes ice cream cookie sandwiches to young children as they exit. I've ridden the slide eight times today, and have eaten eight ice cream sandwiches. When friends ask how many times I've gone I say *"four,"* because I don't want to be judged as a *"glutton."* I encounter some friends who take down their pop-up tents and box up their inventory. They joke about the neighboring **OCCUPY MINIMALISM** booth, which didn't even pitch a tent for the festival. Earlier, a man left a single sheet of paper with the booth name written in tiny font on the pavement. No one else showed up to staff the parcel. No one from the public inquired about the piece of paper.]

[0711.2 / 1795] [THE WHITE KNIGHT (*searching, sharing, and eager*) is cute. I date him, but I'm judged. Some people think he's way too young for me.]

[0711.3 / 1796] [I see playful dogs outside the window on a rooftop. Some are puppies. They don't understand, *"the edge is dangerous."* I pull a couple of them inside just before they fall.]

[0711.4 / 1797] [The cookie slide is permanently installed as an art installation in a giant steel warehouse.] //

✲✲

DATE: #0939, #0944, #1076
POP UP: #0937, #0950, #1041

TINY: #0826, #0857, #0916, #0920
EDGE: #1073, #1105, #1128

⁑

#0712 - June 17, 2019 @ 05:51 (Big Sur, California)

[0712.1 / 1798] [It's THE CHILD's birthday. We play on the same kickball team. THE OBSERVER (*balanced, neutral, and quiet*) referees.]

[0712.2 / 1799] [JOHN LENNON invites people onstage to sing. A drunk woman ruins the experience.]

[0712.3 / 1800] [*"Roadie"* teams take on *"Cyclists"* in West Side Story-style gang combat.]

[0712.4 / 1801] [THE POOL BOY (*hot, social, and manipulative*) and THE AUSSIE (*creative, fair, and triggered*) are on opposite teams.]

[0712.5 / 1802] [I record a video of THE CHILD with a pen camera.]

[0712.6 / 1803] [I sit on my boyfriend's lap saying, *"I Love You"* in his ear as I stroke his shaved head. He doesn't reply.]

[0712.7 / 1804] [I cook Indian food. *"The key to retaining spice and flavor is to reuse water that's been seasoned and boiled."*]

[0712.8 / 1805] [THE OBSERVER (*articulate, clear, and vocal*) leads a yoga class for 12 people. I've agreed to assist her.]

[0712.9 / 1806] [I'm back in the kickball game. I kick a ball just beyond the net. I nearly score a goal. *"It's a near miss!"*] //

[0712.10 / 1807] [THE CATALYST (*astute, influential, and fluid*) and THE CONNECTOR botch the launch of a new ticketing process for Burning Man. THE CATALYST takes a client call as she drives away from a parking lot. The group comes for her with torches and pitchforks. Leaving quickly was prudent.]

⁑

Maj. = 2- THE CHILD: #0722, 4- THE CONNECTOR: #0762
JOHN LENNON: #920
BURNING MAN: #0805, #0826, #0850, #0160
GOAL: #0802, #0811, #0923, #0929, #0957
THE AUSSIE: #0904
THE POOL BOY: #0985
THE CATALYST: #1133

⁑

#0713 - June 18, 2019 @ 06:14 (Big Sur, California)

[0713.1 / 1808] [I celebrate Easter at a bathhouse.]

[0713.2 / 1809] [I'm at the second annual *"something."* After much ado in an auditorium, ELTON JOHN stands in regal attire before our group, issuing each member a distinctive solid gold ring with an inlay of pink psychedelic letters. When worn the rings look like miniature upturned platform boots. They weigh a staggering 20 ounces each. Four words (*unique to the person*) are imprinted on the bottom of their, *"gold boot ring."* The tone is celebratory and sanctified.] //

⁑

ELTON JOHN: #0908
EASTER: #1158, #1177
SOLID GOLD: #1028, #1044, #1101

⁑

#0714 - June 19, 2019 @ 05:00 (Big Sur, California)

[0714.1 / 1810] [THE FIDUCIARY learns to DJ.]

[0714.2 / 1811] [I'm on a grassy two-level field where a social club holds a fancy event. Luxury bars of soap are on sale for $12 each. I have one in my pocket. I don't remember if I've paid for it. A group of drag queens hosts a field day (*games and races*) as a destroyed cityscape smolders behind them, bathed from above in restorative gold light.]

[0714.3 / 1812] [I change homes an hour after graduation. THE ZOMBIE (*pained, erratic, and worn down*) is the only friend who stays to help me move. My bags are hastily taken from my old home to the new lot. My felt hats are left on the lawn in an open cardboard box and ruined by a rainstorm that completes as quickly as it begins. A ⅙ size version of the old house fashioned from dark chocolate appears on the driveway and is casually eaten by me and the neighbors a we reminisce and say farewell. As we consume the chocolate version, the old house disappears.] //

⁑

Maj. = 9- THE FIDUCIARY: #0788
SOAP: #0846, #1010, #1016, #1051, #1082, #1152
DJ. #0883, #0897, #0961, #1045
RUINED: #868, #0929, #1169
THE ZOMBIE: #1099

⁑

#0715 - June 20, 2019 @ 02:13 (Big Sur, California)

[0715.1 / 1813] [I participate in a multi-stage bike ride and attempt to get an early start on today's segment. A variety of interactions and environmental factors prevent my departure and result in lost hours of lead time. I fall to the back of the pack. At dusk, a courtesy bus from our hotel to the next destination departs with me as a passenger. I'm failing. My bike is racked. While riding the bus I see the remnants of a bike accident on an exit ramp that would have snarled the route I intended to take. EMT's on the scene resemble Muppets. Treatment is given to those critically wounded at night under bright flood lights.]

[0715.2 / 1814] [I see two abstract, lung-like images hover a couple of feet in front of my face. They're quite large and overlap on another, "*lateral to medial.*" One is dull orange; the other forest green. "*Yeah, they're really showing you 'existential,' today,*" THE INSTRUCTOR (*knowl-*

edgeable, accessible, and friendly) says with a white toothed grin, referencing the images shown by my guides. I'm curious and a bit confused. I don't receive a clear transmission.]

[0715.3 / 1815] [I'm back at the cyclist hotel. I recall I have a ticket for a CIRQUE du SOLEIL performance given to me by THE RINGMASTER *(generous, delightful, and sweet)* and THE CARDINAL *(dashing, helpful, and tactile)*. From a group of 50, I specifically ask THE ASSISTANT to, *"go to my black backpack and retrieve the ticket."* She leaves and returns empty handed. I'm frustrated and blurt, *"If anyone would understand the need to listen, I thought it would be you."* The scene remains active. People rush around us as I sit on a carpeted floor next to a concierge.]

[0715.4 / 1816] [I'm at an extravagant residence. A woman with straight black hair in a scarlet evening gown *(also wearing a mink stole)* stands with both hands on a kitchen island, looking down at her phone. She's THE PILOT's green card wife. The group gathered is paranoid they're being surveilled, and begin accusing one another of being *"the mole."* As attention turns, the wife promptly walks up to me and pulls a walkie-talkie from the side pocket of my backpack, which was in plain view the entire time. She smashes the device on the table in front of me, making special consideration to snap the antenna clean from the brick. She storms off, and I'm stunned by what just happened. THE KIND HEART hands me the broken pieces as I cry. My hands tremble as I defend myself to the group. I give a rousing monologue that declares all the ways and reasons why, *"I'm in the wrong place at the wrong time!"* THE PILOT's Italian grandfather laughs at me, chewing on a cigar while I plead my case. Doesn't appear this is going to end well for me as I watch them load clips with ammunition.] //

⁕

Maj. = 6- *THE PILOT: #0774, 21-THE KIND HEART: #1059*
KITCHEN ISLAND· #0815
GREEN CARD: #1185
THE ASSISTANT: #0786

⁕

#0716 - June 20, 2019 @ 05:53 (Big Sur, California)

[0716.1 / 1817] [I'm at a 1970's outdoor concert. I'm excited to see the final performance of a globally adored artist.]

[0716.2 / 1818] [I'm at THE EDUCATORS' *(supportive, committed, and graceful)* house. Their pet moose joins us to eat in their breakfast nook. I turn away and walk down a hallway which feels like the interior ring of a Las Vegas hotel. The various levels within occur as rolling hills marked with Incan agricultural plots. THE YOUNG CEO *(smart, quick, and objective)* ducks in and out of arched doorways brightly lit with white light.]

[0716.3 / 1819] [A fraternity practices for its upcoming performance in a Greek Week variety show.] //

⁂

1970'S: #0874, #1080, #1141
GREEK: #0887, #1008, #1091
ADORED: #1139

⁂

#0717 - June 20, 2019 @ 06:42 (Big Sur, California)

[0717.1 / 1820] [I descend a large steep staircase in a dilapidated building. I might be in Beirut, Lebanon or somewhere in the Middle East. I tightly hold a crude white railing as I spin rapidly downwards towards a pile of broken concrete. I and my entire group make it to the bottom safely.]

[0717.2 / 1821] [Young men in a row are pushed from behind in a body of water. They're all naked. On shore, THE SEXWORKER (*fierce, empowered, and somatic*) and THE RAY OF SUNSHINE (*strong, masculine, and silent*) practice humiliation and BDSM live on Instagram. Further away on a grassy field THE BREWMASTER and THE PARKS DIRECTOR (*withdrawn, skeptical, and searching*) crouch behind a set of large antlers and snap photographs in my direction with their recently purchased pair of brand new SLRs.]

[0717.3 / 1822] [A series of large boulders hang suspended like a staircase over an azure blue reservoir like an odd and beautiful 3D surrealist, immersive painting. I blink and find myself in an olive lit corporate meeting room discussing the utility and municipal applications of technology related to the hovering stones.]

[0717.4 / 1823] [I'm in my living room, which doubles as my art space. My assistant uses a 3" black marker and draws meticulous lines from wall to wall. The lines on the floor clearly direct movers how to reposition a series of four-square canvases. When complete, my work can continue. New furniture can be appropriately placed. The geometry is precise. The room can pivot like a Rubik's Cube on demand.]

[0717.5 / 1824] [It's autumn, at a harvest festival. The night air is crisp. THE WEAVER (*19-20 years of age*) is known for being a skilled artisan. She's actively courted by a customer to produce another piece of pottery. THE CARPENTER is a young cadet who arrives on scene with strong opinions, and pops his mouth off at THE WEAVER. She tells him to, *"check the military man at the door."* A General's wife claps and asks THE WEAVER, *"Where did you learn to talk like that?"* A small chalkboard next to a basket of loose bills reads, *"Baby's Laundry Fund - 2020."* A large black cone shaped candle (*~2' tall*) burns down. Once extinguished its residual warmth causes the entire mass to droop to the left like a wizard's hat.] //

⁂

Maj. = 0- THE WEAVER: #0719, 1- THE CARPENTER: #0719
GENERAL: #0829, #0878, #0943, #0979, #1155, #1179
BILLS: #0925, #0931, #0988, #1165

SLR: #0952
THE SEX WORKER: #0726
THE RAY OF SUNSHINE: #0726
THE BREWMASTER: #0803
THE PARKS DIRECTOR: #1017

✳✳

#0718 - June 21, 2019 @ 01:16 (Big Sur, California)

[0718.1 / 1825] [The scene begins at a desk on a construction site composed of four skate-board half pipes positioned in the shape of an X *(when viewed from above)*. We run from our desks on the exterior platforms and exchange paper messages rolled up and placed in clear batons when we pass one another at the intersection. As more interactions on bikes continue, I realize I'm on a Habitat for Humanity build site.

Construction is underwritten and sponsored by *"a big bank."* The house is open to the public as construction continues. I'm not aligned to any particular project.

What begins as cooperative service shifts to a scramble for survival. The energy is similar to a high school hallway between classes. The level of danger constantly increases like I'm advancing through higher levels of a video game. One by one, members of the construction crew begin to turn on me. I'm threatened with hammers, saws, and nail guns by different people in different rooms of the house. I find myself in constant peril. Numerous strong women of color provide me with peripheral emotional support as I'm threatened. Window installers belay from above. Some faces I encounter as I move from room to room include THE BOUNCER *(aggressive, masculine, and threatening)* and THE PIED PIPER *(friendly, welcoming, and calm)*.

"Am I experiencing a, future-perfect transposition of the Underground Railroad?'" I yell as I run, not really knowing what I'm saying.

Among my more perilous encounters is a chance meeting a large muscular man with a tri-colored beard.

He arrives on site riding a titanium frame bicycle. He wears a shiny blackish purple wetsuit. His goggles finish the look, making him appear like a human-beetle hybrid. At first, I believe he's my friend. I know I've misjudged him when he shoves me to the ground and attempts to stomp on my face. I see an American Flag logo on the sole of his boot as it's thrust toward my jaw. His dark female counterpart laughs as I scramble.

"Snuff him out like a cockroach!" she yells to encourage the purple-black-beetle-man.

I run from room to room, installing wiring and sanding sheetrock as I flee. In each succes-sive room I'm put eye-to-eye with a former abuser, some of whom I forgive. THE PIED PIPER leads a light hearted talk on an outdoor deck and nods supportively in my direction even though he can't verbally acknowledge my presence skittering around the property. The group sips beer samples as he explains how he honed his brewing process.] //

✳✳

HALF PIPE: #1189
EYE TO EYE: #980, #1001, #1084
JAW: #0874, #0950, #1001, #1050, #1053
PERIL: #0926
ADVANCING: #0931, #1056, #1169

✳✳

491

#0719 - June 21, 2019 @ 07:41 (Big Sur, California)

[0719.1 / 1826] [I'm inside a remote mountain cabin. It's late afternoon on Summer Solstice. The family is there. The scene is low key and easy. I answer a knock at the door, surprised by the arrival of THE BESTIE (*clear, candid, and real*). Her hair is braided. She wears a backpack. She makes a hilarious wincing facial expression with an accompanying *"mouth fart"* sound. I invite her inside, delightfully surprised by her presence.

I turn to face the other direction and find myself in a luxury high rise condo with a smoky view of an amber and orange sky. I intended to introduce THE BESTIE to the family but instead witness an odd scene where a young drunk frat boy named "Adam" demands his car keys from his girlfriend. They share an infant son, who cries from inside a *"half box"* made of cardboard set on the kitchen countertop. The girlfriend is distressed. "Adam's" agreed to have sex with another woman. He fumbles with his phone with one eye closed. He bites his tongue in an overcompensating attempt to order an Uber. After strenuously focusing for a few moments, he looks up at THE BESTIE and me, and begins to hurl insults at her. I intuitively step out in front of her to immediately curtail his nonsense.

"She's a...she...she's....a cokehead," he drunkenly slurs.

I run toward him and firmly grasp his throat as I slam him back against the wall.

"You need to get better friends," I interrupt him as he gasps, while continuing, *"All I want to hear from you is 'Uh huh.'"*

Pointing at THE BESTIE, I say, *"She's the first person I met in San Francisco. There's no contest between her and you, nor her and your fraternity. I will choose her every time."*

I loosen the grip on his throat. He's embarrassed and pissed off as he slides to the floor. "Adam" is immature, impractical, and needs to be repeatedly, *"shhh'd."*

As I turn to face THE BESTIE, I'm back inside the mountain cabin. *"This is the first person I met in San Francisco,"* I repeat to THE WEAVER, THE CARPENTER and THE DANCER. They smile and listen as THE BESTIE and I share a heart-to-heart conversation.

She briefly offers some simple life truths (*equal parts humor and grit*) before expressing she wants to take a solo hike. She intends to leave before sunset to celebrate the solstice. I invite her to come back after 8pm so we can continue our conversation.

"This is THE ACTOR's best friend," I smile and shout to THE WEAVER and THE CARPENTER.

As she turns to depart, THE BESTIE's nose begins to bleed. Droplets fall to the floor and create splatters that look like infant sized hand and foot prints. I offer her a rag and a handkerchief. As she compresses the bridge of her nose, I tell her, *"You are connected to God. When I met you, I was fully alive and connected too. I must be again, since you've floated back into my life. My life is organized in a very specific way now and I thank you for contributing to it."*

THE BESTIE's presence remains warm and nurturing. I don't want her to go .] //

⚜

Maj. = 0- THE WEAVER: #0722, 1- THE CARPENTER: #0722,
2- THE DANCER: #0731, 10- THE ACTOR: #0772
DEPART: #0804, #0813, #0819, #0885
THANK YOU: #0819, #0828, #0846
HIKE: #0808

⚜

#0720 - June 21, 2019 @ 09:21 (Big Sur, California)

[0720.1 / 1827] [I spend a night at a roadside motel. The next morning THE LAWYER and I move up the time for our lunch meeting.
"Hey Nash! Let's get an early start and meet at the dusty baseball field at 9:00am."
Once we connect at the ball field, we walk towards a diner. Our dress and dialog imply we've met up in 1962. As we take a seat, the sun sets rapidly behind a mountain giving everything a rusty red hue. Across the highway stands the Great Pyramid of Cheops. Just in front of the pyramid is a ¼ scale version of the monument built from modern materials (*framed lumber and 3D printed concrete*). I run out of the diner, across the highway, and up a small hill, hoping to get a sublime golden hour view of the scene.
"The light is perfect right now for that shot you wanted!" I shout back to THE LAWYER with a hand cupping my mouth. A new city has sprung up behind the diner in the short time it's taken to jaunt across the highway.] //

⁂

Maj. = 5- THE LAWYER: #0722
LUNCH: #0823, #0835, #0872
BASEBALL: #0905, #1188
DINER: #1026, #1045

⁂

JOSHUA D. LUNDELL

***

PART 10 - I AM THAT

#0721 - #0826

"Do I contradict myself?
Very well then, I contradict myself,
(I am large, I contain multitudes.)"

-Walt Whitman

* * *

June 22, 2019 - August 16, 2019

⚜

⚜10.1 - THE BOOK OF EQUULEUS: 0721-0724 ⚜

#0721 - June 22, 2019 @ 04:33 (San Francisco, California)

[0721.1 / 1828] [I'm on a tour bus with a group. We take an excursion to ride rollercoasters. THE ORGANIST (*dashing, gentlemanly, and talented*) and his husband invite themselves along. Both are tired from an all-day ride on another bus prior to linking up with our group. He mentions his friends have made special poster board signs for us and other riders on our rollercoaster train to hold up while we ride. The signs will make us conspicuous to other friends in different locations within the park. Will the signs offer a marriage proposal? A pregnancy announcement? It's unclear what will be spelled out whilst the cards are held overhead. THE ORGANIST asks me to retrieve the stack of signs from their prior bus. As I depart the husbands start having sex. I turn around and jack off. I cum, and then to my surprise immediately cum again without touching my dick. I love the sensation.]

[0721.2 / 1829] [I observe construction activities commence on a land mass allocated by a municipality for a future beltway. All tasks (*and those responsible for completing them*) whizz through the sequence in time lapse. Land clears. It's graded. Roads are paved. Cars drive through en masse.] //

⚜

START: #0808 #0811, #0820, #0841, #0868, #0871, #0874, #0883, #0888, #0896, #0899
OVERHEAD: #0811, #0812, #0825, #0831, #0844, #0861, #0874
POSTER: #0841, #0888, #0909, #0916, #0989, #1031, #1161

⚜

#0722 - June 23, 2019 @ 06:37 (Beavercreek, Ohio)

[0722.1 / 1830] [**Mood:** Intense. An accident happens. THE CHILD comes to the house for a visit, and self identifies as a, *"good helper."* A swimming pool with a stone grotto occupies the majority of a property. THE WANDERER (*youthful, exuberant, and curious*) falls and strikes his head on the edge of the pool. He claims he's ok. THE CARPENTER shoved him. Much of the time is spent strategizing how to help THE CARPENTER avoid financial extortion and a criminal conviction. THE LAWYER arbitrates. THE WEAVER and THE CARPENTER decide to have a conversation behind closed doors. They believe their prospective risk of loss falls somewhere between $13,000 and $130,000. While they meet, I tamper with evidence at the scene and gather a series of small objects from the bottom of the pool. In doing so I realize I might be the one who actually shoved THE WANDERER, and not THE CARPENTER. It's unclear at the moment.

THE WANDERER claims he can complete the Pacific Crest Trail on his originally established timeline, even after absorbing that severe blow to the head. I think this renders his civil complaint without merit. THE WANDERER's mother appears to support him, then dissolves in thin air as quickly as she arrives.

"You're such a good helper," I say, validating THE CHILD as she pushes piles of boards

together while surrounded by a team of firefighters. One of the firefighters nearly strikes her in the head with a shovel; another accident narrowly avoided.

I'm playfully stuck in a sandwich hug between THE WANDERER and another faceless person of equal size and stature (*6'4" and slender*). As they press against me, I bring my forearms to my chest and jokingly exclaim, *"Maybe this'll make me taller!"*

THE WANDERER's mother returns and speaks privately with THE LAWYER, having left work early to take an appointment to discuss the case. The less we say, the better the likely outcome will be for everyone.] //

⁎⁎

Maj. = 0- THE WEAVER: #0727, 01- THE CARPENTER: #0727,
03- THE CHILD: #0732, 05- THE LAWYER: #0763
SANDWICH: #0879, #0891, #0909, #1084, #1145, #1158, #1160
ACCIDENT: #760, #1034, #0273, #0714

⁎⁎

#0723 -June 23, 2019 @ 11:47 (Beavercreek, Ohio)

[0723.1 / 1831] [Cookies are stacked, one slightly larger beneath the next to form a conical tower. They're pink, round, flavored like strawberry rhubarb, and topped with a scoop of pink watermelon flavored ice cream.]

[0723.2 / 1832] [Flash animation sequence. I'm struck in the chest by the baton of a Sai tossed high in the sky. Cartoon blood sprays up in a geyser from the wound as I wince in agony. "Cartoon Me" wants to remove the melee weapon, but THE INQUISITOR (*process oriented, seeking, and down tempo*) won't allow it. I start to bleed out and feel cold flood my extremities. I know I'm going to die.] //

⁎⁎

WATERMELON: #0947, #1197
PINK: #0816, #0820, #0844, #0850, #0867, #910
TOWER: #0891, #0916, #0919, #0931, #1028, #0098, #0113, #0150, #0157, #0220

⁎⁎

#0724 - June 24, 2019 @ 01:59 (Beavercreek, Ohio)

[0724.1 / 1833] [PRISON BREAK! Repeated sequence! Each time I break out, less security enforcement is present. Each time I return to the facility, I leave with more and more inmates. Over time this begins to cause problems. Incidences of crime spike. Some of those I help spring from incarceration begin to deify me. Others want me dead. A mass murder happens in a safe house I've set up for those recently emancipated.]

[0724.2 / 1834] [I'm a woman. THE GATOR (*fraternal, dualistic, and commanding*) plays the role of warden of a minimum-security facility. He takes no action as he observes me make sexual advances toward a male orderly. I stay overnight in the facility, eventually waking to

497

note it's 7:00am. The time renders me "Fair Game" for retention. I risk incarceration if I choose to stay and play.]

[0724.3 / 1835] [I'm a man. As I depart and walk by a tall chain link fence, I witness a beautiful, muscular Asian man in the prison yard get teased for having a micro-penis. I hold the fence, swing to the other side, release my grip and slide down the smooth concrete exterior of a mental hospital. While descending, I realize many of those I've freed do not have access to necessary medicines they were regularly administered while inside the institution. By now, they've likely all died without support. I'm not upset. The outcome seems logical and unemotional.

I continue the escape. Many others have followed my lead. As we frolic and skip through a forest at night, I teach each of them a relevant survival skill that will help them navigate their newfound freedom. Some hide in the bushes. Others cover themselves with leaves. A unique solution is administered to each escapee.

Time advances. We all end up working together at a cafeteria. The parent company of the cafeteria merges with another. The new composite company plans a dinner party with the newly minted combined staff. When asked if we're going to attend, our inconsistent answers begin to raise suspicion. If we're found out we'll be sent back to jail.] //

⁂

SKIP: #0866, #0877, #0929, #1174, #0001, #0317, #0359, #0589, #0640
TREES: #0924, #0939, #0963, #0970, #1011, #0008, #0032, #0036 #0048, #0066, #0079
EXTERIOR: #0803, #0877, #0904, #0914, #0973, #0988, #0990, #1037, #1052, #1072

⁂

⚜ 10.2 - THE BOOK OF ERIDANUS: 0725-0758 ⚜

#0725 - June 24, 2019 @ 05:29 (Beavercreek, Ohio)

[0725.1 / 1836] [THE PASSIONATE BRAZILIAN (*soulful, suave, and quietly strong*) and THE FILM PRODUCER explore renting a building to launch their new photography business. I consider becoming their business partner. The unique multi-level property has stone floors and large windows at the back of the space. On the ground floor a windowless bedroom hides within a boiler room. Another room would make a good massage/reiki office. Upstairs, a long retail area with Smurf blue carpeting could be converted into a lofted yoga studio. The rent is $2300 a month.

While upstairs with THE PASSIONATE BRAZILIAN things turn erotic. I push him to his back on a countertop and lunge. We make out and press our chiseled bodies together. My mind wanders and I start contemplating whether it would be fun to create a business relationship with a strong undercurrent of sexual tension. THE PASSIONATE BRAZILIAN and I don't have sex. Another man and woman interested in renting the building catch us and attempt to shame us.

"SEX IS GOOD! You should try it!" I say as we giggle and embrace.

How would my life need to change to run a small business? No time for vacation. I'd be married to it. Would I have diminished flexibility? I have some things to sort out before I could commit. THE PASSIONATE BRAZILIAN has a lot of friends. Getting them to classes would be good for business. With my arms around his neck, I look out a window and see a yellow bus depot with red flags flying in the wind on top. I take this as a cue. Competition in the neighborhood would be fierce. As I weigh the pros and cons, one decision is simple. I'd leave my current team without any hesitation to make a new venture happen.] //

⚜

BOILER: #0243
EMBRACE: #0134, #0218, #0367
THE PASSIONATE BRAZILIAN: #0826
THE FILM PRODUCER: #1083

⚜

#0726 - June 24, 2019 @ 07:27 (Beavercreek, Ohio)

[0726.1 / 1837] [I'm at an elevated fast casual Asian restaurant in a mall food court that features a $16 "Grab 'n Go" menu. The ads on LCD screens are sleek, colorful with snarky catch phrases. *"Don't add THAT kind of honey to the soup. Say 'No No No to GMOs,'"* text set next to a wagging cartoon hand reads.

I enter a store called "PLANCHA," a woman's boutique that occurs as a mashup of ZARA and DOLLS KILL. All looks are $87. THE PEDDLER (*witty, devoted, and soulful*) and his drag queen boyfriend share a changing room in the basement level as I select a gold dress and a pair of matching pumps to try on. I discover myself sitting by a bathroom on a couch next to THE RAY OF SUNSHINE (*confident, cool, and musky*). We lean backwards to see if THE SEX WORKER (*playful, candid, and paid*) is home, but it appears he's still with a client downstairs.]

. . .

[0726.2 / 1838] [THE TAR HEEL *(tipsy, flirtatious, and explicit)* owns a home in a Seattle suburb and offers a bedroom for rent. I inspect the property and like the steel ladders he's installed that dually function as stairwells. The interior spaces are vast, unobstructed and artfully decorated. A guy enters and leaves a tray of snack foods *(Chips, RxBars, etc.)* in the dark and then promptly exits.

A night passes and snacks remain available on the table. The table has become an event information station on the final morning of a global convention. I leave the house and jump in a convertible. I wave at a homeless Black man as a friendly gesture for him to cross the street. He mistakes it for an invitation to hitchhike and attempts to enter the car. I speed away and make a sharp left-hand turn into oncoming traffic. I drive aggressively to escape and stop at a large open-air mall. I exit the car and pass a group of men wearing leather bulldog harnesses, walking toward me from the opposite direction. They walk a fuzzy bulldog on a green and black neoprene leash. I fawn over the dog and accidentally kick it in the face as I squeal in anticipation of petting it.]

[0726.3 / 1839] ["The President of the USA" gets hair and makeup done in advance of a live TV broadcast. He begins exhibiting signs of shock *(pale, cool, and diaphoretic)* and no one on the scene can help him but me. I say, *"Hey, we have the same undercut,"* as I push a sweaty mass of hair back over his head. This calms him down. I'm annoyed I'm obligated to help him.] //

⁎⁎

SNARKY: #0012
ONCOMING TRAFFIC: #0215, #0260, #0309
COOL: #0023, #0073, #0080
LIVE: #120, #0144, #0169
THE SEX WORKER: #0788

⁎⁎

#0727 - June 25, 2019 @ 03:07 (Beavercreek, Ohio)

[0727.1 / 1840] [THE WEAVER and I look to purchase mountain property. THE CARPENTER and I build campfires from large twigs stacked inside large iron cages. A small ceramic ghostly object is splattered with blue paint and left on a table, intended to create a spooked/unsettling response in anyone who encounters it.] //

⁎⁎

Maj. = 0- THE WEAVER: #0731, 1- THE CARPENTER: #0728
CERAMIC: #0090
FOR SALE: #0149, #0201, #0264

⁎⁎

#0728 - June 25, 2019 @ 06:41 (Beavercreek, Ohio)

[0728.1 / 1841] [I'm deeply immersed in a home renovation project with an intention of moving into the property, once complete. THE THINKER and THE FEELER both help me and work until they both fall down from sheer exhaustion. THE CARPENTER and I go grocery shopping. He tells me about a military gas drilling project that has gone wildly over

500

budget. A counterparty developer on the project didn't understand that, *"95% gas purity was a high enough standard for all consumer cars on earth and that 80% of the project budget has been spent attempting to move from 96-98% purity."*

On the walk home we pass a Black child in a diaper living in squalor after its home has been destroyed by a hurricane. Another huge storm front rolls through. We sit around a campfire with a group of strangers until it subsides. THE CARPENTER and I don't have umbrellas, yet we don't get wet. The rain breaks and the sky overhead remains day-lit.]

[0728.2 / 1842] [I lay on my back. Spiders spin webs towards my face as I stream a cut of a new BEYONCÉ album that was performed live and in entirety, once.]

[0728.3 / 1843] [Everyone working on the house from the earlier segment sleeps. We decide not to wake anyone up. THE CARPENTER and I leave breakfast food on the counter and assume they'll all sleep soundly through the night.] //

✯

Maj. = 1- THE CARPENTER: #0731
Min. = ♠*- THE THINKER: #0740,* ♣*- THE FEELER: #0740*
BEYONCÉ: #0765
PURITY: #0010
ONCE: #0009, #0017, #0019

✯

#0729 - June 26, 2019 @ 05:22 (Sandusky, Ohio)

[0729.1 / 1844] [I'm outside a lodge trying to find my dorm room. I carry a big round devil's food cake. I ask for help multiple times and attempt entering from the street, the mailroom, and other side doors of what becomes a casino. Once inside I'm unable to find my room. No one is able to assist me. Mailroom operations in the belly of the casino are vast.] //

✯

CASINO: #0010, #0012, #0293, #0332
BELLY: #0116, #0147
VAST: #0048, #0077, #0079

✯

#0730 - June 26, 2019 @ 07:45 (Sandusky, Ohio)

[0730.1 / 1845] [I find my dorm room. I have two roommates. We have king sized beds set side by side with the same teal-turquoise sheets and comforters.] //

✯

KING SIZED: #0039
ROOMMATES: #0015, #0194
TEAL: #0170

✯

#0731 - June 27, 2019 @ 04:45 (Sandusky, Ohio)

[0731.1 / 1846] [I'm annoyed. I discover I'm being surveilled by a government agency who say they're *"not impressed"* with me. I snap and go off on a huge unnecessary diatribe about THE CARPENTER's career accomplishments. *"You wear those stripes on your shoulders, MR. USAF? Well, let me tell you who MY dad is,"* I scoff wryly at a uniformed man wearing mirrored sunglasses.]

[0731.2 / 1847] [People are corralled and pushed to the center of a town square. I observe from above. Deer ticks cling in a random constellation on the inside of a car window by my face. I try to shoo them away. I fly down into the crowd and find THE DANCER in the public square. We leave quickly in search of THE WEAVER and THE CARPENTER to warn them about what we've experienced. The time has come to flee.] //

✱✱

Maj. = 0- THE WEAVER: #0733, 1- THE CARPENTER: #0737, 2- THE DANCER: #0749
IMPRESSED: #0214, #0379, #0383
RANDOM: #0211, #0248, #0273

✱✱

#0732 - June 27, 2019 @ 08:07 (Sandusky, Ohio)

[0732.1 / 1848] [THE CHILD sits on a table and pretends to understand every word spoken by the group of adults gathered.]

[0732.2 / 1849] [I'm at a spa that's under construction. On a balcony I encounter "David" and we strike up a conversation.
"This place looks outstanding! What's been the biggest challenge to overcome?" I ask.
"Getting experts involved," he says plainly, walking away with a tape measure and a stack of thin books under his arm. I stand on a floor covered in bright blue Astroturf and lean with my back against a steel geometric catwalk railing.]

[0732.3 / 1850] [An artist works behind a glass window, refining a sophisticated water filtration technique. *"We've all been drinking discarded paint, drinking blood. We've had no idea what's been in our water supply and we're going to expose it,"* he says as a test completes wherein layers of fractal patterns of extracted toxic waste flow downstream from the plant in swirls of reds, purples, and white floral impressions. The complex geometric patterns of waste products are "peeled out," leaving purified drinking water.
I peek over a makeshift wall and discover a line of people queued up. Old, empty liquor bottles have been left as a reminder of "bad habits." A small Asian man looks lost so I give him directions,
"Go past the wall of giant tongue depressors / Popsicle sticks, then make a left."
He's with a partner. Much more occurs in this Robin Hood woodland fort as I rapidly float between rooms.] //

✦

Maj. = 3- THE CHILD: #0746
CHALLENGE: #0047, #0108, #0169
SOPHISTICATED: #0028, #0158, #0315
TOXIC: #0013, #0030

✦

#0733 - June 28, 2019 @ 08:23 (Sandusky, Ohio)

[0733.1 / 1851] [The dream is dynamic and full of quick, precise motion. The mood is supportive and loving. Action rises up quickly and then fades. A group of us pack in preparation for a long journey. THE WEAVER is intrigued by my collapsible cup and bowl. *"Wilderness survival tools are amazing,"* she says as I leave the items out for view on a round table. I have some items that don't fit into my pack, but I'm told to not worry as a woman gives me a hug and places her right middle finger on my tailbone for healing.] //

✦

Maj. = 0- THE WEAVER: #0734
TAILBONE: #0012
MIDDLE: #0309, #0336, #0360:

✦

#0734 - June 29, 2019 @ 06:54 (Beavercreek, Ohio)

[0734.1 / 1852] [I'm at a multi-level market where the guests are shuttled between levels in vacuum tubes and slides. I acquire beef jerky and other meat products that should last me a few days. Concession stands feature various types of beer. I give THE WEAVER a small peanut butter chocolate dessert bar in a small brown cardboard box then quickly head back up to a second-floor vendor to make another butcher shop purchase.] //

✦

Maj. = 0- THE WEAVER: #0736
BEEF: #0065, #0083
SECOND FLOOR: #0006, #0066, #0133, #0389

✦

#0735 - June 29, 2019 @ 08:13 (Beavercreek, Ohio)

[0735.1 / 1853] [I set up a makeshift emergency room on a snowy mountainside with two other men. As we set up curtains to separate patient spaces, I suggest hanging whiteboards on the 2'x4' stands to help doctors quickly identify patients and their conditions. We only have blue whiteboard markers. We work quickly until our shift ends at 4:00pm. We promptly depart the field.

THE DESERT NYMPH (*scholarly, seductive, and voluptuous*) asks for help moving trekking backpacks, but I decline. I watch a man perform L-Sit muscle ups on a set of nearby parallel bars. I turn to face out a window and run my energy while staring off at a tall fresh snow bank. After some time, I notice THE ICEMAN flash freezing flowers in fresh powder nearby.

I'm intrigued and want him to teach me his technique. He gives me a lesson in immortality. He teaches me how cold slows down time.]

[0735.2 / 1854] [I discover myself in an arts and crafts workshop where we're taught to weave small leather goods *(wallets/purses/etc.)*. A teacher creates an oversized model of a foldable trivet with 2" interwoven straps of brown and tan leather, and plastic. It's intended to help us see the detail and intricacy of the technique, which we're expected to copy at a much smaller scale.]

[0735.3 / 1855] [I make it back to the ER whiteboards and write the word "BLOW" *(swirled)* in blue marker. As I step away, I realize I should've written the word "BOWL" *(swirled)* instead.] //

✦

IMMORTAL: #0006
FIELD: #0006, #0008, #0010
SWIRL: #0249, #0360
THE DESERT NYMPH: #0871
THE ICEMAN: #1006

✦

#0736 - June 30, 2019 @ 06:24 (Beavercreek, Ohio)

[0736.1 / 1856] [The living room of my house seems like an outdoor courtyard. I spend some time deciding which way to orient my sleeping tent. I decide to set it up perpendicular to the Feng Shui of the room. THE WEAVER serves slices of vegetable pizza for breakfast which I declare are, "SAVORY!" I have a smooth skinned, muscularly toned Caucasian boyfriend. I ask him if he wants to have sex. He says he wants to top. This excites me so much I give myself a blowjob.] //

✦

Maj. = 0- THE WEAVER: #0746
BREAKFAST: #0017, #0019, #0124, #0171, #0382
SMOOTH SKIN: #0194

✦

#0737 - July 2, 2019 @ 06:31 (Beavercreek, Ohio)

[0737.1 / 1857] [I discover myself behind a chain link fence, waking up and getting dressed as a mass of people casually pass by. I'm preparing for my next assignment. THE CARPEN-TER's done similar work in the past and offers some insight as I ready myself. I've been tasked with leading the setup of an Olympic media outlet and television studio. The team my group will replace mid-stream attempts to rush the setup, to prove their competence. They achieved the desired outcome last cycle. The same approach won't work this time. They're failing.

The ramps on the media stage are fairly steep and complex to construct. It requires preci-

504

sion and care to unload and roll wooden carts down the ramps and place them appropriately around the site.]

[0737.2 / 1858] [THE TRIATHLETE (*entrepreneurial, team oriented, and engaging*) and his wife ride through on bikes. They've built their relationship on challenging each other to physical competitions.]

[0737.3 / 1859] [I quickly return to my makeshift dorm where I place an arm through a portal in the closet to reach under the media stage floor while attempting to grab a pair of clean socks. When I thrust my arm through, I don't notice the group of people sleeping side by side on the stage. The weight from above traps my arm and I'm unable to wiggle free. I'm not able to get my crew's attention as I wave helplessly out of sight.] //

⁎⁎

Maj. = 1- THE CARPENTER: #0740
CARE: #0206, #0250, #0306
STUDIO: #0085, #0175, #0191
SOCKS: #0021, #0040, #0083

⁎⁎

#0738 - July 3, 2019 @ 01:29 (Beavercreek, Ohio)

[0738.1 / 1860] [I'm in a reality where a debate participant who's losing can stop a discussion and concede by saying their opponent, *"drinks their own pee."* This exchange is considered polite in the new media.] //

⁎⁎

DEBATE: #0012, #0045, #0286
REALITY: #0019, #0023, #0024

⁎⁎

#0739 - July 3, 2019 @ 03:08 (Beavercreek, Ohio)

[0739.1 / 1861] [I'm asleep and awakened by a dark shadow tugging on my longest left toe. I begin hyperventilating on the floor when I notice a witch in my bed. I surround myself in gold bubbles.] //

⁎⁎

GOLD: #0119, 0124, #0125, #0127
FLOOR: #0098, #0100, #0101, #0107
SHADOW: #0006, #0035, #0086, #0092

⁎⁎

#0740 - July 3, 2019 @ 06:13 (Beavercreek, Ohio)

[0740.1 / 1862] [Chaos. Boys play basketball in front of a gated community. THE WILD-

CARD (*analytical, grieving, and accomplished*) lives in one of the homes. I'm embarrassed to disclose my long-term relationship status with THE WILDCARD to THE CARPENTER.]

[0740.2 / 1863] [I meet THE THINKER and THE FEELER in a parking lot. We drive trucks. THE FEELER has cancer, has miscarried, and is now pregnant again as she undergoes chemotherapy. I hug her and offer her any help she wants.] //

⁎⁎

Maj. = 1- THE CARPENTER: #0757
Min. = ♠- *THE THINKER: #0785*, ♣- *THE FEELER: #0785*
PREGNANT: #0041, #0117, #0189
RELATIONSHIP: #0181, #0197, #0382
CHAOS: #0367

⁎⁎

#0741 - July 4, 2019 @ 05:12 (Beavercreek, Ohio)

[0741.1 / 1864] [THE POLYMATH (*epicurean, experienced, and playful*) and I walk around a suburban plat on a sidewalk in a neighborhood called, "Kingswood Forest." We discuss starting a relationship. Initially, THE POLYMATH is more fervent and direct. I'm steady in my perspective.

"*I'm totally open to it, and I don't want any drama. I want the core of our relationship to be easy. I want it to be a refuge.*"

He walks a few steps ahead of me, occasionally turning toward me to ask, "*Am I less social than I was a year ago?*"

"*Yes, 90% less,*" I say, proceeding to respond to each round of questioning. He needs some convincing when I say, "*I love you.*"

We discover ourselves walking down the center aisle of a grocery store. The questioning continues. I'm distracted by oddly large, "SINGLE SERVING" dinner bowls that have foil pull back tops. They would easily feed a family.] //

⁎⁎

AISLE: #0034, #0053, #0149, #0201
I LOVE YOU: #0009, #0082, #0148, #0150
DRAMA: #0035, #0042, #0171, #0281
SUBURBAN: #0010, #0037, #0063, #0200

⁎⁎

#0742 - July 4, 2019 @ 07:11 (Beavercreek, Ohio)

[0742.1 / 1865] [I hover a couple inches outside of my body and see an outline filled with anatomical elements of my nervous system. I'm able to understand the way, "*neurotransmitters speak to and through the other systems of the body.*" I observe the interior of my body in a lab-like setting where I see the impact of various life situations (*work, romantic relationships, eating, physical activity, prayer, etc.*).]

. . .

[0742.2 / 1866] [I pass through a turnstile and enter/exit a public swimming pool multiple times wearing wet clothes.] //

⁎⁎

NERVOUS SYSTEM: #0031
WET CLOTHES: #0293
INCHES: #0022, #0031, #0045, #0125

⁎⁎

#0743 - July 5, 2019 @ 02:38 (Beavercreek, Ohio)

[0743.1 / 1867] [I'm on an airplane where passengers have a rigorous discussion about the use of gender pronouns. My family and I are the service staff that focuses on meticulously inventorying food and first aid on board. The priority changes. We begin stacking books tightly into overhead compartments. We complete the flight. As we disembark with our roller boards we're forced to return to our point of origin and repeat the flight without luggage. We're all confused by this sequence of events. It seems unnecessary and inefficient, but our opinions don't seem to matter.] //

⁎⁎
PRONOUNS: #0245
BOOKS: #0028, #0088, #0233, #0317, #0323
POINT OF ORIGIN: #0160
⁎⁎

#0744 - July 5, 2019 @ 08:08 (Beavercreek, Ohio)

[0744.1 / 1868] [It's the last day of college. I've overslept and will fail the final exam for a course I've previously failed. I've also confused myself by returning to a house where I'm no longer a tenant. I startle a young Asian woman when I enter the front door. She's leaving for work. She doesn't question my being in the house. An open laptop on a table in my former bedroom increases my confusion. I make flirty conversation with a gay couple who lounge nearby on a futon. We start playing around/hooking up until the identical twin of one of the men enters. I leave with the twin after I quickly change clothes. Walking across campus, I want to check my grades, but I don't know how to do it. I pass THE EPICUREAN sitting in an amphitheater, who's just aggressively "shhh'd" an annoying young man.]

[0744.2 / 1869] [THE CONSERVATIVE NEIGHBOR (*confident, opinionated, and righteous*) has retired. In his retired life he's an attendant to a short and slim childlike alien being. They walk out the back door of their home holding hands.] //

⁎⁎
Min. = ❤- THE EPICUREAN: #0748
SHHH: #0045, #0204, #0250
RETIRED: #0193
THE CONSERVATIVE NEIGHBOR: #1259
⁎⁎

#0745 - July 6, 2019 @ 06:22 (Beavercreek, Ohio)

[0745.1 / 1870] [I search for a Burning Man ticket. No one I know has one. I pile into the back of a 15-passenger van with a production crew. I seem to know the woman sitting next to me, who's quick to verbally confirm she's, *"annoyed by small children."* Artistically mutated cars are staged for a parade along a dusty road framed by skyscrapers.]

[0745.2 / 1871] [I quickly walk through the atrium of a mansion, passing a table of assorted objects. Beyond the table, ornaments line the edges of a pathway. *"Am I in the NOME KING's lair in "Return to Oz?""* Outside the hall, everything is a black void.]

[0745.3 / 1872] [I drive a car off a bridge, bank the vehicle, and swerve back on a lower segment of the bridge. Drifting out of bounds helped me to find a missing man exhaustedly clinging to the bridge by an elbow. He clutches a bike between his thighs. The water level has risen up to his neck. If I don't attempt saving him, he will surely drown.]

[0745.4 / 1873] [I'm on a soundstage to take a final exam. The exam's to be completed with a partner. Each member of the pair is supposed to have a different form in order to collabora- tively solve the cryptography segment. My female partner and I are flummoxed by the exam and fail. We raise an objection only after the proctor notices we've both been incorrectly issued the same form.] //

⁂

EXAM: # 0065, #0220

OFF A BRIDGE: #0365

15 PASSENGER VAN: #0038, #0069, #0204

⁂

#0746 - July 7, 2019 @ 01:00 (San Francisco, California)

[0746.1 / 1874] [We're in the home of an eccentric billionaire. We walk through the modern palatial estate where I take note of his extensive boot collection. He also boasts a marvelous fine art collection rivaled only by major museums. He is similar in size and stature to GEORGE WASHINGTON. He's bald on top and wears small round glasses. He points our attention to an area on the living room floor covered with a sectional couch to hide the space from which his prized Picasso was stolen. Prior to the theft people walked on the piece without their knowledge, as an intentional part of the interactive installation.

I tell him I know where the stolen Picasso is, and that I've noted its location in a dream journal entry. Internally, I cogitate on how I want to inform my peer that my, *"premonition about the rich guy on the news has come into reality."* The man's tone becomes more urgent. He's subletting the giant apartment while away on vacation. He's scheduled to leave in the morning. THE CHILD sits nearby playing with a remote control that operates a large hearth/fireplace. She giggles every time the propane tank spews a fireball. She cradles an injury to her belly under a set of overalls that she refuses to let us see.

The man returns with short purple hair, wearing a violet ZORRO mask and similarly colored aubergine suede jacket with beaded fringe.

"We enjoy the feeling of the fringe pressing on our faces," he says dragging a jacket sleeve oddly overhead like a set of miniature car wash bristles.

"He's a nice one," THE WEAVER whispers to me, implying I best ask him on a date. She's smitten.

At golden hour the purple fringe masked billionaire takes THE CHILD for a ride in a Bugatti down a dusty country road. THE WEAVER fills the gas tank when they return using an on-property fuel pump. Some gasoline sprays out of the tank, splashing carnival glass droplets in a nearby fish pond. Cattails pop up from the marsh. I turn the other direction and see JFK JR and a sister *(both middle aged)* talking about starting a new company. Both are on board a grounded antique AIR FORCE ONE. JACKIE O stands out of sight under a set of gymnasium bleachers, wearing a peach ensemble *(camisole, pillbox hat, and gloves)* silently admiring her children.] //

⁂

Maj. = 0- THE WEAVER: #0760, 3- THE CHILD: #0748
POND: #0129, #0277
MASK: #1076, #1083, #1196

⁂

#0747 - July 7, 2019 @ 03:42 (San Francisco, California)

[0747.1 / 1875] [I'm in a cafeteria line, flanked by young "bro-y" men who have been invited by a billionaire to compete for venture capital.

"Dude did you go to 'Garden Fest?' We were looking for you," one yacht-rocker guy *(khaki shorts, sandals, tan skin, blonde hair)* says to me as a waft of smoke from a skillet fried steak hits my nose. He discloses that he suffers from heroin addiction, but keeps his comments quiet so the man pan frying steak won't overhear. The chef *(and all other men in the scene)* are incredibly tall. I notice burns on the chef's legs where he mistakenly touched a hot stove or oven. A group of students stroll by proudly declaring their low-grade point average is evidence of, *"how stupid this university really is."* They seem self-aware of their stupidity and intellectual shortcomings.]

[0747.2 / 1876] [I'm in the basement headquarters of a burgeoning start up. All of the walls are clear glass. The family is present and working. I pass through a break room stacked floor to ceiling with tubs of snacks, no fewer than 20 of a particular item are on hand at any time. Inventory appears infinite. Jugs of S_____. Berries. Licorice. A conference room hidden toward a back corner is unlit and has an upright piano against a wall. The team *(including the family)* gathers in a conference room, where a desk houses an oval shaped piano/keyboard with translucent keys that light up when depressed.

VICTORIA BECKHAM is onsite to discuss a sponsorship proposal for the company. She's much shorter than I expected. She wears a clean line white pant suit and a nurse's hat. She's so small she actually tucks up under the desk in the conference room. I ask to take her photo but she doesn't consent. I'm bummed because I wanted to send it to THE JESTER with the caption, *"A MINOR MAJOR"* making a joke in reference to her vernacular, size, and the sound produced by the musical instrument on the desk.] //

⁎⁎

Min. = ◆- THE JESTER: #1096
SPONSORSHIP: #0227
STUPID: #0053, #0054
HEROIN: #0143, #0245

⁎⁎

#0748 - July 7, 2019 @ 05:26 (San Francisco, California)

[0748.1 / 1877] [I'm in an underground corridor, lit only in the segment where I stand. THE RADICAL FAERIE *(fluid, observant, and sexual)* lags behind a single turn, occupied with his own priorities. His dick hangs out from his shorts. I shout back that I'd give him a blowjob. I feel intoxicated. I'm not sure where I am.]

[0748.2 / 1878] [I pass through a gift shop being stocked for a 20th anniversary college reunion. "Welcome Back Class of 2001" banners hang overhead. Ball caps with a commemorative design are assumed to be the biggest sellers.]

[0748.3 / 1879] [On the lawn of a well-manicured Tudor manor THE EPICUREAN and another aristocratic gentleman *(with white hair and short beard)* openly debate who has the most eclectic peer group. Each lean back comfortably in white Adirondack chairs positioned near a small circular fire pit. It's unclear, but they may have talked all night.
The sun rises.
I enter the property and pass through an atrium, observing tile floors and stained glass bent around warped pieces of ancient wood, filled crudely with white plaster.
A father *(the son of the wealthy homeowner)* has been discharged from a rehab program to combat meth addiction and is kicked hard in the shin by his teen son at their initial reunion.]

[0748.4 / 1880] [THE CHILD is a backup dancer in a music video produced by her school. GRANDMA stands nearby wearing a light green shag rug inspired outfit. THE CHILD's break-dancing moves are quite impressive.]

[0748.5 / 1881] [All television channels are overtaken by DONALD TRUMP and scroll a list of every self-purported vote and order he's taken.
It's on all channels.
I'm annoyed as I fling the remote control at the screen.] //

⁎⁎

Maj. = 03- THE CHILD: #0749, 11- GRANDMA: #0780
Min. = ♥- THE EPICUREAN: #0757
DONALD TRUMP: #0795
REHAB: #0063

⁎⁎

#0749 - July 8, 2019 @ 04:00 (San Francisco, California)

[0749.1 / 1882] [I'm in an amphitheater. I'm surrounded by professionally dressed people who attend a global leadership summit, which doubles as a networking event. There's lots of chatter and handshaking between various motivational speakers. The theme of the conference centers on "convenience." I feel deep aversion to the theme rise up within me. As entrepreneurs espouse the benefits and efficiencies of their proposed applications, I take broad issue with the forum, declaring the service and experience economies as *"irresponsible and dependent on poor behavior. And all in all, bullshit."* Conversation ceases. Silence briefly reigns. I hear a pin drop.

The scene shifts and I discover the group has gathered at a sought after/trendy Brazilian steakhouse. The service team, furniture, food and utensils all seem giant sized. Perhaps we're all miniature, it's not clear. A large device holds 25 chickens in a 5x5 grid. A square of 24 roasts surrounds the 5x5, creating a 7x7 grid. It's heavy, hot, yet turned with ease from a fire pit to a presentation tray at the center of our table by our server.

THE DANCER, THE CHILD and I leave the table en route to the bathroom but instead enter an office with mahogany shelves and a stately roll top desk. We open the top desk drawer and find a payload of chocolate (*similar to Cadbury Flake*) segmented in two piles. 80% of the drawer holds chocolate with 80% cacao. The other 20% of the drawer has chocolate with 20% cacao.

Grilled chickens rest on the book shelves. All the chicken breasts have been cut off.

"Ugh, they're all blackened. I hate that," a random guy yells as he passes by.] //

⁎⁎

Maj. = 2- THE DANCER: #0751, 3- THE CHILD: #0751
DRAWER: #0017, #0039, #0073, #0086
SUMMIT: #0015, #0047, #0204

⁎⁎

#0750 - July 9, 2019 @ 00:21 (San Francisco, California)

[0750.1 / 1883] [I'm chased through a mansion. I've taken something and it's not clear whether I'm a hero or a villain. I fall out a window and land in a bramble bush. The scene restarts and now I'm in pursuit of myself. The quicker "Me" runs away and I stop following.]

[0750.2 / 1884] [I'm in the middle of a long stone corridor in a castle. I gymnastically descend through a Victorian-era boiler room. I look down and see a detective staring up expectantly towards me. I stop and feel fearful. A series of table sized playing cards, made of steel, painted, and sharpened like razors on all sides rise up and create a closing circle where my dangling legs will most certainly be sliced off. The detective is happy. The scene is exhausting and replays multiple times, with me winding up in situations that will substantially maim or kill me.] //

⁎⁎

CASTLE: #0836, #0871, #0904
WINDOW: #0906, #0912, #0926

⁎⁎

#0751 - July 9, 2019 @ 03:00 (San Francisco, California)

[0751.1 / 1885] [I'm in a large modern log cabin, staring out a giant rain spotted window that boasts a sunrise view of a serene mountain landscape. I turn to the right, descend a staircase and realize I'm in a retreat center lodge. I join a line of people, all blindfolded, who hold cafeteria trays waiting to be served breakfast. I've been here before. I sneak around looking for new rooms to explore, which irrationally seems dangerous. I find THE CHILD and THE DANCER in a bedroom. THE CHILD's happiness impedes her willingness to listen to "Mommy."] //

⁂

Maj. = 2- THE DANCER: #0755, 3- THE CHILD: #0775
SUNRISE: #0170

⁂

#0752 - July 9, 2019 2019 @ 04:45 (San Francisco, California)

[0752.1 / 1886] [I make my bed and prepare for the day. It feels like I live on a ranch in pioneer times.]

[0752.2 / 1887] [I sit at a counter in a 1950's malt shop and overhear two women outfitted in 1980's garb discuss and congratulate each other on their new jobs. It turns territorial for a moment when they discover they have to share management duties for an IKEA brick and mortar as a condition of their promotions. They decide to collaborate.]

[0752.3 / 1888] [I'm a cameraman for a documentary following BECK through the process of recording an album. I take a spiraling path in the air from the back of the recital hall to the stage to craft a shot that captures the essence of the artist.]

[0752.4 / 1889] [I read a newspaper article that discloses which drugs bands either currently take or have given up. NOFX is on their current tour without the help of steroids. WHITESNAKE is about to hit the road with a selection of erectile dysfunction meds (*small blue pills*).]

[0752.5 / 1890] [I'm backstage before a CELINE DION show. CELINE swims in an ivory lined pool, then takes a lukewarm shower. I've purchased a ticket, but am asked to play silent cameo roles of "Jesus" and "The Lion" in tonight's performance. I was hoping to sing. I hear CELINE critique a backup singer, *"No, you sing the lower third,"* as she dons an elf costume and heads towards the stage with an attendant. I would much rather sing.] //

⁂

JESUS: #1080
RANCH: #0124, #0175, #0323
LION: #0070, #0124, #0267, #037

⁂

512

#0753 - July 10, 2019 @ 05:25 (San Francisco, California)

[0753.1 / 1891] [I'm at a laundromat intent on washing precisely 20kg of clothing.]

[0753.2 / 1892] [I'm in a lit classroom on a black soundstage. I sit at a "Righty" desk working through an exam. THE TRANSLATOR enters, takes a seat on the teacher's desk and asks, *"So how are we doing?"* I realize I've checked in to the 2:00 am class. The first four questions on the test request I "fill in the blanks (0-10)." I've written "9" as my answer for all four items. The "correct" answer for all four is "10," but I'm given partial credit.

Another portion of the exam is disputed because of an unclear instruction on how to read test content. Two arrows pointing in different trajectories provide guidance. THE TRANSLATOR circles the arrow and taps the page with her pointer finger to provide a clue, but I don't understand.

Later, I'm relieved to learn I passed the test. A rich and well-dressed woman *(who looks like ENYA)* gives me a chauffeured ride home from class.] //

✷
✷✷

Maj. = 19- THE TRANSLATOR: #0759
GUIDANCE: #0070, #0391
INSTRUCTION: #0026, #0210
CREDIT: #0016, #0024, #0189, #0220, #0356
✷
✷✷

#0754 - July 10, 2019 @ 07:12 (San Francisco, California)

[0754.1 / 1893] ["BLACK BABIES!" is a controversial documentary and early favorite for the upcoming awards season. The film follows the lives of 10 children raised in the same house with the same access to nutrition and education. The outcomes 18 years later are disputed and deeply polarizing within the court of public opinion.]

[0754.2 / 1894] [A temple construction crew fills out forms in pursuit of grant funding. I'm responsible for distributing and collecting the forms.]

[0754.3 / 1895] [I've created an expose that demonstrates it costs $435K to get your preferred legislation to the floor of the US House and Senate. That amount gets your opinion prioritized over every pending VA appeal in the queue for lawmaker review. That payoff also gets you 15 minutes of facetime with your elected official.] //

✷
✷✷
DOCUMENTARY: #0027, #0060, #0063
GRANT: #0217, #0250, #0359
QUEUE: #0027, #0032, #0094, #0396
✷
✷✷

#0755 - July 11, 2019 @ 04:11 (San Francisco California)

[0755.1 / 1896] [I'm at a party attempting to buy drinks. I have a stack of $20 bills that stick together. I'm unable to separate them. The vendor refuses to complete the sale and I leave empty handed. No one else will accept my "sticky dollars." No matter though, all that's available for purchase is cheap nutrient deficient food that people overpay for and begrudgingly force down their throats. I'm particularly repulsed by cheap loose meat sandwiches / sloppy joes that bleed grease through round white paper plates.]

[0755.2 / 1897] [THE MAGICIAN purchases ride coupons for a group of children, then promptly disappears in a puff of smoke.]

[0755.3 / 1898] [A brick wall with a skyline backdrop has a large brocade curtain suspended in front of it like a screen. A one million candle power search lamp focused on the curtain reveals x-ray-like silhouettes of performers who act out scenes from silent films. A Wurlitzer organ provides accompaniment. THE DANCER and I discover ourselves backstage and thrust into the limelight. Our task is to act out a love scene between a man and a woman. Our faces can't be seen. We're able to fake a passionate kiss by placing a hand between our mouths. I still find it gross to come in that close of contact with my sister's mouth. She feels the same way about me.]

[0755.4 / 1899] [I'm going on a six-week global sojourn. As I plan, I'm concerned that at its conclusion I won't be able to gain entry to the United States. That fear subsides as I consider the places I want to go, things I want to experience in London, and places I wish to enjoy on the south easterly coast of Romania.]

[0755.5 / 1900] [I stand at a doorway at the back of a concert venue. I hold the door and encourage others to pass me. THE CHEERLEADER (effervescent, compact, and directive) is among those I recognize. A bro-y, blonde haired, muscular guy sets up food stations on buffet tables. We're attending his party and he's delighted to set everything up for his guests. A guest picks on "the popular kid" by holding the popular kid's face in front of a handheld device. Two small saucers and a red/black set of pipes splash water spun by silver spheres collected in the saucers into the restrained person's face.]

[0755.6 / 1901] [THE DANCER puts a CD in a stereo under an industrial bridge next to the venue at dawn. Gold green light enhances the smell of freshly cut grass. The stereo is placed on damp gravel. The song, "DOWN IN IT" by NINE INCH NAILS plays. The CD is scratched and skips. I'm annoyed. I love that song.] //

*
**

Maj. = 2- THE DANCER: #0758, 14- THE MAGICIAN: #0858
NINE INCH NAILS: #0857
LOOSE: #0024, #0026, #0034, #0080, #0348, #0356
CD: #0070, #0169

*
**

#0756 - July 11, 2019 @ 06:40 (San Francisco, California)

[0756.1 / 1902] [*"Those particular boxes are extremely popular in Tanzania,"* a familiar feminine voice says behind my left ear, referencing a grid full of refrigerated yogurt and granola products. Empty promotional cases made of colorful printed cardboard indicate the store has sold out, though a line remains to purchase inbound stock.
"Welcome back!" I exclaim as I turn around and see an unfamiliar face.]

[0756.2 / 1903] [I'm in a cellar beneath a country farmhouse looking through multiple bushel baskets of ripe fruit. I select peaches that I can stick my entire thumb in and am also keen to inspect bananas with the correct proportion of "sugar freckles." I carry an armful up to the main house and make breakfast smoothies with THE CONFIDANT. Next to the kitchen sits a row of desks, atop one of which I've placed the extra fruit. In a parallel row to the desks are a series of hospital beds. All are sterile and ready to take new patients.]

[0756.3 / 1904] [I spend a brief time in a pastel-colored future world, driven by artificial intelligence. A large interface is placed in front of me and I'm told to admire the wiggling heart graphics on the chests of my friend's avatars. It's sweet and simple. People here seem to be happy.] //

☆☆

Maj. = 16- THE CONFIDANT: #0782
SMOOTHIES: #0053, #0054

☆☆

#0757 - July 12, 2019 @ 01:51 (San Francisco, California)

[0757.1 / 1905] [*CRASH! * *INJURIES! * *INSTANT DEATHS! * I'm inside a castle on a bright sunny day. A wall of the castle collapses inward. People on a catwalk/ledge fall. Those underneath are crushed and immediately killed. I hear their screams and can feel their bones break in the roots of my teeth. At least 20 people have died. A few could be rescued from the rubble. I'm able to assist and direct EMT's and other first responders as they arrive on scene of the mass casualty event. One of the female first responders is 100% dismissive of my insight and support.]

[0757.2 / 1906] [A muscular female bodybuilder in a pink bikini flexes repeatedly in front of me. She seems unnecessarily tan.]

[0757.3 / 1907] [A second building collapse occurs. The dismissive EMT suffers a crush injury when her leg becomes trapped under a mass of stone. I text THE EPICUREAN to troubleshoot. He's certain our friendship is dying. I assure him it's not while seeking advice on how to support someone who doesn't want help.]

. . .

[0757.4 / 1908] [I purchase a five-string bass for my new role in a rock band. THE CARPEN-TER's at the store and supportive of my career choice. He suggests six and seven string basses, but I laugh and call the idea absurd. I've narrowed down the color choices for the instrument to red, blue and black. I'm pretty much sold on the black one because it looks, *"Metal as fuck."* Once I select an instrument, I'm given a complimentary marijuana Popsicle. I don't want it and politely refuse. The flavor would be revolting. BLECK! I hear a rumble and the floor shakes. A third wall of the castle has collapsed, out of view.] //

※※

Maj. = 1- THE CARPENTER: #0763
Min. = ♥- THE EPICUREAN: #0998
RUBBLE: #0053, #0157

※※

#0758 - July 12, 2019 @ 04:57 (San Francisco, California)

[0758.1 / 1909] [I sit on a stone staircase leading up to a large cathedral with two older Black women. We attend a midweek choir rehearsal for weekend services.]

[0758.2 / 1910] [I hydroplane with THE DANCER who criticizes, *"Anyone using therapeutic services at a church is usurious!"* Our car spins around six times.]

[0758.3 / 1911] [People are all in S_____ while on retreat.]

[0758.4 / 1912] [I'm apprehensive about pending test results.]

[0758.5 / 1913] [L_____ family sings in the church choir.] //

※※

Maj. = 2- THE DANCER: #0764
RESULTS: #0036, #0047, #0064, #0069, #0134
CHOIR: 0023, #0030, #0347, #0384

※※

⁂ 10.3 - THE BOOK OF ARGO: 0759-0804 ⁂

#0759 - July 12, 2019 @ 06:49 (San Francisco, California)

[0759.1 / 1914] [I walk towards two men riding bikes, who approach from the opposite direction. I turn sideways to squeeze between them as they quickly roll by.]

[0759.2 / 1915] [I spend an eternity ugly crying. I'm alone. Everything around me is black and empty. I feel as though I've utterly wasted my life. I feel lost.
"HELP ME, CREATOR!" I cry out as I extend my arms up towards a sky that isn't there.]

[0759.3 / 1916] [I'm at a brunch. The event is held in the recessed level of a tri-level home. Many familiar faces work to change out hotel pans of food on the buffet. Brunch is still being served, but the final hotel pans have just left the kitchen. THE DEVOTEE lets me grab an oversized cinnamon roll as she passes by wearing oven mitts while she carries the pan. I realize I'm dreaming and run upstairs to find a pen so I can write everything down. I find a pile of pens in a desk drawer, but none of them produce ink when I scribble which leaves me feeling frustrated.
I swing around the center pole of a spiral staircase by my left hand and float down, body parallel to the floor. At the bottom I encounter a family with a dog, who've arrived to clean up after brunch concludes. It's their house, after all. I've finished my work and leave the property with the family's blessing. I step out on to a stone staircase and briefly encounter THE TRANSLATOR. After a pregnant pause she says, *"Let's get a drink some time,"* then ducks into an Uber and heads home. I find it odd that twilight has just shifted to dark and remain puzzled but satisfied as I wake up.] //

⁂

Maj. = 19- THE TRANSLATOR: #0782
Min. = ♠- THE DEVOTEE: #0896
CREATOR: #0071, #0143, #0153, #0166, #0175, #0204, #0271
BRUNCH: #0306
TRI-LEVEL: #0036, #0101
CINNAMON ROLL: #0294, #0334

⁂

#0760 - July 13, 2019 @ 05:04 (San Francisco, California)

[0760.1 / 1917] [THE PARATROOPER *(confident, patriotic, and rugged)* breaks his left leg below the knee in an accident. When he looks at me, we immediately change bodies. He gets up and walks away. I look down and see my new leg dangle like jelly from femur to foot as I hoist its dead weight up from behind my knee. I'm injured. I'm sad. I cry. I spent so much time and effort sculpting the physical body that my friend's spirit just walked away using. The crippling injury in THE PARATROOPER's legacy body renders me without an identity. Mobility and dexterity both minimized, I have no experience of pain but rather a dead, heavy, fleshy marionette leg.
I wait hours for transport to a hospital. A woman at the house seems to have some level of

517

nursing skill, but she and others on the scene don't know specifically what to do. They dismiss my suggestions for splinting and immobilizing the limb. Another woman sits nearby on the grass. She's suffered a similar injury and never recovered. The leg injury ruined her life. Repeated jostling of her unset bones resulted in tiny calcium fragments cutting through the supporting muscles of her leg like a serrated knife, rendering her entire leg useless.]

[0760.2 / 1918] [A crazed drunken woman erratically drives a white Lamborghini. I leave my body and over float near the car as she spins donuts in the dust. I scribble with a black paint marker from the passenger window down the side of the vehicle all the way to the trunk. The car continues to spin in a parking lot.

"GO IN THE HOUSE! GET INSIDE NOW!!" I scream to THE WEAVER.

We don't know what the woman wants from us.] //

✺

Maj. = 0- THE WEAVER: #0763
RUINED: #0026, #0154, #0204, #0320
LEAVE MY BODY: #0009, #0045, #0093, #0101, #0301
DEAD: #0151, #0162, #0172
THE PARATROOPER: #1059

✺

#0761 - July 14, 2019 @ 05:03 (San Francisco, California)

[0761.1 / 1919] [A single Nazi stands in a public square shouting hateful speech. The words aren't given any attention by the large mass of people funneling around the square in all directions. Those who notice his presence encourage him to keep speaking so they'll know exactly where he is at all times.]

[0761.2 / 1920] [A group of artists discuss collaborating with a "genius" on a future feature film. The "genius" is of Indian heritage, and seems to favor GEORGE LUCAS in his general appearance.]

[0761.3 / 1921] [THE FILM "DICK TRACY" is remade as a combination live action/animation feature similar to "Who Framed Roger Rabbit." Critics chatter about the CGI version of "Breathless Mahoney" perfectly matching the artistic tone of the film's intended time period. Public frenzy towards the character is on par with HEIDI KLUM's Halloween homage to cartoon bombshell JESSICA RABBIT. HEIDI already plans to create a similar "Breathless" honorarium with her Halloween costume later this year.] //

✺

SQUARE: #0004, #0006, #0040, #0043
GENIUS: #0040, #0048, #0060, #0100
PRESENCE: #0015, #0082, #0101, #0298, #0393
JESSICA RABBIT: #0960

✺

#0762 - July 14, 2019 @ 05:32 (San Francisco, California)

[0762.1 / 1922] [I'm on an airplane that banks strongly to the right immediately after take-off. It attempts to ascend by executing a helix maneuver on its side, but this doesn't yield any additional height. I'm over beautifully blue Bahamian waters en route to a movie premiere.]

[0762.2 / 1923] [I'm a photographer at a red-carpet event, celebrating the film directed by the Indian man in dream [0761.2 / 1920]. No one can believe the young seeming director is actually 77 years old. Adding to the astonishment and confusion is a comment made during an interview that he's RICHARD GERE's uncle. The interviewer doesn't know what to make of the statement.]

[0762.3 / 1924] [TRENT REZNOR gives a snarky interview while smoking a cigarette. *"It's always a special day when someone does something 'genius level' like repackage and distribute something as 'new.' Like the standard form country pop single. What...the same thing has made it to number 1 six times? Seven?"* He blows smoke in the interviewer's face and snuffs out the cigarette in a round gold foil Burger King ashtray.]

[0762.4 / 1925] [A witness for a major case is treated with hostility by THE CONNECTOR. She returns to court after a recess where she was permitted to remove a box truck from an evidence warehouse, drive it around the city, and then return it. I exit the courtroom, and mistakenly leave my ID behind. THE CONNECTOR whistles from behind me to get my attention. She promptly brings me my ID, curtailing any need to backtrack.]

[0762.5 / 1926] [I walk briskly down a set of wooden bleachers in a dark gymnasium. I'm halted mid-stride by an invisible force. I recognize it's my guide, "L." No words are spoken, but I'm given a very clear instruction: *"DON'T SKIP ANY STEPS."*] //

⁂

Maj. = 4- THE CONNECTOR: #0772
MAJOR: #0026, #0077, #0125
WOODEN: #0380, #0396
EVIDENCE: #0260, #0278

⁂

#0763 - July 15, 2019 @ 04:00 (San Francisco, California)

[0763.1 / 1927] [Mid-discussion with THE WORLDBRIDGER, I direct my attention towards a playing card size image of an exalted woman named "Q." She emerges from the card, grabs my hand, and takes me on a rapid journey across space and time that I don't fully grasp, nor understand.
Images flash in rapid succession so quickly that they blur into pulsar-like clicks of diamond light. The cosmic flip book of images slows to a homesteader's scene displaying

THE POSTMASTER and THE FARMHAND. "Q" and I pause to look at each other and smile, but say nothing.

The pages of the flipbook advance as if blown by the wind until "Q" stops it on a picture of a messy house where THE LAWYER and THE DULCE DE LECHE (conflicted, dramatic, and afraid) live together in squalor. Garbage is scattered on the floor. Feces (human and pet) has been ground into the carpet. The circumstances aren't lovely.

Another flipbook image shows me side by side with a guy who's completely missing both legs. He uses a skateboard and his hands to roll back home from a trip to the grocery store, with a plastic bag full of milk and break set just in front of his torso. I flirt with him. He's my partner, lover and best friend.

Another page shows me on a white-water raft with my family. I'm a teenager. I'm sitting between THE WEAVER and THE CARPENTER who laugh as we race extremely fast through the course of rapids. I'm concerned my phone will be ruined by the water.

Another yet, shows me with friends eating ice cream bars frozen to solid chocolate tongue depressors that melt in our hands.

The next flip shows me at the feet of "FarMor's" parents in the 1950's watching THE CATHOLIC (age 5) throw a tantrum at a funeral.

"Q" closes the book. I take the cue I need to write down as much of this interaction as I can recall. I scribble pen to paper 6-7 times before the ink starts to flow. I get a few pages of detail recorded before I pause and realize I'm still dreaming, which wakes me up.] //

✷

Maj. = 0- THE WEAVER: #0764, 1- THE CARPENTER: #0764,
5- THE LAWYER: #0810, 7- THE WORLDBRIDGER: #0771
Min. = ♥- THE FARMHAND: #1107, ♣- THE POSTMASTER: #0905,
♣- THE CATHOLIC: #1117, ♣- THE DULCE DE LECHE: #1205
FUNERAL: #0124
DETAIL: #0044, #0185
FAMILY: #0096, #0112.

✷

#0764- July 15, 2019 @ 06:06 (San Francisco, California)

[0764.1 / 1928] [I observe an odd clinical, grisly scene where a large aquarium full of blood is, "raked for plasma." Small bands of white and yellow separate from the vat of red liquid as it coagulates. The process functions as designed.]

[0764.2 / 1929] [I'm outside THE WEAVER and THE CARPENTER's house at night. I'm drawn toward an odd "haunted passageway," at the right side of the property. I turn the knob on the peculiar ¾ sized door. Its paint shifts from deep red to green tones like an ink bomb dropped in water. The door remains locked. I can't go in.]

[0764.3 / 1930] [I tour a village in Switzerland and take an excursion to experience views from a central observation platform. The top of the platform is surrounded by a thrill ride made of L shaped bars that swing, extend and spin outwards from the center like spokes on a bike wheel around the stationary deck. Those who choose to ride can only reenter the deck via a small 2′ x 3′ rectangular opening, which must be precisely targeted, else riders risk either slamming into a window or sliding across and off the top of the building where they'll fall hundreds of feet to their death. When I ride, I suffer the fall. The adrenaline rush to the ground mitigates any pain I feel when my bones crush on impact. One of my eyes flickers. It's cloudy and cold. I catch intermittent, non-centered images of the town square. My body powers down like a camcorder with a dying battery set randomly on the street.]

[0764.4 / 1931] [I observe a team of inspectors audit a family-owned restaurant. An employee makes futile attempts to mop an open courtyard as it rains down from the night sky, like a polite version of "Kitchen Nightmares." The inspectors sit at a long table and are served obscenely large portions of ham (*5lb per plate*). One inspector eats a bowl of green peas as the group trash talks the quality and presentation of the food. They're disgusted to learn the same black plastic basins used to wash dishes also serve as the customer restroom. The building has no plumbing.]

[0764.5 / 1932] [I am 8 years old. I'm in a double occupancy hotel room, sitting on a bed. THE CARPENTER hands THE DANCER and I each ½ of an oatmeal snack bar saying, *"THE WEAVER said give this to you before you dogpile."* I sit and eat my half, eyeballing a small brown paper bag, full of specialty chocolates. *"THE WEAVER knows best. You don't,"* is scribbled on the bag in tiny black letters. The bag rests on a mirrored vanity.] //

⁂

Maj. = *0-THE WEAVER: #0775, 1-THE CARPENTER: #0775, 2-THE DANCER: # 0775*
GREEN PEAS: #0088
DISGUSTED: #0044
SWITZERLAND: #0097, #0098, #0141
BROWN: #0035, #0084, #0086, #0098

⁂

#0765 - July 16, 2019 @ 03:45 (San Francisco, California)
* I enjoyed this dream tremendously. It was so vivid I believed I was awake. *

[0765.1 / 1933] [I'm on a light and enjoyable tour of an eastern European country. I share a house with a group where the hosts nickel and dime me throughout my stay. We're offered excursions that can be taken individually. I select one that takes me to a dilapidated and graffiti covered concrete wall that extends for miles. I have different guides at different moments by the wall. Some are male. Some are female. It's possible I'm in the Czech Republic. I may have lost my passport, but that doesn't seem to matter.]

[0765.2 / 1934] [I enter a large venue and am offered an impromptu job as a cameraman for BEYONCÉ on her upcoming tour. She rehearses on a catwalk on a dark soundstage. We have tremendous fun framing different angles and stage marks as she flips her hair and experiments with various walks, hand gestures and eye contact. The experience is so immersive I forget the Czech Republic trip. For a moment I feel frustrated and sad. I quickly center and create another moment on stage with BEYONCE. I remind myself, *"I'm the stand in"* to stay humble.] //

⁂

BEYONCÉ: #0770
CZECH: #0093, #0184
SOUNDSTAGE: #0066
PASSPORT: #0122, #0182
⁂

#0766 - July 16, 2019 @ 06:00 (San Francisco, California)

[07661.1 / 1935] [*THIS DREAM UNINTENTIONALLY LEFT BLANK*] //

⁂

LEFT: #0193, #0199, #0200, #0204, #0210
BLANK: #0033, #0037, #0186
⁂

#0767 - July 16, 2019 @ 06:53 (San Francisco, California)

[0767.1 / 1936] [I'm at the "best" party of the year. It takes place on a cobblestone court-yard on the penthouse level of a downtown building. A young woman in a pastel blue skirt walks by. *"I love your glasses,"* I shout as she winks at me. The crowd is mostly 20 somethings in casual dress. HILLARY CLINTON and another blonde woman enter wearing green evening gowns. They engage in a playful argument about, *"who gets the first hug and who gets the most hugs?"* I don't hug either of them. I'm more interested in finding my music composer friend.

Cool tracks groove in the background at low volume. I'm eventually informed it's my friend's work. I'm dedicated to finding him. I want to collaborate. I want to learn how he constructed the piece shared at the party. I figure he's already moved on to a bunch of other projects. I'm mostly thrilled to know someone who has the patience and precision to create something complex that simultaneously seems like simple, accessible pop music. What does it require to exist at such a level of full-on auditory wizardry?

I open a door to the back exit. I look down from a fire escape stairwell and see a ¾ full pizza box dropped into the alley below. A tan woman with long brown hair, giant breasts, and wearing a lime green bikini top suspends herself across two stairwells by her hands in an "iron cross" expression as she talks to me.

"There is so much I've let go of. So much more I want to remember. I hope I have the opportunity to return to this reality and remember more. Please let me come back to visit, when aligned." I ask God.] //

⁂

HILLARY CLINTON: #0792
COLLABORATE: #0062, #0114, #0158, #0326
PIZZA: #0006, #0045, #0104, #0123
GOD: #0080, #0143, #0172, #0386
⁂

#0768 - July 17, 2019 @ 04:11 (San Francisco, California)

[0768.1 / 1937] [I'm oriented toward violence, as an objection to racism. The cadence of images I'm shown is rapid and confusing. I confront two men deeply kissing while wearing KKK robes. It's dark. They're not wearing hoods. I'm shocked to discover two Black men.
"Is this what you want to be remembered for? Is this your legacy?" I shout at them chest forward and arms flared back.
Next to the men is a purple and pink glitter glass topped coffee table which has been fully covered in a thin "clear black" top coat. I use the blade of a steak knife to scrape away dry black paint. The cut swirls and scraped patterns expose tiny glitter skulls and pica pica anime graphics. The tone is childlike and juvenile.]

[0768.2 / 1938] [THE PROMOTER (*polished, influential, and focused*) and I stand curbside to a suburban housing plat, sharing conversation. THE PROMOTER's son rides by us slowly on a bicycle. It becomes clear the KKK spectacle was related to a college fraternity recruitment event. THE PROMOTER's son is embarrassed because he had intended (*for a time prior to the expose*) to rush the racist, self-hating organization.
I give him a tip on how to, *"best smoke out organizational absurdity,"* whispering quietly in his right ear as he pedals by.
THE PROMOTER and I have agreed to buy groceries for a brunch, with a shared intention of exposing the incongruence and integrity bleeds in a different peer group with whom we're affiliated. The reckoning will come later. Right now, we're focused on how delicious our pancakes, waffles and mimosas will be.] //

⁎⁎

GLITTER: #0014, #0064
LEGACY: #0040
RAPID: #0158, #0306, #0400
THE PROMOTER: #1131

⁎⁎

#0769 - July 18, 2019 @ 01:41 (San Francisco, California)

[0769.1 / 1939] [I'm at an amusement park. The family is present. We're having fun together, but I go on a mission by myself. The park is vacant aside from the ride operators. I'm a roller coaster tester. My job is to ride in every seat, of every train, of every ride. The current ride has a challenge. I have to push the train partially up the hill to get it to catch the lift chain. It takes precision to hop back in, as the train darts up the hill at tremendous speed.
I'm responsible for latching my own lap belt and harness, as the train zooms vertically hundreds of feet. I repeat this process 20+ times. On one pass, I exit the train and rush to grab carnival plush toys from shopping bags set off to the side. I hold a toy under each arm, realizing there's a seat at the front of the train I haven't yet tested. I debate putting the toys down as I watch the train speed away. No loss. The next train inbounds immediately. There's no queue for the attraction. Waiting for the next train is the sensible choice.
I repeat this process for multiple other massive coasters. I find it a quite fulfilling job.
On another attraction, I discover three loose classroom chairs insufficiently bolted to the train car. They bounce and topple erratically when the ride is in motion. I make a detailed

note and recommend that the ride be put through additional rounds of testing before being opened for public use.

One ride is designed for families with large bodies.

Another makes special considerations to accommodate people with disabilities.] //

☆☆

AMUSEMENT PARK: #0274, #0308, #0339, #0376
PLUSH: #0009, #0084, #0128
FULFILLING: #0039
TOYS: #0010, #0121

☆☆

#0770 - July 18, 2019 @ 03:04 (San Francisco, California)

[0770.1 / 1940] [BEYONCÉ and BLUE IVY stand in front of a steel garage door as it rolls up, swarmed by paparazzi.]

[0770.2 / 1941] [THE PELVIS *(evocative, and sensual)* and THE PORTRAIT ARTIST *(reverent, calm, and observant)* lead a twister-like game where the score is tabulated on an odd image of a spine that's been disembodied from tailbone to skull. Players straddle and step to large brown, orange, yellow and tan colored pill shaped platforms suspended over a deep chasm.]

[0770.3 / 1942] [I meet THE EVIL TWIN *(wily, tricky, and fun-loving)* and another guy at the top of a staircase. *"We're heading back into the park to ride other rides. You should join us!"* they shout over a BEASTIE BOYS mixtape blaring from a vintage ghetto blaster.

The words from the song are absurd and I laugh out loud. I surf down a sparkly white granite staircase, momentarily confused by THE EVIL TWIN who now emerges from the bottom of the spiral staircase in the opposite direction. I'm flummoxed, having just walked away from him above board. He's pranked me well.

"Go doppelganger!"] //

☆☆

BEYONCÉ: #0974
BLUE IVY: #1213
BEASTIE BOYS: #1193
SPIRAL STAIRCASE: #0044, #0056, #0083, #0120
PILL: #0084, #0112, #0151, #0183
SPINE: #0077, #0231, #0376
TWISTER: #0317

☆☆

#0771 - July 18, 2019 @ 04:45 (San Francisco, California)

[0771.1 / 1943] [People walk into a room with prizes under their arms, along with a baby. They're ready to have a food eating contest. I sit on the floor and work on putting my left foot behind my head, while sitting up as straight as possible. I'm even leaning backwards a little bit to give myself deliciously deep psoas stretch.]

[0771.2 / 1944] [I have a 1:1 healing session with THE WORLDBRIDGER. He's supportive of my growth. We spend a great deal of time in uninterrupted eye contact while his hands are placed on my head. *"I don't know if you should be in level 4. Maybe you should go back to Level 3."* I concurrently say *"5,"* in my head and am a bit perplexed by the invitation to go backwards. Then I notice a karmic cord of energy tied between my 3rd and 8th chakras.
"Oh, THE NEUTRAL GUIDE helped me find this once before. Suppose it's time to get rid of this old concept again." I cut the cord. We create healing. My next steps become obvious.] //

⁎⁎

Maj. = 7 -THE WORLDBRIDGER: # 0792
Min. = ♥- THE NEUTRAL GUIDE: #0773
BACKWARDS: #0015, #0140, #0168, #0235, #0392
LEVEL: #0231, #0249, #0293

⁎⁎

#0772 - July 19, 2019 @ 05:12 (San Francisco, California)

[0772.1 / 1945] [I participate in a contest with two other people. We are prompted to select either a sledgehammer or an axe, and for a limited period, demonstrate which can best destroy an automobile.]

[0772.2 / 1946] [THE ACTOR is in town for the summer. We make plans to get together for a "catch up" drink downtown. He's happily living the thespian's life, taking roles with regional theater companies around the country. He's particularly lit up by the mention of a guy named "Roland." A woman passes us and winks at THE ACTOR. He winks back, and then for "Good Luck" he decides to give her his autograph. He scribbles one on a napkin, another on a bar coaster, then hands them both to me. He holds a series of paint markers in his hand.
"Champion. Like me," he says, noting the brand name of the markers and pointing his thumb to his chest.
We leave the hotel bar and share a few final moments on a staircase chatting.
"Yeah, the thing with "Roland" just sort of happened. We started chatting. Occasionally, we spent nights with each other. Now we're pretty much together every weekend. I guess that means something?" Our exchange is sweet and fun. I'm delighted THE ACTOR's so taken by being in this coupled up situation.]

[0772.3 / 1947] [THE CONNECTOR and I move a rented Aston Martin through a narrow serpentine passage composed of large cube concrete barricades placed on opposite sides of the street. I drive the vehicle 5mph and stop when I feel the driver's side door grind on the edge of a block. Our task is to move the concept car from an interior display space to a busy city street outside. I think it's been scratched but upon inspection, don't find any exterior damage. THE CONNECTOR grabs the keys and takes the car for a joyride. She squeals the tires and spins a couple donuts before speeding away.] //

⁕

Maj. = 4- THE CONNECTOR: #0773, 10- THE ACTOR: #0837
AUTOGRAPH: #0244
CHAMPION: #0126
KEYS: #0023, #0046, #0219

⁕

#0773 - July 19, 2019 @ 09:21 (San Francisco, California)

[0773.1 / 1948] [Abstraction of four Saudi Arabian princes *(men of different sizes, shape and disposition)* all sitting on the edge of a palace catwalk, laughing and joking. The fat bearded one picks on his smaller statured brothers. It's late afternoon, sunny, dusty and smells of hookah smoke.]

[0773.2 / 1949] [I hover above a game show set. The WHEEL OF FORTUNE is submerged in a pool of water. The wheel segments are large enough for people to swim in.
   I pass two parents pushing their special needs child in a motorized carriage along a catwalk above the set. VANNA WHITE waves up to us from down in the water.]

[0773.3 / 1950] [I'm at a Walmart-like store. A missing iPad has been turned in to customer service and casts a series of my personal photos on to all the demonstration TV screens around the entire store.
   I stand in line. The woman in front of me verifies another found tablet computer as her own, based on the bas relief floral case. I briefly interact with a neighbor who only wants to be called by a new self-assigned nickname. I advance in line and notice that the screens now stream video from a sex party I attended.
   I see my blue purple hat sail through a crowd of naked testosterone laden bodies.
   I leave the line and go to the basement in search of a bathroom. I encounter THE NEUTRAL GUIDE and realize I don't have a hat on. My hair is disheveled. I need to use the bathroom. I realize I'm shoeless and have to daintily tiptoe across the white tile floor to avoid stepping in piles of shit.
   When I finish, I return upstairs and am stopped by THE CONNECTOR. She comments that she, *"needs to get accustomed to being 'in charge of you,' on the crew."*
   We've gone grocery shopping. She's allowed everyone on her team to take possession of a "Crew Card."
   She realizes the cards are linked to her personal checking account. No spending limits have been set as people run around the store filling up carts with food and supplies.
   A female associate expels a rowdy woman from the store for aggressively complaining to customer service.] //

⁕

Maj. = 4- THE CONNECTOR: #0800
(mind the gap)
Min. = ♥-THE NEUTRAL GUIDE: #1178

⁕

#0774 - July 20, 2019 @ 05:32 (San Francisco, California)

[0774.1 / 1951] [I'm super stoked to have box seats for an APHEX TWIN show. Me and my crew have an awesome view up and left from the stage. The house lights go down and the opening performer begins to warm up the crowd. RICHARD DAVID JAMES occupies a suite directly beneath my box. I lean over and take photographs, which he encourages. He departs for the stage. I tumble over the side railing of the box and roll to the ceiling beneath where I walk down a wall and into the artist's suite.

The space is set up to stimulate creativity. It's full of carefully placed, prized effects including an original STORMTROOPER mask prop, and a series of daguerreotype photos of corpses. I realize I'm being surveilled as I snap photos for my own amusement and posterity. I've been in this room many times before. I'm tickled by the novelty and call THE ATHEIST and THE PILOT to, *"Come down and check this shit out. It's amazing."* My attention is drawn to a black t-shirt with white letters on it. It reads, "IMBECILE," a relic from my long-disbanded garage band now an oddly cherished artifact owned by a musical genius. I'm confused as to how he would have gotten it. I take it.

The music starts. The crowd is active and roars. Visuals to accompany the music are generated in real time from candid images texted to a server by the crowd. Faces in the images are upsettingly distorted in expectedly jarring ways. A heterosexual Asian couple take the stage and create an interpretive dance.]

[0774.2 / 1952] [I'm on a walk through a tunnel down a mountain pathway. THE PILGRIM *(seeking, contrary, and aware)* walks next to me. She guides me around a large man who steps in front of us. He intends to block us. She mentions a law that compels the man to stand aside and give us instant access to a secret trailhead. Once on the path we're overwhelmed by the beauty of the rivers, streams, and carnival glass walkways that extend shimmering through a serene valley.]

[0774.3 / 1953] [I work on a building maintenance project next to a grand cathedral. Someone on site is incredibly insistent that I not proceed. They prefer I take a very clear and narrow path in the opposite direction. I have a special laminated credential hanging from my neck on a gold lanyard which allows me to stay on my original course.]

[0774.4 / 1954] [Someone works on a ballistic device that will chip away at the exterior of buildings. Tests for the machine are executed on a long-paved corridor. The device shoots hotdog-like projectiles. They bounce off the walls without producing any damage. The man running the test morphs into a woman who speaks angrily in a Russian dialect.] //

✲✲

Maj. = 6- THE PILOT: #1001, 8- THE ATHEIST: #0777
GLASS: #0071, #0079, #0080
CORRIDOR: #0026, #0038, #0054
MUSIC: #0371, #0385, #0393

✲✲

#0775 - July 20, 2019 @ 07:52 (San Francisco, California)

[0775.1 / 1955] [It feels like a brisk winter day. We're nearing the end of a family vacation. We thoroughly enjoyed our stay at a luxurious stone mountain lodge. I've gone out for a walk to grab a coffee and the morning paper. I incorrectly think I know where we're meeting up for breakfast. I'm responsible for getting us all checked out from our accommodations. When I finish at the clubhouse, I turn the wrong direction and am unable to find a staircase that descends to the floor below...*which is where I need to go.*

I attempt to climb out onto a ledge that I think will allow me to dangle and drop, but grow afraid of the height. A fall would break my legs. I pull myself back on to the upper level. Over shoulder I catch a glimpse of a bus we've intended to take from "A to B." It's unclear if the departing bus is ours. Adding to my confusion is the marked absence of a route schedule.

I walk down the corridor stopping to look inside an unlit boutique that sells highly orna-mented and "light sensitive" chocolates and desserts. I encounter the family and we make an in-the-moment decision to have seafood for lunch. I'm surprised at how inexpensive the seafood menu is. *"$6 or $7 pay what you can"* for two full sized, fully prepared fish presented in austere white cardboard pizza boxes. When opened, the box contains a poached fish heat sealed between two sheets of wax paper, each holding a skinned, star shaped portion of cod. The entire fish as presented is edible. The meat falls away like ribbons from the bones. THE DANCER hands me a pair of chopsticks and we share one of the two boxes. We're both a bit confused and amazed by this presentation. It's familiar to THE WEAVER and THE CARPENTER who remark they've eaten here many times before.

THE DANCER points to a car magazine on a nearby table and asks when I think I'm going to buy my next vehicle. As I'm about to answer, THE WEAVER interrupts and strongly suggests that we let none of the skinned fish go to waste, and to *"eat it while it's still hot."* THE DANCER and I roll our eyes. Nothing will go to waste.

All the adults move to an observation space on a lower level where we look in on THE CHILD in a classroom. She's the only one in the class who's wearing a pink glittery formal suit coat. She loves the coat and the attention she gets for wearing it. She loves all the ques-tions the other kids have about the coat. We all stand as a group watching through the one-way glass as she giggles. Her first day of school was really fun!] //

✶
✶✶

Maj. = 0- THE WEAVER: #0776, 1- THE CARPENTER: #0783,
2- THE DANCER: #0777, 3- THE CHILD: #0800
FISH: #0153, #0349, #0360
A TO B: #0088. #0125, #0231
RIBBONS: #0023, #0033, #0105

✶
✶✶

#0776 - July 21, 2019 @ 04:49 (San Francisco, California)

[0776.1 / 1956] [I'm on a massive farm in rural Iowa. I'm introduced to a very fancy woman by the name of "Kristen Kevin" who is a great granddaughter of GREAT GRANDPA, born out of wedlock. She's familiar with THE WEAVER, but this is their first meeting. We're there to take delivery of a new herd of dairy cattle that are airdropped from giant bombers that fly over the land. I remote view the event from above the planes and notice the cows' hind legs have been stretched abnormally and are fastened to wooden fixtures to make them aerodynamic as they plummet from above. GREAT GRANDPA jokes with me to let him shave my head, but I don't let him do it. Even though he continues pestering me, it remains playful.]

[0776.2 / 1957] [A heavy metal band plays a concert and invites a variety of special guests on stage. It feels like an odd juxtaposition of the REAL HOUSEWIVES OF WHEREVER and avatars from organized religions.

Christians, Muslims and various other sectarian representatives are forced together. Though publicly celebrated as a successful social experiment, it seems awkward and manufactured for some political end.] //

⁂

Maj. = 0- THE WEAVER: #0780
IOWA: #0162, #0281
REMOTE: #0037, #0212, #0379

⁂

#0777 - July 21, 2019 @ 05:43 (San Francisco, California)

[0777.1 / 1958] [I sit on a fast-moving bus, across from two young founders of a new successful startup. I'm invited to be their third founder. I'm intrigued by a series of three brown leather-bound books they remove from a cellophane wrapper, page edge side torn through with a thumbnail. One guy blows sawdust from the cover and brushes a straight pin off the edge of the meeting table and on to a thick red shag rug. Me and the other guy drop to the floor and run our hands across the rug searching for the sharp object. The other is disinterested and believes it's best solved by letting someone step on it. I pull an emergency cord to get the bus to stop.

As I step off, I proceed down a stone promenade lined by central offices of successful companies. My attention is drawn to an "Apple" building. I'm amused to know that the company began the same as mine...small! I walk by a series of giant 5-foot-tall bird feathers stuck in the ground. A handwritten paper note next to the feathers reads:

"Limit yourself to 2. They're gifts generously provided by the wild VANE spelled W A V E."

I arrive at a train station and notice THE DANCER and THE ATHEIST have decided to take a short time apart. THE ATHEIST gets on a train.

THE BOSTON MARATHONER *(smart, embodied, and honest)* arrives at the station and gives THE DANCER a hug. It's very sad. They talk about children who've recently passed away.

A tear rolls down my cheek and I wipe it away quickly so no passersby will see.] //

⁂

Maj. = 2- THE DANCER: #0787, 8- THE ATHEIST: #0798
APPLE: #0149, #0309, #0342
LEATHER: #0012, #0015, #0052, #0060

⁂

#0778 - July 22, 2019 @ 01:45 (San Francisco, California)
**Amorphous abstractions. **

[0778.1 / 1959] [I'm at a drive-in movie. THE COMPASS *(discerning, expansive, and deep)* sits next to me. We make out during the entire film.]

[0778.2 / 1960] [*"Is what you have better?" "Oh, so much better,"* I hear two voices banter in the dark.]

[0778.3 / 1961] [A nutrition influencer gives a client poor guidance when he advises she, *"drink 1L of water per hour to stay attractive."*]

[0778.4 / 1962] [People gather for a picnic on a municipal lawn, grilling sausages and serving each other potato salad. I float above a set of bleachers positioned behind a wooden fence, and separated from the grassy picnic field. I notice a car's lights flood out the image on a drive-in movie screen far off in the distance.] //

⁂

MAKE OUT: #0083, #0148, #0170, #0218, #0317
PICNIC: #0094, #0188, #0260, #0350
WATER: #0360, #0364, #0365, #0374
BETTER: #0144, #0353, #0358
THE COMPASS: #0845

⁂

#0779 - July 23, 2019 @ 04.00 (San Francisco, California)

[0779.1 / 1963] [A black spider crawls across a wooden table.]
[0779.2 / 1964] [I chat with friends as I mix an activated charcoal supplement with water. The supplement bottle has much less weight to it than I imagined.]
[0779.3 / 1965] [I teach a class. Students take no direction. They do what they want and I'm simply stuck in chaos.] //

⁂

SPIDER: #0154
SUPPLEMENT: #0002, #0136, #0159
FRIENDS: #0265, #0312, #0320, #0350

⁂

#0780 - July 23, 2019 @ 06:03 (San Francisco, California)

[0780.1 / 1966] [I've been tasked to record some information on paper, from an arcade game screen. Two other women sit with me. We're seated to the left of a larger group. Even when I squint, I'm barely able to make out the screen's content. It just looks dead to me. A Black teenage girl looks on from over my right shoulder. She wears a turquoise knit sweater.

She pushes me aside and holds her left arm across my throat. I push back by jamming a paperback novel into her face saying, *"Do you like how that feels?"*]

[0780.2 / 1967] [I sit side-by-side on a motorized bench with "my girls" as we drive across town. We don't like each other, though we've been part of the same "posse" for a long time. We discuss whether or not I should leave town. We never make eye contact. Overhead in the middle of the road, a shelf hovers and displays cartoon hats. The hats are each a single, solid color. A green one (and a gold one) are high on my list to purchase. *"They'd really "pop,"* at next year's Easter services." After a moment of confusion, I realize I'm a young Black girl living somewhere in the southern United States during the mid-20th century.]

[0780.3 / 1968] [I stop at a red barn. I enter and go upstairs. THE WEAVER sits at a kitchen table wearing an apron. GRANDMA passed away some time ago. I need to take a shit really badly and make my way to the bathroom. I'm startled by a scribbled list on a piece of white cardboard from a cigarette carton, on the floor next to the commode written in GRANDPA's handwriting. The need to poop goes away. Tears flood from my eyes. I run to the kitchen table asking THE WEAVER,
"Is that GRANDPA's list by the toilet?"
"Yes, I just left it there," she says, continuing to read the newspaper.
"Why?" I ask, crying. I wake up just before THE WEAVER answers.] //

⁎⁎⁎

Maj. = 0- THE WEAVER: #0783, 11-GRANDMA: #0807
Min. = ♥- GRANDPA: #0815
EASTER: #0106, #0240
SWEATER: #0024, #0293, #0321

⁎⁎⁎

#0781 - July 24, 2019 @ 04:33 (San Francisco, California)

[0781.1 / 1969] [Class continues with THE PSYCHIC DOCTOR *(connected, polished, and intentional)* who repeats a postulate to remain open to success. We oscillate between various high frequency tones as a meditative exercise. He's grounded and available to his students. He offers healing generously and freely. I feel a strong affinity for him as a teacher and am eager to learn more. Things move faster than my mind can track. Spirit gets what it came for.]

[0781.2 / 1970] [I walk down the back staircase at a restaurant with THE HIPSTER *(witty, stylish, and gruff).* We're familiar and friendly as we join a dinner table with a variety of gregarious beings. I'm seated next to the evening's guest of honor; a 54-year-old boy who takes a shine to me. He asks me to pass the potatoes. I hand him a French fry basket with a hard starchy brick at its center. Much frivolity and play ensue as a result.]

[0781.3 / 1971] [TINA TURNER wears a red dress. She shouts and urges others to, *"burn down the patriarchy,"* as she struggles to open her body into "bow pose."] //

531

⁂
⁑
TINA TURNER: #0948
FRENCH FRY: #0081
PLAY: #0074, #0081, #0102
SHINE: #0014, #0065, #0072
⁑
⁂

#0782 - July 24, 2019 @ 05:35 (San Francisco, California)

[0782.1 / 1972] [I've arrived in a Jeep at a mountain lodge. My counterpart is a small chiseled Asian man who sports a highly intricate throat tattoo. His dark frame glasses make him seem mysterious and sexy. He's the CFO of my tech company. We grab our bags and head for the door. THE DENTIST (*jovial, funny, and civic minded*) meets up with us as we enter. Initially, we can't find our rooms. I walk in on a few people who are sleeping, but they don't wake up.]

[0782.2 / 1973] [I'm in a large room with a recessed gathering area in the center. THE TRANSLATOR provides me with a piece of information, which I quickly forget. An abstract painting hangs on the wall composed of various simple geometric forms (*cubes, circles, etc.*). The painting is framed by a thick 2" layer of brown toffee colored wood. I look away for a moment. When I turn back around the brown border has transformed to light pink, making the piece incredibly beautiful to me. THE CONFIDANT hugs me from behind. After staring at the painting, we turn to each other and begin kissing. Then we make love.] //

⁂
⁑
Maj. = 16- THE CONFIDANT: #0798, 19-THE TRANSLATOR: #0792
CUBES: #0270, #0320
TATTOO: #0043, #0140, #0232
GEOMETRIC: #0018, #0346
⁑
⁂

#0783 - July 24, 2019 @ 10:38 (San Francisco, California)

[0783.1 / 1974] [*"GODDAMNIT don't bring that through the house!"* THE CARPENTER yells at a woman who inhabits the second bedroom in an apartment. She's carried a pink assault rifle past the family and out to the back patio, likely to shoot at *"dogs and other damned pests."* *"It's going to kill power in the house if she uses that."* Power to the house cuts off. THE WEAVER sits nearby in an easy chair with her left hand pressed into the armrest so strongly that one of her fingers dislocates. A curious series of events unfold as she nurses her injured digit. Everyone in the family takes multiple rapid-fire paths through their lives, living, dying and repeating as THE WEAVER stays seated in the chair. I die of different diseases. THE CARPENTER has a heart attack. Multiple grandchildren are born and pass away. THE WEAVER sits still and observes all of it.

Tears occasionally stream down her face, but her focus on the advancing movie is unwavering. She outlives all her children and grandchildren. She sits quietly and alone in her well-kept home in a place where she's well looked after. She's easily over 100 years old. I've died and float nearby.] //

⁂

Maj. = 0- THE WEAVER: #0789, 1- THE CARPENTER #0799
HEART: #0047, #0060, #0069, #0015
MOVIE: #0001, #0014, #0016, #0149

⁂

#0784 - July 26, 2019 @ 03:41 (San Francisco, California)

[0784.1 / 1975] [The scene is uplifting, playful and creative. I quantize an electronic music composition. While the music renders, I play a game of snooker with THE MIDWESTERN GENT (*committed*) and THE HOBBIT (*aloof*). The object of the game is to scatter pill bottles of differing shapes and sizes around the table by striking them with a cue bass. Glass dishes are pressed into the giant table's corners. A carnival glass candy dish recessed in the center of the green felt table looks like a pink amoeba. I line up a shot that ricochets rapidly back and forth, "PING! PING! PING! PING! PING! PING!" An orange pill bottle drops into a corner pocket. Both THE MIDWESTERN GENT and THE HOBBIT are amazed by the outcome. Once I hit most of the bottles in their pockets, my phone notifies me I've won access to a set of master musical stems to remix and publish. Looks like I'll spend the next few nights arranging a new dance mix of "YOUNG BLOOD" by THE NAKED AND FAMOUS. The raw piece sounds solid, but unpolished. Later, I'll work the files through mastering, one at a time] //

⁂

CARNIVAL GLASS: #0390
AMAZING: #0189, #0263, #0353, #0359
NAKED: #0035, #0044, #0153
THE MIDWESTERN GENT: #0888
THE HOBBIT: #0855

⁂

#0785 - July 26, 2019 @ 06:01 (San Francisco, California)

[0785.1 / 1976] [After a house party, I pack my bags to leave on a weekend excursion. As I gather my things, I look out a window and over an edge. I won't be able to make the steep climb down with everything I want to bring. I take some time to bargain and consolidate. Empty bottles and half eaten food is scattered everywhere. The calendar suggests today's a fasting day, but I choose to eat anyway. I believe the more quickly I eat strawberry wafer cookies, they won't "count." I jam 10 of them in my mouth as fast as possible. I grab my coat, two bags, and troubleshoot how to descend down the exterior of the condo building on the fly.

Once on the ground, I go to a fast-food restaurant and order a combo meal from an exhausted version of THE FEELER. A large group walks in to order just as I finish eating. THE FEELER goes on break and eats sitting across from THE THINKER. I step towards them to talk. She's sick. I'm there to support her. THE RODIN (*statuesque, beautiful, and sinewy*), my crush from the house party, sits nearby on a couch. We flirt, but I decide to not take it any further. I have no social media profiles. He only dates friends of friends on Facebook.] //

⁂

☆☆

Min. = ♠-THE THINKER: #0924, ♣- THE FEELER: #0924
COOKIES: #0058, #0080, #0148
TROUBLESHOOT: #0058, #0264
THE RODIN: #1226

☆☆

#0786 - July 29, 2019 @ 18:55 (San Francisco, California)

[0786.1 / 1977] [I awaken from sleep and discover I'm lying on a floor. A group of people quarrel outside my door. All parties are outraged. I know if I speak a word through the door, I'll wind up sucked into that energetic trap, and will wind up in blind outrage as well. I stay quiet, lay down, and go back to sleep as the argument intensifies.]

[0786.2 / 1978] [THE KANGAROO is on the move again. He throws a massive, lavish going away party at what will soon be his former residence. We remark to one another about how many mutual friends we share, who we've just recently become aware of. THE INTERIOR DESIGNER *(exceptional, intuitive, and loving)* and THE KANGAROO clink champagne flutes then make conversation on a grand staircase. They met through a person named "Gary Marshall," of whom they are both exceptionally fond. More details blur by. As the edgy world around me softens it's clear that I'm attracted to THE KANGAROO. I make no mention. He's leaving. We have a nice conversation at the end of the party as a catering staff *(some visible / others invisible)* resets the space for inbound tenants. The numerous tablecloths and chairs flying around the room seem like ordinary circumstances.]

[0786.3 / 1979] [I witness a process where musicians look at a sequence of photographs to help them generate the mood and tone for cover versions of their favorite songs. It's as though they step through the frame and into a psychedelic Polaroid world when they do this. Full immersion.]

[0786.4 / 1980] [I'm seated next to THE BLACK BEAUTY *(mysterious, heavy, and resilient)* on what occurs as a helicopter powered chair lift. From high above an ocean scene, she allows me to select colors, shapes, pigment and images and layer them into the background. Each color has a corresponding soundscape. I create a song scape for THE ASSISTANT, which begins with me specifically commenting on what I see on top of *(and beneath)* the surface of the water.]

[0786.5 / 1981] [Pictures spontaneously print from and hang on invisible nearby walls, adding layering to existing lush nature scenes.]

[0786.6 / 1982] [I fly with THE BLACK BEAUTY above an island over a vast body of deep blue water. I'm acknowledged wordlessly by both THE BLACK BEAUTY and THE ASSISTANT for being, "tapped in." I've agreed to share what I see as I concurrently witness a variety of other realities. Scene action speeds up and becomes blurry. I'm roused from sleep, slightly disoriented.] //

⁎⁎

Min. = ♠- *THE KANGAROO: #1280*
POLAROID: #0044, #0132, #0266
CHAMPAGNE FLUTES: #0341
LUSH: #0079, #0101, #0147
THE BLACK BEAUTY: #0787

⁎⁎

#0787 - July 30, 2019 @ 01:44 (San Francisco, California)

[0787.1 / 1983] [I'm seated around a slim ovular white conference table, lit overhead softly in a black walled room. I play THE HUMBLE MAN (*suffering, fleeing, and tired*) and another man a new dance track through a pair of rectangular table top speakers. The speakers have remarkable low-end resonance, given their small credit card-like size. They belong to THE PIZZA DELIVERY BOY (*wealthy, manipulative, and musical*).
THE HUMBLE MAN and the other guy stand up and leave the room soon into the listening party. They don't understand my art. THE PIZZA DELIVERY BOY sits to my left. THE DANCER sits to my right. As the music continues, we're startled by a flash of fire created by a dollop of lava that spontaneously appears atop a single sheet of loose-leaf paper on the conference room floor. THE DANCER blurts out a surprised scream.
New faces fill empty seats around the table. I restart the presentation. The newly gathered group listens to my creation in its entirety. When it concludes I thank them for their presence, attention, and consideration. THE PIZZA DELIVERY BOY leans over, whispers in my ear, and reminds me that he lent me the speakers. I apologize for being so enraptured in the music; I'd forgotten to acknowledge him for his generous in-kind support.]

[0787.2 / 1984] [I'm near LA watching a massive volcanic eruption after a magnificent earthquake. Ash and smoke spew high into the atmosphere. A similar sized dollop of lava from [0787.1 / 1983] lands a few feet from where I stand, causing a brush fire.]

[0787.3 / 1985] [Another volcano unexpectedly erupts in Iowa, covering rolling green corn fields with colorful red and orange lava.]

[0787.4 / 1986] [In a maximum-security prison, a female detainee in solitary confinement is under suicide watch. She uses a stapler-looking instrument like a Theremin to create simple and unsettling musical tones. All the inmates in the prison are elderly artists. The woman kneels on the floor of her cell with her eyes closed and runs her index finger on the length of the device, which softly lights up as it generates sounds. The guard responsible for her is not supportive and yells. It's difficult to watch, but I can't turn my head to look away.]

. . .

[0787.5 / 1987] [A group of Indian women, festively dressed in colorful saris, are gathered at a busy intersection in a major metro area to make and sell naan and pakora for a fundraiser. I'm delighted by their expressions of color. None of them really want to be there.

I step away from the women and on to a street car (*a grocery car*), stocked with amazing fare. Everyone is issued a single bag to fill however they wish. I'm drawn to big bowls of fresh mozzarella cheese and packages of plant based hot dogs. I have to be discerning with my choices. I want to take everything, but there's no way it'll all fit into a single bag.]

[0787.6 / 1988] [THE BLACK BEAUTY (*helpful, magnetic, and feminine*) has become the regional VP for a cosmetics company. I've written THE BLACK BEAUTY a note. Upon mailing it, I realize I didn't send it to her new address.]

[0787.7 / 1989] [I wake up in the grocery car, thinking I've written THE BLACK BEAUTY a thank you note. I have not. Instead, she's left me a designer briefcase stocked and lined with specialty chocolate bars as a gift. A note within informs me she's relocated to San Juan, Puerto Rico. She's responsible for launching the mobile grocery concept car and has left me an extra bag to fill with sundries. I ponder what to grab from the shelves. The EDM playing overhead makes me ponder why I prefer certain music producers.] //

⁂

Maj. = 2- THE DANCER: #0791
EDM: #0271, #0340
INDEX FINGER: #0088, #0106, #0113, #0148
THE BLACK BEAUTY: #0878
THE PIZZA DELIVERY BOY: #1145

⁂

#0788 - July 30, 2019 @ 03:27 (San Francisco, California)

[0788.1 / 1990] [I pass an Asian man on the street, who I've previously dated. As we talk, he morphs into THE FIDUCIARY who is deeply angry with me and screams, "YOU LEFT ME!" The energy between us is charged up, and throughout the interaction various friends and spirits drop in to watch the scenario unfold. His upset and energy flinging continues unwaveringly for a lengthy period. It does not drop in intensity, nor neutralize. My space feels calm. I have clarity around why I made my decisions in past lives. He doesn't understand why I walked away, a deep irony being he was so wrapped up in his fantasies he has no idea he walked away from me.]

[0788.2 / 1991] [A team of people gather to support a giant social event titled "RIDDEN," as noted on a black block letter wall sign written on a giant green "Post-It." The sign has 14 empty spaces for participant names. Someone has written my name on a line with the title: "Leader." I didn't select this designation. Those striving to be the "leader" are tremendously upset.]

. . .

[0788.3 / 1992] [A popular augmented reality game involves using one's finger to glide a small fast moving silver pinball around a grid to gather coins, set in lines and clusters. At times the ball can lose velocity and become stuck to a cluster's "gravity." A special maneuver can yield a "breakaway" from the group, and can result in high volumes of bonus points. I attempt the game once and achieve a global all time high score, frustrating thousands of other players. Some have dedicated months to practice yet have not achieved anywhere near my first-time result.]

[0788.4 / 1993] [People switch faces with each other after they share eye contact. I keep a detailed journal of every switch I make. It has an augmented reality feel. Each switch burns off a karmic valence. I continue writing down detailed notes and musings. I'm paired with a partner who wants to leave immediately. I request 5 minutes of his time, affirmed as a reasonable period to write down my impressions. When we complete, the partner requests five minutes to get grounded. I oblige and commit to sit silently for the full time. He becomes impatient as I honor his request. I keep reading and writing as time clicks by one second at a time. My journal has loose change inside. Nickels, dimes, quarters, fall on to the table as I turn it over and give it a shake.]

[0788.5 / 1994] [BARBRA STREISAND is a friend who checks in with me from time to time.]

[0788.6 / 1995] [THE SEX WORKER (*seductive, playful, and honest*) updates his profile photo on social media. Now, a soft lit black and white image (*shot from above*) shows him resting on the sand. His eyes are sweetly closed. The sound of a soft breeze blows upward from the image.]

[0788.7 / 1996] [A group of people gather near a train after taking exams. A woman leaves a binder that holds all of her test preparation notes. She hasn't yet passed the bar. An easement in the law allows her to charge a "reasonable rate" for advisory service she provides while unlicensed. All monies earned in such a way must be fully applied to her education expenses. She's given someone "caveated" legal guidance under this new standard, and intends to do so again to whittle away at her large financial burden.]

[0788.8 / 1997] [I return to playing the face switching game. My field of vision is framed in a vertical chevron shape, like a medieval battle shield. I'm disoriented for a moment, then realize I'm inside a large magnolia tree and see what it sees.] //

⁎⁎

Maj. = 9- THE FIDUCIARY: #0891
BARBRA STREISAND: #1379
SPIRITS: #0018, #0039, #0357, #0358, #0367

⁎⁎

⁎⁎

JOSHUA D. LUNDELL

#0789 - July 30, 2019 @ 06:55 (San Francisco, California)

[0789.1 / 1998] [THE BARISTA *(good natured, surprised, and simple)* is recognized in a Sunday morning news piece for his work with a symphony of grade school children who are unable to afford their instruments.]

[0789.2 / 1999] [THE WEAVER and I watch AEROSMITH perform at a bar. During the band's second set they play, "EAT THE RICH." Something seems fishy as I sit and swig a beer. I run to the side stage to see what's going on and discover the band is playing a CD through the house PA and faking their performance. The front man's antics *(who turns out isn't STEVEN TYLER)* distract the crowd. He thrusts a microphone stand into the crowd to gain their participation. Their goal is to get the crowd drunk and rowdy. THE WEAVER runs into a woman she knows on the opposite side of the bar.]

[0789.3 / 2000] [I walk with friends discussing the timing of our next big trip. I'm insistent it'll occur next May after I've finished my work. Brief mentions of paying rent and possibly moving into a new place follow. THE PORN STAR *(evolving, defiant, and exploring)* describes what it's like living in a house with a "Wall of Mirrors." Quite literally a mirrored wall, reflects the morning light beautifully through the space and also creates the possibility of an odd intrusion from those outside who can easily see whatever action occurs inside, from down on the street.
He chooses to point the mirrors towards the breakfast nook, which cascades shards of diamond light into a cozy and nourishing neutral space for peepers to peep. The mirrors in THE PORN STAR's home migrate from the wall to a staircase where they're displayed like opaque letter tiles on a WHEEL OF FORTUNE game board. He changes one tile at a time from frosted to clear with a light touch and a smile. A large crowd waits for the "full show" on the sidewalk.]

[0789.4 / 2001] [I consider leasing an extravagant condo to run down financial resources and expose any deep attachments I have to the "energy of money." The point of the exercise would be: *"Get neutral to going broke."*]

[0789.5 / 2002] [I consider going back to Africa.] //

⁎⁎
Maj. = 0- THE WEAVER: #0795
PORN: #0021, #0184, #0201, #0254
DIAMOND: #0013, #0170, #0271
COZY: #0010, #0017, #0040, #0124
⁎⁎

#0790 - July 30, 2019 @ 08:11 (San Francisco, California)

[0790.1 / 2003] [I live in a highly desirable neighborhood, on the first residential floor of a

538

condo building. I'm aware a public open house is underway. I'm not sure what time it is. I go for a walk. It's dark out. I pick up my backpack. I take out my phone and receive a call.

"What did you do for your 40th?"

"Not a whole lot. Just kept to myself and stayed connected."

I turn a corner and a woman hands me a neighborhood news flyer. I'm able to accept it after I put a box of cereal I've purchased under my arm, that hand also holding a ½ gallon plastic jug of milk.

I turn back in the direction of my home and see a massive line formed to inspect and interview for a few new units on the market. The front and side doors of my unit are wide open. Curious people trickle in a couple at a time. I take care when inviting them *(who may be my new neighbors)* to graciously depart. I've left a pair of jeans and my Peruvian fedora scattered on the bathroom countertop. A small TV in the back of the unit rests atop a stately piece of solid oak furniture. The walls are painted a cool ice blue. Plush grey carpet softly soothes under foot.

Everyone wants to live in this neighborhood. I'm lucky I chose to live here on the ground floor. I have some reservations about leaving this place and not being able to come back. I remove my shoes. I pour cereal and milk in a bowl. I know as long as I continue to pray and stay connected it will be clear when it's time to stay, and go. It won't be an issue if eventually I have to live somewhere else. I feel good as I stare off through the kitchen window, pondering and enjoying the crunch of a bite of cereal on a steel spoon.] //

✢

CONDO: #0036, #0114, #0133
STEEL: #0021, #0023, #0024
CURIOUS: #0117, #0124, #0135
OAK: #0045, #0088

✢

#0791 - July 31, 2019 @ 06:10 (San Francisco, California)

[0791.1 / 2004] [I'm at an amusement park with my family. We agree to ride a Ferris Wheel together. We're on the ride for an extended amount of time. It's night and not very well lit. I become suspended upside down beneath our carriage. I'm stuck, but I think it's funny. When I exit the ride, I rub the small of my back. A finger brushes a small shunt or plastic pipe, the size of a drinking straw. It's implanted just above my tailbone and needs to be surgically removed. The surgery occurs instantly and is delivered "business as usual" with little fanfare or commotion. Aftercare involves regularly irrigating the wound. The nearest place I can do this is by an exhibit of highly contagious cats who all have been similarly wounded. I take special precautions to keep my distance from the cats as I wash with hot soapy water to stave off infection. It's a bit confusing and becomes more so when I realize that I'm seven years old and THE DANCER is three.] //

✢

Maj. 2- THE DANCER: #0798
SURGERY: #0198, #0260, #0293, #0353
SEVEN: #0014, #0026, #0033, #0105, #0378
TAILBONE: #0012

✢

539

#0792 - July 31, 2019 @ 07:03 (San Francisco, California)

[0792.1 / 2005] [Behind podiums and communicating through different TV screens, Two beings debate while rapidly changing faces. One debater takes on the valence of a joker mouthed HILLARY CLINTON, the other a dog-eyed incarnation of RHIANNA. They debate on a cruise ship. HILLARY humiliates RHIANNA who, face in hands, runs away and down a staircase supported by four bodyguards dressed in white uniforms. RHIANNA must get off the boat as quickly as possible. HILLARY just stands there laughing.]

[0792.2 / 2006] [I'm in the "2:00am class." I walk down the wide hallways of what could be a modern zoo or an "educational gallery." The place has a high vibration and an intention to support children in their connection to God. I may be at a camp for gifted children. Regardless of title, it's a place that's changing the world. My spirit is moved. It could be quite lovely to work here.

Long horizontal rectangular windows are framed in black. I enter a doorway and find myself in a waiting room behind a classroom. THE WORLDBRIDGER pops out from behind a room divider, freshly showered and wearing a towel. He unintentionally flashes me as he wraps himself up. He taps me on the shoulder and smiles as he slips by to prepare for class. I'm humored by the interaction. I enter a large classroom where THE TRANSLATOR leads an exercise. I'm asked a question and I respond in kind, interrupted mid-thought by someone who notices the time is fairly late (*10:45pm, but it's light out*). THE TRANSLATOR calmly responds, *"We'll be done when we're done."*]

[0792.3 / 2007] [I tap in and learn the band TOOL used meditative tools and ecstatic technologies to source and write their forthcoming album. A pan shot of JUSTIN CHANCELLOR being interviewed catches him saying, *"Every note on this record will come from a place where I am grounded and protected. It will be sourced (the entire album) from my place of connection."*]

[0792.4 / 2008] [I awaken in a classroom answering a question: *"Everything I identify as good or bad is something I have created."* As I look out towards the classroom, I see a long hall, full of desks occupied by spirits who come and go when they get what they need.] //

⁕⁎

Maj. = 7- THE WORLDBRIDGER: #0856, 19- THE TRANSLATOR: #0831
RHIANNA: #1012
TOOL: #0933
TOWEL: #0182, #0194, #0375

⁕⁎

#0793 - July 31, 2019 @ 09:18 (San Francisco, California)

[0793.1 / 2009] [I'm at a wedding with THE WHITE RABBIT and THE AYURVEDIC. We gather by a little river to cut off locks of our hair. We drop them in the running water as a gift to the bride and groom, just before their ceremony begins.]

. . .

[0793.2 / 2010] [I ride in a 1950's automobile with two women as we drive up a steep hill. The car barely moves enough to crest the hill. We make a joke at the driver's expense, referring to her as "SLOWWW-IS." Everyone in the car including "Lois" breaks out in laughter.]

[0793.3 / 2011] [I'm on the set of a Hollywood production. THE NASTY PIG (*dirty, confrontational, and vocal*) stands ready in the basement of a house across the street. He hollers at me while waving a cheeseburger. He requests I toss him the cheeseburger I'm holding. I throw it at him with more force than intended, and it breaks one of the "sugar glass" windows on set. The director screams, *"CUT!"* Another actor is deeply annoyed with me. They believe my hasty response, *"wrecked the perfect moment."*

I stand on a table between takes and observe the flurry of activity between producers, actors, directors and prop masters who reset the scene.] //

✳

Min. = ◆- *THE WHITE RABBIT: #1345*
WEDDING: #0024, #0026, #0098, #0151, #0154, #0176
1950's: #0055, #0089, #0112, #0159, #0183, #0185, #0377

✳

#0794 - August 2, 2019 @ 02:37 (San Francisco, California)

[0794.1 / 2012] [I may be in Beverly Hills. A large house has a trampoline and a pool in the backyard. I ask the owners if I can come by and practice later.
"Sure, just give us a head's up so we can make sure no one else is around."
When I return THE MUSICAL PANDA (*inspired, uplifting, and engaging*) pulls a wagon with a large bucket of fertilizer hitched to the back.
"There's a guy who looks like he could use some help," I say cupping my mouth with my hand. He waves back in agreement.
We both look out over a giant emerald lawn, freshly cut like a diamond patterned fairway. The odd double shadows cast from the trees confuse me.]

[0794.2 / 2013] [I observe and inspect a series of black wooden frames on a vast wall. Within each frame is a panel of black corduroy fabric. Some of the frames contain black striped wallpaper instead of corduroy.]

[0794.3 / 2014] [I exit to another "backside" of the house and wave to a group of people who don't know me. I have a curt interaction with some very possessive children who constantly want to "bounce." They're more interested in jumping on the trampoline next to the pool instead of swimming.] //

✳

EMERALD: #0001, #0004
TRAMPOLINE: #0026, #0306
HELP: #0238, #0251, #0271, #0280

✳

541

#0795 - August 2, 2019 @ 04:01 (San Francisco, California)

[0795.1 / 2015] [I've experienced this previously in a different dream within a dream. THE VIP (*generous, curious, and adventurous*) gifts me a ticket to Burning Man. I learn this through viewing a Facebook feed. I've been given three, but must go to "will call" to retrieve one.]

[0795.2 / 2016] [DONALD TRUMP has actually been President since before the Vietnam War. Over time the power of the office has been eroded through a process called "Forced Supplementation." I find myself dictating into a phone in a reality where the world has only known a politicized DONALD TRUMP for four years.]

[0795.3 / 2017] [I'm alone in an ice-cold room submerged in cold water up to my eye line. It remains such for some time until more people arrive to socialize. I choose to sit in a heated pool away from the chatter. A young girl is at the far end of the hot pool. I keep as far away from her as possible. Any male presence near her will upset her father, who is large and lingers at the center of the hot pool. A guy with no feet wants to show me how to *"find the center of the best part of the pool,"* a stone square platform in the center of the maze. The hot pool has many cascading levels, similar to an ESCHER sketch. It's beautiful, comforting and restorative.]

[0795.4 / 2018] [We travel. I've forgotten my phone charger and dream journals, so it appears I have no way to continue my project. THE WEAVER's there. We travel together through different mental pictures of being on beaches in costumes. This helps me come to terms with the likelihood I may not ever go back to the desert. I've had a variety of good times in my life, and things are just as they need to be. We drive a van. THE WEAVER drives from the back seat on the opposite side from me. My vision is obscured by the captain's chair in front. It's frustrating for a moment until another steering wheel appears in front of me, allowing me to collaboratively drive with THE WEAVER.] //

⁂

Maj. = 0- THE WEAVER: #0799
DONALD TRUMP: #0920
FACEBOOK: #0081, #0237
COSTUMES: # 0017

⁂

#0796 - August 2, 2019 @ 05:14 (San Francisco, California)

[0796.1 / 2019] [I move through various spaces in an office building and showroom to help someone with their HR paperwork. I hold a pair of earplugs in my hand. My counterpart and I stop and place our paperwork down on a roll top desk at the back of the showroom. We spend some time autographing all documents that require both of our signatures. The order in which I get him to work through the documents is important. Specific role assignments are dependent upon signed contracts. It's illegal for him to even look at some before we're complete. We discover ourselves at the end of a long conference table, with others seated at the far end. I suggest we change locations completely. We do, and it was the prudent choice. My counterpart begins to disclose medications his former employees take. Among other HIPAA violations, he's compelled to give me updates on all their conditions from the most recent six months.

"Please stop."]

[0796.2 / 2020] [I hold a remote control with a greyscale image of a male celebrity that changes in its middle. One minute it's PAUL RUDD, the next it's LEONARDO DICAPRIO.]

[0796.3 / 2021] [I omnisciently observe a workshop at a fitness studio. The instructor encourages students to hold positions for five minutes. I'm not impressed. I whisper in his ear,

"That's all it takes to master leading this style of practice. Put people somewhere and then let them do it."

One attendee is a joyful topless woman who claims that, *"It's easy!"*

"Did you hold the expression the whole time?"

"No, of course I didn't!"

She stands adjacent to a large waving banner of a labia that celebrates her womanly power and femininity.] //

⁎⁎
CONTRACTS: #0031, #0096, #0097
JOYFUL: #0012, #0098
BANNER: #0004, #0024, #0092, #0286
⁎⁎

#0797 - August 2, 2019 @ 05:59 (San Francisco, California)

[0797.1 / 2022] [BARON BAPTISTE provides me with some insights into how he organizes his weeklong immersions. In the middle of an experience, he lays down and places his head in a grey conical pillow which gives him a Nefertiti-ish, appearance from where I sit. He speaks slowly, deliberately, and reinforces the importance of, *"never giving medical advice."* He's seated next to an oversized lantern in a square cube of black wrought iron. Panes of opaque glass are lit softly by a candle in the center.

"Speak just slowly enough so you sound like an observant and calmly reprimanding mother." He flows in fluid conversation on various forms and alignments.

He continues, *"I want them to hear me. I give them no advice...and for some reason they think I'm their mom."*]

[0797.2 / 2023] [I'm driving.]

[0797.3 / 2024] [I have free time and spend an afternoon searching for a gymnastics club. I double check my teaching schedule to avoid any conflicts before I take time for myself to practice and exercise.] //

⁑

BARON BAPTISTE: #0800
PILLOW: #0013, #0063, #0140
WROUGHT IRON: #0212, #0301
SCHEDULE: #0271, #0297, #0367, #0385

⁑

#0798 - August 3, 2019 @ 05:59 (San Francisco, California)

[0798.1 / 2025] [THE DANCER has an ultrasound that reveals she's pregnant with triplet boys. The other two pop out from behind the one they knew of previously and seem to shout, *"SURPRISE!"* with their miniature jazz hands. THE DANCER and THE ATHEIST are both startled and excited.]

[0798.2 / 2026] [I'm with musicians. We discuss and compare our favorite polyrhythmic sections of progressive compositions. A particular piece written in 25/8 has us all delightfully in agreement that it would be a challenge to perform live. We break it down and practice slowly. We enjoy it.]

[0798.3 / 2027] [It feels like we're somewhere in Northern Canada. I've forgotten my passport. I gather with members of a permaculture community before an international trip. The retreat space where we meet has a greenhouse and a garden store. THE HARBINGER (*vivacious, rambunctious, and curious*) is roughly seven years old and playfully runs the register in the shop. We go about gathering items from the fully stocked shelves of the store.
I climb down a steep stone ladder carved to look like large roots. I meet the group at the bottom. I eat and share my bag of truffles (*coated in dark chocolate and rolled in diced nuts*). I'm surprised at how *"liked"* they are. Their taste is strong, and their odor pungent.
I realize I've also committed to attend a celebration with THE CONFIDANT's family on the same dates of the international excursion, in another town I've never previously heard of. Finding both a black shirt and white shirt suddenly becomes very important.
"A wedding? Oh shit! I don't have travel arrangements, documents, nor the proper clothing." I call home in a panic. It's unclear which trip I end up taking.] //

⁑

Maj. = 2- THE DANCER: #0807, 8 THE ATHEIST: #0804, 16- THE CONFIDANT: #0895
BLACK AND WHITE: #0005, #0016, #0026, #0052, #0063

⁑

#0799 - August 5, 2019 @ 03:03 (San Francisco, California)

[0799.1 / 2028] [I empty a roll top desk in the middle of the woods. I take a photograph to prove that I did it.]

[0799.2 / 2029] [I've founded a new company. I attend a celebratory breakfast where I encounter THE CEO (*influential, exceptional, and motivated*), who after a short two-week tenure, has taken a new role he believes he'll *"love for life."* We surrender our driver's licenses to be seated for lunch and are informed there are no available tables inside.

We're seated on the lawn near a perimeter fence at "Table 19." A waiter comes by, sits down with us, and very casually takes our order. THE MALE MODEL *(strong, sexy, and brotherly)* sits down and starts describing a former living situation where a roommate was in a relationship with a dying partner. A woman briskly passes us and shoves my chair in towards the table. She's seated with the group next to us.

"Hey Ma'am did you know that hurt me?" She ignores me.

"Hey Ma'am...psst Ma'am....um helloooo. MA'AM!" My voice raises and disrupts the other table.

A man named "Mr. Wolf" sits next to her as things escalate. He shouts back at me and I curtly cut him off shouting, *"STOP IT!"*

A third person walks by and yells at us, intending to disrupt our entire luncheon by claiming we're transphobes.

"What are you talking about? I was just sitting here. I was shoved for no reason by her and now I have bruised ribs," I say expressing confusion.

"She isn't she. That's 'ZE!' GET IT RIGHT!" they yell at me.

"If 'ZE' didn't SAY, how could I possibly know?" I clap back.

A fourth person comes over to our table, so angered they want our group ejected from the venue. He screams in my face.

"I'm queer and fluid. You're full of it," I mutter when he pauses to catch his breath.

Circumstances become increasingly polarized when someone from our table decides to go to the other table and spank "ZE."

"GET UP AND GO APOLOGIZE RIGHT NOW!" I scream as he returns to his seat laughing.

"GET UP AND GO SOLVE THAT NOW, OR IT'S JUST GOING TO MAKE EVERYTHING WORSE!"

After an intense moment of silence locked in a glare with me, he stands and leaves the table. The interaction subsides.

"If you were wondering why I haven't gone back to work yet, it's because I'd have to deal with THIS. SHIT. ALL. DAY. LONG. All I wanted to do was eat my fucking breakfast and celebrate the start of something new," I look down the table and say to THE WEAVER, THE CARPENTER, and THE FAIRY GODPARENTS. As I lean in to take a bite, I wake up.] //

✳

Maj. = 0- THE WEAVER: #0807, 1- THE CARPENTER: #0811
SURRENDER: #0010, #0019, #0193
SILENCE: #0017, #0365, #0371
THE FAIRY GODPARENTS: #0824
THE CEO: #0858

✳

#0800 - August 5, 2019 @ 04:58 (San Francisco, California)

[0800.1 / 2030] [A family of public officials goes into hiding at a biker bar. They're being hunted. The bar lounge serves as a stage for them to observe their collective malfeasance towards others acted out by angels and demons: embezzlement, racial slurs, defamatory slander, stealing candy from children...farting on busy street corners...a full range of "bad deeds" from which none are excluded. Certain they'll be murdered by the

Hell's Angels (*or whatever group bangs at the door*), they wish to atone before they die. They ask for my help. The parents are receptive to my quiet, neutral guidance, for which I demand no reciprocity. *"Not today, but on your time, you need to clean that energy up."*]

[0800.2 / 2031] [BARON BAPTISTE passes me, sweating profusely while talking on his phone. *"BASTARDS!"* he exclaims when he learns his dog trainer was not successful weaning his pups off their habit of licking their genitals.]

[0800.3 / 2032] [I kick a small ball down a long corridor to a child on my way back to a suite where my family has gathered. They tell me, *"The at-risk family at the bar in dream [0800.1 / 2030] has taken the recommendation to 'go neutral.'"* Multiple threads emerge at the same time with a similar notion: *"CLEAN IT UP."*]

[0800.4 / 2033] [THE CHILD is five years old. She covers herself with bath towels piled in the hallway. She wants to play hide and seek, but keeps talking under the towels which makes her easily identifiable.]

[0800.5 / 2034] [A social scene at a restaurant occurs with family and friends. Everyone enjoys "free refills." THE CONNECTOR joins. I decide that I don't want to be there when I notice everyone getting fucked up. As I depart, a female server runs after me.
"Sir, even if you don't party your card will be charged."
"I'm not drinking. My card is in my wallet. I'm going to leave now. Thank you."
The woman gives me a silent nod, then returns inside to make the rest of the staff aware of my decision.] //

⁂

Maj. = 3- THE CHILD: *#0815*, 4- THE CONNECTOR: *#0804*
FIVE: #0141, #0147, #0163, #0172
SILENT: #0005, #0019, #0048, #0136

⁂

#0801 - August 5, 2019 @ 06:14 (San Francisco, California)

[0801.1 / 2035] [I'm overfed. I stand at a buffet filling a plate with various items shaped like cones (*slices of pizza, pastries with a circle of filling in the center, chocolate chips, "SPORA"- (nitrogen filled wrappers that hold sliced strawberries dipped in cream/chocolate)*).
My attention goes to partial wheels of cheesecake served upturned on their sides. Single serving sizes vary. The food tastes gross and doesn't nourish me. I don't want to eat it, but I feel obligated to because I've taken it.
I'm hustled out of the way by an aggressive server who makes way for a set of business partners who have paid to eat. Members of another team choose to gather behind me in a grandstand. A third set stops for a post-celebration ceremony after completing their LGBTQ community fundraiser.

The celebration occurred adjacent to a mini-mall *(to the right)* which houses a variety of small business frontages.

As I stand to the side, I watch fit muscular men walk around in neoprene harnesses and jockstraps amongst young heteronormative families who are seated and dining. Attendees occasionally pause to introduce themselves by first whispering in each other's ears, then announcing new friendships to the group with a microphone that drops from the ceiling on a coiled black spring-like cable.

My team walks a couple steps ahead of me as we pass a large celebration occurring along a strip of hotels. Each hotel party fundraises for a different nonprofit beneficiary.]

[0801.2 / 2036] [I learn I have a large amount of cash in an account. I decide to leave it untouched, indefinitely. I want the story to be that I've taken odd jobs as a handyman, barista, etc. that generate enough revenue to give the appearance that I'm *just getting by.*" There will be a day when I can take it all out and instantly become a multi-millionaire. I'll write a book about the exquisite experience of delaying gratification.] //

⁎⁎

WHEELS: #0012, #0066, #0204, #0220
MICROPHONE: #0009, #0012, #0060, #0069
GROSS: #0045, #0193, #0218
LGBTQ: #0212

⁎⁎

#0802 - August 6, 2019 @ 02:00 (San Francisco, California)

[0802.1 / 2037] [I attend a party. I arrive *"on time,"* just slightly ahead of a *"deadline,"* and share knowledge about *"embodied cognition."* THE HEDONISTS *(expressive, sharp, and direct)* attend and stand out among a sea of faces as I give my talk. I've become well practiced and apt at *"stretching time"* through simply stretching my body. I make it my goal to invite everyone else to experience a similar mild non-ordinary state of consciousness.] //

⁎⁎

EMBODIED: #0045
DEADLINE: #0081
NON-ORDINARY: #0026, #0200

⁎⁎

#0803 - August 6, 2019 @ 03:02 (San Francisco, California)

[0803.1 / 2038] [I attend a gala/birthday event at a massive mansion, surrounded by a variety of engaging characters. In a grand hall intricate floral patterns are projected in soft gold light on a vast wall, demonstrating a new tool *(the size of a grain of rice)* placed inconspicuously in the center of a room. THE BREWMASTER stands in a side room in front of a series of decorations and ornaments incongruent to the season. People drink champagne nearby and disregard the haphazard, unkempt storage concept. Part of their invitation asked that they assist in resetting the ballroom for the forthcoming season.

The gathering marks the 50th birthday celebration for the "MASTER PRANKSTER"

547

whose title is spelled out in bubble block letters on a cake. One group watches an interactive movie in the basement, while rowdier festivities occur one level up. I stop and make conversation with THE NOMINEE *(independent, visionary, and resolute)* on a stairwell and "tag in" THE ROMANTIC who proceeds downstairs to claim my vacant spot on the couch between a crew of flirtatious queer boys.

A cable car system on the exterior of the house makes for more rapid transport between the giant levels of the property. I ride it from the top floor to the bottom taking in majestic views of grand cities of the world at night. I spot an emerging *"Black Rock City"* off in the distance. Another feature on display at the party are *"reality portals."* I stick my head in one and note people with prestigious titles *(but who are barely present)* have rented office boxes that overlook the 405. They work while they're on vacation. Some support actors, Pulitzer Prize winners, etc.] //

✻

Maj. = 15- *THE ROMANTIC: #0820*
CABLE: #0321, #0370
MANSION: #0128, #0143, #0151, #0184
THE BREWMASTER: #0805

✻

#0804 - August 7, 2019 @ 04:29 (San Francisco, California)

[0804.1 / 2039] [I march into a meeting with THE AUDIOLOGIST *(provocative, revealed, and true)* and a bunch of new faces. I sit down at a conference table and realize I'm across from the band "GHOST" who all work day jobs as bank tellers. During the meeting I'm informed I've been laid off, though because I've been a member of the band it makes the blow of that decision much easier to stomach.

"I'm sorry I didn't have more opportunities to create with you," I say as I look at the group and exit the conference.

I pass THE AUDIOLOGIST at a corner as I depart the building.

I'm captivated by a wall with a giant projection screen. A blue background with a white lined grid expands and contracts like a massive, "breathing mesh." Upon inspection of the projection above a couch, I notice the grid lines are strings of code. I take a moment to write THE ATHEIST a note which reads:

"FUCK YEAH DUDE! I WAS PART OF GHOST!
They're my buddies. It made getting laid that much easier!"

I call THE CONNECTOR who's already aware of my professional news.

"Have you been eating enough nourishing food? No. Sure, you've haven't! What you need is all the California produce you can eat. I'll send it home with you later if I have to," she commands.

The situation feels good, obvious, and complete. I have zero concern about finding another job. I'm left with the image of undulating lines of code for a product on which my *(now former)* team continues development.

I recall flashes of text strings from within the undulating grid as I walk further and further from my former place of employment:

Syntax Matters.] //

✲✲

Maj. = 4- THE CONNECTOR: #0815, 8- THE ATHEIST: #0818
GRID: #0012, #0017, #0021, #0079, #0125
CODE: #0060, #0077, #0113, #0123, #0240
MESH: #0006, #0021, #0028

✲✲

#0805 - August 7, 2019 @ 05:30 (San Francisco, California)
*Four levels deep in a dream state. I awaken and record this content three times before actually waking up to write it down. *

[0805.1 / 2040] [THE RECONCILIATOR decides she wants to give me $8000 in cash after we spend a night out with THE AGONY *(just, committed, and vocal)* and THE BREWMASTER.
"I left a big stack of paper in your bag."
"Well, I'm a proponent of the banking system and let me tell you why. It takes away the risk of you losing your stack of paper. I can transfer it to you electronically anywhere in the world, very simply, with the click of a button. I can also open an account for you."
She takes some time to contemplate as we depart her condo building to get some late-night grub.
A woman overhears our conversation shift from banking to prospective real estate acquisitions and interjects, *"Oh I live right down the street from there!"*
THE RECONCILIATOR nods, mildly annoyed by the prospect of this woman as a neighbor. She already comes off as too nosey.]

[0805.2 / 2041] [People spin around and become possessed after a group of witch doctors touch them. All those handled, fall into a soul-loss trance. Their eyes turn completely white. The witch doctors want to give me a similar treatment, which I accept as a challenge. As I spin around, I'm able to identify all the cords from different beings attempting to gain entry to my personal bubble. I cut the cords. The entities shoot new cords at me, but I spin out of the way before they stick.]

[0805.3 / 2042] [A wizard hat made out of crepe paper stands adjacent to a temple. It burns up in a bright flash. An uneducated man comments on the construction of the hat, not believing people's conjectures that it would burn very quickly.
"I need to learn more about math. You guys are talking about things I just don't understand," he plainly states.
Note: *I've recorded this scenario twice in different deeper states*]

[0805.4 / 2043] [I'm guided to keep an impression of "the artist" in my space as a way of working with doubt and creative impasse. Energies exist that I need to get neutral to, and have no thing about when they "pop around." Things to allow. Allies. Things to let be. Resistance to release.] //

⚛

Min. = ♥- THE RECONCILIATOR: #0880
WIZARD: #0045, #0056, #0124, #0134, #0143, #0371, #0396
THE AGONY: #0880
THE BREWMASTER: #1017

⚛

#0806 - August 7, 2019 @ 06:25 (San Francisco, California)

[0806.1 / 2044] [I stand outside a large building by a crosswalk. I'm mesmerized by two Russian Men who walk by. One wears "Heelys." He rolls by effortlessly, to which I goofily respond by pointing and saying, *"Hey look! He floats!"*]

[806.2 / 2045] [I find myself in a red-lit restaurant where a cute young man I don't know extends his arm in my direction. He offers me a pineapple margarita in a mug, right as the surrounding group rises to offer him a toast. I raise my arm and cheer for him with the group.
"What do you suppose he's up to next?" the woman sitting next to me at the table asks.
I take a big gulp from the mug before disclosing I don't know who he is. When a waitress returns, I hand her an envelope full of old receipts.
"Throw these away please."
"Do I need to know what they are?"
"No, they're just old Russian propaganda that can be eliminated. They wanted to use them on me, but I discovered them before they could. It's time to get rid of 'em."] //

⁂
ENVELOPE: #0037, #0055, #0232
WAITRESS: #0226
PINEAPPLE: #0219
⁂

#0807 - August 7, 2019 @ 07:07 (San Francisco, California)

[0807.1 / 2046] [I'm on my way to see THE DANCER and the baby. When I enter the ground floor of their apartment complex, I pass a wall that discloses there have been 13 births in the last week. As I look through the window with THE WEAVER, waiting for THE DANCER to arrive, I see a woman hit a neighbor's garbage can with her car in a driveway. She and her three kids exit the vehicle and swiftly move towards the door. The woman has annoyed every neighbor on the block, after similarly striking fences, vehicles and other property with her car. She's considered a loose cannon. I go outside and in the company of various other neighbors we collectively yell, *"HEY! The cops have been called!"*
"Don't call us for something like that," the cops clap back after they arrive and inspect the scene.
GRANDMA and I go back inside and sit at a table. We plate small portions of sliced strawberries and mangoes, which we then use in our own adapted version of a sculpture game. I decide a fun prank would be to stack equivalent sized pieces of strawberry on top of one another.
"Oh Dear," GRANDMA says as she attempts to determine what I've created.
THE DANCER calls the landline to let us know she's been delayed in traffic but will arrive shortly.
The female neighbor comes out face made up, with a huge bouffant hairdo topped by an enormous white bow. She exaggerates her gestures as she publicly apologizes for all the chaos she's caused on the street.] //

⁂

Maj. = 0- THE WEAVER: #0808, 01- THE DANCER: #0818, 11- GRANDMA: #0808
DRIVEWAY: #0037, #0151, #0214, #0231, #0300, #0361
MANGO: #0035, #0319

⁂

#0808 - August 8, 2019 @ 04:46 (The Presidio of San Francisco, California)

[0808.1 / 2047] [I stand at the start of a trailhead overlooking a vast mountain range. I wear a base layer, flip flops, and a cute powder blue cycling cap. We're about to start a significant climb across the mountain range with a group. The trek is planned to take multiple days. A group of three people ahead of us are just about to begin. *"Shall we go on a hike?"* I playfully shout in their direction, laughing and knowing I'll need to layer up before I'm actually ready. Two of the three laugh at my comment, the third one doesn't respond to my brand of humor and believes I'm being flagrant and irresponsible based on how I'm currently dressed.]

[0808.2 / 2048] [I go into the bathroom to take a shower. Along one side are baker's racks stacked with boxes. I've been asked by THE WEAVER and GRANDMA to puncture the sides of each box near the bottom and leave a, *"waning crescent impression."* When I finish that task two other stacks of boxes on the same racks require similar handling. I need to take a shower and refresh before I can meet my group for the hike.] //

⁂

Maj. = 0- THE WEAVER: #0810, 11-GRANDMA: #0851
PUNCTURE: #0035, #0180, #0389
SHOWER: #0036, #0044, #0058, #0146, #0172, #0182, #0209, #0330, #0379, #0394
HIKE: #0200, #0246

⁂

#0809 - August 9, 2019 @ 02:22 (San Francisco, California)

[0809.1 / 2049] [FRANK ROBINSON gives me a tour of his home. An escalator with a piece of carpet on the top stair prevents him from tripping when he steps off. Everything is covered in plastic, including the device that keeps his bed warm at night, which he ritually unwraps and rewraps every day. Common desk drawer items are loosely scattered on the floor. *"Access for today's necessary tools is simple!"* he jovially exclaims. His mood is elevated. He's fully ambulatory and able to keep moving, which he considers important at, *"his age."* I'm humored and enriched. I love connecting with my out-of-body friend in this heaven adjacent dimension.] //

⁂

FRANK ROBINSON: #1343
TOOLS: #0009, #0233, #0360, #0396
HUMORED: #0012, #0025, #0027, #0070, #0089, #0097
ESCALATOR: #0027, #0045, #0089, #0106, #0311, #0337

⁂

#0810 - August 9, 2019 @ 03:49 (San Francisco, California)

[0810.1 / 2050] [THE LAWYER helps a young Black woman complete her law school applications. One in progress for "UAB" is spread out on a dining table along with various alumni publications from other universities under consideration. THE LAWYER is precise and meticulous when giving feedback to the woman on how to frame her admissions essays as they participate in an active teleconference with an unknown third party. The young woman becomes agitated and screams into the phone. *"Michelle. They STOLE it! They stole THIS! They stole THAT! I'm straight HOOD!"* When the emotional waves subside, she's given guidance on how to conduct herself during business networking lunches.]

[0810.2 / 2051] [I wear a safari hat and become preoccupied with tying up one half that's come loose and flaps down over my left ear. Oddly the string has come unthreaded from a brass eyelet. Should be a simple thing to remedy, but fixing it befuddles me.]

[0810.3 / 2052] [I'm in a garage looking through boxes of bulk food items intended for use in a community "India Day" celebration that THE WEAVER's agreed to produce with THE TIGER MOM *(firm, emotive, and energized)*. I take a diet cream soda from a box and drink it as I traverse the garage, unable to find other items I've been tasked to pull out. I mutter in to a phone, *"I've been inside this hologram before."*] //

✻
Maj. = 0- THE WEAVER: #0823, 5- THE LAWYER: #0835
INDIA: #0117, #0223, #0224, #0225, #0226
HOLOGRAM: #0004, #0024, #0132
THIRD: #0012, #0022, #0023, #0062, #0066, #0088, #0176, #0234
THE TIGER MOM: #0811
✻

#0811 - August 9, 2019 @ 05:15 (San Francisco, California)

[0811.1 / 2053] [My goal is to get a new key cut. I climb up a structure THE CARPENTER built, filled with stacks of decorative boxes. On the top is a stainless-steel tray that has various pills *(Aspirin, Aleve, and Motrin)*, uncut keys and a single crisp dollar bill upturned on its side in the shape of an "S." Appraisers arrive to inspect THE CARPENTER's garden. The garden's been built in an interior greenhouse in a subterranean cave-like basement that is very tall overhead. One of the appraisers is fascinated by THE CARPENTER's taffy plants.
"You've really built something marvelous here. It's absolutely WONDERFUL," one of the young men remarks, in astonishment to THE CARPENTER.
"Well, I'll eventually go back to work just as soon as I stop having fun spending money and want to go make it again," he playfully responds.]

[0811.2 / 2054] [I text myself during a yoga class. THE TIGER MOM *(flirtatious, abstract, and honest)* asks me to leave immediately.]

. . .

[0811.3 / 2055] [THE CARPENTER says, *"I'll go back and get a job after I'm done playing music."* ***"Well...you better start practicing so you actually start playing."*** I see him sitting with a guitar in a chair on a long gravel driveway, playing some licks. One of the uncut keys I've grabbed confuses me. I'm not certain if it's a skeleton key or a blank template. It appears to be made of sterling silver smelted in the form of a miniature spoon.] //

⁂

Maj. = 1- THE CARPENTER: #0823
KEY: #1256, #1276, #1310
GARDEN: #1261, #1301
THE TIGER MOM: #1422

⁂

#0812 - August 10, 2019 @ 04:06 (San Francisco, California)

[0812.1 / 2056] [I enter a massive gothic cathedral, lit dimly by candles. I proceed to the front row and take a seat in front of THE EXCOMMUNICATED *(shocked, hurt, and dismissed)* and a woman I've never met. I wait to perform a Bach Organ Concerto. I hold the music gently on my lap.
"You don't have to do any of it!" An omniscient voice playfully whispers overhead.
I sit in presence and watch group after group after group of people walk by as the voice repeats the same phrase. In each group I constantly make eye contact with one person. The same face shows up, overlaid on different bodies. Sometimes we laugh. Other times we cry. Other times still, we stick out our tongues. Sometimes we don't acknowledge one another. This continues infinitely. My inner monologue is consistent: ***"Tat Tvam Asi." "Tat Tvam Asi." "Tat Tvam Asi."*** Neutral and quiet. I am that.] //

⁂

PRESENCE: #0015, #0082, #0101, #0298, #0393
MONOLOGUE: #0002
GOTHIC CATHEDRAL: #0032, #0158
THE EXCOMMUNICATED: #1023

⁂

#0813 - August 10, 2019 @ 06:14 (San Francisco, California)

[0813.1 / 2057] [It's the 13th of a month. I'm reminded by my female host that she and I have scheduled a tarot reading. She regrets to inform me that based on "astrological reasons" our appointment must be delayed until the 27th and that she must immediately depart for Lake Tahoe.]

[0813.2 / 2058] [I'm invited to join a party with a group at an upstairs apartment. The hosts just left a young girl's birthday celebration in the unit below theirs at the trough of a U-shaped staircase. Two men at the adult gathering share the same birthday with the young girl. They're determined to attend her party and harbor some annoyance toward her parents. In the men's opinion, the parents celebrate the young girl's developmental achievements too frequently.

We're careful as a group to not step too heavily on the upstairs floor. They've gone to bed downstairs. We want to be respectful neighbors while continuing to celebrate the men. The apartment is a bachelor pad. It could use updated carpet, fixtures, and a fresh coat of paint on the dingy stained walls.] //

⁂

RESPECTFUL: #0155
BACHELOR PAD: #0144
OPINION: #1248
DELAYED: #1294

⁂

#0814 - August 11, 2019 @ 03:57 (San Francisco, California)

[0814.1 / 2059] [*"The key to understanding dreams is to ask yourself the question:* **'How is this familiar?'**"]

[0814.2 / 2060] [I've gone out to party with a group of people. I discover myself in a bed as other people come home from being out, and I'm not certain how I got there. I overhear THE NURSE talking to a group of people on the street corner beneath my window. She tells them she's, *"40."* I'm guided to rouse, walk to my balcony and call down to her.
"50. You're 50. She's 50."
This upsets her. I walk away and go to the bathroom. I run into THE PSYCHIATRIST and a group of young people who've gathered and sit on the sinks. The entire group scatters, taking off in Ubers that instantly travel away from each other in different directions. I'm left alone, and weigh whether or not to walk home as deeper detail quickly fades.] //

⁂

Maj. = 13- THE NURSE: #0902
Min. = ♠- THE PSYCHIATRIST: #0839
FAMILIAR: #0006, #0012, #0014, #0016, #0017, #0019
OVERHEAR: #0029, #0033, #0045, #0088, #0100

⁂

#0815 -August 12, 2019 @ 02:58 (San Francisco, California)

[0815.1 / 2061] [The family moves back into a house on a cul de sac, where they lived in 1983. Some of the rooms have been untouched by the current family who's occupied the residence for many years. The current inhabitants use social media platforms to generate income. Two gazebos stand in the backyard. One is modern and elegantly up fitted with white cabinetry and luxury fixtures. Its use is shared by the entire neighborhood. The other gazebo is located near a pond surrounded by autumn leaves (*which seems odd and novel as it's 4th of July weekend*).
A few houses down, a man stands on his driveway, arm outstretched and holding a hula hoop that spins quickly on a tether of fishing line creating the appearance of a carnival glass globe alongside his torso. He casually tells his young mesmerized daughter (*who stares vacantly into the globe*) that, *"Lady Liberty has been arrested."*

555

Standing in the kitchen of the old family house, THE CHILD says she's hungry for breakfast. GRANDPA proceeds to make her pancakes on a hot griddle installed in the kitchen island. I pull her hand back before she can touch the hot surface. I see her little hand severely blistered moments before it happens, and act to prevent the injury. We all encourage her to take a step back. Old tool kits, cleaning supplies, and medicines in the pantry (*Nyquil bottles*) are all dated to expire in 1983.
"*Who spends their time and money looking at the Instagram account of a family that lives in Beavercreek, Ohio in 1983?*" I ask the outgoing owner.
"*Really dumb bored people,*" he states matter of factly.]

[0815.2 / 2062] [I'm in a mall populated with predominantly ultra-high end retail frontages, each hidden behind flat marble walls on the basement level of a building. One simple space with circular tables offers a violet leather fold over satchel for $5000. This maker's retail space is next to a bridal gown designer, which closes its marble door in my face before I can enter and browse. I turn around and am introduced to the QUEEN OF KENYA, a stunning Nubian goddess who stands tall, slim and statuesque in her gown. She and I have met multiple times.]

[0815.3 / 2063] [I've arrived at the old family home at 11:00pm, when I awaken from a nap after attending the awards celebration where I first met the QUEEN OF KENYA. THE CONVERT sits on the couch in the sunlight, which confuses me based on the time of day. THE CONNECTOR and THE FIREFIGHTER have both fallen asleep on another segment of the sectional couch. Earlier, they attended the awards ceremony with me.]

[0815.4 / 2064] [I descend a long passage near a highway, en route to a gathering space for team members. When I get to a cabin, THE KIWI (*brotherly, strong, and timid*) passes me. I participate in an exhibition tennis match with a woman. The ceilings are just 9 feet tall. The ball ricochets wildly as we bat it back and forth. I strike my opponent with the ball multiple times. I'm not fully participating. She quickly wins the match with ease, to thunderous applause. A group of teens hold up a large pastel blue foam totem that denotes where we've agreed to gather down around the next bend of a mountain highway after the tennis competition concludes.] //

⁂

Maj. = 3- THE CHILD: *#0846,* 4 - THE CONNECTOR: *#0820*
Min. = ♥- GRANDPA: *#0846,* ♥-THE FIREFIGHTER: *#0830*
BREAKFAST: #0017, #0019, #0124, #0171, #0382
KENYA: #0378

⁂

#0816 - August 13, 2019 @ 03:22 (San Francisco, California)

[0816.1 / 2065] [It's my first day of work at a new job. It's 1:00pm. I'm rushed with others to an elevator through a dimly lit space. On the way I'm accused of pushing a woman in a short pink dress (*when in fact shoves me from behind before I ever see her*). I trip and strike the right toe of my fine Italian leather wingtip, which splits from the sole, and exposes frayed stitching with a large chunk gored from the shoe. It'll need to be repaired ASAP.

We all wait for a prolonged period for the up-level managers to get clear on their talking points. The meeting was scheduled for 1:00pm. I feel like going home at 3:00pm. At that hour, the meeting still hasn't commenced which suggests that I won't like this organization, much less the job.]

[0816.2 / 2066] [A young couple both work for a marijuana dispensary. They decide to hook up while at work. They're interrupted by another pot dealer who charges into the scene. Their goods are sold in a box with a lenticular case that sequentially animates the word "NOW" in bold capital letters printed in vibrant tones of orange and yellow. The colors radiate outwards from the center.] //

⁜
NEW JOB: #0151, #0274, #0306, #0323
MARIJUANA: #0017
FRAYED: #0386
⁜

#0817 - August 13, 2019 @ 04:54 (San Francisco, California)

[0817.1 / 2067] [I'm in line and handed a coupon for 10% off a coffee, which I present as an admission ticket to a boat ride. Two boats, equally full of people, motor out to the middle of the bay and spin wildly and donut-like in opposite directions, with an intention of coaxing sharks to come to the surface for observation. It makes me feel dizzy and unsafe. Off in the distance on the water is a building sized cube of pineapple bobbing and floating above the surface. It's decorated with cherries, grapes and vibrantly colored fruits to entice the giant fish to come near, feast, and visit with us]

[0817.2 / 2068] [I've taken a part time job at a trampoline factory as a data processor. I fill out a few rows of information in a single spreadsheet, and have satisfied all requirements to get paid. I have three interactions with people via email. I'm most interested in corresponding with a person who's currently in South Africa. An office contest revolving around "name" is in play, but I'm not certain what to do to play along. The reward for winning is an extra vacation day.

I write on a white board in black capital letters:

"SENIOR LEADERS - 87".

In small red letters between and beneath I write:

"i n t e r n s - 86."

Those who've been with the group for years best those who've been there for one day, by just one point. I'm embarrassed for the bosses for their slim margin of victory. Their days of running the firm are dwindling.]

557

. . .

[0817.3 / 2069] [I go to the back door of the home of a well-known public figure whom I know, admire and respect. It's night time. I consider breaking into their house. The purpose for my visit quickly is forgotten and I wake up.] //

⁑

TRAMPOLINE: #0026, #0306
SOUTH AFRICA: #0218
SHARKS: #0223, #1354

⁑

#0818 - August 13, 2019 @ 06:08 (San Francisco, California)

[0818.1 / 2070] [I run around the back of a field, amidst a crowd attempting to record this dream. Some yell at me with an intention to distract me. I come to, and duck under a split-rail fence, while recalling that the dream I woke from involved being in a converted brick factory space which had two different sculptures on display. The art was created by "Daniel Day," and was gifted to the space before the artist had achieved any critical acclaim.
The "valuable" sculpture is a three-foot-tall visage of a man, unidentified and without title. My attention fixates on a large mixed media sculpture on the opposite end of the hall composed of bent, twisted train track metal *(shaped roughly like a human body)*, with draped chains of casted concrete surrounding its wrists, which extend upward and out in prayer. Both pieces are highly sought after.]

[0818.2 / 2071] [THE DANCER and THE ATHEIST arrive for dinner and conversation with a second woman with them. They went on vacation together and THE ATHEIST slept with her. They tell me they're divorcing and I feel deep sadness.
"It's my circumstance to get complete with," THE DANCER says to me.
"Why didn't you reach out and let me know sooner?" I ask with tears streaming down my face.
"I didn't want to trouble you or anyone else with my burden."
My mind races and I feel helpless.] //

⁑

Maj. = 2- THE DANCER: #0846, 8-THE ATHEIST: #0846
MIXED MEDIA: #0175
SADNESS: #0045, #0066, #0102, #0129, #0389
BURDEN: #0034, #0047, #0171, #0281
OPPOSITE: #0301, #0339, #0384, #0395, #0396

⁑

#0819 - August 13, 2019 @ 07:36 (San Francisco, California)

[0819.1 / 2072] [I go to the gym. I encounter an older man whom I've previously met once. He's sweet and fumbles through his words as he asks me to join him in the showers to play. I respectfully decline and continue to manually power a stair step machine, allowing my bottom foot to fall off at the lowest point of the machine. It strikes the floor before I step up again.

Three younger fit guys briefly have a conversation on their phones, while standing around a weight bench next to my machine then quickly depart. A woman taps me and requests to use the stair stepper. I dismount and let her use it. I turn around and am face-to-face with a tall frizzy haired guy named "<u>Kyle</u>." He wears glasses. His hair is partially pulled back. He's funny and full of wit. He's an actor that lives in "the valley." I live up on the hill. "<u>Kyle</u>" shares an apartment with his sister and his mother.

He suggests we get together, but I decline without discussing my other plans.

"Sooooo you live with the snobs?"

"I dunno about that. I just like the views of the city from up there."

Thank you cards are scattered on a nearby table next to a box of old magazines *(including playboy #1 with Marilyn Monroe)* left by the owners of the gym as evidence of who their friends and family are.]

[0819.2 / 2073] [I attend morning yoga in the inner courtyard of a villa. Ambient music by "FOUR TET" gently dances on air. Participants are positioned in the form of a square at the perimeter, facing out towards the courtyard walls. A tall man with a haircut similar to mine *(but 2" longer)* pulls his hair back while staring intensely at a thick vertically growing vine. *"Wow, that guy is really patient and persistent,"* I think just before waking.] //

⁂

FOUR TET: #0877

OLDER: #0066, #0172, #0198, #0209, #0275, #0354, #0380

PATIENT: #0011, #0111, #0293

FRIZZY: #0163

THANK YOU: #0010, #0059, #0063, #0125, #0390

WEIGHT: #0019, #0088, #0189, #0322

⁂

#0820 - August 14, 2019 @ 04:19 (San Francisco, California)

[0820.1 / 2074] [I'm the basement level of a grand estate, like a BELK mansion in a southern state. People gather around a nun and celebrate her life well lived. She's seated on a chair in the round. When formalities conclude the crowd mingles and the nun transforms into an elderly male wheelchair using veteran, who sloppily gorges himself on pie and cake, eating indiscriminately from a tray set across his lap. He grotesquely shoves piece after piece of cheesecake and pie in his mouth.

I spend time trying to connect a next generation Bluetooth device to the property sound system, to support a group exercise led by THE INTERVENTIONIST *(clinical, thorough, and genuine)*. I'm passed over as a participant, but am asked to sign in and verify I've completed the course.

"I'll sign, but indulge me and let me touch the play board," which I do with the toe of my right shoe.

A large conical pit in the center of the floor allows participants to slide down the sidewalls and rebound off a soft pink air filled bladder.

I move to a couch and have conversation with THE CONNECTOR and THE SCHOOL

559

TEACHER *(anxious, overworked, and mildly neurotic)*, as we eat a mound of white cake with strawberry filling off a large silver platter. They incoherently discuss "Friends and Family" campouts and their absurdly expensive ticket prices.
  "Do you know how much fucking money I paid for those friendships?...and the miracles?...and the magic?"
  "No, I just remember being really fucked up and having this guy tell me...*pregnant pause*"
  "She should have at least let you look at it."
  THE CONNECTOR requests a ride home, but it's a bit unclear if she's going with me, or someone else. Before exiting I see a teenage boy head upstairs wearing a red "MAGA hat." I shout up to him, and when he turns back the hat changes to a dark blue from red. I turn to go upstairs and encounter THE ROMANTIC, who's occupied with entertaining a small group of friends. He's surprised to see me. When I attempt saying hello my words are garbled, muddled, and inarticulate from the start. The interaction becomes delightfully odd.
  "Maybe I'll see you at the burn?" I prod.
  "I just got a new job at LinkedIn, so I'm hoping to go, but it's not likely. I'll have some time later to sauna if you want to come back later," THE ROMANTIC replies.
  I exit the front door, walk across a large cobblestone parking lot, and retrieve a bike. I pause and consider texting THE ROMANTIC that we likely won't cross paths. I decide not to text. I raise the bike's kickstand and move towards an exit. Giant serpentine glass doors swivel rapidly, cautiously monitored by a young bald man seated in the center of a round desk. It's unclear why this technology was selected. Pressurization? Sterilization?
  "If I had your job I'd just sit here and stare at these things all day," I say in momentary wonderment of the doors. The man doesn't respond.] //

⁂

Maj. = 4- THE CONNECTOR: #0848, 15- THE ROMANTIC: #0905
SERPENTINE: #0025, #0042, #0148, #0154, #0312, #0326, #0371
BLADDER: #0035
STERILIZATION: #0145
THE INTERVENTIONIST: #0826

⁂

#0821 - August 14, 2019 @ 05:14 (San Francisco, California)

[0821.1 / 2075] [I'm in an industrial kitchen in front of a stainless-steel prep table. A pair of hands opens a small red igloo cooler and reveals my kidneys, which have been placed on ice for transport. They're taken from the cooler and set on a soiled plastic cutting board. Food residue from a recently prepared meal remains. I stare at the organs and marvel at the miracle they are, and wonder what purpose removing them from my body serves. A large sharp knife readies itself to thinly slice and serve them up, *"a carpaccio."*]

[0821.2 / 2076] [My GUIDE "L" gently touches me on the right nape of my neck, as I walk down a stone staircase to a basement. I'm given a parody of a song to sing when things seem to get challenging: *"The only job...is a burden. The only job...is a burden."*]

· · ·

[0821.3 / 2077] [An interactive painting hangs suspended in the air. It's wall sized and a group of women stand near it, discussing, and contemplating. The painting is in an upstairs gallery and seems to predict and verify the paths of natural disasters in real time across the earth. A large volcanic eruption in the ocean has pushed up a new island chain, whose ripples send off waves that grow into tsunamis as they spread across the vast body of water.] //

⁂

PARODY: #0021

RIPPLES: #0038

MIRACLE: #0019, #0126

⁂

#0822 - August 14, 2019 @ 06:29 (San Francisco, California)

[0822.1 / 2078] [I enter a music studio with rough cuts of multiple tracks. I use my mouth to create additional percussion overdubs which will be used in the next phase of mixing. A toilet in the center of the room fills to the brim with clean water and almost spills out on the floor just as I flush it.]

[0822.2 / 2079] [I stand with a group on a platform overlooking a marathon finish line. A woman casually strolls against the flow of traffic eating a banana. *"You! Hey you! You're being REALLY annoying right now! Yes YOU! You are better than that!"* I exasperatedly crow at the woman.]

[0822.3 / 2080] [A man and woman leave for a morning walk with their golden Labrador puppy. When they return the dog is 10x larger, with short bronze curls and exceptionally long, slender legs. I go down to greet them *"Wow, you're beautiful! What a good boy you are!"* I say to the dog who stands at my eye level.] //

⁂

BANANA: #0054, #0183, #0375

PUPPY: #0249, #0255

BEAUTIFUL: #1247, #1253

⁂

#0823 - August 14, 2019 @ 09:22 (San Francisco, California)

[0823.1 / 2081] [A red faucet pours out a steady flow of viscous red paint onto a terracotta template, which will be used to press vinyl records. *"You can have any amount of healing you want, whenever you need,"* an omniscient voice neutrally states in the center of my head as I observe the abstraction.]

[0823.2 / 2082] [At a lakefront property, three young men ask us if they can park our cars on the other side of the land. All they want, they say, is to be fed lunch. It's clear to us that they're up to no good. We recommend they leave, which angers them. They shout, swear, and slur at us as they gallop away.

A robbery takes place at the lake house. Two female burglars bungle the job. The house is owned by two men, whom the women have corralled in the bathroom at gunpoint. The women ask their captives to rob themselves. This triggers one of the men who leaps at one of the women and crushes her windpipe with his bare hands. He's later charged by the police with, "bridal-cide." THE WEAVER's pretty neutral when I tell her about it later.

"Well, that makes perfect sense," she says without much response.

I take off my blue pork pie hat, and in so doing cut a long segment of my hair off that was pulled through and held out by a length of brown razor ribbon. Part of my forehead is shorn bald. I cry a little as I show THE WEAVER. Neither she nor THE CARPENTER are taken by my emotional response to unintentional hair loss.] //

⁂

Maj. = 0- THE WEAVER: #0865, 1- THE CARPENTER: #0846
HEALING: #0019, #0037, #0039, #0046, #0125, #0143, #0158
RAZOR: #0079
SENSE: #0035, #0036, #0044, #0065, #0090

⁂

#0824 - August 15, 2019 @ 03:57 (San Francisco, California)
*Multiple sequence fragments occur intermittent and unclear. *

[0824.1 / 2083] [Theater company at night. Star of the show. A group of young actors play out a family scene.]

[0824.2 / 2084] [THE FAIRY GODPARENTS follow up with me on our conversation we had last Christmas.]

[0824.3 / 2085] [Relationship celebration sequence that highlights THE ADVOCATE *(tenacious, resilient, and miraculous)* and his husband.]

[0824.4 / 2086] [Donating blood.]

[0824.5 / 2087] [I exit a building and am shielded by my team as we pile into a truck.]

[0824.6 / 2088] [The varnish on a single panel of wood flooring begins to peel. I grab it and pull it to strip it off.]

[0824.7 / 2089] [A young couple embraces. I know them. They're friendly. They're sensual and sexual with one another. When I grab my cheeks and say, *'I can't believe it's been 72 hours since they've seen each other,'* a studio audience is revealed and lightly applauds.]

. . .

[0824.8 / 2090] [A substance known to cure multiple cancers in adults is found to amplify the spread of brain cancer in some children.]

[0824.9 / 2091] [An emotional support chinchilla is brought through the blood center to distract donors and keep them calm.]

[0824.10 / 2092] [A banner in a hallway next to an art exhibit has a giant set of sparkling green, menacing snake eyes. They're upsetting to look at. THE NINER'S FAN (*contrary, free, and rebellious*) hands me a stack of poker chips with LCDs illuminating their dynamic value. One moment they're worth $10, the next $55. She places them in my hand and gives me a kiss. I know when I leave the parking lot, I won't see her again for a very long time.] //

✳

THEATER: #0133, #0147, #0170, #0359
VERY LONG: #0117, #0170
$55: #0021
CONVERSATION: #0025, #0037, #0039
DONORS: #0128
THE FAIRY GODPARENTS: #1126
THE NINER'S FAN: #1233

✳

#0825 - **August 16, 2019 @ 04:57 (San Francisco, California)**

[0825.1 / 2093] [I observe an exam. The grading scale is strange. The number of people influenced is the denominator. The numerator is the number of questions answered correctly. Two different scores compiled in a similar way are added together to create a cumulative score.]

[0825.2 / 2094] [I make music with the RED HOT CHILI PEPPERS at a beach front property. I'm tasked to write the outro to a song. I ask them to, *"cue up track 17 for overdubs."* I take a seat at my keyboard and begin to play sequences of incomprehensibly fast chromatic flourishes. Strobe lights flash overhead as I play. I experience my hands as half the size they are when I'm not playing. They shrink at speed.]

[0825.3 / 2095] [Children walk their oversized black dog around a parking lot. They drop the leash and the dog sprints away. The dog is quick and it's a challenge to corral it, but I'm able to grab the leash, give it back to the boy who dropped it, and calm the dog down.] //

✳

LEASH: #0211
SCALE: #0248, #0360, #0393, #0394

BLACK: #1255, #1275, #1284
DOG: #1204, #1268
⁂

#0826 - August 16, 2019 @ 6:13am (San Francisco, California)

[**0826.1 / 2096**] [I hear voices talking up and back to the right side of my head. I tune in to see if it's "L̲." It sounds like a male voice. Low resonance. I feel like we're calibrating agreements prior to heading out to the desert to work.]

[**0826.2 / 2097**] [I pass THE PASSIONATE BRAZILIAN (*sweet, strong, and unwavering*) on my way to the gym. We hug and have a conversation while embracing. He's on his way to see his husband. We both step away when we get erections. He comments on my physical appearance and asks if I'm on my way to hook up. *"No, I'm just going to Burning Man."*]

[**0826.3 / 2098**] [I see THE INTERVENTIONIST (*clear, informed, and sharp*) and THE BISEXUAL (*affable, honest, and unique*) at a bus stop. I glance away. When I look back two different faces stare at me. I pass a kiosk that sells tiny printed vanity t-shirts. (*Slogan: "Wife beaters for little girls"*). One shirt says, *"i.like.to.play.crazy."* in all lowercase. The shirts are extremely popular and quickly sell out.]

[**0826.4 / 2099**] [I'm on a flight to Asia. We're encouraged mid-flight to get up and exchange seats with a stranger. I wander the cabin and find a seat near the nose, as the plane dips into its initial descent. Two hours of flying time remain.] //

⅄
BURNING MAN: #0070, #0185, #0246, #0260, #0295
EXCHANGE: #0033, #0043, #0077, #0079, #0084
KIOSK: #0033, #0056, #0066, #0104, #0319
"L": #0968, #1157, #1318, #1385
THE PASSIONATE BRAZILIAN: #0930
⁂

INTERMISSION

CONSTELLATIONS: 2

CONTENTS

JOSHUA D. LUNDELL

⁎⁎⁎

MAJOR CONSTELLATIONS (22):
DESCRIPTIONS

✣

~Most frequently encountered reflections and select, non-exhaustive qualities~
Follow a constellation by turning to their dream of origin (#0000).

✣ **0 - THE WEAVER** ✣ *Encountered in 262 dreams between #0010-#1423 (18.2%)* = [The monad. Mother. Unity. Unconditional love. Infinite light of consciousness. Receptive. Tender. Nurturing. Supportive. Kind. Patient. A steadfast guide which nurtures the walk on the pathway of evolution.
   Likely to say: "True happiness is only possible when shared." "There is always something to learn." "Everything is a product of creative expression."] //

✣ **1 - THE CARPENTER** ✣ *Encountered in 207 dreams between #0012-#1433 (14.3%)* = [The dyad. Father. Courageous. Resilient. Consciousness. Aware. Unwaveringly supports true creativity.
   Likely to say: "I am you. You are me." "We're the dream and the dreamer." "Part of me is you." "Namaste." "Om Mani Peme Hung." "Aloha."] //

✣ **2 - THE DANCER** ✣ *Encountered in 173 dreams between #0002-#1434 (12%)* = [The self. Invisible force that unifies polarities. Dot connector. Prone to lose sight of itself along its multivariate quest. Highest expression of spirit and creative spark. Access to unconditional love. Unifies and balances aspects of the monad and dyad.
   Likely to say: "Hello Me!" "Love is naturally available to each of us. Our awakening is shared."] //

· · ·

567

⚜ 3 - THE CHILD ⚜ *Encountered in 107 dreams between #0102-#1437 (7.4%)* = [The spark of true nature. The seed of true creativity. Vulnerable, tender, and innocent. Unwaveringly determined. Learns with openness. Plays as an access to ingenuity. Helpless at times. Can't yet engage with life's cruel circumstances. Constantly reminded it's ok to not know. Explores and expresses the evolutionary essence held at its core.
Likely to say: *"Let's do that!" "I don't know." "Can I try? Let me try, please."*] //

⚜ 4 - THE CONNECTOR ⚜ *Encountered in 62 dreams between #0071-#1421 (4.3%)* = [The joy of full engagement. Confronts conditioning. Roils against superficiality, avoidance, and coping mechanisms. Essential to the transformation of entitlement and injustice, though occasionally their creative downloads can become distorted and bring overwhelm.
Likely to say: *"I'm in constant motion." "I struggle to find balance in all aspects of life." "This impressive mask hides my most extremely sensitive aspects."*] //

⚜ 5 - THE LAWYER ⚜ *Encountered in 54 dreams between #0080-#1438 (3.8%)* = [The armor. Reliant upon form. Reflects the conditioned ego. Often seems like a dictator. Dominating. Masculine. Tends to give power to the mind before the heart. Their growth depends on bringing the mind in service of the heart through compassionate confrontation.
Likely to say: *"I wear this face to engage an uncertain world, and it controls my life." "Much has happened to me. I act in certain ways because I haven't yet fully metabolized unjust trauma."*] //

⚜ 6 - THE PILOT ⚜ *Encountered in 37 dreams between #0129-#1404 (2.6%)* = [The friend. Awe. Excitement. Willing to evolve. Alive. Vital. Sees deeper meaning. Fascinated with evolution through play. Smiles. Tastes. Bends. Breaks. Throws. Sees objects through many different sensory capacities. Quickly assimilates knowledge and information.
Likely to say: *"I'm fascinated by learning, exploration, and direct experience." "I'm computation wielding, airplane flying, laser loving, faggot millennial Eurotrash."*] //

⚜ 7 - THE WORLDBRIDGER ⚜ *Encountered in 35 dreams between #0010-#1430 (2.4%)* = [The wise one. The elder. The healer. The Bishop. The headmaster. Represents the more transcendental, spiritual aspects of existence. The "at cause" directed energy of the "surren-dered spirit in right action." Wizard. Serves the non-conditional. No longer lives for the sake of the world, but attuned to broad spectrum creation. Sets challenges that support various stations of development.
Likely to say: *"Use your tools. Nothing is more powerful than you."*] //

⚜ 8 - THE ATHEIST ⚜ *Encountered in 35 dreams between #0020-#1380 (2.4%)* = [Resistant. Intermittently engaged. Righteous. Rational. Tends to protect their vulnerability by over-clocking masculinity. Part time relativist. Benefits from invitations to soften. Dutiful spouse, father and ally. Holds strong, fact-based opinions. Occasionally withdraws when threatened. Accustomed to being manipulated and abused. Working to release conditioning. Healing.
Likely to say: *"I'm more bark than bite." "Your argument is invalid." "I'm not wounded...you're wounded."*] //

. . .

⚛ **9 - THE FIDUCIARY** ⚛ *Encountered in 30 dreams between #0007-#1407 (2.1%)* = [Conditioned masculinity. Publicly polished. Privately messy. Impulsively paradoxical. Orderly. Compartmentalized. Avoids irrational fears at all costs. Triggered when reminded of unprocessed experiences. Tends to react in a familiar pattern without being aware of the trap of conditioning. Intellectually engages questions.
   Likely to say: "What conditioning?" "What circumstances bring me in and out of integrity."] //

⚛ **10 - THE ACTOR** ⚛ *Encountered in 29 dreams between #0066-#1426 (2%)* = [Soul guide. Anima/Animus. Lover. Calls forth suppressed energy, and things for which the spirit longs. Expressions of intimacy. Spark and flame. Screen on which perfection is projected. Attraction. Magnetic longing. Strides confidently along their own evolutionary path.
   Likely to say: "I'll show you deeper aspects of yourself that other friends avoid."] //

⚛ **11 - GRANDMA** ⚛ *Encountered in 27 dreams between #0013-#1433 (1.9%)* = [Wholeness. Provides a sense of fulfillment and completion. Acknowledges and closes prior evolutionary cycles. Offers an invitation to return to the original state. Often invisible, yet felt along the journey. Playfully points to areas of disintegration behind the scenes. Occasionally takes the role of coach.
   Likely to say: "Don't be overwhelmed and consumed by compulsive states." "Take a deep breath." "Would you like a slice of pie?"] //

⚛ **12 - THE LITTLE PRINCE** ⚛ *Encountered in 25 dreams between #0915-#1437 (1.8%)* = [The joy of curiosity. The sensitive masculine. Steward between epochs. The glimmer of optimism. The single candle shining courageously in the void. The seed of genius. Intrepid spirit. Trusting. Reminder of "tender surrender" among over utilized conditioned expressions.
   *Likely to say: "Wow! Wau-wooow! WOW!" *Sings and babbles in a youthfully exuberant developing language**]//

⚛ **13 - THE NURSE** ⚛ *Encountered in 24 dreams between #0026-#1319 (1.7%)* = [Conditioned femininity. Witch mother. The area in the subconscious where fears, withholds and traumas are stored. Begs for confrontation. Somewhat defined by the past. Comfortable navigating the swamp, and serving as a guide to those in shadowy parts aching to be made light.
   Likely to say: "The story of my life defines who I am and what I can do." "I'm loyal, hardworking, well intended, empathetic, fearful, loving, forgiving, and introspective."] //

⚛ **14 - THE MAGICIAN** ⚛ *Encountered in 22 dreams between #0472-#1430 (1.6%)* = [Generally emerges as the polychronic trickster. Consistently appears as a gatekeeper between realms of "The Great Game." Proposes challenges to test the character, intention, and motivations of "the rescuer," "the persecutor," and "the victim." Provides playful reminders when backslides into comfortably numb states become areas of risk to mitigate and backstop.

Likely to say: *"Are you sure you're ready?" "You can never go back." "Tempting, isn't it?" "Cause flow. How? You know." "Stay awake. Build stuff."*] //

✿ **15 - THE ROMANTIC** ✿ *Encountered in 21 dreams between #0318-#1432 (1.5%)* = [Represents attraction. Clear and eager. Libido. Deeper expressions of friendliness and creative thrust. Wishes for other's happiness without wanting anything in return. Seems fleeting to the conditioned ego. Occurs as fecund, playful, somatic, and a whispering muse to the burgeoning artist.
Likely to say: *"I encourage you." "Take on unimaginable hardship to get closer to meeting your true self." "Get back to basics...and be tender along the way." "Your mind is ridiculous. Let's get naked."*] //

✿ **16 - THE CONFIDANT** ✿ *Encountered in 20 dreams between #0022-#1437 (1.4%)* = [Represents liked qualities in others, as yet uncultivated within. Appreciated. Unique. Courageous. Candid. Stable. Present. Possesses the qualities necessary for evolution.
Likely to say: *"You've got this. It's attainable. Go." "Stop. You're doing that bullshit again."*] //

✿ **17 - THE LOBBYIST** ✿ *Encountered in 18 dreams between #0129-#1296 (1.3%)* = [The powerful, positive "NO" in a sea of inauthentic, cowardly "YES." Willing to apply resources when systemic logjams emerge. Unapologetic. Action oriented. Speaks what's wanted into being. Plays the game with nuance and elegance. Though comfortable presenting as bristly and sarcastic, their heart space holds tremendous compassion and broad-spectrum Love for humanity.
Likely to say: *"I'm among the world's most egregious assholes." "People are the worst." "Here. Get this." "Shit."*] //

✿ **18 - THE PUBLIC MEDIUM** ✿ *Encountered in 17 dreams between #0028-#1407 (1.2%)* = [A spiritual guide with common past life karma. An ascendant master in training. Has shared trench warfare, far flung extraterrestrial adventures, and healing encounters with entities from unconditional and non-conditional realms in an ethereal, prayerful, and increasingly soft tone.
Likely to say: *"I'm praying for you. Thank you for the opportunity to serve."*] //

✿ **19 - THE TRANSLATOR** ✿ *Encountered in 17 dreams between #0322-#1412 (1.2%)* = [Consistently points out pockets of resistance. Teacher. Guide between prime material and non-physical dimensions. Surrendered and in service to God, Guides and Self.
Likely to say: *"The bar is being held for you to tap back in whenever you want." "God embarrasses you? Now that is funny." "I commit to being God's love. I commit to Love as a presence (not as a verb). I commit to alignment. I commit to living God's truth. I commit to non-conditional guidance...continuously. I commit to growth. I commit to anchoring to the deep here and now."*] //

✿ **20 - THE HEALER** ✿ *Encountered in 16 dreams between #0010-#1412 (1.1%)* = [The pure listener. Unconsciously competent across practiced traditions and modalities. Soul gazer.

Masterfully adept at navigating the "Deep Now." Effortlessly bounds between ecstatic, cathartic, and sober/rational realms.

Likely **to say:** *"Attempts to label me generally prove futile. None are comprehensive. Healer. Teacher. Facilitator. Steward. Medicine Man. Ayahuascero. All are part time roles. My work is to 1) transform the capricious ego into a humble servant of the shared heart of humanity and 2) embody* <u>T</u>*rue nature." "Love and compassion to all beings now, then, everywhere, and every-When."*] //

⚜ **21 - THE KIND HEART** ⚜ *Encountered in 15 dreams between #0179-#1404 (1%)* = [Commits to co-creative relationship. A voracious and quick learner. Manifests friendships that support their being themselves fully, more of the time. Celebrates its kinks and quirks. Creates space to take refuge within itself, for the benefit of those they love. A being *(purposefully)* of few words

Likely **to say:** *"Bonjour à tous. De quoi parlerons-nous aujourd'hui? Quel problème est le plus intéressant à résoudre?*] //

CONSTELLATIONS, ASTERISMS, AND BRIGHT STARS

~ANCESTORS~
GRANDMA - #0013
GRANDPA - #0014
GREAT GRANDMOTHER - #1041
GREAT GRANDPA - #0776

* * *

~A~
THE ACCOUNTANT - #0987
THE ACTOR - #0066
THE AD EXECUTIVE - #0321
THE ADONIS - #0371
THE ADOPTIVE FATHER - #0337
THE ADOPTIVE MOTHER - #0386
THE ADVANCED STUDENTS - #0613
THE ADVOCATE - #0824
THE AESTHETE - #0170
THE AFFLICTED - #0007
THE AGONY - #0082
THE AIR TRAFFIC CONTROLLER - #0379
THE ALCOHOLIC - #0239
THE ALIEN NATUROPATH - #0527
THE ALLY - #0533
THE ALPHA - #0385
THE AMBASSADOR - #0941
THE ANESTHESIOLOGIST - #0241
THE ANGRY SPRITE - #0158

THE ANIMATOR - #0249
THE APIRIST - #0833
THE ARBITER - #1439
THE ARBORIST - #0640
THE ARCHITECT - #0198
THE ARMY ANGEL - #0126
THE ARTIST - #0089
THE ASH - #0498
THE ASSISTANT - #0613
THE ATHEIST - #0020
THE ATTRACTOR - #0254
THE AUDIOLOGIST - #0804
THE AUDITOR - #0033
THE AUSSIE - #0645
THE AVENGER - #0829
THE AWAKENING - #1190
THE AYURVEDIC - #0002

* * *

~B~
THE BAD IDEA - #0841
THE BADASS - #0495
THE BAKER - #0595
THE BANDANA - #0430
THE BANKER - #0076
THE BAPTIZED ONE - #0637
THE BARBIE - #0657
THE BARISTA - #0789
THE BARKEEP - #0323
THE BASS - #1039
THE BENEFITS ADMINISTRATOR - #0901
THE BESTIE - #0719
THE BISEXUAL - #0826
THE BLACK BEAUTY - #0786
THE BLACK KNIGHT - #0402
THE BLUE HAIRED BLOKE - #0284
THE BLUES SINGER - #0019
THE BODHI PUNK - #0539
THE BODY BUILDER - #0593
THE BOND TRADERS - #0009
THE BONES - #1383
THE BONSAI - #0569
THE BOSNIAN - #0202
THE BOSS - #0271
THE BOSTON MARATHONER - #0461
THE BOUNCER - #0701
THE BRAIN - #0656

THE BRAND MANAGER - #0154
THE BREAKS DJ - #0144
THE BREWMASTER - #0204
THE BRIGHT SATELLITE - #0950
THE BRITS - #0670
THE BROKER - #0210
THE BUBBLE - #0117
THE BURLESQUE PERFORMER - #1073
THE BUTCH LESBIAN - #0260

* * *

~C~
THE C-SUITE - #0124
THE CAMERAMAN - #0561
THE CANINE SAVIOR - #1384
THE CARDINAL - #0410
THE CAREGIVER - #0204
THE CAROLER - #1159
THE CAROLINA REAPER - #1207
THE CARPENTER - #0012
THE CARTOONIST - #0284
THE CATALYST - #0712
THE CATCHER - #0703
THE CATERER - #0848
THE CATHOLIC - #0678
THE CENTERLINE - #0836
THE CEO - #0799
THE CHALLENGER - #0071
THE CHAMPION - #0260
THE CHAMPION OF LOVE - #0703
THE CHANNEL - #1078
THE CHARLATAN - #0134
THE CHEERLEADER - #0755
THE CHEF - #0014
THE CHEMISTS - #0150
THE CHICKEN - #0953
THE CHIEF OF STAFF - #1236
THE CHILD - #0102
THE CHOCOHOLIC - #0044
THE CITY EMPLOYEE - #0387
THE CLUB KID - #0037
THE COACH - #0071
THE COCK - #0434
THE COLONEL - #0069
THE COMBAT MEDIC - #0045
THE COMIC - #0082
THE COMMUNITY ORGANIZERS - #0861

THE COMPASS - #0778
THE COMPUTATIONAL LINGUIST - #1155
THE CONCIERGE - #0094
THE CONDUCTOR - #0097
THE CONFIDANT - #0022
THE CONJURER - #1243
THE CONNECTOR - #0071
THE CONSERVATIVE NEIGHBOR - #0744
THE CONSULTANT - #0131
THE CONTRAST JUNKIE - #0170
THE CONVERT - #0009
THE COOK - #0696
THE CORD CUTTER - #0134
THE CORPORATE PLANNER - #1066
THE COSMIC WHITE HEART - #0045
THE COUNSELOR - #0969
THE COUTURIER - #0204
THE COWBOY - #1184
THE COYOTE -#0603
THE CRAZY DIAMOND - #1094
THE CREATOR - #0071
THE CROWN PRINCE - #0528
THE CRUNCH - #0082
THE CRUSH - #0951
THE CUDDLER - #0317

* * *

~D~
THE DANCER - #0002
THE DANDY - #0298
THE DAUGHTER - #0259
THE DEAR HEART - #0624
THE DELIGHT - #0251
THE DENTIST - #0782
THE DESERT NYMPH - #0735
THE DESIGNER - #0472
THE DEVOTEE - #0384
THE DIPLOMAT - #0038
THE DISNEY PRINCE - #0453
THE DOCTOR - #0184
THE DOMINATRIX - #0073
THE DRAGON TAMER - #0281
THE DRAMA QUEEN - #0353
THE DRONE PILOT - #0672
THE DRUM MAJOR - #1166
THE DRUMMER - #0064
THE DULCE DE LECHE - #0363

~E~

THE ECSTASY - #0082
THE EDITOR - #1208
THE EDUCATOR - #1360
THE EDUCATORS - #0716
THE EMPYREAN - #1240
THE EMT - #0939
THE ENGINEER - #0200
THE ENTREPRENEUR - #0969
THE EPICUREAN - #0233
THE EPITOME - #1375
THE EQUESTRIAN - #0401
THE ERROR PROOFER - #0206
THE EVIL TWIN - #0666
THE EXCOMMUNICATED - #0812
THE EXECUTIVE DIRECTOR - #0891
THE EXECUTIVE PRODUCER - #0070
THE EXPAT - #0134
THE EXTERMINATOR - #1003
THE EXTROVERT - #1320

* * *

~F~

THE FAIRY GODMOTHER - #0209
THE FAIRY GODPARENTS - #0392
THE FAITHFUL ONE - #0215
THE FARMHAND - #0201
THE FASHIONISTA - #0170
THE FBI AGENT - #0115
THE FEELER - #0094
THE FELLOW - #0108
THE FIDUCIARY - #0007
THE FIFTY POUND BRAIN - #0710
THE FILM PRODUCER - #0124
THE FIREFIGHTER - #0668
THE FIRST GRADER - #1031
THE FIT BOY - #0650
THE FLASH - #0568
THE FLIRT - #0076
THE FLORIDIAN - #0603
THE FLUFF - #1094
THE FLUTIST - #0023
THE FOUNDER - #0581
THE FRATERNITY MAN - #0237
THE FUJIYAMA MAMA - #1330
THE FUNDAMENTALIST - #0461
THE FUNDRAISER - #0874

THE FUNKY MONKEY - #0598
THE FUR TRAPPER - #1028

* * *

~G~
THE GAME DESIGNER - #0608
THE GAMER - #0307
THE GANG BANGER - #0182
THE GARDENER - #0045
THE GATOR - #0724
THE GDMF UNICORN - #0147
THE GENIUS - #0162
THE GENTLEMAN - #0995
THE GERMAN - #0205
THE GINGER - #0185
THE GODFATHER - #0428
THE GOGO BOY - #0913
THE GOLDEN ONE - #0931
THE GOLDEN SHADOW - #0547
THE GONG MASTER - #0128
THE GOOD WEED - #0917
THE GOTH - #0445
THE GRACE - #0353
THE GRANDDAUGHTER - #1000
THE GRANDSONS - #1000
THE GREASED PIG - #1126
THE GREAT UNCLE - #1066
THE GREEK - #0367
THE GREEN TARA - #0012
THE GREGARIOUS CONSULTANT - #0158
THE GROOMSMAN - #0302
THE GUITARIST - #0025
THE GYM TWINK - #1129
THE GYMNAST - #1202
THE GYPSY - #0066

* * *

~H~
THE HABERDASHER - #0137
THE HIATUS - #0035
THE HANDYMAN - #0021
THE HARBINGER - #0010
THE HEADBANGER - #0899
THE HEADCASE - #0914
THE HEALED WOMAN - #0098
THE HEALER - #0010

THE HEDONISTS - #0195
THE HILL - #0283
THE HILLBILLY - #0014
THE HIPSTER - #0781
THE HIRING MANAGER - #1057
THE HOBBIT - #0784
THE HOMECOMING DATE - #1079
THE HOPE - #0830
THE HOST - #0831
THE HOT HEAD - #0443
THE HOUSEWIFE - #0231
THE HULA HOOPER - #0962
THE HUMBLE MAN - #0039
THE HUSBAND - #0297
THE HUSTLER - #0307
THE HYPE MAN - #1439

* * *

~I~

THE ICEMAN - #0317
THE IMPRESSIONIST - #0046
THE IMPROV ACTOR - #0847
THE INQUISITOR - #0723
THE INSIDER - #0887
THE INSPIRATION - #0595
THE INSTRUCTOR - #0715
THE INTELLIGENCE OFFICER - #0271
THE INTERIOR DESIGNER   #0786
THE INTERN - #0015
THE INTERVENTIONIST - #0820
THE INTROVERT - #1320
THE INVESTMENT BANKER - #0141
THE IRISHMAN - #0248
THE IRONMAN - #0633

* * *

~J~

THE JAZZ TRUMPETER - #1145
THE JESTER - #0127
THE JEW - #1402

* * *

~K~

THE KANGAROO - #0279
THE KANSAN - #0193

THE KENYAN - #0378
THE KETTLE - #0143
THE KIDDO - #0661
THE KINDERGARTENER - #1031
THE KIND HEART - #0179
THE KINKSTER - #1045
THE KINKY MD - #0218
THE KITKAT - #0481
THE KIWI - #0560
THE KOAN - #0557
THE KOKORO - #0512

* * *

~L~

THE LACHRYMOLOGIST - #0573
THE LACROSSE PLAYER - #1080
THE LALA - #0561
THE LAMPLIGHTER - #0972
THE LANDLORD - #0212
THE LANDSCAPE ARCHITECT - #0159
THE LATIN FIREBALL - #0901
THE LAUGHING MONKEY - #0692
THE LAWYER - #0080
THE LEGEND - #0400
THE LINEAGE HOLDER - #1100
THE LINGUIST - #0249
THE LION - #0267
THE LIONESS - #0070
THE LITIGATOR - #1056
THE LITTLE BROTHER - #0029
THE LITTLE PRINCE - #0915
THE LOBBYIST - #0129
THE LOGICIAN - #0126
THE LONGFELLOW - #0957
THE LOVE STORY AUTHOR - #0610
THE LOYALIST - #1440
THE LUCKY MAN - #0025
THE LUMBERJACK - #0021
THE LUTHERAN PASTOR - #0098
THE LYRICIST - #0040

* * *

~M~

THE M&A ATTORNEY - #0106
THE MAGICIAN - #0472
THE MAKE UP ARTIST - #1025

THE MAKER - #0016
THE MALE MODEL - #0799
THE MANAGING DIRECTOR - #0015
THE MARATHONER - #0097
THE MASSEUR - #0868
THE MASSEUSE - #0376
THE MASSIVE HOMOSEXUAL - #0084
THE MBA CANDIDATE - #0620
THE MEDIA TEAM - #0261
THE MEDICINE WOMAN - #0003
THE MEEK - #0302
THE MEME - #0193
THE MIDWESTERN GENT - #0784
THE MIDWIFE - #0226
THE MINIATURE - #1117
THE MINISTER - #0618
THE MIRROR - #0114
THE MODEL - #0144
THE MODERN CAVEMEN - #0563
THE MOTIVATIONAL SPEAKER - #0683
THE MOTO - #0291
THE MUSICAL PANDA - #0794

* * *

~N~
THE NASTY PIG - #0793
THE NAYSAYER - #0048
THE NEIGHBOR - #0672
THE NEIGHBORHOOD WATCH - #1058
THE NEUROSCIENTIST - #0573
THE NEUTRAL GUIDE - #0010
THE NEWLYWEDS - #0556
THE NINERS FAN - #0394
THE NOMINEE - #0803
THE NORSE DEMIGOD - #1016
THE NOWHERE MAN - #0874
THE NUN - #0165
THE NURSE - #0026

* * *

~O~
THE OB/GYN - #0518
THE OBSERVER - #0070
THE OCCUPATIONAL THERAPIST - #0590
THE OFFICE ADMIN - #0394
THE OFFICIANT - #0013

THE OLD SOUL - #0001
THE OLDEST FRIEND IN THE BOOK - #1354
THE ONE NIGHT STAND - #0218
THE ONE WHO GIVES A DAMN - #0834
THE ORACLE - #0134
THE ORANGE PIG - #0401
THE ORATOR - #0237
THE ORGANIST - #0721
THE ORIGAMIST - #0481
THE ORPHAN - #0302
THE OWNER - #0502

* * *

~P~

THE PACHAMAMA - #0878
THE PAGE - #0182
THE PAINTER - #0113
THE PANDA - #0028
THE PARATROOPER - #0760
THE PARKS DIRECTOR - #0281
THE PARTNERS - #0640
THE PASSIONATE BRAZILIAN - #0173
THE PEDDLER - #0726
THE PEDIATRICIAN - #0271
THE PEER - #1147
THE PELVIS - #0770
THE PERFORMANCE ARTIST - #1016
THE PERVERT - #0545
THE PHILANTHROPIST - #0170
THE PHOENIX - #0452
THE PHOTOGRAPHER - #0120
THE PHOTOGRAPHIC MEMORY - #0080
THE PHYSICIST - #0030
THE PIANIST - #0640
THE PIED PIPER - #0718
THE PILGRIM - #0216
THE PILOT - #0129
THE PIXIE - #0115
THE PIZZA DELIVERY BOY - #0276
THE POCKET GAY - #0653
THE POINT GUARD - #0044
THE POLISH PRINCE - #0394
THE POLITICIAN - #0531
THE POLYMATH - #0710
THE POOL BOY - #0712
THE PORN KING - #1220
THE PORN KING'S MOTHER - #1220

THE PORN STAR - #0393
THE PORTRAIT ARTIST - #0363
THE POSTMASTER - #0201
THE POWER PLAYER - #0234
THE PRACTITIONER - #0980
THE PRAGMATIST - #1003
THE PRANKSTER - #0256
THE PRECIOUS ONE - #0322
THE PRESS SECRETARY - #1124
THE PRETZEL - #0269
THE PRIESTESS - #0391
THE PROFESSOR - #0306
THE PROM DATE - #1104
THE PROMOTER - #0768
THE PROPERTY MANAGER - #0384
THE PSYCHEDELIC STEWARD - #0595
THE PSYCHIATRIST - #0259
THE PSYCHIC - #0241
THE PSYCHIC DOCTOR - #0781
THE PSYCHONAUT - #0030
THE PUBLIC MEDIUM - #0028
THE PUBLIC SERVANT - #0231
THE PYRO IN TRAINING - #0088

* * *

~Q~
THE QUEER - #0263

* * *

~R~
THE RABID RABBIT - #0834
THE RADICAL FAERIE - #0748
THE RADICAL HIPPIE - #0523
THE RAINMAN - #0491
THE RAJNEESH - #1211
THE RAPTOR - #0176
THE RAY OF SUNSHINE - #0717
THE REANIMATOR - #1319
THE REBEL - #0337
THE RECONCILIATOR - #0317
THE REFLECTION - #0007
THE REIKI MASTER - #0010
THE REINCARNATED - #1066
THE RENAISSANCE MAN - #0106
THE RENEGADE - #0085
THE REPATRIATES - #1117

THE REPEATER - #0071
THE RESISTANCE - #0034
THE RESTAURATEUR - #0297
THE RETAILER - #0210
THE REVOLUTIONARY - #0069
THE RICH MAN - #0097
THE RINGMASTER - #0715
THE ROADRUNNER - #0642
THE ROBOT - #0176
THE ROCK STAR SPOUSE - #0281
THE RODIN - #0701
THE ROLLERGIRL - #0495
THE ROMANTIC - #0318
THE RUBY - #0169
THE RUMBLER - #0963

* * *

~S~
THE SAMOAN - #0004
THE SCHOOL TEACHER - #0820
THE SEASON - #0585
THE SEER - #0050
THE SENSOR - #0858
THE SERVANT - #0144
THE SEX FRIEND - #0524
THE SEX THERAPIST - #0647
THE SEX WORKER - #0697
THE SEXUAL SACRED - #0022
THE SHAKTI SISTER - #0143
THE SHARED HEART - #0070
THE SILVER BOYS - #1131
THE SIRENS - #0014
THE SIXTH DEGREE BLACKBELT - #0422
THE SKATER - #0285
THE SKEPTIC - #0656
THE SKYWOLF - #1389
THE SLUT - #0894
THE SMILE - #0532
THE SMOKE SCREEN - #0400
THE SMOKER - #1113
THE SOCCER COACH - #0514
THE SON - #0259
THE SOOTHSAYER - #0135
THE SOUL SISTER - #1275
THE SOUL SINGER - #1185
THE SOUND ENGINEER - #0641
THE SOUTHERN BELLE - #0273

THE SOUTHERN GENTLEMAN - #0698
THE SPECK - #0520
THE SPOTTED DOG - #0237
THE SQUIRREL - #1340
THE STRATEGIST - #0136
THE STUDENT - #0114
THE SUMERIAN - #0964
THE SURGICAL TECH - #0024
THE SURVIVOR - #0400
THE SWAB - #0291
THE SWEET D - #0699
THE SWIM COACH- #0365

* * *

~T~

THE TAR HEEL - #0291
THE TATER - #0705
THE TEACHER - #0144
THE TEAM LEADER - #0239
THE TECHIE - #0117
THE TEETOTALER - #1236
THE TEMPLAR - #0052
THE THEM - #0157
THE THERAPIST - #0579
THE THINKER - #0056
THE TIGER MOM - #0602
THE TINKERBELL - #0862
THE TINY ROMANIAN - #0089
THE TINY TODDLER - #0081
THE TOP OF THE WORLD - #0476
THE TORCH RUNNER - #0070
THE TRAIL RUNNER - #0094
THE TRAINEE - #0595
THE TRAINER - #0532
THE TRANSLATOR - #0322
THE TRANSPARENT HEADCASE - #0075
THE TRAVELER - #0950
THE TRIATHLETE - #0737
THE TRICK - #0887
THE TRINITY - #0589
THE TRIUMVIRATE - #1078
THE TRUST FUND BABY - #1130
THE TWIRLERS - #0219

* * *

~V~

THE VAULT MANAGER - #0113
THE VEGAN - #0837
THE VENTURE CAPITALIST - #0904
THE VETERINARIAN - #1402
THE VICAR - #0151
THE VICE BROTHERS - #0028
THE VICTOR - #0027
THE VIKING ELF - #0117
THE VINTNER - #0150
THE VIOLINIST - #1034
THE VIP - #0795
THE VISIONARY - #0594

* * *

~W~
THE WALKER - #0892
THE WANDERER - #0722
THE WARD OF GAIA - #0010
THE WARRIOR WOMAN - #0989
THE WEAVER - #0010
THE WHISTLE - #0143
THE WHITE KNIGHT - #0711
THE WHITE RABBIT - #0014
THE WHITE RUSSIAN - #0933
THE WIDOW - #1072
THE WILD WEST - #0337
THE WILDCARD - #0740
THE WILDERNESS GUIDE - #0304
THE WINE PURVEYOR - #0871
THE WINO - #1057
THE WITNESS - #1005
THE WORLDBRIDGER - #0010
THE WRANGLER - #0022
THE WRITER - #0238

* * *

~Y~
THE YIMBY - #0188
THE YOGI - #0119
THE YOUNG AUDITOR - #0703
THE YOUNG CEO - #0716

* * *

~Z~
THE ZOMBIE - #0714

ZEITGEIST VALENCES

~A~

AC/DC - #0381
ADAM JONES - #0012
ADOLF HITLER - #0466
AEROSMITH - #0789
AL JARREAU - #0392
ALAN WATTS - #1010
ALANIS MORISETTE - #1157
ALBERT EINSTEIN - #0995
ALEX GREY - #1078
ALEX JONES - #0237
AMON TOBIN - #0548
AMY CUDDY - #0043
AMY POEHLER - #0457
AMY SHUMER - #0186
ANA GASTEYER - #1023
ANDERSON COOPER - #1032
ANDREW W.K. - #0219
ANDY SAMBERG - #1033
ANNE FINUCANE - #0074
ANTHONY KEDIS - #0015
ALEXANDRIA OCASIO-CORTEZ - #0390
APHEX TWIN - #0774
ARCA - #1392
ARCHANGEL RAPHAEL - #1025
ARETHA FRANKLIN - #0346
ARIANA GRANDE - #0629
AXL ROSE - #0249

AYANNA PRESSLEY - #0390

* * *

~B~
BARACK OBAMA - #0172
BARBRA STREISAND - #0445
BARON BAPTISTE - #0070
BASSNECTAR - #0251
BECK - #0249
BELA and MARTHA KARYOLI - #0017
BENJAMIN FRANKLIN - #0033
BERNIE MADOFF - #0979
BERNIE SANDERS - #0979
BETTE MIDLER - #0498
BETTY WHITE - #0359
BEYONCÉ - #0063
BILL GATES - #1386
BILL MURRAY - #1315
BILL ODENKIRK - #1117
BLUE IVY - #0770
BOB BARKER - #0538
BOB DYLAN - #1163
BRADLEY COOPER - #0612
BRIAN WELCH - #0298
BRITNEY SPEARS - #1176
BUDDHA - #1251

ʌ ʌ ʌ

~C~
CAITYLYN JENNER - #0248
CARLOS SANTANA - #0954
CAROL BURNETT - #1434
CATHERINE O'HARA - #1247
CATHY BESSANT - #0117
CELINE DION - #0752
CG JUNG - #0671
CHARLIE CHAPLIN - #0005
CHER - #0708
CHEVY CHASE - #0364
CHLOE SEVIGNY - #0533
CHRIS PRATT - #1379
CHRISTOPHER HITCHENS - #1251
CHUCK NORRIS - #0627
CLAY AIKEN - #0683
CLEVE JONES - #0124
COLDPLAY - #0271

COLONEL SANDERS - #1370
COREY TAYLOR - #0666

* * *

~D~

DANNY CAREY - #0012
DANNY ELFMAN - #0563
DAVE CHAPPELLE - #1016
DAVE GROHL - #0265
DAVID BOWIE - #0534
DAVID FRANCO - #0625
DAVID LEE ROTH - #0183
DEATH GRIPS - #0251
DEFTONES - #0961
DENISE MENELLY - #0640
DIANE FEINSTEIN - #0151
DICK CHENEY - #0446
DIPLO - #1380
DISTURBED - #0666
DONALD GLOVER - #0162
DONALD TRUMP - #0009
DRAKE - #0346
DREAM THEATER - #0024
DREW BARRYMORE - #0865
DUFF MCKAGAN - #0860
DUKE ELLINGTON - #0476

* * *

~E~

EDGAR ALLAN POE - #0995
ELTON JOHN - #0713
ENNIO MORRICONE - #1261
ENYA - #0552
ERYKAH BADU - #1286
ESCHER - #0053
ESTHER HICKS - #0119

* * *

~F~

FLEA - #0015
FLEETWOOD MAC - #0033
FOO FIGHTERS - #0968
FOUR TET - #0819
FRANK ROBINSON - #0124
FRANK ZAPPA - #0183

FREDDY MERCURY - #0573

* * *

~G~

GARTH BROOKS - #0007
GAVIN NEWSOM - #0530
GAY HENDRICKS - #0247
GENESIS P-ORRIDGE - #0303
GEORGE LUCAS - #0761
GEORGE WASHINGTON - #0746
GORDON RAMSAY - #0045
GORILLAZ - #0919
GOV. MIKE DEWINE - #1326
GWYNETH PALTROW - #1061

* * *

~H~

HARRIET TUBMAN - #0346
HEIDI KLUM - #0538
HILLARY CLINTON - #0767
HUGH JACKMAN - #0154

* * *

~I~

IDRIS ELBA - #0426
IMOGEN HEAP - #0327
IVANKA TRUMP - #0102

* * *

~J~

JACK DORSEY - #0682
JACKIE O - #0746
JAMES FRANCO - #0523
JAMES LABRIE - #0024
JAMES MUNKY SHAFFER - #0372
JANE KIM - #0174
JANET JACKSON - #0007
JARED KUSHNER - #0102
JARED LETO - #0696
JAY-Z - #0147
JEFF SESSIONS - #0458
JENEANE GAROFALO - #0457
JENNIFER ANISTON - #1127
JENNIFER LOPEZ - #0954

JESUS CHRIST - #0127
JFK JR - #0746
JIMMY PAGE - #0554
JODIE FOSTER - #0405
JOE BIDEN - #0573
JOE ROGAN - #0682
JOE STRUMMER - #0620
JOHN GOSSLING - #1017
JOHN LENNON - #0712
JOHN MCCAIN - #1144
JOHN MYUNG - #0024
JOHN OLIVER - #0944
JOHN PAUL JONES - #0554
JOHN PETRUCCI - #0024
JOHN SPENCE - #1057
JONATHAN DAVIS - #0073
JORDAN PETERSON - #0676
JORDAN RUDESS - #0024
JOSEPH CAMPBELL - #1010
JOSH GROBAN - #0627
JOSH HOMME - #0234
JUDGE JUDY - #0965
JULIA ROBERTS - #1028
JULIA STILES - #0225
JULIE ANDREWS - #0144
JUNYA WANTANABE - #1251
JUSTICE KAVANAUGH - #0341
JUSTIN CHANCELLOR - #0012
JUSTIN TIMBERLAKE - #0466

* * *

~K~

KAMALA HARRIS - #1341
KATIE HENDRICKS - #0247
KATY PERRY - #0897
KELLY CLARKSON - #0079
KELLY OSBOURNE - #1090
KEN RYKER - #0403
KENDRICK LAMAR - #1237
KIM KARDASHIAN - #1349
KMFDM - #0526
KORN - #0073
KRISTI YAMAGUCHI - #0855
KYLIE MINOGUE - #1061

* * *

~**L**~

LADY GAGA - #0367
LARRY DAVID - #0065
LARS ULRICH - #1071
LAYNE STAYLEY - #0235
LCD SOUNDSYSTEM - #0365
LEONARDO DICAPRIO - #0796
LESLIE JORDAN - #0452
LEWIS CARROLL - #1001
LINDA RONSTADT - #1082
LINDSAY GRAHAM - #0341
LIZZO - #0909
LORIN ASHTON - #0326
LOUIS ARMSTRONG - #0827
LOUIS CK - #0154
LUDWIG VAN BEETHOVEN - #0668
LUKE PERRY - #0568

* * *

~**M**~

MADONNA - #0266
MARILYN MANSON - #0027
MARC BENIOFF - #1057
MARK ZUCKERBERG - #0113
MARTIN SCORCESE - #1028
MARIANNE WILLIAMSON - #0828
MAYA ANGELOU - #0346
MAYA RUDOLPH - #0457
MAYNARD KEENAN - #0012
MELANIA TRUMP - #1139
MICHAEL BLOOMBERG - #1058
MICHAEL EISENER - #0113
MICHAEL JACKSON - #0515
MICHELLE OBAMA - #1214
MICK JAGGER - #0872
MIKE MANGINI - #0024
MIKE PATTON - #0175
MIKE PENCE - #0255
MITCH MCCONNELL - #0341
MOBY - #0827
MOLLY SHANNON - #0948
MR. BUNGLE - #1092

MR. ROGERS - #0851

* * *

~N~

NANCY PELOSI - #0907
NAO - #0313
NEIL PATRICK HARRIS - #0698
NIECY NASH - #0863
NINE INCH NAILS - #0394
NOFX - #0752

* * *

~O~

OKSANA BAIUL - #0859
OPRAH - #0007
OZZY OSBOURNE - #0012

* * *

~P~

P. DIDDY - #0346
PAMELA ANDERSON - #0880
PANTERA - #0601
PARIS HILTON - #0580
PARKER POSEY - #0040
PARLIAMENT FUNKADELIC - #0006
PATRICK DEMPSEY - #0084
PAUL MCCARTNEY - #0242
PAUL REUBENS - #0898
PAUL RUDD - #0796
PAUL RYAN - #0129
PAUL YOUNG - #0441
PEMA CHODRON - #0032
PETE BUTTEGEIG - #1096
PETE STEELE - #1097
PHISH - #0336
POGO - #0244
PRINCE - #0069
PRINCESS DIANA - #0401

* * *

~R~

RAGE AGAINST THE MACHINE - #1218
RASCAL FLATTS - #0557
RASHIDA JONES - #0055
RASHIDA TLAIB - #0390
RED HOT CHILI PEPPERS - #0015
RHIANNA - #0792
RICARDO MONTLBAN - #0597

RICHARD DAVID JAMES - #0774
RICHARD GERE - #0762
RICHARD NIXON - #1188
ROB LOWE - #0055
ROB SCHNEIDER - #0220
ROB ZOMBIE - #0137
ROBERT PLANT - #0914
ROBIN WILLIAMS - #0361
RODNEY DANGERFIELD - #0014
ROSEANNE BARR - #1055

* * *

~S~

SAINT PETER - #0023
SAM NEILL - #1247
SANDRA BULLOCK - #0863
SARA GILBERT - #1055
SARAH PAULSON - #1028
SARAH SILVERMAN - #0541
SCARLETT JOHANSSSON - #1426
SCOTT WEINER - #0220
SELENA GOMEZ - #0683
SERJ TANKARIAN - #0183
SHAKIRA - #1117
SHAQUILLE O'NEAL - #0188
SHARI BAPTISTE - #0482
SHARON OSBOURNE - #1090
SHAUN WHITE - #0126
SHELDON ADELSON - #0218
SHIRLEY MACLAINE - #1434
SID - #1069
SINBAD - #0007
SIR PATRICK STEWART - #1131
SKRILLEX - #0672
SLASH - #0460
SLAYER - #0468
SLIPKNOT - #0666
SOPHIE - #1026
ST. FRANCIS OF ASSISI - #0998
ST. MICHAEL - #1251
ST. RAPHAEL - #1251
ST. THOMAS AQUINAS - #0924
STANLEY KUBRICK - #0405
STEPHEN COLBERT - #0587
STEPHEN KING - #0490
STEVEN TYLER - #0789
STOCKARD CHANNING - #0905

STS9 - #0495

* * *

~T~

THE BEASTIE BOYS - #0770
THE BEATLES - #0935
THE BELKS - #0655
THE BLACK MADONNA - #0350
THE BLUE ANGELS - #0867
THE BUSH PRESIDENTS - #0336
THE CHEMICAL BROTHERS - #0524
THE DALAI LAMA - #0009
THE LONELY ISLAND - #1033
THE NAKED AND FAMOUS - #0784
THE OSBOURNES - #0619
THE QUEEN OF ENGLAND - #0100
THE ROLLING STONES - #0872
THE VELVET UNDERGROUND - #1420
THE VON TRAPPS - #0417
THERESA MAY - #1250
THOMAS EDISON - #0461
THROBBING GRISTLE - #0303
TINA TURNER - #0229
TOM BRADY - #0538
TOM HANKS - #0899
TOM MORELLO - #1275
TOOL - #0012
TRENT REZNOR - #0394
TWIGGY RAMIREZ - #0860
TYPE O NEGATIVE - #1097

* * *

~U~

UNCLE FRED WAHPEPAH - #0396

* * *

~V~

VANILLA FUDGE - #1259
VANNA WHITE - #0773
VICTORIA BECKHAM - #0747

* * *

~W~

WAH! - #0626

WARREN BUFFETT - #0396
WHITESNAKE - #0752
WILLAM - #1073
WOODY HARRELSON - #0960
WU TANG CLAN - #1012

* * *

~Y~
YEAH YEAH YEAHS #0624
YOKO ONO - #1308
YUL BRYNNER - #0597

* * *

~Z~
ZACHARY QUINTO - #0040
ZACK DE LA ROCHA - #0294
ZOE KRAVITZ - #0421

AMALGAMS, HYBRIDS, AND SPIRITS

~A~
"Abigail Bumby" - #0055
"Adam.jdl" - #0272
"Adam" - #0719
"Agape" - #0558
"AL" - #0392
"Albert Fart" - #1356
"Amber" - #0493
"AMELIA" - #0394
"Andrea" - #0147
"Angel" - #0474
"Annie" - #0371
"Anthony" - #0024
"Anthony" - #1111
"Ashleigh" - #0897
"Ashley" - #0556
"Aunt Jemima" - #0334
AEOS - #0842
ALEXIS ROSE - #1074
ALFRED E. NEWMAN - #0357
ANNA MADRIGAL - #0641
ANNIE WARBUCKS - #0115
APRIL LUDGATE - #1007

* * *

~B~
"Ben" - #0133

597

"Ben" - #0908
"Blanket" - #1036
"Blue 'L'" - #1385
"Blue Elwood" - #1123
"Brad" - #0075
"Brad" - #0518
"Breathless Mahoney" - #0761
"Brent" - #0495
"BRIAN" - #0263
"Britney & Ava" - #1365
"Bryan and Ashleigh" - #1115

* * *

~C~
"Carla" - #0645
"Casey" - #0903
"Chris McGill" - #0654
"Chris" - #0482
"Chris" - #0675
"Chris" - #1258
"Colton" - #1068
"COMPACHA" #0304
"Cosmin" - #0967
CAPTAIN CAVEMAN - #0950
CHARLEE - #0089

* * *

~D~
"Daniel " - #0056
"Daniel Day" - #0818
"Daniel" - #0408
"Dave" - #1073
"David" - #0935
"David" - #0732
"David" - #1299
"Dawn" - #0945
"DONNELLAN" - #1078
"Doris" - #1343
"Dr. Habib Rajnesh" - #0611
"Dwight" - #1307
DICK TRACY - #0761
DR. EMMETT BROWN - #0063
DR. ZOIDBERG - #0131

* * *

~**E**~

"ECNIV" - #1286
"Elf Boys" - #0435
"ERIC WHITEMAN" - #0154
"Eric" - #1326
"Eric" - #1340
"Eros - #0558
EROS - #0972

* * *

~**F**~

"FLEABAG" - #1170
"Francis" - #1442

* * *

~**G**~

"Gary Marshall" - #0786
"Gatekeeper" - #0169
"Genius" - #0761
GHOSTBUSTERS - #0461
"Gizmo" - #1029
"Greg" - #0069
"Grim Reaper" - #0535

* * *

~**H**~

"HERK" - #1439
"HRR" - #0496
HAN SOLO - #0875

* * *

~**I**~

"Ian" - #0910
"ILSE" - #0878

* * *

~**J**~

"Jacob" - #0637
"Jared and Jaret" - #0600
"JEFF and CHRIS" - #0218
"Jeff" - #0357
"Jeff" - #1155
"Jennifer" - #1168

"Jeremy" - #0909
"Jim" - #0975
"JJ" - #1045
"Joe" - #0176
"John Helmwhast" - #0313
"JOHN" - #0532
"John" - #0959
"Joseph" - #0252
"Josh and Brent" - #0547
"Josh" - #0570
"Joshua" - #0047
"Joshua" - #1052
"Junior Storyteller" - #0402
"Justin" - #0130
"Justin" - #0416
JAMES BOND - #0006
JESSICA FLETCHER - #0406
JESSICA RABBIT - #0761

* * *

~K~
"KATIE" - #0645
"KATIE" - #1085
"Katie" - #1323
"Kelly" - #0079
"KIKO and CHRIS" - #0169
"Kris Kraftsman" - #0876
"Krishna" - #0611
"Kristen Kevin" - #0776
"Kuma" - #0375
"Kyle" - #0819
KING KONG - #1221
KUMA - #0222

* * *

~L~
"L" - #0610
"LEANDRA" - #0576
"Linda Evans" - #1166
"Lois" - #0793
"Lucas Dvorak" - #1171
"Lucas" - #0008
LESLIE KNOPE - #0508

* * *

~**M**~

"MADONNA'S HERO" - #0316
"Maeva" - #1023
"Maggie" - #0979
"Maid Marian" - #1085
"MARK" - #0153
"Mark" - #1410
"Mary" - #1177
"Mary" - #1336
"Matthew" - #0897
"Max" - #0922
"Melanie" - #0302
"Meredith" - #0259
"Mom" - #0317
"Mom" - #0410
"Mr. Beaselman" - #0971
"Mr. Wolf" - #0799
"Mrs. Leavenworth" - #0907
MARTY MCFLY - #0063
MARY POPPINS - #0332
MICKEY MOUSE - #0376
MORPHEUS - #0913

* * *

~**N**~

"Naomi" - #0175
"NAOMI" - #1187
"Nelson from Norway" - #1073
"NICOTINE" - #0384
NOME KING - #0745

* * *

~**P**~

"Patrick McFadden" - #0435
"Patrick" - #0975
"Paul" - #0414
"Pete" - #1164
"Phil and Kim" - #0284
PEE WEE HERMAN - #1243

* * *

~**Q**~

"Q" - #0763

* * *

~R~
  "RAJ" - #0579
  "Ray" - #0557
  "Red Man" - #0010
  "Rhonda" - #0834
  "RIDLEY SCOTT" - #1381
  "Rob" - #1082
  "Roland" - #0772
  "Ryan" - #0929
  RON SWANSON - #1007
  ROSE NYLON - #0704

* * *

~S~
  "SAKUNE" - #0919
  "Santa Claus" - #0194
  "Scarlet" - #1410
  "Scott" - #1116
  "Sean" - #1015
  "Sebastian" - #0902
  "Sentinel" - #0071
  "SHE" - #0850
  "Sherri" - #0608
  "SOWL" - #0209
  "Stephanie" - #0938
  "Steve Jobs" - #1353
  "STEVE" - #0176
  "Steve" - #1411
  "SUPERMAN" - #1146
  "Susan" - #0611
  SOPHIA PATRILLO - #0549
  SPIDERMAN - #0956
  STANLEY THE DOG - #0101

* * *

~T~
  "TARA" - #1188
  "Tayisha Busay" - #1068
  "TEAM NITRO" - #1243
  "Terrie" - #1080
  "The Daughter of the Chief" - #0498
  "The bassist" - #0953
  "The Consciousness" - #0047
  "the director" - #0042
  "The Four Founders" - #0178
  "The Governor" - #1136

"The Guitarist" - #0953
"The Master of the House" - #1409
"The Origin" - #1285
"The Performer" - #0177
"The President" - #1287
"The Priest" - #1084
THE SIMPSONS - #0384
"The sound" - #0884
"The Uncle" - #1434
"Theresa" - #1410
"Todd" - #0701
TARZAN - #0950
TASMANIAN DEVIL - #0871
TENAYA THE CAT - #0574
THE QUEEN OF KENYA - #0815
The Twins - "Sarah and Brad" - #0909

* * *

~**V**~

"V.O." - #1385
"Vertin" - #1052
"Vicente" - #0926
"Victoria" - #0885
VAMPIRE LESTAT - #0953

* * *

~**W**~

"Will" - #1080
"Willy Wonka" - #0578
WONDER WOMAN - #0956

* * *

~**Z**~

"ZE" - #0799
ZORRO - #0746

Made in the USA
Monee, IL
19 February 2021